No QUITTERS HERE

Quest for the Dome

A STORY ABOUT HIGH SCHOOL FOOTBALL
AND THE POWER OF A DREAM

B. M. Woodward

Brenda Woodward

Library of Congress Cataloging-in-Publication Data

NO QUITTERS HERE, Quest for the Dome

B. M. Woodward, 1st Edition

ISBN: 0-615-12218-3

Library of Congress Control Number: 2002096217

First printing   November, 2002

Second printing   April, 2003

Additional copies of this book are available through Amazon.com and bn.com

Visit: NoQuittersHere.com

Printed in the United States of America by

Morris Publishing
3212 East Highway 30
Kearney, NE 68847
1-800-650-7888

CONTENTS

THIS BOOK IS DEDICATED
TO ALL WHO WORE THE
RED AND BLACK;
THE MOST DETERMINED
AND ENERGETIC GROUP
I HAVE EVER MET.

YOU RAISED THE BAR.

1. RESPECT - 1988

There isn't a person anywhere who isn't capable of doing more than
he thinks he can.

-Henry Ford

The great Silverdome crowd roared. The din was almost deafening. The home kicker tapped his kicking toe nervously behind him. The average built athletic senior felt unworthy to be the one to start the show. He had not made a touchdown all season – a few tackles, which he was unmercifully kidded about, some extra points, and a couple of field goals.

Still.

He shook his head to rid his mind of negative thoughts: 'be cool- act like you've done this a hundred times before. Don't miss it. Just hit it. Head down...'

He raised his left arm and silently counted each of his coverage squad mates that flanked him, '. . . nine, ten,' he pointed to himself and mouthed, 'eleven.'

The shrill tone of the back judge's whistle cut the noise and echoed eerily about the cavernous building. The kicker gave the scene a final panoramic scan and committed it to memory, reckoning that he'd need the mental snapshot some day to explain it to his kids. He closed his eyes and breathed deep like he always did. He approached the teed-up ball gracefully in a lazy 'j' and, after what seemed like an eternity, met the ball with an outstretched foot. Barely a second later, the dull explosion of foot meeting pressurized leather rocked the 'Dome.'

Another State Championship game was on.

Everyone seemed to want Barry Paxton. That idea was reinforced every day when he opened mail addressed to Mr. Barry Paxton, a name he shared with his father. The Army wanted him to 'be all he could be.' The Marines wanted him to be one of their 'few good men.' The Navy, well, it didn't matter what they wanted. Barry would *never* be a swabby. He didn't know why, maybe it was the hat. He cringed at the thought of anyone seeing him sport that floppy, white thing on his head. The local community college, and just about every other college within the reach of the U.S. Postal Service, wanted his parent's tuition money. A good student with dreams to eventually attend medical school, Barry Paxton was indeed, a young man in demand.

When he walked back to the house from the mailbox, Barry wiped the sweat from his brow – a consequence of having just pushed a small mower over the lawn in front of the Paxton's modest cape cod. The well-built 17 year-old considered the bundle of mail he just harvested. He sighed. *What will it be today? Vinyl siding? No, that would be for dad. An offer for free swimming lessons to join the Coast Guard? Another plan guaranteeing weight loss?* Barry chuckled at the idea of weight loss. That he didn't need. At 6'1"-200 pounds he wasn't the biggest frog in the pond, let alone the biggest lineman in the league or the team.

Barry scooped up the hose from the freshly manicured yard. The familiar sweet smell of freshly cut grass conjured up images of football. He could smell the air of pre-game warm-ups, a combination of just cut Ryegrass, Kentucky Blue, and the first sweat of the evening thrown in for good measure. All that was missing was the aroma of hotdogs and the buttery fragrance of popcorn from the concession stand behind the bleachers.

He took a long pull of the cold water. His throat welcomed the cool relief. For a moment he could taste football. For a moment he hungered for it – hitting the sled until you could hit it no longer, the pleasingly sore muscles, jumping through mental and emotional hoops week after week. Butterflies danced in the pit of his stomach. Barry wanted football to start *now.*

He took another cool gulp from the garden hose and tossed it down. With a cleansing breath, however, Barry realized that like Christmas, football would eventually come, and it would be his last.

Barry sat on the cold cement of the front porch. It felt good. He flipped through the small stack of mail when a plain white envelope caught his eye. It was personally addressed to him. 'Coach Annese' was stamped as the return address. *Why would Coach send him a letter in the middle of summer?* His heart pounded noticeably while he slowly, deliberately, opened the envelope. He reverently unfolded the letter and read it word for word, like a kid reading the assembly directions to his favorite game. He felt his heart rate twist a notch when he read the last half of a letter addressed to Montrose Football Players:

> . . . *When double practices begin, we will commit our practice time to fundamentals and execution and not to physical conditioning. If you want to contribute to the success of a championship team prepare yourself physically and mentally now.*
>
> *We will conduct conditioning sessions for two weeks. We will start these sessions at 7:00 PM and finish no later then 8:30 PM. You are required to attend these sessions unless you are on a family vacation or are involved in another important commitment. Remember, it is your football team and you must become accountable and responsible to the team. It is my hope that you would anxiously participate in these conditioning sessions for the simple reason that you want to prepare yourself to become a contributing member of the team. Seniors should start to take a leadership role during these conditioning sessions.*
>
> *Remember, the most important qualification for becoming a CHAMPION is an intense, burning desire to succeed! If we believe that we can win the championship, and if we work relentlessly to achieve that goal, we will win it. Birch Run week is only seven weeks away so begin to think of accomplishing our first goal – 'Beat Birch Run.'*
>
> > *Respectfully,*
> >
> > *Coach Annese*

Barry sharply looked up when he heard the sound of grinding gravel in the driveway. He was glad to see Joe Morse, his best friend.

'Hey Bear, you're all sweaty,' the happy-go-lucky Morse noted as he whipped shut the driver's side door of his rusty Chevy S-10. 'You look like you've just finished two-a-days. How come you're so red?'

Bham. Joe instantly saw blue sky. He landed on the ground with a resounding thud, just short of the roadside ditch. Joe was a bit larger than Barry was and not exactly the easiest guy to take down. But down he was.

'Dang Barry!' Joe gasped while he tried to collect himself.

Barry laughed, 'Sorry, I couldn't resist.'

He began to cough hard, alternating between deep hacks and bursts of laughter. He wasn't able to speak. At length, 'Bear' collected himself and admitted, 'I just read the letter from Coach Annese. I guess it just got me too pumped up and I needed to hit somebody.'

They both fell into a comfortable laugh, a laugh that only two closest friends are able to share after one has plowed the other into the turf. It was the summer of 1988 and both boys looked forward to their senior year. While Greg Louganis, Jackie Joyner-Kersee, and Florence Griffith-Joyner waited for the Olympic torch to be lit in Seoul, South Korea, Barry and Joe awaited football season. It was their chance to be the top dogs at school. They especially looked forward to football season with a premonition that their new coach, preparing for his second season, could make things happen.

Bear and Joe sat on the porch, reminiscing about the season past. They laughed about the huge senior who faked a heart attack to get out of practice. The poor boy was nearly 400 pounds and couldn't fit on the school's scales.

'Remember him laying there, wearing two pair of the biggest practice pants they had?' Joe asked.

'Yeah, they had to sew 'em together. Remember how the team huddled around him, waitin' for the ambulance? Think Coach Annese wanted to give him mouth to mouth?'

They both roared.

'I wasn't doin' it!' Bear piped in. He started coughing again.

'Me either.' Joe asked, 'Hey, you okay?'

'It's the grass. Been allergic to it since I was kid.'

'Oh, yeah, that's right.'

Between coughs Bear managed, 'What about Clyde and the time he tried to get us to stop swearing?'

Joe feigned seriousness, 'You guys' (gasp – gasp). I'm gettin' tired of runnin' gassers' (gasp – gasp). 'Stop yer damn swearing!'

Bear, now under control, with his best Coach Annese impersonation, 'Back on the line, Boys!'

They lost it. For a team that lost more games than it won, there were a lot of interesting moments.

Their banter that day was one of those stitches in time that weaves the fabric of friendship: sharing common experiences and caring about one another. The boys, on the cusp of being men, laughed about their past and dreamed about the future. They had no idea that in nine short months, the time it took both to be conceived and born, they would walk away from Montrose High School and rarely see each other again.

Joe remembered their pre-season scrimmage over Labor Day last, his junior year. After an especially poor performance, the team thought that they would shower and go home upon their arrival at the school. Coach Annese, however, had other plans. He was disgusted in his team's effort that afternoon against teams they should've dominated. As soon as they struggled off the bus, Coach announced, 'Let's hit the practice field!'

Joe sounded as incredulous as he could, 'Could you believe it when Annese told 'em to turn on the stadium lights? People driving down Feher Drive had to wonder what was up.'

The team practiced an exhausting eight hours that day, but they were too stubborn to give up. They would not quit.

Barry recalled, 'Remember when that senior quit last year? He couldn't handle it anymore and he mumbled some crap like, 'I quit!' Coach asked him, 'What did you say?'

'Humph,' the dumb kid said. 'I quit!' replied Joe.

Both boys were quiet for a moment, as if engaged in a moment of silence for a fallen comrade. They recalled how Annese shot back, 'Then quit! But take off all of your stuff, right here, right now!'

Just as though it happened the day before, they could only imagine how humiliated the exhausted player felt when he stripped off his helmet and the rest of his armor while his teammates smirked. He stripped completely down to his girdle and started to walk away.

Coach Annese yelled, 'Hey, that girdle belongs to the school too!'

Feeling two feet tall the boy pulled the girdle pad off, leaving him clad only in his underwear, and threw it down. His squadmates stopped laughing. They didn't know quite how to respond to this awkward situation. Each player knew that he didn't have the balls to quit, not even if he wanted to, and not like that.

'Man,' Joe said, almost whispering. 'Right there we knew Coach Annese was for real. He wasn't afraid of anything.'

In that instant, that defining moment, it became clear to all that the fire that burned in the eyes of Coach Annese wasn't a reflection, but came from a furnace that burned within.

A lot of things changed since then, including the weight room. It was in very poor shape when Annese arrived at Montrose High. It's no wonder it wasn't a favorite hang out. The team needed strong kids to institute the veer, not just kids with bulging biceps like Brutus, but strong legs. Annese and assistant Coach Dennis Reinhart both believed in the value of team strength and made it a priority to build a first-class room.

In the meantime, there had to be a way to increase team strength and build camaraderie. One Sunday, after a film session, Annese showed up with a bundle of what looked like two-foot broomsticks. The kids paired up and Annese led them through a number of isometric exercises using resistance.

Senior Charlie Lange asked Joe, 'Is this for real?'

The guys had never heard of Isometrics and thought it was a fancy word Coach created that meant stretching. After all, he was pretty convincing. It looked half-ass at first and the kids goofed around like they had a substitute teacher for gym class. But as the hour progressed, so did the kids. Annese got them sweating, working, and busting it out as best they could with dowel rods. He produced a team of young men who all felt muscles the next day that they didn't realize existed. And they didn't have to touch a weight to do it!

The weight room that followed a year later made that Sunday afternoon ancient history. It showed that the kids began to believe in their coach on a new level. The school purchased new weightlifting equipment with a substantial amount of money donated by the Montrose Blueberry Committee.

The Rams became seriously involved in weightlifting by meeting four times a week during the season, and five days a week the rest of the year, including summer. The coaches manned the weight room from 8 AM to 8 PM during the summer and committed to spend whatever time it took, realizing benefits would be reaped later.

Reinhart was a national powerlifting champion himself and had the muscles to prove it. His solid frame still held the look of a serious bodybuilder. He was short and fit with a face that resembled Mike Ditka, then head coach for the Chicago Bears. His polo shirt stretched so tight around his biceps that he pushed the elbow length sleeves up his forearms to prevent cutting off his circulation. It was either cap 'em or rip 'em, and ruin a good shirt. Reinhart's thick mustache only added to his tough guy appearance, while his thighs appeared as large as the slim cheerleaders' waists. He had a way of standing stiff with arms pushed from his sides, as if expecting someone to throw a tackle at any moment. Reinhart was unaware that his stance alone intimidated the defensive players. No one really wanted to mess with him.

His credentials alone earned him recognition from his squad, along with an eagerness to learn the proper technique. Looking at him was like watching a live infomercial; they wanted his results. Naturally, freshmen were in a hurry to bulk up, falling victim to thick seniors strutting their machoism. 'Hey, is that all you can lift?'

Reinhart constantly harped on the big guys to not push the smaller ones around. He wanted them to increase their strength, but didn't want any injuries, and showed them firsthand what *not* to do. Ron Newton watched wide-eyed, observing how Reinhart could hardly reach the back of his head to comb his hair. His elbows just wouldn't give. 'Newt' discovered that his head defensive coach fell prey to what happens when you don't fully extend your arms during reps.

Joe wanted that strength and undeniably surfaced as the leader of the team. He wasn't the biggest guy on the line, but he was one of the strongest and could motivate the others. He was a likable guy, the one his classmates later voted as 'The Most Wanted to be on a Deserted Island With,' long before the birth of the Survivor series. He and Charlie became the catalyst to get the team in the weight room consistently during the off-season. Reinhart caught them both, hook, line and sinker, into firmly believing in their new weightlifting program. And so they went to work. If someone didn't wrestle or play basketball during the winter, they had better be lifting. Joe even called teammates on snow days, regardless if school was canceled and told them, 'Walk to school if you have to or find someone with a snowmobile but you better show up.'

And they did. Joe, Charlie, Bear and Matt Leeseberg were a part of the first group of lifters to vie competitively at the state meet. Charlie, the Mr. Goody-Two-Shoes of the group, was a good smiling, Christian boy. He was their pioneer who tested the waters at the first competition. That was back in the day when the entire powerlifting team was small enough to ride in one car with Reinhart at the wheel. Charlie won his weight class at States, opening a new chapter in Montrose Football.

Charlie had a modest confidence and already proved that he possessed characteristics necessary for success. He was a tall, slender brown-haired lad whose shoulder pads complimented his athletic physique. By the end of the season, he proved to his coaches and his squad to be the greatest team player. An honor that would claim him the recipient of the prestigious new 'Coaches Award.' He also set weightlifting records in the newly formed 'Champions Club.'

The 'Club' was introduced as an incentive to help players improve their agility skills, stamina, strength and to be proud of a high G.P.A. The goal was to increase each player's awareness; they had the ability to do their best every day. It served as an inspiration during the off-season, nurturing their will to compete, while bringing out the champion in all of them.

Kids were tested or timed on the bench press, parallel squat, 40 yard dash, 20 yard backward run, box jumps, T-test, mile run, jumpovers, and their G.P.A. Initial testing took place during March, then players were retested three months later. If they improved in each of the ten areas, they were inducted into the 'Champion's Club' and received a T-shirt. Eighteen players were inducted that first year, feeling nothing but pride when the results were posted in the school's newspaper -- *The Rampage.*

Some players couldn't compete in all ten areas but were able to specialize by capturing records in a few events. Records were reset each year, but the

`88 squad was the forerunner, the baseline that future years compared to; so they worked hard.

Matt Venturino, a junior punt returner, demonstrated his ability in the jumping events. Chris Clolinger showed his agility by winning the T-test event, and Chris Wright set the G.P.A record with a 4.0. Wright loved football and worked hard, yet appreciated that his coaches recognized the importance of an education.

The coaches wanted the team to realize that playing football at the high school or college level wasn't only about building strength by lifting weights. Their football careers would eventually end. It ends for everyone. It's over during high school for most, for some after college, and only a handful make it to the pros. Either way, players needed to realize that their skills could only take them so far.

What would happen if practice didn't start on time? No one really wanted to find out, but Newt, a sophomore, was about to. Newt was barely a teenager and had already become a tough risk taker. He looked older because he could grow a distinct, dark mustache while everyone else in gym class sported peach fuzz. He had difficulty getting to practice some days since his mom worked two jobs and wasn't always available, but that wouldn't stop the determined 15-year-old who was now under the spell of Coach Annese. He was too young to have a driver's license, yet old enough to know better. Newt did it anyway. He was desperate, and no one could miss the first day of pads. *No one.*

Especially him. He couldn't let them down after being selected as one of the few sophomores moved up to Varsity. He had dues to pay and respect to earn. A dangerous house-throwing twister wouldn't stop him from missing practice. After Newt tasted football during his first year of high school, he thrived on the straightforward expectations that were placed on him. He already experienced things beyond what veteran players had. Somehow, football filled the huge empty void he lived with every day since his dad checked out of life two years earlier.

How does a young boy deal with that? Saying it was hard or tough doesn't come close. Devastating, disturbing, or shocking fit better. *What does a kid do when his entire life is turned upside down and he felt abandoned?* At 13, Newt found himself in the fast lane headed the wrong way on a one-way journey and wasn't sure how to get off.

The coaches wondered, *Could they reel him in?* Newt was just a mixed up kid who needed answers, some kind of purpose to his life. Both Annese and Reinhart saw a fight to survive and succeed in Newt. They quickly saw through his toughness and spotted the slightest glimmer in his deep blue eyes that he wanted to belong. Both realized that Newt was at a crossroads, and challenged him to choose the right path.

Annese and Reinhart were both in their mid-twenties and had yet to experience the joys and heartaches that came with fatherhood. They discovered that coaching also dealt with the real stuff; the game of football suddenly didn't seem as intrinsic as they originally thought. Both felt the need to shape his future and fill the void in his young life and offered him an avenue to vent his unexplicited, yet justified anger.

In Newt's eyes, the coaches were older and wiser and willing to give him all the help he needed at a time when he needed it most. *Was it chance? Or were they guardian angels that came along at the perfect moment, giving him something to believe in?*

Himself.

Their drive transported itself deep into Newt's very soul, like a jackhammer gashing through concrete; it wouldn't stop until it punctured completely through. Newt realized that he would accomplish something big one day, if on sure determination alone. He developed a sense of survivorship escorted by an excitable spirit, and the drive of an Olympic athlete.

Football became Newt's lifesaver, the helping hand that rescued him and set him on the right course . . . for life. No way would he screw up and miss practice. So Newt did what any panicked 15-year old would, he listened to the nasty `72 pickup call him from the driveway. He grabbed the keys, jumped in, and headed for practice; confident that he'd be home before his mom was any wiser. Newt needed that 'ol truck more than it needed him. The old green Dodge sputtered more than a few times before it conked out and died two miles from the school.

Shit!

Newt slammed the door then rushed to the first house. His compelling fist desperately pounded on the stranger's front door. The antsy way he shifted his weight from left to right made him appear like he had to take a leak. Finally, a head peeked from the large picture window then cautiously opened the front door of the white ranch. Newt fought to catch his breath and forcefully pleaded, 'You gotta let me use your phone!'

The homeowner must have thought Newt had been in an accident and needed help. But the young lad didn't look banged up nor did his truck. What was the emergency? Newt anxiously dialed several phone numbers, his frustration increasing when he couldn't reach anyone. Newt thought, *Damn. Everyone must already be at the school. That is, everyone but me!* That thought terrified him even more. Newt didn't remember if he even thanked the homeowner before he swiftly dodged out of the front door, his feet barely touched the ground.

Newt sprinted the remaining two miles to the high school, running as fast as his legs would go. He swallowed panic with every swig of air; his stomach burned. By the time he arrived, he felt like a kid on his way to the principal's office. Annese noticed the alarmed look on Newt's face while he listened to his explanation between gasps of air. Newt watched the stern look on his coach's face, the same look he saw on the face of his friends' dads when they brought the car home past curfew; glad you're safe but pissed you're late.

Practice was expected to start exactly as scheduled. No excuses or everyone ran gassers. Newt was afraid to look up and sensed daggers sharply attack him from every direction. They hated to run and soon discovered Annese designed a training program to push them beyond the standard. *Dependability was taught.*

Annese arrived in August of '87 barely before the first game, like adopting a newborn baby without time to paint the nursery. He didn't have an off-season to implement the program that supported his coaching philosophy. He recruited Dennis Reinhart to run his defense, a hometown guy that he played football with at Alma College. Two other assistants joined, along with teacher Jamie Kitts. Kitts stood a head taller than the rest of the staff, a former high school All-American who played football at Marysville High School. An injury robbed him of his college football scholarship so he gladly accepted the position. He missed football.

By and large, the '87 seniors disliked Annese even though they sensed something special about him. The transition was tough especially when Annese punished them by running gassers whenever a player cursed. Running dead sprints from one sideline and back in the exhausting heat, over and over, got old fast.

It was a two-way street. The undisciplined kids also frustrated the new coaching staff. In order to curb their profanity Annese issued gassers to all, adnauseam, as a peer pressure tactic. In one sense it worked, in another it didn't. The seniors were used to Coach Bob Hayes who didn't fight what he considered unimportant battles -- like swearing. A few seniors had enough and quit during Annese's first year. They didn't want to make the commitment; it just wasn't worth it to them. So the staff went to work rebuilding their program by starting several juniors just a few games into the '87 Season. They hoped it wouldn't take two years to sell them on the new system that was to come -- *the veer.*

Annese wasn't blind and realized the resistance to his hard-nosed tactics. Some players and their parents thought his techniques were too tough, and that he swore too much. They blamed it on his young age. School officials listened to their concerns, but the high school principal wanted to give Tony Annese a chance. After all, he hired him so it was his neck on the line. He was wise enough to realize the benefits a disciplined football program can bring to a high school. Seniors had adapted to the cool, calm style of Coach Hayes, who didn't stress discipline much. Not that the kids wouldn't run through a wall for Hayes, but with a new guy, like any new situation, the kids were going to test it. *They flunked.*

Annese started a system based on trust and discipline -- like the Army. Something unique developed for those that stayed. They worked harder than they ever thought they could, and learned more than they ever thought they would. Players respected their new coach who proved to work harder than anyone else; they started to see results.

Even though they went 4-5 in '87, Annese managed to lay the foundation and whet their appetite. Younger players valued the lessons; yet willingly admitted they were a bit intimidated by Coach Annese. He had earned their respect.

It was the first day of pads, previously known as 'The Meat Grinder,' but Annese called it 'Ram drills.' Joe stretched his pads over his muscular legs and looked at Bear. He knew Bear sensed it too, that familiar, comfortable feeling like putting on your favorite shirt. Joe grinned as they headed out of the locker room, 'Let's go hit somebody.'

Two other sophomores, who appeared as intense as Newt, worked out with the Varsity. All three of them wanted a permanent spot on the big team even if it meant being the low man on the totem pole. It meant Varsity, a year ahead of schedule. Each fought to confirm they had something to prove. Jason Katt paired up with Newt on a Ram drill, like two young bucks going for the ultimate prize. *Who would break? Who would survive?*

Their adrenaline skyrocketed and they felt their hormones kick in while the squad shouted. 'C'mon, is that all you got?'

Neither stopped when the whistle blew, as their internal drive consumed them. Male egos flew high with every drop of sweat that tempted the drill into a fistfight. Annese and Reinhart exchanged an unspoken glance that said, *This team loves to hit!* It wasn't anything personal, just a result of constant drilling from the coaches. The strong level of competition pushed them over the edge. The coaches realized they needed to channel that energy and control the overactive testosterone that surfaced. Everyone seemed to thrive on the vigor and liveliness of the rookies, until it appeared unashamedly obvious that neither planned to quit. Seniors stood back admiring their tenacity; they wanted those stubborn sophomores on Varsity.

The juniors were more skeptical, especially Venturino. Once the fight reached an intense point, 'Vinnie' felt slightly uncomfortable watching his teammates exchange hard blows. *Maybe the coaches just wanted them to get it out of their system, being the first day and all.*

About that time Charlie glanced at Bear. His raised eyebrows sent a questionable glance that said, *Just how long will they let this free-for-all go on?* Annese and Reinhart stepped in about then. Each grabbed an arduous sophomore, placing their arms behind their backs like cops busting a bar brawl. 'All right, that's enough!'

They unintentionally started a new tradition for Ram drills. When it came time for the buddy drill, Vinnie was wiser than he was a year ago. Since he was the smallest guy on the team, he avoided senior Matt Leeseberg. 'Cheese,' a name his mom even adopted, was a huge tackle that stood 6'3"; Vin didn't want to be paired with him. Vinnie quickly found his friend Paul

Wixson, 'Hey Wix, run with me. I got stuck with a 400 pound guy last year and that was awful!'

Wixson laughed when he recalled the scene, 'Yeah, you guys looked like David and Goliath.'

Vinnie was a high-energy pip-squeak that stood 5'5" and weighed about 125 pounds, dripping wet. He could run around the 400m track fairly fast; hardly a match for his heavyweight partner. Maybe he was driven by fear, afraid to make the big guy do too many ups-and-downs while he ran. When they switched, Vinnie did more ups-and-downs than the entire team combined. The fat guy's feet were heavy and sluggish, as if dragging a ball and chain during his lap. His unhurried pace caused Vin's arms to grow heavier by the minute as 'Fatman' dragged his ass. Vinnie was only a scrawny sophomore then, afraid the fat guy might sit on him if he complained.

Something drastically changed for Vinnie during the summer of `88; his life would never be the same. While most of his friends enjoyed their youthful summer days, he had serious decisions on his mind. One involved football . . . *Should he play or not?*

When Wixson stopped by to pick him up for their first Varsity two-a-days he beeped and yelled, 'Hey Vinnie, you ready?'

Vinnie sprinted to Wixson's car then hesitated after hooking his hands over the open passenger window. He threw Wix a look of uncertainty, while trying to decide if he should get in or not. Wix studied the serious expression on his friend's face, immediately feeling a level of compassion. Wix was a head taller than Vinnie and outweighed him by a good 90 pounds. One played on the line, the other in the backfield, yet they were good friends. Friends that shared an undisclosed secret. Wix felt the weight on his friend's shoulders and secretly hoped that Vin wouldn't bag football for a job bagging groceries. 'C'mon, get in!'

Vinnie stared at the door handle while contemplating, *Should I go or not?* He looked at Wix who thought about their J.V. Season. Vinnie proved to be the spark plug for the Rams; his teammates wanted him to share in their first Varsity experience. They were all anxious to play for Coach Annese even though they didn't know him very well . . . *yet.*

The truth was, Vinnie wanted to play football more than anything else in the world, but he worried about what others thought. It played on his mind constantly. *Heck, she was still planning on being a cheerleader this season. What would people say about that? He still couldn't believe it happened to 'them'. Those things always happened to 'other couples' and here he was in a heap of trouble and a baby due in five months. Even though he was only 16 years-old, he didn't want to stop doing everything he enjoyed.*

His parents, as well as his girlfriends', wanted them to have a normal high school experience. They planned to do more than their share to make that happen. Mr. Venturino wanted the best for his only son -- a college education and hopefully a football scholarship. Some laughed at their dream of a 5'5"-125 pound kick returner playing Division I football, but then they didn't know how quick Vin was on the field. Vinnie wouldn't fully appreciate all that his father did for him until years down the road. The father and son were determined not to let their ambition be ruined by a few cynical pessimists or a single innocent baby. Their dream gave Vinnie the encouragement he needed to face decisions during his darkest hours.

Wix remembered the day his friend broke the news to him. Vin drove over to his house the very day he found out, totally catching Wix off-guard. Wix looked shocked and asked Vin, 'What are you telling me?'

'I'm going to be a dad.'

Once Vinnie shared his news with Wixson it brought them even closer, although Vin thought it was strange to see his happy-go-lucky friend look so serious. Wixson threw a look at his friend and seemed to read his mind when he calmly said, 'Let's go Vin. It'll be okay.'

Vinnie exchanged the glance and felt the tug between boyhood and manhood. For a moment he felt carefree and excited when he jumped in his friend's car and thought, *I sure hope you're right.*

Vin felt the energy the moment he walked into the locker room. Everyone seemed glad to be there, anxious to start football practice. He thought some of the guys looked at him differently and he wondered, *Did I just imagine that or do they know? Do they think I shouldn't be here? What will the coaches think?*

It was difficult enough to explain his situation to his parents, now he had to repeat the scene with his new coaches. He wondered if he had the nerve and decided to hold off telling Coach Annese, until he got to know him better. Vin planned to keep his situation quiet for as long as he could, and just be *one of the guys.*

The team gathered together before the second session of two-a-days. They joked around, unable to hide their enthusiasm for their upcoming season. Coach Annese started preaching about his expectations and what they could and couldn't do, and should and shouldn't do. His talk made Vinnie choke on the curt words. His crisp, deep voice caught Vin's undivided attention when he ended with ' . . . so don't get your girlfriends knocked up!'

Vin felt all eyes drill through him, and naturally hung his head. He realized how fast big news traveled in a small town and wondered who all knew. *Is this speech intended for me? 'Cause if it is - it's a little late!*

Wixson sensed Vin's discomfort and placed his large hand on his friend's smaller shoulder. His loyal friend leaned toward Vin, speaking in a low, hushed voice. 'Hey, it'll be okay.'

Vin nodded, appreciating that his friend stood by him. A few guys gave Vin sympathetic nods. They'd heard the news from their girlfriends, and were thankful that it didn't happen to them. Most teammates were shocked when they heard, especially those in relationships. They didn't pretend to comprehend what Vinnie and his girl must be going through, but it gave them one hell of a scare. They suddenly realized that everything had consequences, no matter how fun and harmless it seemed at the time.

Someone informed Coach Annese during practice. Annese searched for Vinnie after practice finished. 'Hey, come with me for a minute. I want to talk to you.'

It was the first time Coach found himself in that situation. After a year, he had already helped more troubled boys than he ever expected, but this situation was more complicated. Vin was going to be a dad and was only starting his junior year of high school. The young coach quickly discovered that his position involved much more than understanding the offense and defense. Vinnie's heart raced. A quick, fearful chill shot from his gut to his head when Coach Annese placed an arm around Vin's heavy shoulders, leading him away. 'Hey, I apologize for the way I blurted out earlier. I really didn't know about it then. I would've stated it a little differently.'

He stopped and faced Vinnie, 'What can I do to help?'

Vin felt his stomach swap anxiety for relief. 'Don't worry about it Coach, you didn't know.'

Vinnie listened while Coach persuaded him to stick with football, repeating the same words of wisdom that his father said. Neither wanted him to look back one day and feel resentment about what *could have been*.

Vin left his first day of Varsity practice exhausted, yet had a skip in his walk, feeling calmer than when he arrived. He felt lucky that the people who mattered most in his life wanted to help him make the best of his situation. Between the support at home and encouragement from his coaches he thought, *Maybe this could all work out.*

Wixson had a reputation of being a cut-up, a fun-loving spirit . . . until the day he got hit in the privates during a drill. The pain was excruciating and he couldn't control the words that emerged from his mouth. Annese wouldn't put up with swearing and hovered over Wixson. The moment Wix swore again Annese responded, 'You better shut up or you're giving me a gasser.'

Wixson doubled over in pain and swore again, unaware of the world around him. Coach repeated, 'That's one. You better shut up or the whole team's gonna give me a gasser!'

The team laughed after Wixson swore again. But Coach wasn't smiling when he yelled, 'There's another one!'

Cheese, their biggest tackle at 265 pounds, hated to run. He was tall, his frame already resembled a college football player. His large athletic build and olive complexion made even his tanned friends look pale when standing next to him. His mood was the first to switch from jovial laughter to fuming anger, after huddling with the others around Wix and Coach Annese. Suddenly, it didn't seem so funny. 'Hey, shut up Wixson. Just shut your mouth! I know it hurts, but just shut up!'

Coach Annese ran his football program somewhat like the military. The rules were black and white; players abided by them or were not invited to stay. Matt Anderson liked Coach Annese because he gave him a chance, in spite of being one of the smaller players on the team. Maybe it was because being small never stopped Coach Annese. Anderson appreciated getting a chance after being overlooked through the years. Coach made Anderson feel like he could make something out of anybody, bringing out his best no matter how big or small he was. But when it came to long hair and earrings, they butted heads. After Anderson arrived at the first practice with shoulder length blonde hair and an earring is his left ear, his teammates sensed trouble brewing. It usually took a year or so for West Coast fads to hit the small midwestern town of Montrose. That particular popular trend tagged the phrase, 'Left is right and right is wrong.' Joe stood back and asked Bear, 'How do you think Annese will handle this?'

'I don't think he'll overlook it.'

He was right. Coach came right out and told Anderson what the rules were. He wanted him to stay on the team, but he wouldn't budge on his guidelines. Anderson's step-dad later stormed into Annese's office to stick up for his step-son, embellished in his own earring and long hair. The step-dad came to discuss some of the rules that were too strict, considering the times. The entire scene caught Anderson by surprise. He wasn't close with his step-dad, yet felt proud that he stood up for him. His teammates stood in the background and wondered, *How would Coach react to this?*

They should've known better. Annese had a better understanding of Anderson's environment, but he still wouldn't budge on his policies. *Rules were rules.*

Anderson respected his coach's values, even if they clashed with his own personal preferences. Anderson knew it was a battle he couldn't win, so he compromised after walking into the coach's office the following day. Annese greeted him, 'Hey, somebody got a hair cut. What about the earring?'

Anderson had a great smile and a pleasing tone to his voice that made him easy to like. Likable enough that his schoolmates later elected him as their Homecoming King. After a few moments of debate, the average-sized senior smiled, 'Okay, I promise I won't wear it to practice.'

Anderson didn't mention that he planned to wear his earring during school, except Fridays. *Fridays were sacred.*

The coaches and players gathered to discuss their upcoming season and set goals. The '88 Rams were inexperienced at certain positions; their season depended on how fast they matured. They needed to become football players very quickly.

'We're a 31 man roster, 15 of you are back from last year. We're counting on your experience. We'll use our seven returning starters to run a balanced offensive attack. You gained a lot of knowledge from a year ago, and you got bigger and stronger during the off-season. We're looking good so far. You guys can run and throw and we've got guys who can think on their feet. We want to be able to finesse people yet run over them with a 5-2 defense.'

Charlie and Joe shouted 'Yeah' after high-fiving each other, proudly representing Reinhart's defense.

Traditionally, Montrose's strength was its defense. They focused on shutting people down. The Rams were breaking tradition from their normal style of power football and were becoming a dive and veer team. The staff wanted their tradition-rich Rams to regain the form that propelled them to League Championship seasons five times in the '80's, including playoff appearances in 1981 and 1985.

Just 12 brief months ago, Annese had the Rams run shotgun and the T-option while he eased them into the veer. Shotgun gave the junior quarterback, Chris Clolinger, extra time to move around and throw. The offensive line was terrible then and allowed 'Goose' to get abused. The guys called Clolinger 'Goose' after pro relief pitcher Goose Gossage. Joe gave Goose the nickname after catching for him during baseball season. Like Gossage, Goose had a mean fast ball that turned a few heads; the nickname carried over to football season.

Goose got sacked eight times in one game. Eight times. The following week, he couldn't practice until Thursday because of back spasms. But he wouldn't say anything because he was a sophomore on a Varsity team, with a group of seniors who weren't thrilled with Annese changing everything. Goose took things in stride. He was a good-looking, fit, sandy-haired teenager who had an arm. Goose learned fast and rarely got upset, just banged up more than he liked. The veer was difficult for players at first, but Goose studied the offense so thoroughly that he made it easier on the team.

After school, Bear caught up with his friend Joe and headed toward the locker room. In just a few short days they would dress for their first game. Both felt anxious when they reached the glass entrance doors between the administration offices and the gym. Bear stopped walking and stared outside, 'I don't know. It looks pretty dark out there.'

Joe asked Coach, 'Hey, we practicing inside today?'

He wasn't surprised at his response. 'No. Outside.'

Bear stepped out of the back school entrance near the football locker room. Before he put his helmet on, he tipped his head back to gaze at the dark gray sky. He noticed a nasty storm ranging in the near distance. Clouds appeared angry as they raced through the sky, like they were in a hurry to get someplace. His nostrils sensed the musty smell of rain as a wet mist sprinkled his face. It looked like a daunting downpour was quickly headed their way, yet it felt good.

A brief half-hour later, it didn't feel quite as refreshing. It bit. The line barely heard their quarterback's cadence over the hail thumping against the top of their helmets. As much as they wanted to practice, it felt weird; the conditions made it difficult to concentrate. Hailstones felt like bullets, making a pinging sound before the frozen rain boomeranged from their helmets. It was like acting out one of their favorite shows -- 'Tour of Duty,' only they dodged from hailstones instead of wild fire during the heat of the battle.

Charlie didn't want to be the first to quit, but it was getting difficult to ignore the hail striking the back of his calves. He looked at Kevin Salter when they took their positions on the line, 'Hey, you think he's gonna call practice?'

The tall lean athlete replied, 'I'm sure he will any minute now. This is crazy.'

But he didn't. The thought never entered his head. It was Birch Run week; their first game was only days away and they needed to work on several things. The high school principal watched practice from his office, wondering when the team would surrender to the weather. But this group appeared to be tough as nails. He respected their work ethic, but he had to stop them. The principal finally slipped his raincoat on then headed to the field, forcing the squad to move to the gym -- *immediately!*

Maybe that was an indication of how their first game would go. *It wasn't pretty.* **Birch Run** had tremendous team speed, making it difficult for the Rams to contend with their quickness. Montrose lost the contest in '87 and Birch Run appeared three times faster in '88. The Rams missed two scoring opportunities after driving to the Panther ten, only to come up empty handed. The third quarter was just as ugly when Montrose dropped a ball -- all alone in the endzone.

One could sense the frustration that Goose felt after each series. He led the Rams to nine first downs, but only hit on two of his nine aerials. Goose led them to a 4-5 record the season past. He was only a sophomore then, and two of those losses were within two points. He earned the faith that the seniors and the coaches placed in him. Annese worked with Goose during the off-season, teaching him the veer option. Coach even set up fake players on the gym floor. He helped Goose become a better quarterback in a faster time then the staff expected, but Birch Run challenged him.

The Rams took their 0-21 loss and boarded their wounded pride on the stuffy school bus. They worked so hard to have such an ugly beginning. Defensively, linebackers Joe and junior Cliff Casteel turned in 21 tackles. The defense grabbed two fumble recoveries and an interception, but on the flip side -- they allowed three TD's. Annese was irate, but realized they lost to a very good team. The road ahead wasn't going to be easy. The Rams needed to get better week-by-week. He wondered, *Would the Rams start out 0-2 for their second straight season?*

They all wanted a win for their season opener, to build some confidence before facing the perennial Class B power of the **Chesaning** Indians. Most of the standing room only crowd of nearly 2,000 had not found a seat when it happened. Chesaning coughed up the pigskin on the initial possession of the first quarter. Ram junior back Chris Kies picked-up the loose ball then rambled 30 yards to pay dirt, as Montrose hosted their closest neighbors to the west.

Kies was a short, stocky kid with one of the proudest dads on the team. Mr. Kies watched every move that his son made, unable to resist yelling at the top of his lungs, 'That's my boy!'

The extra point put the Montrose Rams on the scoreboard first, 7-0. With :18 seconds left in the first quarter on a third and 14 play, the Indian senior signal caller hooked up with his receiver on a 20 yard scoring toss. The extra point knotted the board at seven apiece. The war was on.

The Rams pushed inside the five yard line, looking like they'd break the deadlock. Kies plowed through a gaping hole, but the ball squirted loose and Chesaning recovered.

Goose shook his head, showing his frustration. 'Guys - we're too close to the goal for a critical turnover like that.'

Annese knew that the second half would be even bigger, and tried to prepare his squad for the emotional battle. Cheese sat in the locker room during the half, totally focused on every word. Annese had a way of captivating each of them, hypnotizing them with his words aimed straight at their hearts. He made them look deep inside, completing a serious gut check.

Cheese didn't want to lose that game, not after last year. He drifted for a moment, recalling the half-time talk in Chesaning's locker room in `87 when Coach yelled, 'If Chesaning scores one more time, we're going home.'

The young team felt uncertain of what to do at the start of the third period after the Rams kicked off to Chesaning. The Indians managed to run the ball all the way back for a TD. They were a bunch of 16-17 year-old kids who wondered if their first year coach literally meant what he threatened. Insecure looks revealed their lack of confidence; unsure if he expected them to quit and get on the bus. But the squad quickly got their answer when Annese fumed at them, scaring them into scoring.

Cheese was one of 15 returning seniors anxious to even the score, after Chesaning handed them a 7-36 whipping in `87. The Montrose Varsity felt their school and fans didn't have high expectations like they did in previous years. It was a natural letdown after mediocre seasons in `86 and `87. The Rams dominated as League Champs five of the six years before that under Coach Bob Hayes. But the `88 Rams started to work good together as a team. They wanted to show Annese that they were capable of playing much better during his second year as head coach. The Rams were believers as well as overachievers.

Goose threw a pass to Kevin, hoping to open things up during the third quarter. He watched Kevin's tall frame stretch as far as he could, but the ball only glazed his fingertips then went airborne another 20 yards.

Tafoya played the other end position and ran a pattern. He happened to be in the right spot at the right time, turning the pass into a theatrical play. In spite of the close score, Tafoya had fun at his new position. He got tackled earlier in the game, yet still managed to dive and make an awesome one-handed catch. Even though his team didn't score on the down, it became one of those perfect football moments that a player never forgets. It was also a moment that made Tafoya want to thank Coach Annese for insisting he play Varsity football. Annese wasn't around when Tafoya broke his hand during his freshman season. It was a nasty break that developed a severe internal infection that led to surgery. He gave up football his sophomore year, and became satisfied with basketball, track, and cross-country. Tafoya made up his mind, *I don't need football. I still have basketball* (which was his favorite sport anyway). But Coach Annese kept after him -- 'You're playing football Tafoya.'

Tafoya finally gave in, feeling thankful that the seniors accepted him. He had a slight reading disability and didn't have many classes with seniors; therefore, didn't feel as popular or outgoing as some. He never had a problem with it, yet felt maybe some of the seniors did. But once they hit the field, Tafoya was aggressive and outgoing, proving that he could compete with the best of them. He quickly earned their respect; they all soon discovered that they didn't have any differences.

Cheese became frustrated after watching Chesaning's offensive line assert itself in the third period by marching 80 yards on 13 plays, for what could be the game winning score. But the Rams had another shot. Coach had faith in his strong right side and ran the same play over senior tackles Joe Morse and Cheese. At 265 pounds, Cheese was their biggest weapon aided by Joe's strong 200 pounds, but they couldn't help the Rams break through. If determination alone could break a hole, the Rams would easily have split a gash in the dam, but Chesaning's brick wall frustrated them to no end.

It became scary at the end of the game when Bear told Goose in the huddle, 'We can't keep running the same play, they're looking for it. We've got to try something different.'

Nothing against Joe and Cheese, they were his closest friends. In fact, they were inseparable their senior year, even their girlfriends hung out together. Bear and Joe were neighbors and knew each other since birth. Cheese hung around them ever since he moved to Montrose back in the sixth grade, but none of that mattered at the moment. They ran three straight plays on the strong side, *and it wasn't working.* Goose wanted to win the game just as much as Bear did, if not more. They were in the same situation against Birch Run last week, and the left side didn't get the down when they had their chance.

The signal caller concealed his frustration, pausing to think before replying. 'What am I supposed to do Bear? Coach keeps calling it in!'

There was something in the serious tone of Bear's voice that caught the second year quarterback off-guard. Bear was usually the one cutting up and goofing around with the guys. But he knew in that defining moment, that the Rams could do whatever they set their minds to. Bear looked at Goose, 'Run it on my side just once. I promise we'll open it up.'

Bear was not the type to openly go against the grain. He played tackle and was one of the big guys on the line. For the most part, Bear was an obedient student who possessed a likable honesty. His integrity coupled by his powerful, serious expression, made Goose think twice before finalizing his decision. 'Okay guys, listen up...'

They broke huddle. Charlie took his position at center, while nervously fingering the ball. He instinctively lined up the threads until they felt comfortable in his hand. Charlie had exchanged enough hand-offs with Goose that he could snap the ball in his sleep, but he also knew they could botch one in an instant. Goose had a way of taking things in stride and rarely got upset. He rehearsed the play in his mind then slowly looked to his left. When he glanced down the right side of the line, he intentionally threw a glance at Coach Annese from the corner of his eye. Coach always stood straight down the line of scrimmage, monitoring every move. Goose took a deep breath, forcing his brain to ignore his conscience, then bravely changed the play.

The Rams could've made the down on their fortitude alone; Goose felt thankful for that. Annese appreciated their spunk, but was displeased with their sneaky method . . . and the squad knew it. It was bad enough to go against your coach, but if you botched it . . . practice would be hell.

After an interception and four minutes remaining in the game, Montrose had one last chance to score. Twenty-four seconds of sustained fury remained and everyone wondered, *Could the Rams pull it off?*

Intense adrenaline surrounded the stadium, saturating both teams, as well as their supporters. Fans felt every ounce of their emotion, noticing how midfield looked like a cluster of smokestacks. Players' mouths served as chimney flues, allowing white steam to escape when heavy breathing met crisp, evening air.

The Rams moved the ball down the field within the five yard line. Joe thought, *For sure we can bust in from three yards in four downs and challenge the lead.*

Annese weighed his options from the sideline. *Should he settle for a tie and kick the extra point, or roll the dice on a two-point conversion to win or lose the game?* He decided he had to go for it -- no guts, no glory. He planned on calling a 48-counter option pass to junior Jason Tafoya. He knew that he'd catch it. Tafoya had the best hands and he never dropped the little three-step drop throws from Goose.

Both fear and adrenaline rushed through Kies who emitted a petrifying scream when he ran directly at his opponent on second down. Kies was a fearless bulldog who would rather run through you than around you. The entire Montrose sideline grew restless. Anderson, another back, couldn't sit still on the sideline and wanted a piece of the action, but realized they needed the power of Cliff and Kies. Joe and Cheese blocked like there was no tomorrow, and thought for sure the Rams could punch through from two yards out. Again, no gain.

Annese called the same play behind Joe and Cheese who fought back hard against Chesaning's brick wall. It became a nightmare for both of them. Emotions flew high and Kies again screamed fiercely, like a wild man determined to strike at anything in his path. He feared no one. Neither did his opponents. The Chesaning defense protected their endzone like a sacred burial ground, denying the Rams one final chance to cross. Bob Sager's Chesaning Indians hung on for a hard-fought, '7-14' gridiron victory over the Montrose Rams.

The dejected Rams huddled midfield after the game, aggravated that they didn't score. Coach Annese knew their faces so well, sensing their frustration. He was a small, but feisty giant who enthralled their full attention when he spoke. They failed to capitalize on a golden scoring opportunity -- not once but *twice* inside the five yard line that would've turned things around. Coach told the squad, 'That turnover was critical. We fumbled on a play where we could've walked the ball into the endzone.'

Cheese felt his words were specifically meant for he and Joe. His dark eyes focused at a thick blade of grass, while he stared at the ground, lost in his own frustration. They ran all four downs over the two of them, the strong side, and couldn't score from the five. It burned a spot in the core of his soul that instantly became his biggest regret; one that stayed with him for more than a decade.

Cliff wondered, *What could we have done differently? What more could I have done to help the team? Whatever it was, he would've done it in a heartbeat.*

Annese analyzed their expressions, feeling a metamorphosis transpire in front of his very own eyes. He saw it in their faces and heard it in their voices. His Rams sincerely felt the honest pain of loss. It became a defining moment, as translucent as it was. Annese welcomed the revolution he witnessed; his steadfast Rams were becoming committed. He told them, 'You came far enough tonight to almost beat a team as good as Chesaning. We were beaten tonight by the class of the MMB (Mid-Michigan B League).'

Losing hurts. Especially when it's a very, very close game; a game that would have more impact years down the road, more than anyone could even begin to imagine. It was tough to end with a goal line battle. Their pain intensified after realizing how close they came. Saturday's headline read, 'Tribe Earns Victory, Rams Earn Respect.' Indian Coach Sager told the press, 'I give Montrose all the credit in the world. They played one heckuva game.'

Coach Annese silently hoped after the disgruntled fans read the article they wouldn't only focus on the loss, but realize just how hard the Rams had played. He overheard their comments and knew they were questioning the direction of the coaching staff, wondering if they were on the right track. Annese's overall record was now '4 and 7.' So far in '88, the Freshmen were 0-1, the J.V. had lost two, and his Varsity was winless. For the Montrose coaching staff, that added up to 0-5. Yeah, they were in a rebuilding phase at Montrose, *but how long would it take? When would the W's come? Would the Rams give up?*

Their efforts were not rewarded, but the Rams were far from quitting. They honestly believed their work ethic and commitment would eventually pay off. They were learning what hard work was and hoped good things followed, but at the time it felt like a big battle. Coach was building attitude. His Rams were becoming physically strong as individuals and emotionally strong as a unit, after playing two tough opening games. Annese felt they were ready to play hard-nosed football in the Genesee Eight Conference (GEC).

Newt was late for practice again, hoping to slip in unnoticed, but quickly learned that it was hard to sneak anything by Coach Annese. His deep voice sent a chill through Newt when Annese yelled, 'Give me 50!'

Newt hit the hard ground with a sigh. He already felt frustrated for being late and now was embarrassed that he was busted. He counted loudly, then toned it down after Annese moved down the field. Newt mouthed '18' and thought his coach was sidetracked, so he stopped to rest for a moment.

Annese's voice startled him, 'Newt, I can't hear you, better give me another 50!'

Newt started over. *Shit! That man must have eyes in the back of his head.*

Annese watched the game films over and over, becoming fanatical about personal fouls. If he could justify in his mind that a play had the potential of a personal foul, even if the referee had not called it, Annese rendered the punishment. He used peer pressure to discipline the entire team, not just the player involved. For every possible penalty, the entire team had to run 15 gassers, which the team dubbed 15-for-15. They hated running but understood his message -- no personal fouls. *Responsibility was implied.*

The Rams prepared for their first league game against **Hamady**, as if it were the start of a new season. The League Championship was still an achievable goal, but the Hamady Hawks already had two wins to open the GEC League, while the Montrose Rams had two losses. They didn't want anymore.

Montrose won the toss and elected to take possession the second half. Instead of taking the pigskin into the endzone, it seemed like they ran up-and-down the field at will. The Rams coughed up the ball twice inside the Hamady ten in the first quarter, wasting good scoring opportunities.

Wixson took a hard hit in the first quarter of the game. His right arm hurt like hell, but he managed to make a left-handed catch. When he reached the sideline he took several Motrin, his trademark drug. The guys called Wixson 'Motrin Man' whose motto was, 'Stop the pain before it stops you.' His mom was a nurse and he conveniently 'borrowed' from her supply of Motrin, generously sharing them whenever his teammates were in pain. But he didn't just hand them over; Wix asked questions. He made guys justify the severity of their pain, then evaluated if they needed 600mg, 800mg or 1200mg. That night, he popped a couple strong ones, wondering if it would even touch the pain in his right arm.

Goose finally connected with Vinnie on a nine yard TD with 2:30 left in the half, then handed off to Kies who bullied over for the conversion. On the ensuing kickoff, Hamady ran 75 yards to pay dirt, then made the conversion to even the score. With time running out, Montrose booted a 25 yard field goal, taking a slight three point lead by the half.

Jimmy Harris played nose-tackle, and wished he could have the type of game that he did a year ago against Hamady. He still remembered the night he sacked the quarterback five times and blocked a punt; linemen don't easily forget games like that.

Fans who couldn't resist the smell of buttery popcorn, wished they had ignored their hunger twinges. They felt like uninvited guests at an ass-chewing contest when they passed by an embarrassed team tucked in a corner of the field counting push-ups -- in unison. It was obvious to passer-bys how displeased Annese was when he stood over them, unsatisfied with their performance. His message came across loud and clear; he had expectations for his team . . . and they were not being met!

But other forces were involved, some beyond player's control. Wixson managed to play the entire first half of the game before he surrendered to his pain, hoping to catch a brief rest during the half. It was the one thought that kept him going and helped diminish his pain. He didn't expect to be reprimanded and ordered to drop fifty push-ups during the half. Wixson tried to do them until the pain took over. He couldn't conceal that something was definitely wrong with his arm. It throbbed continuously; he couldn't put any weight on it. The Motrin didn't touch his pain, forcing him to make a decision – one that he hated. The fun-loving defensive end was extremely serious when he approached the two assistant coaches. He held up his swollen arm, 'I can't play the rest of the game.'

Coach Hayes called him 'a wimp' and Coach Kitts called him 'a baby,' causing the young lad to doubt his own toughness. That in itself would've persuaded Wixson to play above the pain under normal conditions, but that night he couldn't. No matter how much he wanted to, the pain was overwhelming, and he realized that even tough, macho guys had their limits. His body wasn't just sending him a warning sign; it conveyed a roadblock. Wixson swallowed his pride, hung his sweaty head while holding his aching arm, then found a place on the sideline. But Wixson got a chance to redeem his ego at school on Monday, when he sported a shiny new cast on his broken right arm.

Players focused on every word that Coach Annese spoke. The squad wanted to believe they were capable of accomplishing everything he said they could. 'We're going out and setting the tone for the second half. The most important drive of the game is second half, first possession.'

And they did.

They believed in themselves enough to march 63 yards to the 12 yard line on their opening second half drive. Cliff bolted in for the score then flaunted the leather ball high in the air, exposing it like a valuable trophy. His buddies joined in the celebration, but soon discovered just how much Annese despised showboating. Cliff wondered, *Why is Coach so furious? After all, I gained 95 yards during the game and made seven unassisted tackles.* He had a funny feeling that he'd pay for his little celebration at practice on Monday.

It would be worse than Cliff imagined. In just two days, his arms felt like rubber and he was dog-tired. He wondered if he could ever hold a football that high above his head again, for what seemed like an eternity. One could safely bet that Cliff Casteel would never be seen showboating a football in the endzone. *Tenacity was understood.*

Goose pulled them ahead when he scored on a five yard keeper. With some help from Kies, another workhorse who contributed 114 yards, Montrose handed Hamady their first loss of the season. The Rams boarded the bus with their first League victory, but the ride home was not a festive one. The bus smelled of sweat, a strong offensive odor that seemed to attach itself like an ugly parasite on their inexcusable performance. In spite of their '24-8' victory, they sensed Coach Annese wasn't happy about their three fumbles, especially the two within the red zone.

Joe and Cheese talked about their next contender and the type of defense **New Lothrop** played. Their deep conversation took place over food from Mr. G's Pizzeria. Linemen had a habit of resolving issues over food and this was no exception. They followed New Lothrop's season that had two big wins and one close loss that fell in overtime to Bentley. The line wondered if the offense would get the job done. They were still in transition, trying to adjust to the complex veer, which still felt new to them. It was a tricky offense for a high school team to learn quickly, and the Rams seemed to lack confidence in running it successfully.

Things seemed to turn around for the Rams who dominated the New Lothrop Hornets from the onset. On one offensive series they ran the veer the same direction all the way down the field. The Rams never huddled and a pleased Coach Annese stood on the sideline yelling, 'Run it again!'

The veer finally started to work.

New Lothrop must've known they were running it again, and still couldn't stop it. It ignited the Rams' confidence. The fans loved it! Everything clicked. The finally got a paycheck on Friday night for all of their hard work. Instead of fumbling the ball, they forced fumbles. Things started going bad for the Hornets and the Rams capitalized. The shoe was on the other foot when the Hornets fumbled three times in the first half.

Cliff and Kies sparked the offense after passing the century mark for rushing yards. Goose came into his passing game when he hooked up with Vinnie on a TD pass, then dazzled the crowd with a 55 yard pass caught by the tall, lean Jason Tafoya. He was a player who worked hard and made great progress; an honor that his teammates later bestowed as their 'Most Improved Player.'

The Rams came together as a team, performing their best game yet with a nearly flawless '33-14' victory over New Lothrop. They tasted the sweet kiss of victory two weeks straight, knowing what it took to win. They finally saw the results of their hard work during the off-season.

The line's performance was what made the backfield successful; their execution would make or break their season. They demonstrated how far they had progressed in a year. The option was coming along for Kies and Cliff, the Rams all junior backfield. Goose felt confident running behind Cheese, whose massive size made huge holes for him. His entire offensive line was phenomenal; Charlie, Joe, Cheese, Bear, Kevin, Tafoya and sophomore tackle Brody Mier, showed ability to drive off the ball and move opponents.

Fridays were special -- the most important day of the week. Football players dressed in shirts and ties instead of traditional football jerseys. It was a new tradition that Coach Annese started when he took over. From the moment they dressed for school, Coach wanted the squad to feel that game days were special; the tight knot around their neck was a constant reminder.

Spirit-filled festivities consumed the school during Homecoming week, while the Rams prepared to host the **Bentley** Bulldogs. But Newt didn't feel very festive after separating his shoulder earlier in the week. The only good thing about getting injured was that Coach Annese's good-looking wife took him to the doctor. The young sophomore knew he was the envy of every senior on the team, when he perched himself next to Chris Annese in the front seat. The guys thought she was the new girl in school the first time they saw the attractive, petite blonde a year ago. She was hard to read and they sensed their youth annoyed her, but it didn't stop their constant flirting when Coach wasn't looking. They completely overlooked the fact that she was a smart college graduate just starting her career as the new business manager for the Montrose School District.

Later that week, Newt stopped to read a freshly hung poster outside of the coach's office. It seemed Annese constantly instilled the importance of a good attitude. The injured player crossed his arms, allowing his eyes to follow the words while soaking in the significance of its message:

Montrose Football - Which Way Today?
'How You Use Today Will Determine How Tomorrow Uses You'

Many of the words on the poster implicated what he was about to do when Newt reported to Annese on game day, 'Hey Coach, my doctor gave me a support brace and said I was able to play tonight.'

Maybe he stretched the truth a bit. Just a bit. If he repeated what his doc really recommended, he'd be stuck on the sideline and he hated watching. After all, he was one of the chosen sophomores who made the Varsity. Nothing would get in his way. *Nothing.*

The seniors could tell by the way Newt played that he'd be a future star. Even though Newt couldn't raise his arm above his head to intercept the ball, he planned to bat it down. That was his game plan.

Vin dropped a punt early in the game and Bentley scored a one yard TD. Vinnie felt his stomach churn when he approached the sideline. His heart pounded so loudly that the noise echoed in his helmet, forcing him to gasp when Coach grabbed his facemask, 'Forget it Vin. Just get it in the endzone!'

So Vin did. He was jumpy and felt his heart pump quicker than normal. Maybe his quickness caught them off-guard when he caught the ball, then confidently strode down the sideline while layers of pads added mass to his size. Vin ran the kickoff the entire length of the field, giving Montrose a one-point lead after a good PAT. Vin's happiness quickly turned and he got pissed when Bentley scored their second TD. He funneled his energy to breakup the conversion, but the Bentley Bulldogs were up.

Montrose drove 89 yards, then Kies capped it with a five yard TD. A successful conversion gave the Rams a 15-12 half-time edge, but there wasn't any room for bragging rights. Montrose knew they were far from being out of the battle. Bentley was the defending GEC kingpin and Annese was worried about their offense.

Their half-time strategy became, 'Bentley can't score if they don't have the ball!' That seemed the logical way to contain the speed Coach Cal TerHaar's Bulldogs had. Montrose exercised their game plan, maintaining ball control after driving 63 yards on the third quarter's opening possession. Kies capped it off again with a one yard run, then kicked the PAT for a 22-12 lead.

Annese wanted to run the trap later in the game, but Goose wouldn't run it. Coach sent the play in twice with senior Jimmy Harris, but Goose decided to change the play in the huddle. It wasn't a good time for a pissing contest between a coach and his quarterback. Newt watched his coach stomp up-and-down the sideline, screaming at Goose who intentionally ignored the head coach. When the team met in the huddle Goose asked his teammates, 'What is Annese so mad about?'

For the third time, Annese sent the play in with Harris along with explicit instructions. 'Harris, go in there and tell Goose exactly how I'm telling you, to run the FREAKING play. Tell him exactly how I'm telling you.'

Harris nervously ran to the huddle, repeating Annese's instructions verbatim. Every single Ram in the huddle exchanged glances with raised eyebrows. They all knew that one didn't argue with Coach Annese and win. The quarterback thought for a second then replied, 'You go tell him that I'm not running his FREAKING play!'

Harris was just the messenger and didn't plan for a second to get in the middle of their stupid pissing match. He didn't always agree with Annese either, but at least tried to do what he was told; and was surprised that Goose didn't. Harris played on the line and was known for being outgoing and outspoken, but he was unsure of how to handle this escapade. The tension was so thick in the huddle they all grew nervous. Harris threw Newt a cautious glance. Newt listened to the dialog in the huddle, growing anxious with each passing second, astounded that Goose had the nerve.

The offense anxiously broke huddle. The moment they lined up, Annese knew that Goose didn't plan to call his play. The offense glanced at the sideline just in time to see Coach throw his clipboard, before signaling a timeout. They realized he was furious the moment he turned his ball cap around and stomped to the middle of the field. Annese burned a timeout to void the power struggle between a coach and his quarterback.

The entire offense tensed. They had never been in this situation. No one ever challenged Annese before, especially in front of everyone. Newt looked at Goose, who stared back at him before he mouthed the words, 'Oh Shit!'

Two simple words that spoke for the entire offense. Coach Annese kept his head down the entire walk to the huddle, which seemed to take an eternity. He looked directly at Goose, then firmly stated in his distinct intimidating voice, 'WHO IS THE COACH? WHO IS THE COACH HERE?' YOU TELL ME RIGHT NOW, WHO IS THE COACH?'

His words bit. Harris' heart pounded. He felt somewhat responsible for not getting the message across to Goose. He was caught in the crossfire, afraid the two might overtly duke it out in the middle of the huddle. *Confrontations were nerve racking.* Goose looked at his coach, calmly petitioning his case. 'We're moving the ball down field. We're getting the yards. I don't see why you're so upset.'

Goose placed his coach in a difficult situation as the two stared each other down in a battle of the wills. Perhaps Goose reminded Annese of himself as a high school quarterback and eased up. Goose remained cool, something a good quarterback should always do in a crisis situation. Annese calmed down after realizing that Goose used his best judgment, and wasn't intentionally trying to piss him off. Annese gave Goose a delayed final glare before pointing his finger directly in the young quarterback's face, 'If you screw up, it's your ass!'

Goose had immeasurable respect for Coach Annese, but he was young and eager to prove his own ability. Goose gave a confident nod, noticing that his teammates all breathed a sigh of relief. Newt felt thankful that the power struggle was finally over, while trying to control his heart rate to a somewhat normal pace. He looked at his quarterback, 'Damn Goose!'

An easy smile formed on Goose's face. All he said was, 'Let's go guys!'

Cliff added an insurance TD for a final score of '28-12.' Cliff and Kies both set new records for having more than 100 yards in three games. Cliff Casteel was the workhorse but split a lot of time with Chris Kies. They were both hard-nosed, productive backs that possessed unbelievable determination and strength. Strength that opponents found hard to bring down.

Later that night after everyone had left the locker room, Annese found Goose. 'So, you wanted to call the freaking play, did you?'

A sheepish look fell over Goose's face and he suddenly felt embarrassed.

Annese knew he had him, 'Well, I'm glad to see you take some initiative.'

Goose breathed a sigh of relief and decided not to pull that stunt again. *Authority was respected.*

The Rams got down to business right away against their next league opponent -- **Atherton**. Cliff scored on a 14 yard TD. Just 34 quick seconds later, the Rams scooped up a fumble, then bolted 33 yards to put Montrose up 14-0. Chris Wright hauled in a 38 yard TD reception to join in the scoring with Kies and Vinnie. Kevin hauled in five of Goose's six completions for 108 yards and a TD. The coaching staff noticed their team fought better when things were going their way.

The team noticed that Coach's talks were becoming more strategic. He didn't seem to yell at them as much during the half. They knew each other so well after spending so much time together. The Rams started to win and reaped the results Annese talked about. Coach even padded up for some practices, threw some passes, and ran with them. In a way it felt like he was one of them, not just the commander in chief shouting orders.

The '39-8' Atherton victory put Montrose in an enviable position. Several teams were in pursuit to lead the League after week four. Before the Rams left the field they learned that the unbeaten Lake Fenton Blue Devils lost to Bentley by ten points. Lake Fenton was the team to beat to claim the GEC League Title. Annese didn't want his team getting a big head before the top two teams faced each other in a week. But he didn't need to worry; the Rams had their own motivation after losing to Lake Fenton, in overtime, a year ago. The Rams still tasted the sour tang from that loss. The Rams wanted revenge; and they wanted to be the '88 GEC League Champs.

Jason Katt, a J.V. defensive end, amazed the coaches when he stopped the veer in a scrimmage against the J.V. Annese ripped into the Varsity; he couldn't understand how a sophomore figured out how to stop the veer, when other Varsity teams had trouble shutting it down. Katts' efforts earned him a spot on the Varsity for the final three games of the '88 Season.

Katt felt strange when he attended the J.V. game on Thursday night. It felt odd to sit with the Varsity in the bleachers, watching his J.V. Team on the field. He couldn't understand why he didn't feel like a big shot, or why his J.V. squad called him one of the chosen ones. Instead, he felt weird not being on the field with his buddies, the guys that he played with since little league football. He knew their moves so well, as they did his. He felt peculiar when his J.V. Team won that game without him, like he was in a dream looking for himself in the midst of the celebration.

Montrose had the inside track for at least a share of the GEC Title, but Annese knew his Rams wouldn't be content with that. Montrose was in the driver's seat and a win would widen the margin, but a loss would make the two teams even. Montrose wanted to win a championship the way you're supposed to -- outright.

A friendly but competitive rivalry started to brew over the past summer when Cheese, Joe, Bear and Charlie attended a football camp at Michigan State University (even though they were all University of Michigan fans at the time). They bumped into some Lake Fenton guys who bragged about beating Montrose in overtime in '87 and listened to their plans to beat the Rams again in '88. The offensive line thought they were tough at MSU with the four of them averaging 6'1"- 220 pounds. They soon ate humble pie after standing beside players measuring 6'8", pushing 300 pounds. It made them realize that they were all small fish in a big pond.

How does a team of linemen win Air Force Football without their quarterback at the camp? The Rams did. They became the proud recipients of 'Air Force ball,' beating 500 players at the camp. Coming off baseball season helped. Bear and Cheese were also respectable pitchers that could throw a decent football pass.

With three games left in the season, the show down had something even more important than the League Title on the line -- heavy bragging rights. The Rams took the field for their pre-game warm-up, while listening to **Lake Fenton** chant their plans to win the GEC. Naturally, the Rams wanted to dish it back, but Annese coached them to save it for the field.

Kevin knew he'd remember that night for a long time. He felt the contiguous energy jump from one bench to the other when he found a spot in the locker room. Maybe he wouldn't remember word-for-word *what* Coach said in that pre-game talk, but he'd never forget *how* he said it or the excited emotion that filled the room. Annese delivered a motivating talk, like none they'd ever heard. Players stared wide-eyed as his voice fluctuated from a subdued mute to an intense roar. Their hearts pounded; no one had ever spoke to them like that. Swallowing hard, they tried to control the emotion that started in the tips of their toes, then quickly shot to their brains. The entire team felt so high when they stepped foot on their home field, they felt ready to take on the reigning Superbowl Champs -- the Washington Redskins.

The Rams wanted to earn respect; that had been their motto all season. They wanted to prove that they were a decent football team. They admitted they were not as talented as Lake Fenton, *but were just as determined.* Montrose finished the past two seasons in the middle of the pack, after winning five League Championships during the 80's. Tony Annese wanted his first, and so did the team. When Lake Fenton beat Montrose 18-20 in overtime in 1987, they also broke a long losing streak against the Rams -- one that held since 1978. That was the last time Lake Fenton won the GEC Title; now they wanted it in `88. Everyone knew Lake Fenton had the talent, but the Rams had the veer and a lot of formations; they could run or pass.

The juniors gathered in the locker room, reminiscing about the last time they faced Lake Fenton. Annese laughed as former J.V. players rehashed the story when Vinnie became a hero in his Grandpa's eyes. Vin's Grandpa worked with a Lake Fenton player's grandpa. Since blood is thicker than friendship, both fellas constantly bragged about their grandsons. That game, Vin intentionally ran the entire distance of the field to tackle the other grandson, even though it wasn't his man. He did it just so his Grandpa could go to work and say, 'My grandson got your grandson.'

They ruthlessly teased him about it, which lead to Vinnie receiving the 'Hammer Award' for his heroic show. Annese wiped the smile from his own face and set him straight, 'Hey Vin, I know you love your Grandpa, but you'll have to tell him that we don't do those things on Varsity.'

Vin nodded his head. He got the message.

When the opening kickoff was booted, the 22 guys on the field knew what was on the line. Montrose made mistakes early and found themselves stalled at the Lake Fenton 35. If that wasn't bad enough, they allowed a fumble to stuff another threat, but the determined Rams never quit. They executed when they had to and fought a hard-hitting first half.

Who wanted it more?

The Montrose J.V. Team came to watch like they always did on Friday nights except tonight was different, one of *their own* was on the field. The J.V. went crazy whenever Katt went in. He played with the big boys now, which tempted them to both admire and envy him. Katt turned into a fireball, playing his best, in the biggest game of the season. The sophomore wasn't intimidated, which earned him more respect than he imagined.

With less than a minute before the first half expired, the game was still a scoreless battle. When Goose connected with Kevin in the endzone, the crowd screamed with delight. Goose was nearsighted, which created a bit of a challenge to find his receivers on long passes. It stemmed back to the first game of the season when Goose wore his contacts. Because he felt that game stunk, he decided not to wear them the rest of the season. He didn't want to jinx the Rams.

The crowd went nuts when their Rams got on the board before the intermission. Kevin played end, using his tall athletic frame to snatch passes.

He had a long face and narrow chin and often tried to smirk instead of smile. Kevin was a quiet guy, like Charlie, who played with dedication. He earned a position as one of the defensive captains and was good enough to play at the college level. When Northwood University later recruited Cheese, they asked about Kevin from watching gamefilms. But Northwood had a business curriculum and Kevin wanted law enforcement, regardless of a football program.

What was the key to winning this game? That was the main thought on the minds of the coaching staff when they entered the locker room. Annese listened to their deep breathing while looking at their sweaty faces, sensing their anxiousness. The composed tone in his voice seemed to calm them down, 'Don't worry about the scoring opportunities we missed. Our most important key is to sustain a drive on our first possession of the third quarter and score.'

That was the key to winning the game. The Rams took the second half kickoff and drove 70-plus yards. Montrose fans went nuts when Goose connected with Kevin on a slick 36 yard over-the-shoulder catch.

Goose hit Vin on a scoring pass then again with trustworthy Tafoya on the conversion. The Rams forced Lake Fenton to punt, then picked-up a safety when the snap sailed over the punter's head on fourth down. The Blue Devils drove 96 yards to score with 6:45 left in the game, then quickly tried an on-side kick in an effort to regain possession. The Rams were geared up, recovered, then cleverly ate up the remainder of the clock to secure a '16-8' victory.

Cheese felt good about his game. He won a personal battle and was able to block and dominate a Lake Fenton lineman who was pretty good. The entire defense performed spectacular, limiting their opponent's passing game by shutting down their key running back. The offense also did their job against a tough team. Cliff turned in his best performance by racking up 163 yards to shatter another 100 yard mark for the fourth time.

It was an amazing battle that gloriously intensified on the short walk from the field. By the time they reached the locker room, they were wacky, especially the seniors. The huge rowdy linemen felt a fierce excitement, letting their emotions run loose. Bear turned on the showers and nodded at Joe. He helped Cheese snatch anyone close, chucking them into the wet steam. The crud and dirt from their uniforms quickly cast into mud when they plunged into a huge pile on the shower room floor. Some underclassmen joined in the chaotic, unruly scene to celebrate their huge victory. Katt played on the line with them and did his job, and did it well, especially for a sophomore. He stood back and laughed at them, tasting the sweetness of their success, while absorbing the wonderful feeling of a hard-fought victory. He suddenly felt like the new kid on the block, thrilled they let him play, but couldn't ignore the gnawing feeling in his gut. Something was missing. He knew exactly what it was -- *his* football buddies. He only wished the J.V. guys were around to throw in that muddy heap of happy, smelly players.

The win gave Montrose a 5-0 mark in the League, one full game better than Bentley, Goodrich, Hamady and Lake Fenton. The Rams knew the hunt for a League Championship required two more wins.

*So how did the **Bendle** Tigers catch the Rams off-guard from the get go?* The Tigers were not even in the hunt for a League Championship, but that didn't stop their spirit. Montrose fans barely found a parking spot when the Tigers stunned the visiting Rams by returning the opening boot 88 yards, putting six points on the board only seconds into the game. It only pissed off the offense, who shouted commands in the huddle.

It worked. Before the Bendle crowd finished celebrating, Montrose quickly recovered on its first play from scrimmage. Annese came out with a trick play. His voice sparred confidence when he stated that it would work. Goose pitched to Cliff who hit Vinnie in stride on a flashy 53 yard passing TD. This time, the Montrose crowd went nuts.

Cliff became the man of the night. Not only did he throw a TD pass he ran for two TD's in the first quarter, one in the second, three in the third. The grand finale was a 55 yard run with 35 seconds left on the clock. He scored six TD's and passed for a seventh. The guys compared it to hitting 'the cycle' in baseball. Cliff racked up 288 yards on 28 carries. His spectacular performance surpassed the school's single game record; not bad for an extremely muddy field.

Coach Annese was extremely proud of Cliff who became the benchmark that Annese gauged future backs against. Not only was Annese his coach but his confidant, who was well aware of the personal battles Cliff fought. Coach admired how such a young kid could put all of his troubles behind him the moment he put on his uniform. The football field was his sanctuary; a place to release his frustration. Football provided him with some control of the outcome. Cliff transformed his circumstances behind the façade of a bulldog that just wouldn't go down, like he was in some sort of fight-for-his life. Going down would be like giving in, and he'd never do that. He battled with even more intensity on the wrestling mat to prove he was a fighter, a determined warrior. On the surface he appeared as a rigid, hard-nosed old time player, but Coach saw a vulnerable childlike side that he hid from most. In a situation where many would foil, Cliff moved in the opposite extreme. Athletics became his refuge, protecting him from some of life's hard knocks. Football gave him the opportunity to excel in something he loved to do and at the same time take his mind off other things. His efforts secured total admiration from his coaches, which mirrored Cliff's feelings. Like Newt, Cliff needed his coaches at that point in his life, appreciating how they personally cared about him as an individual -- both on and off the field.

In spite of playing in a sloppy downpour most of the game, Bear, Cheese, Charlie, and Brody did their part on the devastating offensive line, by helping the Rams compile 571 yards in total offense. Even though neither team scored in the final quarter, Newt and Joe turned in standout defensive performances. They both pounced on fumble recoveries to defeat Bendle '46-12.' Goose had a remarkable night when he hit on six of ten passes for 166 yards, and ran for 80 yards on two attempts. His efforts, along with Cliff, earned them the 'Most Valuable Player Award' at the end of the season. Both demonstrated how well they deserved the honor and forced a tie. Their plaques read, 'To a person who we depended on more than any other player on the team. He should be the most difficult player to replace.'

And they were.

The smile on the young, second year head coach appeared to be permanently stuck there. He didn't want to conceal his bliss, realizing the win allowed Montrose to clinch the GEC Championship Title outright. He knew how much hard work went into the Title and he wondered if his kids realized what they had accomplished. The Rams started working for the Title in November, preparing as hard as any team in the state during the off-season, but it wasn't over yet. He challenged the team to step up and finish 7-0 in the League. They gladly consented, primed to face the **Goodrich Martians** -- their final opponent. The Martians were in the running for a second place spot and would be tough to beat.

The seniors lingered a bit longer in the locker room that Thursday night, as if they didn't want to go home. They had been together for months, enduring bruising, draining practices, every single day. Without speaking, Joe, Bear, Charlie, Cheese, and Kevin exchanged a concluding look. Without a shot in the state playoffs, the empty realization began to sink in -- *they just finished their last football practice.* The seniors felt good about what they accomplished, yet sad that the end was near. Cheese and Joe had plans to play college football, but this was it for the rest of the squad. That night was the last time they would yank a raunchy practice jersey over their head. Their uniforms held a pithy fragrance, a respectful, human scent. It was a competition sweat, which was different from the foul stench of three-day-old socks and jocks they kept in the bottom of their lockers.

Sweat that secreted from their pores wasn't like the typical body odor of one that neglected to shower. No. Competition sweat was pure -- almost a tribal thing. It was a bizarre smell that each one of them knew they would surely miss, but their moms would not. By the time they handled their sons' vulgar uniforms, they had lost their sweetness. By then, they just plain stunk.

Coach wanted each of them to prolong their drive and play their very best right until the end of the game. Even though they had the GEC League Title locked in and no chance to advance, they needed to win for the seniors, since it was their last game. He wanted to end the season with a strong victory, so underclassmen felt that champion feeling during the entire off-season. *He wanted them hungry.* Annese joked, 'Hey, I won't let you order your Montrose Football jacket unless you beat Goodrich.'

They knew Coach didn't mean it verbatim, that was just his style. He always raised the bar one notch higher, wanting each of them to push himself a step farther. Before they left, Coach handed each Varsity player a letter. Joe stood over Bear's shoulder, feeling an emptiness swell in his throat as he read:

> *'So it's time to hang 'em up again. Another season gone. The end of a long period of suffering and joy. For the seniors it's over, no more complaining to each other during conditioning, no more butterflies before the game, nor will you feel the crack of the pads or the impact of your helmet against another.*
>
> *Remember all the good times at camp and practice, the camaraderie we all shared with each other, the ups-and-downs, victories and losses. These things will be with you for the rest of your life.*
>
> *For the juniors it's the beginning of the end. Make the best of your senior year. I always heard, 'You'll be sorry when it's over,' but never believed it while doing ladders or gassers. Believe me when it's over you'll wish you worked harder, done better, and had more success.*
>
> *Just remember success in life is what we leave behind not what we take with us. All that is left now are the memories of the greatest times of our lives.'*

Joe felt tears sting his eyes when he read Coach Annese's personal hand-written note at the bottom. Bear looked away, while gently folding his letter, before sliding it back into the white envelope. He wanted to be alone when he read his personal message. He quickly picked-up his gym bag and headed to his car. Bear was usually famished after practice, appreciating that his family patiently waited for him so they could eat together. But that night, he barely said hello as he rushed past the dinner table to his room. Bear stared at the letter for a few minutes then closed his eyes, relaxing his body. He fell back on his bed and stared at the ceiling for the longest time. That letter reminded him of the one that Coach sent last July gearing him up for the season. He felt a pang of guilt when he remembered how he dreaded the thought of two-a-day practices. Now the season was almost over and he wondered where the time went. Only one game remained and Bear was determined to play his best.

The seed Coach Annese planted with his letter appeared to work. Joe hardly slept all night; beating Goodrich was all he could think of. He thought about all of the things he learned from playing Montrose Football, and how it gave him more confidence in himself. He learned about tenacity and hard work, leadership and success, how to set goals and accomplish them and most importantly -- how to never quit. Finally, he closed his eyes and laid still . . . until he fell asleep.

Cheese woke up Friday morning and panicked. His head pounded and his body ached with chills. He thought, *Of all days to come down with the flu.* He went back to bed for a few hours, hoping the extra rest helped him make it through the last half day of school, or he wouldn't be eligible to play. He would go even if it meant carrying a bucket to class; one could get away with that when you're as big as Cheese. Nothing would stop him from playing his final football game. *Nothing.*

Cheese managed to get through the day. Once he donned his uniform, he forgot about his fever. He worked hard with the rest of the line, wanting to go out in style for their grand finale. Their performance helped Cliff crack the 1,000 yard mark and score two more TD's. Goose also cracked the 1,000 yard mark when he combined his rushing and passing yards for the season. Chris Wright broke free on a 40 yard romp to score with less than a minute in the game to end the lopsided '34-8' triumph over Goodrich.

The Montrose Rams posted seven straight victories after a rocky start. Their first two losses were to quality teams; Birch Run was playoff bound and Chesaning ended up being the MMB League Champs. Just like 1988 would see the end of the Reagan Era when George Bush took office, the Montrose Rams saw the end of the Bob Hayes era when Tony Annese took over. Before they walked off the field, the Rams lifted their hands to the center and shouted out seven breakdowns -- one for each victory. They stood tall and walked two-by-two with locked hands when they made their exit under the goal post one final time.

Jimmy Harris knew he'd miss the tradition and the camaraderie with his teammates. He injured his knee at the end of the Bentley game that later required four surgeries to repair. He was bummed that he lost his starting position but glad when he got to play, in spite of the pain.

Kevin felt sad after the team celebrated their success at the end of the game. He had a flashback of their last game in '87 when those seniors told him, 'Enjoy every minute of the season because when it's over you can't go back.' At that time, Kevin's last game seemed so far away. After all, he had another year to go. Now, the hard reality hit him like a stiff punch, leaving him with the realization that once he walked off the field, he'd never play football again.

Tafoya felt bad that it was over for Kevin, the senior that took him under his wing. Kevin was a quiet guy who didn't need to be the center of attention but was able to use his athleticism on the field. He helped Tafoya develop at the opposite end. When Kevin looked at the other seniors, he knew they experienced the same feeling. They should've felt ecstatic after becoming the GEC League Champions. Instead, they made their final exit with a bittersweet feeling. Of all the guys on the team, Tafoya had grown closest to Kevin and respected him. If he missed a day of lifting, Annese chewed on Kevin and said, 'Hey, Tafoya's your guy!'

Later that night, Bear retrieved the letter he kept on the top of his dresser. As he sat on the edge of his bed, he stared at it for the longest time before carefully removing it from the long, white envelope. Then he read the special handwritten note from Coach Annese:

'Barry, I am very proud of you. You dedicated yourself to success and achieved it. Your efforts in the off-season really paid-off and no one deserves <u>*success*</u> *more than you. I know that you will be a successful person in the future because you know what it takes to set a goal and work to achieve it. We won a* <u>*championship*</u> *when few people gave us a chance. We beat the odds!!! Good luck to you in your future endeavors.*

<u>*7–0*</u> *Make Your Last Your Best. Thanks for the memories.'*

Coach Annese

Bear felt his mattress slightly bounce once the weight of his head settled into his bed. He stared at the ceiling, while memories from this crazy game of football flooded his head. It taught him things like responsibility, loyalty, effort, and respect, and would help him become successful in life. His entire team worked extremely hard, yet managed to combine an element of fun to the greatest team sport ever played. He only hoped the seniors would always value their friendship and remain good, good friends. Football took their friendship to another level, fabricating a strong bond among them, connecting them in a way only athletes and war buddies experienced. Like a house with a strong foundation, friendships were built to last a lifetime; he only hoped they would.

Was there more to it than relinquishing another League Title? Everyone seemed to feel that something unusual transpired with the Team of 1988. Maybe it was the charisma of that particular group of guys who developed a work ethic beyond what any one of them expected. Perhaps it was the pioneers who started the powerlifting competitions. Their slight seven-game winning streak generated a quick spark, like striking a match that burned a desire in the underclassmen. Whatever it was, when the `88 Rams combined their strength and talent with their sheer will and determination, it stirred up something larger than any of them had ever imagined. They earned some respect. Those that remained were left with an addicting taste in their mouths.

They wanted more.

FLINT JOURNAL PHOTO/Mary L. McHale
The Line: #50 Charlie Lange, #52 Joe Morse, #79 Matt 'Cheese' Leeseberg, #67 Barry 'Bear' Paxton and #22 Kevin Salter

33 Cliff Casteel and #79 Paul Wixson

Coaches (from left): Denny Reinhart, Tony Annese and Jamie Kitts

2. BELIEF - 1989

If you want to be successful, it's just this simple:
Know what you're doing.
Love what you're doing.
And believe in what you're doing.

-Will Rogers

Goose wasn't ready to give up Montrose Football. Not just yet. He couldn't stay away from it nor put an end to it. He tried. He gave it up once for the sport of baseball then blew out his shoulder, which required surgery. Now he constantly questioned himself, 'Did I make the wrong decision?' Football haunted him. The sport was obviously still in his blood and he couldn't put it to rest. Not yet. Something was still missing.

His heart thumped so heavily in his chest that it echoed in his ears when he ran through the tunnel -- that awesome tunnel. They sprinted across the turf in front of thousands of people. The welcoming noise from the fans was unbelievable; and it was all for them. The turf was softer and newer than he expected. He bounced on the bright green carpet, feeling the spring of a tumbling mat and thought, 'This could make a turtle think it was fast.' He wanted to cut loose and tear across the turf, but knew he shouldn't and held back. He wished they would open up the playbook and showcase the offense a little more; they relied too heavily on the defense. The eyes of the entire state were upon them; they were playing too conservative for Goose. After working out daily with the quarterback, running backs, and defensive backs, he knew their capabilities, and the willpower they possessed to accomplish their goal. But he also knew his position and respected it. Goose adjusted his headset while trying to conceal his beaming smile, but the aura of being in the Pontiac Silverdome was purely overwhelming.

Only sixteen teams earned the privilege, which was unbelievable and way overdue. He never quit believing that it would happen, feeling thankful that dreams didn't come with expiration dates. Goose looked at the team, then at the fans, absorbing the energy of being in the Dome – a wonderful place where dreams came true and championships were won.

'**W**ake-up Goose.   We're going live today, except for the *wussy* quarterback. We can't have him break a nail or anything.'

Coach Annese waited for a reaction from his third year quarterback. He obviously enjoyed the pleasure of testing him, even though his intent was to protect him. He watched the tanned face of his senior quarterback return a half-pissed smirk. Goose respected Coach but sometimes he annoyed the hell out of him. His blood boiled when Coach made comments like that.

Goose looked at Vin then shook his sandy blonde head, 'Why does Coach constantly try to piss me off? He knows how much I crave live practices. I just want to deliver a hit and make players miss me and grab at nothing but air.'

'I hear what you're saying Goose.'   Vin recalled a few months earlier, during basketball season, when an official abruptly bent over in obvious pain. He looked up at Vin, after gaining his composure and scolded, 'You're out of the game!'

Vin innocently turned around with a shocked expression, 'What'd I do?'

A stern referee replied, 'You know what you did.'

Vin was looking in the opposite direction when he threw the basketball to the official, unaware that it hit him in the privates. It was an honest mistake. Vin told anyone that would listen, 'It was an accident, I didn't do it on purpose. I swear!'

Coach Annese kept his cool. He didn't side with Vin or the official. He finished the basketball game, then requested the officials and the athletic director to stay after. Annese was just as strict with personal fouls in basketball as he was in football. Bad sportsmanship simply wasn't tolerated. Annese told the official involved, 'You're either going to apologize to my player or I'm going to kick him off the team. One way or the other, we're watching this video together and resolving this right here, right now.'

Regardless of how the situation turned out, Vin gained an admiration for his coach while he sat on the bench. *Wow, this man really wants to do the right thing and is willing to go through all of this trouble to sort it out. How many coaches would do that for a player?*

It was tough to be the shortest in the group. Vin tried to peek between them for a closer look, but couldn't see the video. The tape revealed that Vin's action was *not* intentional. The official apologized to Vin, they all shook hands and the episode was settled -- *fairly.* That was how Coach Annese operated. If you screwed up, you knew there'd be hell to pay. If not, at least he made the effort to get to the bottom of it.

The basketball team quickly discovered that Coach Annese was intense no matter what sport he coached. He only coached Varsity Basketball at Montrose for a year, but established himself as a true competitor.

Montrose finished a scrimmage at Linden High School when Annese asked if the Rams could use their gym for 15 minutes to work on a few drills. That 15 minutes turned into another 15 and another 15. The exhausted team felt completely drained and couldn't believe Coach asked for 'a few more' minutes. The Linden coach finally sent his team home, while Montrose continued to practice. Vin was exhausted. *I am so tired. The next time I pass that exit door, I'm running out. I'm gonna do it.* He felt his stomach churn with the same ill feeling as when his dad called him by his first and middle name. Every time he ran by the door, he heard a devilish, inner voice say, *Do it. Just run out that door and don't look back. Do it.*

He couldn't. He simply didn't have enough nerve to quit.

Two-a-days finally arrived. The guys were deeply tanned, buffed, some even sported a six-pack (in their abs) from dutifully lifting weights throughout the summer. Even though they were fit, they forgot how difficult Annese's initial practices were. If they didn't run a play right, they ran gassers. If someone lagged behind and didn't run gassers fast enough, they had to get back on the line and run the play again . . . and again . . . and again. If they messed up too much, they ran more gassers. Annese knew he pushed their limits. Even the diehards had a tough time, so Coach decided to accumulate gassers from two-a-days and spread them over the season.

The Varsity and J.V. worked out together during two-a-days. The freshmen would never forget their first day of pads, especially the linemen. Coach previously warned that every player was required to be at practice *on time*. But one player was absent, causing Coach to announce, 'We're doing ups-and-downs until he arrives!'

Goose had a hunch of what Coach was about to do, and was the first to volunteer to find the missing player. It was a privilege of being a captain, and got him out of ups-and-downs. However, it created a panic-filled atmosphere while he drove around in desperation, trying to locate the missing player. Extreme guilt consumed him while he searched, realizing his buddies' arms had to feel like rubber. The team accumulated over 200 ups-and-downs before Goose returned with the refugee in tow. One could surely bet that his squadmates applied their own pressure. After that, they all made a conscious effort to arrive on time.

Rob Schlicht was one of the largest freshmen, extremely strong for his age. Brody Mier encouraged him to get in the weight room when he was in the eighth grade, coaching him to lift more than Schlicht ever thought he could. Like the others, Schlicht was pumped about starting football . . . until he dropped after completing 150 ups-and-downs. His fair skinned face turned dark red; his body drenched with so much sweat that he thought he would die. It was all his hefty body could do in the summer heat. He soon discovered that he hated ups-and-downs, yet tried to understand the necessity of them. Schlicht was technically a freshman, but hadn't attended a single high school class yet. It wasn't *his* place to question how things were done, but rightfully admitted that he'd never felt so intimidated in his entire, young life. *Accountability was learned.*

Annese knew how to push the right buttons to warrant results from every player, even if it meant going to extremes. Some parents were still unsure of what to think about the young head coach who was starting his third year. Most were impressed with the discipline and hard work ethic he instilled in their sons, yet some remained skeptical of the control he had over them. As parents, they felt responsible for providing guidance for curfews and rules; sharing that role with a coach was difficult. Although a few single moms appreciated his discipline, along with the missing father role model that he provided for their sons. They saw positive traits in the their sons' attitudes and commitment levels. Annese helped them believe in themselves.

The football program also attracted a few lightweights. Bill and Bob stood about 5'10", and probably didn't weigh 300 pounds between the two of them. Neither possessed a killer instinct, when a player intentionally smears his best friend as hard as possible in a drill, then helps him up like nothing ever happened. That was football. Most players collided like a free-for-all demolition derby, while Bill and Bob went through the motion of contact but played bumper cars instead. The contrast was too much for the squad who turned their heads, hiding their laughter.

Tuesday was defense day, also dubbed as 'Bill Day.' Seven defensive backs ran pass patterns against the second team offense. Bill was in the offensive group, and for some reason the backs made a point to try and knock his head off. Maybe it was an attempt to toughen him up, or perhaps he was easy prey to make them appear rougher. The backs knew Annese was a decent quarterback in his day, and wondered if he deliberately hung balls in the air so they could get in position to pound Bill.

The last drill of every practice was 'Bill Drill'. Practice wouldn't stop until Bill caught the pass and scored. The entire team normally united and yelled, 'Don't drop it Bill. Don't drop it.' It ended practice on a lighter note, taking the edge off the intensity. If Bill dropped the ball, Coach yelled out three dreaded words -- 'Run it again!'

Players made theatrical dives to intentionally miss Bill when he ran by them. Bill gave 100% of what he had to give, thriving on the attention, which brought him back day after day, week after week.

One day, Jason Liddell was tired of playing games during practice. 'Led' didn't know what came over him. He watched Bill ferry the ball up the sideline while he hustled to the endzone, waiting for him. With a full head of steam, Led blasted the poor kid with all his might. It wasn't an everyday kind of tackle but an all out, full-force Friday night smear. Led pushed him so-far-so-fast, that the force embedded Bill directly into the chain linked fence. Without giving it much thought, Chris Wright instinctively jumped on the tackle.

The sound was indescribable. Coach Kitts watched from the distant press box, but heard the blast as if he stood three feet away. The first thing that hit the ground was the back of Bills' shoulders, followed by his crumpled body, as if a car had just hit him. Fact is, a car at the same speed couldn't have done more damage unless it ran over him. It geeked the guys up, but the celebration stopped once Bill didn't move. No one got in a prayer circle and sang *We Are The World* or anything, but it registered as an awesome hit.

They didn't intend to hurt him, just got caught up in the moment. Bill didn't know what hit him. One second he enjoyed his moment of glory, the next he felt immense pain, forcing him to cry out. Once they climbed off Bill, Led noticed that his ear pads were thrown from his helmet, which was turned sideways on his head. Later, Led saw Bill in the locker room, and felt bad after noticing his bloodshot eyes. He wondered, *What makes a player want to take that kind of abuse? He doesn't get any playing time, yet he comes back every day.*

Some players didn't need to be in the spotlight or even get any glory during a game. The attention they received in practice, or playing on a scout team was enough. They just wanted to be one of the guys, to be a part of something special -- Montrose Football. Every year there would be another

Bill on the team; for some that was enough. Led respected Bill for that but wondered if he would endure the same torment without the glory, if they had to switch places. *Brotherhood was respected.*

The `89 Season needed a special kickoff. Chris Annese, along with Joe's girlfriend, senior Crystal Tipton, planned an ice cream social. Joe now attended college, and helped Annese as an assistant. The staff wanted to bring football families and the community together to meet the team. They figured ice cream had to be easier than the oversized, striped green footballs they hauled in `88 for the watermelon social. Players didn't care, as long as food was included they would be there; the recognition was an added bonus.

September Friday nights and football went together like July summer breezes and brilliant blue skies. Opening night generated a crisp air of excitement as Montrose fans drove the brief 15 minutes north to **Birch Run**. The tempting smell of buttery popcorn lured fans to the concession stand, whether they were hungry or not. The team sat tucked away in a distant locker room, intently listening to Coach Annese's pre-game speech. Fans couldn't hear the chill pitch in Coach Annese's voice or see the players' apprehensive faces when he yelled:

'We do NOT want to repeat the season opener from the past two years. WE DIDN'T EVEN GET ON THE BOARD! WE DIDN'T SCORE ONE POINT! NOT ONE POINT IN TWO YEARS! BIRCH RUN BEAT THE CRAP OUT OF US. THREE TOUCHDOWNS BOTH YEARS. THREE TOUCHDOWNS! THAT IS HUMILIATING! DO YOU WANT THAT TO HAPPEN TONIGHT? DO YOU?'

The squad shouted in unison - 'NO!' Their nerves grew antsy; their hearts hammered in their chests. Most were angry, excited, and nervous all at the same time. The rookies were scared shitless, but had one thing in common . . . they were ready to play football.

Annese moved them. He was a great orator and a fantastic motivator. Some players thought that given time -- he could convince the dead to live. Ron Newton was no exception. Newt couldn't control how the pitch in Coach Annese's voice made his toned muscles twitch. He couldn't control the cave man style grunts that freely escaped his mouth, or how his entire upper body jerked sharply from left to right. Newt was a great locker room presence. Annese got under his skin, creating an adrenaline rush that flowed like wild fire through his veins. His reaction contagiously spread through his teammates, like an untamed virus casting a Neanderthal ambiance over the room. Every fiber of their souls came alive when Coach Annese spoke, which was exactly what he wanted . . . *results.*

Goose was already a bundle of nerves before the pre-game, but Annese's speech made him jump out of his skin. He felt ready to run through a wall. Tony Annese's brothers, Steve and Phil, both helped as assistant coaches. After closely monitoring Goose, they pulled him aside. 'Hey, that speech wasn't meant for you Goose. You're the quarterback. The team needs you to be calm and focused.'

The restless Rams took the field, out-jumping each other when they formed a heap on the Montrose sideline. It would be difficult for Montrose to sneak up on opponents after ending the '88 Season as League Champs. Twelve of their 16 lettermen were back as starters; that should account for something. Montrose couldn't wait to get on the field and show Birch Run what they were capable of, especially Goose. Competitive Goose, who played a huge part in controlling the outcome of their first game. He was a seasoned quarterback; clueless of the thrill he was about to experience.

The Rams won the toss and elected to receive the second half. They kicked off to the Panthers, then were struck by first game jitters, making continuous mistakes throughout the first quarter. The Panthers took advantage by striking first, after their quarterback connected with their receiver for a 14 yard TD.

Vin was just as determined as Goose. He loosened his new receiver gloves on his hands when he prepared to take the field with the kick return team. Annese was pissed once he saw the gloves and approached Vin. 'Take off the gloves. I told you I don't want you wearing gloves.'

The feisty look on the receiver's face matched his coach. Vin felt overanxious, but held the stare before speaking. 'They really help me grip the ball.'

Annese hated receiver gloves and sternly repeated, 'I said, take them off!'

Their angry eyes locked as both secretly wondered, *Will I win this squabble?* Vin had too much respect for his coach, and too much love for the game to fight about it. He finally gave in, pulled off his receiver gloves, then grudgingly handed them over. Annese felt frustrated about the confrontation, yet satisfied that he'd won the battle. He placed Vin's black receiver gloves in the hands of a nearby player on the sideline, before storming away to his spot on the 50 yard line.

Vin anticipated his reaction, predetermining his own course of action. He waited until the final second before taking his position on the field, then swiftly ran past the player holding his gloves. Vin urgently snatched them from his hands and stretched them over his fingers while running to his deep receiver position. He felt like a disobedient child, both satisfied and frustrated, *Why does Coach require so much discipline?*

The Montrose Rams got off to a rocky start, turning the ball over on three-of-four possessions. They managed only 14 offensive plays, while Birch Run scored on a 14 yard TD pass in the second quarter. Later in the period, the Panthers booted a 36 yard field goal making the score 0-9 at the intermission.

The coaching staff made some adjustments during the half, while Annese tried to settle the Rams down. 'We're capable of playing much better ball. We've practiced hard the entire off-season. We came here prepared. This game is not over. We can beat this team!'

He pumped them up then set them loose in typical Tony Annese fashion. Cliff Casteel felt ready to tackle the world when he left the locker room. Vin took his position as the deep receiver, preparing for the second half kickoff. His gaze followed the ball while he positioned himself for the catch, then used his blazing speed to race 83 yards. It seemed Annese overlooked Vin's receiver gloves after that.

The coaching staff had their eyes on Vin's speed to return punts, and planned to use his good hands at wide receiver. Vin set big goals for his senior year, intending to use his speed to get some attention from Division I colleges. Because of his small frame, he realized he needed impressive stats to raise some eyebrows. Vin helped the Rams get off to a good start, until Birch Run's defense stepped up, stopping the Rams in the red zone.

Vin bent over to catch his breath. *Shit! After all that we lost it.*

Shortly after, the defense collected a safety to get the Rams on the board. Coach hoped it gave the offense some desperately needed confidence and told his quarterback, 'Goose, the defense stepped up. They want to win this ball game. Now go out there and show me what the offense can do.'

The quarterback was the most mentally challenged of all positions, with only a matter of seconds to evaluate the defense and worry about pass protection and the opponent's speed. Goose developed an ability to calm his mind down and come up with a new plan on the fly. It came from hours of practice and study, but to Goose it was worth every minute. After the ensuing free kick, the Rams marched to Birch Run's one yard line, then fumbled away another golden scoring opportunity. It all began with ball control and Goose was frustrated. The quarterback grabbed a few facemasks in the huddle, and shouted at his teammates. He had their undivided attention.

Early in the fourth quarter, Vin turned a routine play into a breathtaking, crowd-pleasing 57 yard TD after catching a 15 yard pass from Goose. Vin faked to the inside then broke free to the outside, using his speed to race to the endzone for a long, overdue score. If Montrose had a 'Prime Time' on the team, Vinnie was the guy. He was a bit hyperactive. His high energy on special teams got the scoring going when the offense was a bit groggy. He wanted the ball and Goose found a way to get it to him -- by air or by land. Vin was a senior leader who led by example. He had a contagious, great smile that his classmates acknowledged as the 'Best in the Senior Class.' He wasn't extremely vocal, but when he spoke the guys listened. Finally, the curse was broken and the Montrose Rams scored a long awaited TD; their first against the Birch Run Panthers in three seasons.

Annese went for the jugular, calling for a two-point conversion. He didn't want to tie. He wanted to win and took on the theme -- *No Guts, No Glory.* He stared at the offense with a look that gave them every ounce of confidence they needed to make the play. Goose hit Tafoya, giving the Rams a 10-9 lead with less then two minutes to play in the game. The Rams appeared to have a lock on their season opener, despite being behind 0-9 at the half. All Montrose had to do was hold on to the ball, which was inside Birch Run's 15 yard line, and run out the clock. *It sounded simple enough.*

Jamie Kitts and Billy Persails arrived just after the Rams scored. Both were J.V. coaches who scouted an upcoming opponent's game, completed enough forms to give Annese ample fodder for a tendency chart, then left early. Annese greeted them with a disgusted look, shaking his head. 'What are you guys doing here?'

Invariably one of them interrupted, waving him off. 'Tony those guys are really BAD. If you can't beat them you're not worth squat as a coach,' and left it at that.

They knew they should've stayed and scouted more accurately, but they hated missing the Varsity games. Annese couldn't blame them. Kitts and Persails only hoped the Varsity could hang on and beat Birch Run. They lost to the J.V. Panthers the night before after being tied at zero late in the fourth. The J.V. quarterback made an ill-timed pitch to the right, and a Birch Run defensive tackle scooped the ball up, running 65 yards for a TD and the 0-6 win.

The Rams got the ball back on their side of the 50, with less then two minutes to go. Goose started the task of running out the clock. Montrose was just beginning to learn the veer. Goose took the handoff from Newt, stepped to the right, exposed the ball to ride the dive back, then handed off to Cliff who ran into a pile of Panthers. It was a sure thing; Cliff never dropped the ball. But then a catastrophe happened, while the Rams watched in horror.

Here they were, ready to lock the game up when the field became chaotic as hell. No one believed how the ball squirted loose, then flipped airborne directly into the hands of a Birch Run defensive lineman who grabbed it in full stride while running in the opposite direction.

Shit.

It happened so fast that it was difficult for their young minds to register. The Birch Run fans created a wave of hullabaloo near the end of their home opener; the louder they yelled, the faster he ran. The optimistic Panther raced 80 yards in an effort to turn his fumble recovery into a game winning TD. It was his chance to become a hero for the Panthers as he raced toward the endzone, a feat that should secure a dance with the prom queen.

Not if Goose could help it.

It played out like a movie in slow motion. Ensnarced in the huge pile of sweaty, heavy breathing rivals was #16 -- Goose. His eyes never left the ball, as an astonished look plastered his face. His movements shifted to auto pilot, reacting like a police officer about to ensue a chase. He was mad but didn't have time to fret; he had to catch the bad guy. In that frenzied moment, he pulled himself out of the pile, allowing his unyielding will to pursue his opponent. His teammates didn't think Goose had a prayer of catching him, but then they never saw their quarterback pushed to that extreme.

Goose thought, *No way in hell would he be beat. No way!* His teammates watched in amazement. They never saw Goose run so fast, wondering if he set a record in the 40. Goose was determined to chase the Panther down because his team needed him to. He needed to. Hell, he just brought the Rams from behind. No way would he give up. *No way.* He narrowed the gap between them, as if his life depended on it. With the endzone creeping up all too rapidly, Goose made a last ditch effort to forcefully grab the Panther from behind, pissed that he almost scored. The pair dropped on the four yard line, lying frozen in their tracks like silhouettes from a crime scene. They tried to catch their breath, oblivious that both sides of the stadium considered *their guy* to be a hero.

The Rams still had a chance, but so did the Panthers.

Would a betting man wager on what seemed like a sure thing or go for the long shot? The Rams were up by one, but the Panthers had the ball at the goal line with four downs, and almost two full minutes. The determined look on Goose's face in the huddle motivated Wixson more than he could explain. Wixson was one of three squadmates that pushed the scales past the 200 pound mark. He loved playing tackle because he could hit people and get away with it. Goose honestly believed the Rams could win, and didn't expect anything less of himself or the entire Montrose defense. It inspired them to become a brick wall. By the time they were set in their positions, the Rams truly believed they were a well-oiled fighting machine, like soldiers protecting their fort.

Adrenaline overflowed, almost to the point of being out of control. A late hit by a Ram caused a personal foul, giving the Panthers half-the-distance to the goal. Now they were on the two with only a minute left. Everyone wondered, *Could the Rams hold them? Who would win this ballgame?*

It was the mysterious thrill that kept football exciting; anything could happen. It undesirably became a moment stitched in time; a game neither team would ever forget. It seemed enough adrenaline existed between the two teams on the field, and the fans in the stands, to stir the dead. The defense tried to think through every possible attack, yet remain calm.

Damn! They could hardly think above the forceful thump of their own heartbeats when they huddled together. The Rams hardly recognized the trembling, begging voice of one of their own. The squad grew quiet in order to hear, 'C'mon guys, we have to stop'em. I don't know how we're gonna do it, but we gotta stop'em!'

It was Newt. Rough, strong, hard-hitting Newt. Even as a junior he was one of the respected, tough guys on the team who already had a year of Varsity experience under his belt. At the moment, his emotionally packed voice sounded more like a pleading child in a toy store, willing to do anything to get what he wanted. The emotion from Newt's voice haunted Wixson when the huddle broke and he took his position. Newt's trembling voice echoed in his head as he faced Birch Run's offense. *'We gotta stop 'em guys, we just gotta stop 'em!'*

Time was almost out, but the game was far from over. It was first-and-goal inside the five for Birch Run. The Panthers had to believe they would win. On first down, Coach Buckel called a pass. Three Montrose linemen hit the quarterback; Katt tried to sack him, but went right over him. Wixson almost had him, then Dave Cayton just missed him, but the quarterback was never tackled. He barely got the pass off, but strategically hit a wide-open receiver in the endzone. Before all of the Birch Run fans had a chance to stand and cheer, the ball bounced off the anxious receiver's shoulder pads, and blessedly dropped to the ground. It was ruled incomplete.

How lucky could the Rams be? Could they make a goal line stand and hold the Panthers for three more downs? Vin felt helpless from the sideline as he buried his face in his trembling hands. He couldn't watch but listened to the excited fans as emotion bounced back and forth across the field like a ping-pong game between Birch Run and Montrose. On the very next play, Birch Run's quarterback hit his receiver dead in the numbers. *He dropped it!*

Their fans let out a group sigh -- in unison, as if they'd rehearsed it like the church choir. Birch Run still had time, feeling confident they could pull off a score. Across the field, the Montrose fans cheered with delight, then anxiously held their breath for the next bloodcurdling down.

Could the Montrose defense possibly hold the Panthers at goal line for two more downs? In anticipation of an important third-and-goal, both sets of fans hit their feet, clapping and cheering as loud as their lungs allowed. Birch Run's quarterback dropped back for another pass, searching for an uncovered Panther. He tried to force the pass to his receiver, drilling it into the endzone one more time. The quarterback didn't anticipate the perfect move from Wright, the safety, who cleverly picked it off. Wright was one of the smartest secondary players Montrose ever had, both on and off the field. Academically he tied for the valedictorian spot, an honor that eventually led him to Harvard. For now, he allowed the Montrose crowd to breathe a sigh of relief in a game so important that it compared to the relief of knowing a good friend really didn't die in a plane crash!

Vin found the courage to look up after hearing the outburst from the Montrose side of the field. He searched for Wright in the endzone, making sure it was a Ram who possessed the precious pigskin. Vin finally breathed a sigh of relief, after surviving the longest two minutes of his life. His heart worked overtime when he rushed the field with the rest of the ecstatic offense, high-fiving their defensive buddies as they exchanged positions.

The Rams received a touchback, which brought the ball to the 20 yard line. With :20 seconds left, Montrose downed the next two, running out the clock to claim a hard fought '10-9' victory that the media dubbed -- *The Wild Thing*.

Adrenaline consumed the entire team, creating a strong bond between them. It formed a priceless memory; a cherished moment they would pull out now and then to recapture the feeling, like a child looking at a picture of the biggest fish he ever caught. Wixson led the defensive charge for the Rams, feeling extremely proud that they didn't fold under pressure. Katt was moved when he saw Wixson, the guy who never took things too seriously, become totally swallowed in the emotion of the moment. He sounded like he was about to sing a mournful funeral hymn when he looked at Katt, then shouted with a cracked voice, 'Man, we're goin' to States!'

Coach Reinhart joined in the celebration, thrilled that his defense made a strong goal line stand. They all realized how anything could happen in a good football game. But the offense made too many slip-ups; mistakes they would need to minimize if they wanted to beat **Corunna**.

The Rams didn't know what to expect from Corunna, since it was the first time they were scheduled to face each other. The Corunna Cavaliers proved their strength was in their defense after defeating Class A Lansing Waverly 10-9, the same score that Montrose squeaked by Birch Run.

The Rams charged their home turf ready to play football, racking up 14 points in the first quarter when Goose threw two scoring passes. Chris Kies made the conversion, allowing the Rams to jump out with an early lead.

Corunna shutout the Rams in the second quarter when they added ten points of their own, making the score 14-10 at the half. Annese ignited his team during the half-time reunion, then displayed a stormy reaction after Montrose fumbled the kickoff. Corunna looked to dominate the second half after scooping it up, but had trouble moving the ball and settled for another field goal.

The Rams took possession with most of the third quarter yet to play. They were ready to show that they wanted the win once Goose led them on an 82 yard drive. Their running game worked. Kies took the handoff, then used his strong legs to bulldoze through from five yards out. Kies was born to be a veer back.   He had the right size and speed, and delivered unforgettable blows to would-be tacklers. He could just as easily run over opponents as he could outrun them, often making the decision on the fly. Ironically, his classmates voted him as 'The Friendliest Guy' in their class, but he sure wasn't nice to opponents.

His dad was also funny. The cheerleaders and fans actually missed the abhorrent voice of Mr. Kies during the season opener.   Since he was recovering from pneumonia, he couldn't yell into his annoying megaphone. The other parents bought a custom sweatshirt with the words, 'That's My Boy - #42.' and presented it at the beginning of the Corunna game. Every time his son carried the ball, Mr. Kies stood up, turned around, then wildly waved his arms while pointing to his new shirt. His wife stood by his side, ringing a deafening cowbell; they both overflowed with pride for their son.

The Rams executed better and kept possession most of the second half. Goose connected with Jason Tafoya in the beginning of the final frame for an eight yard TD pass. Newt led the defense with 12 tackles, and scooped up a fumble recovery that set up Kies' final TD to end the game '35-13.'

The win allowed Annese to show his alma mater, Corunna, what the ex-high school quarterback could do as a Varsity head coach. The Annese name carried weight with Corunna, where Tony's dad, Nick Annese, was a former legendary football coach and the athletic director. But Tony Annese quickly learned that his loyalties now resided with Montrose Football.

Winning two non-league openers gave the Rams confidence in each other, and an eagerness to work hard during **Hamady** week. It was a legitimate time for superstitions to kick in. Players started to replicate their exact actions in hopes of obtaining the same results; Annese was no exception. He went home and took a small nap before the Hamady game, feeling rested as he dressed. He wore the same game shirt before making the five-mile drive to the school. Mike and the Mechanics popular hit, *In the Living Years,* blared from the radio as he approached the Flint River Bridge over M-57 near Polk's Pub.

The song made him think about his father who died during his college years, leaving him with a lifetime of uncreated memories. Tony Annese inherited his dad's love for the game, and wished they could've shared his coaching experience together. The significant lyrics seemed to help him connect with his dad.

A few hours later, Goose felt the finger of a Hamady opponent poke through his facemask, digging his eye. His contact popped loose causing Goose to frantically search the field, but knew it was hopeless on the worked up ground. It was only the first quarter and he feared, *What would happen if I lost the other one?* He decided to play with one contact in, while trying to adjust to the unbalanced sensation, like a surgical patient feeling the room sway before going under.

The game turned into a track meet when the visiting Hamady quarterback threw for 187 yards and one TD. Hamady used its great team speed on offense, letting their passes pester the Montrose secondary. Hamady was quick getting to the ball on defense; proving that the Rams didn't play as well against a fast team. Montrose fumbled three times, surrendering several prime first-half scoring opportunities. Both teams rolled up impressive yardage despite a scoreless first half, sending a frustrated Montrose team to the locker room.

Wixson felt relieved that they didn't have to do push-ups like they did in '88, but Coach's words were just as demanding. Newt felt the bite from his words. They all did. 'We're having too many breakdowns here and there throughout the course of the game. We're flirting with disaster. We can't afford to give them momentum because they're gunning for us!'

The half-time speech motivated them. Three minutes into the third quarter, the ice was broken when Cliff burst loose and romped 55 yards to score. Goose grabbed Tafoya's facemask in the huddle, glaring at his brown eyes, 'Don't you dare drop it!'

Goose knew that he'd catch it. Tafoya never dropped one of his passes, but he wanted to make sure they were all on the same page. The play unfolded. Goose found trusty Tafoya in the endzone and let it rip. Goose watched Tafoya make the catch, hanging on until the scoreboard lit up another two points.

The lead didn't last long after Hamady came back on their initial possession, scoring on a six yard run. Two minutes later, the margin tapered to 8-6. The Rams managed to control the offense for the bulk of the third quarter, until Goose plunged over on a one yard sneak boosting the Rams ahead by a TD. Kies scored on a 15 yard jaunt with five minutes left in the final period, but the game was far from over.

Goose was very competitive, becoming mad at himself when he screwed up. He wasn't shy about taking control in the huddle, yelling at the others to provide an extra fraction of intensity. Tafoya rarely screwed up, but Goose made sure he was completely focused. He didn't want anyone botching the play, since the game was so close. Several times during the game he grabbed Tafoya's facemask, screaming directly at him, 'Make sure you get your block!'

Hamady drove down the field, connecting on a 20 yard scoring strike with three minutes left in the game. The Hawks were within one TD to tie. Hamady wanted to win the contest and tried an on-side kick, but the Rams expected it and jumped on the pigskin, claiming possession. A huge sigh of relief shook the Montrose side of the field. The seemingly slow clock counted off the final seconds, allowing the Rams to claim a '20-14' victory. The media dubbed Cliff and Kies as 'The Cream of the GEC Crop' after amassing 278 of the Rams 323 total yards as a rushing tandem.

The Rams escaped a potential scare from Hamady, and scored a 'W' for their league opener. It was their third victory of the season, and kept the Rams curt winning streak alive. The streak was in its infancy, like a small rolling pebble that fostered momentum, eventually turning itself into a burly boulder that provided a source of motivation to all it touched.

Coach Annese left school in a hurry after the bell rang the following Friday afternoon. Like many of his players, he once again surrendered his superstitions by repeating his pre-game routine. He hoped to yield the same results as he dressed for the **New Lothrop** game. When he approached the Flint River Bridge, he hoped that the radio once again played *In the Living Years.*

It did. Unmindful that radio stations often played prerecorded segments, the coach allowed an eerie sensation to brush over him. *Was that coincidence or was his dad sending him some form of message?* Either way, he considered it a good sign and relaxed while he listened to the lyrics of Mike and the Mechanics. He intentionally bypassed the street to the high school, making a detour through town so that he could listen to the entire song, absorbing every word. He felt confident by the time he walked into the locker room.

That confidence was challenged on the first play from scrimmage when the Rams fumbled the football. A New Lothrop Hornet recovered it at the Montrose 26. Seven plays later, the Hornets connected on fourth down, taking a 0-6 lead. Newt could tell that Coach was pissed before the words ever left his mouth. His heart raced so fast that he didn't absorb everything, but he saw spit fly from his coach's mouth. 'You're a bunch of pansies for letting them score first.'

It was gut check time. The offense mentally stepped up before they ever set foot on the field. Goose led them on a 54 yard march, helping them gain confidence on every down. After 13 plays, Kies bullied his way over from the four yard line, while Goose made sure his PAT was good. It gave the Rams a one-point lead with only minutes left in the opening quarter. Montrose fans experienced a rush of excitement that Goose planned to continue. On the next series, he swept right on the quarterback keeper before breaking across the field, outlegging the defense for a 53 yard TD. No way would the quarterback for the Rams surrender defeat. Cliff had the same mentality when he took the handoff from Goose, then made the conversion.

Moments later, the Hornet punter bobbled the snap, but attempted to pass. Newt jumped up and grabbed it, but his helmet was thrown off during the play. It didn't take long for Newt to realize that his nose was broken. It hurt like hell but he wasn't about to tell any coach, especially since his interception gave Montrose possession at its own 45. Kies' powerful legs and physical strength shook off several would-be tacklers on his way to the endzone. He scored on a 31 yard run six plays later.

Then a possible disaster struck for Cliff, after scoring a two yard run half way through the third quarter. He went down. His parents held their breath, while Cliff was carried off the field with a knee injury. Cliff tried to be tough in spite of his pain. He attempted to bottle his frustration and leave it on the field. Cliff was only midway through football season and had even bigger expectations for wrestling; a knee injury was not in his plans.

The Rams tried to establish their running game but the Hornets stacked things up. Montrose reverted to their air game and it worked. Vin hauled in four passes for 82 yards. He helped the offense make some big plays, converting six times on fourth down. The Montrose defense played extremely well, proving that Coach Reinhart had them well prepared for New Lothrop when they closed the score '30-6.'

Superstitions were as sacred to players as Indian burial grounds. The team didn't always discuss them openly, but most everyone accepted them. Even coaches made decisions to repeat a particular play under certain conditions. Double numbers brought good luck to some -- Cliff needed #33, Corey Lake wore #44 and Newt had #55. Changing numbers from J.V. to Varsity was bad luck for others. Goose still wore #16, and Wright #12, but it was different for Wixson. He switched jerseys and wanted the same results that #79 gave Cheese in the `88 Season.

Vin crafted his own set of rituals. He shaved his head in the shape of an arrow, then asked the young trainer, Matt Noble, to paint it red and black before each game. He also wrapped his cleats in white tape, believing it helped him run faster. So did Ricky Diem who had to wear the same socks and T-shirt every game. Tafoya rubbed Icy-Hot on his hands and arms before every game. *Every game.* He wouldn't even think of playing in a game without it. He rubbed the top of his left hand and then his right, followed by his left forearm and then his right, working his way to his upper left arm and then his right. Always in the same order. *Always.*

Last season, Goose wore a faded Detroit Tiger T-shirt that his cousin Scott Aldred gave him. Aldred was their All-State Quarterback in `85, leading the Rams to a Class B playoff berth. Aldred had an arm and was a rookie pitcher for the Detroit Tigers, an accomplishment that classified him as one of the most famous Montrose alumni. Aldred was probably unaware of just how closely many local baseball fans, of all ages, followed his career. Even non sports-minded people were interested in their hometown boy who made it to the big leagues, casually dropping his name whenever discussing sports. Goose knew that a T-shirt coming from Aldred had to be special. He wore it to every game throughout the `88 Season, and planned to do the same in `89, hoping it gave him a competitive edge.

Like Goose, Brody wore the same T-shirt every game. He refused to wash it since the season started, fearing it would rinse the luck out. The same was true for his foul-smelling socks. They were only into week four, and he reeked so badly that his teammates held their breath when they passed his locker. It gave the entire room a musty odor, like the smell of an overripe, gutted cantaloupe mixed with spoiled meat. Players were surprised the maintenance staff didn't complain, but neither did any of them. They just did their best to avoid being his partner on the bus.

No one messed with superstitions. Rituals started subtly and could appear as excessive disorders to outsiders, but players weren't embarrassed about them. Superstitions were a part of football and were simply accepted, no matter how eccentric they seemed. If it worked, you went with it. Game day rituals also spanned the world of pro athletes. Even superstar Michael Jordan admitted to wearing blue basketball shorts from his alma mater, the University of North Carolina, under his Chicago Bulls uniform.

Coach Annese didn't plan to break his rituals either. Constant interruptions after school caused him to become short with everyone. *Didn't they understand? He needed to get home and be asleep by 3 PM for that quick pre-game nap. He didn't want to change his ritual and jinx the team.*

Annese stirred in his seat as he approached the Flint River Bridge. *What were the odds of a radio station playing his song at the same spot for the third week in a row?* He knew they were highly unlikely.

Still.

He took his chances, becoming anxious when he approached the bridge. He even touched the brake to slow down his speed, as if giving the radio station a second chance. He didn't hear the start of the opening beat, so he intervened by quickly jamming in his new cassette. He wasn't about to risk his luck then relaxed when *In the Living Years* devoured his car, soothing his frame of mind. His anxiety diminished as he drove around town, welcoming his time alone. It was *his time* to mentally prepare for the game. He thought about the motivating talks that his dad gave him at Corunna High, remembering his inspiring words. He wished that he could tell his dad what a mentor he had been. He knew that his dad would've enjoyed watching the next generation of Annese coaches, but that wasn't meant to be.

When Annese reached the locker room, he was glad to hear that Cliff's doctor gave him the green light to play. Cliff nursed his injured knee throughout the week, attempting to brush off the severity of his own pain. Annese realized that Cliff wanted to play as much as the rest, and didn't complain one iota to his doctor. He knew better. Cliff was a tough, hard-nosed back; the toughest Annese had ever coached. He just wanted to play football and didn't think about the consequence arthritis played on old athletic injuries. Growing old was the farthest thing from Cliff's mind. He was the most quiet and serious of the three backs, but held a silent determination. It was his turn to play Montrose Football with the boys on Friday night. He wouldn't let a knee injury get in his way, and fed off the pre-game hype.

Both **Bentley** and Montrose were undefeated coming into their league contest. When they approached the field, Cliff proudly marched with his teammates in their traditional two-by-two fashion, joined at their hands in a reflection of their brotherhood. It was Montrose tradition; their proud trademark. It pissed them off, especially Cliff, when a few Bentley adults called them *fagots* as the team walked past them. Kies listened to their biting words and thought, *Let's just show them who's the toughest. Let's make them eat their words.* Coach Annese instructed them to shake it off, 'Be proud of what you represent.'

The Rams hit the field with an edgy intensity, then celebrated when Kies scored half way through the opening quarter. Both teams continued to move the ball, but were able to stop the other. The Bulldogs drove to the Montrose seven early in the second quarter, but were unable to advance when the determined Rams blocked their attempted field goal on the fourth down. Bentley scored midway through the second period, but the undiscouraged Rams came right back on the ensuing possession when Kies scored two minutes before the half ended.

Kies scored his third TD with :39 seconds left in the half. Kies was a physically dominant back who fought for more yardage on every play. Grown men enjoyed watching him explode into the secondary. Once he broke through he knew where to run, preferring to use his strength to plow over an opponent. Kies wore opponents down after a few hits, making it tougher on them once they felt the full impact of his strength. His score exhilarated the Rams; the entire team felt the momentum once the buzzer blared.

During intermission, Annese reminded them of their last contest. 'We had the possession at the start of the second half. The score was 15-12. We came out, went down the field, and scored. That was the decisive drive then and it will be again tonight when we go back on that field and score!'

The Rams were emotionally charged after the half. The sixteen point lead gave Kies added confidence; he held his head a bit higher as the Rams marched past the same Bentley fans that earlier called them fagots. Kies was the guy that constantly pulled shenanigans. He earned the name 'Barney Rubble' for his very distinct laugh that was both loud and boisterous. But Kies restrained from boasting, realizing Coach Annese would be furious if he retaliated. *Yeah, it's funny that no one's saying anything now that the scoreboard shows 22-6. He hoped they ate their words!*

Bentley kicked off, then Montrose held on to the ball for 11 plays, then marched 82 yards until Goose snuck across to score the TD. The Rams were up 30-6. Goose had an edge when he played defensive back because he knew how a quarterback thought. He watched for signs the Bentley quarterback made after their huddle broke and they took their positions. His hunch was right, and he followed his instincts to intercept the ball. Goose was so competitive that he found it hard to enjoy the game while playing, because he was so focused on wanting to do more.

Vin ran behind Goose ready for the pitch back and yelled 'Goose, Goose.'

The quarterback had become the master at knowing when to pitch and when to keep it. That time he pitched to Vinnie who accelerated for extra yardage, just as they orchestrated in practice. Vin added the *flash* on the field, making the big plays at the right time.

Goose added a second score on a 20 yard option keeper. The reserves kept the chains moving for the Rams on their final drive. They took the words seriously that Coach Annese constantly stressed during practice, 'Second teams are what wins games!'

Ricky Diem enjoyed every minute that he was on the field, and had his best night. Ricky was small, about the same size as Vinnie and just as wired. His high energy made everyone laugh when he got in the game. It was obvious that he enjoyed life, especially his senior year. He used that energy to set the Champions Club record for jumpovers with 72. Ricky had a lot of tackles and saw a lot of action on special teams, and considered it a great night.

They all gave 100% during practice and Coach was glad he got them in. Junior Jerry Kovl scored from 23 yards out with four minutes left to play. Kovl was a good back waiting in the wings behind two of the strongest running backs in the League. Kovl was thrilled to get some action when their conversion made the final score 'Montrose 46 - Bentley 6.'

For the Rams, it was their best performance all season. They scored in every quarter, rolling up 455 yards in total offense. Reinhart was proud that his defense checked the Bulldogs to a minus seven yards in the third quarter.

The offensive line was commended for the good seams they opened for the backs. Kies rushed for a phenomenal 174 yards, his third consecutive game to eclipse the 100 yard mark. Annese told the press, 'Kies was the best kept secret in the League and the County.'

His efforts helped the Rams improve to 5-0 overall, extending the area-winning streak to '12 straight.' Annese proudly stated in his post-game interviews, 'I don't know what the rest of the county has as far as backs go, but I tell you, I wouldn't trade my three for anything. They are just tough, dedicated, hard working kids who lead by example.'

Annese didn't have anything good to say at practice on Monday though. His squad had never seen him so angry. Spit actually flew from his mouth when he yelled. No matter how strict his rules were, some teenagers still managed to break them. But they didn't get away with it that time. A few Varsity players, and six from the J.V., were suspended for drinking after a weekend party bust. Coach meant business. The busted players felt like the scum of the earth after he finished with them, feeling lower than a petty officer getting caught going AWOL. It was a degrading punishment to have the face of their head coach so close to theirs, that they could actually count the pores in his skin. His heated voice echoed in their ears, while they wondered if the ass chewing would ever end.

Annese got the last word in throughout the week. The busted players knew they were in trouble after Coach changed the game plan for the annual J.V. scrimmage. Instead of facing the second string Varsity, Coach substituted the over anxious first string. It didn't take a rocket scientist to assume that Annese offered a 'no holds barred' invitation to the Varsity. The suspended players felt like sitting ducks, realizing they were easy prey. Coach conveniently looked the other way throughout their scrimmage each time a cheap shot occurred. It wouldn't do an ounce of good to complain; they all knew it went on deaf ears. By that point, the party and drinking didn't seem quite as much fun as it did on Saturday night. They all agreed if they had it to do over, they wouldn't drink, *they just wouldn't!*

Corey Crockett, the star J.V. quarterback, was included in the bust and couldn't play the rest of the season. Without him, the J.V. Team lost their final three games. Annese already recognized Crockett's potential and felt, with work, he could be Division I material. Crockett quickly learned Coach Annese expected more from him when he gave the quarterback a choice.

'You can either practice with the Varsity the rest of the season or you won't be playing football next year.'

Crockett's worst expectations came true. The cheap shots continued the rest of the season, especially once the Varsity realized they went under blind eyes. Brody enjoyed roughing guys up during practice on a normal day and took advantage of the green light. Coach wanted to see what Crockett was made of and how he reacted at the Varsity level. Crockett needed a taste of Varsity football. He quickly learned about commitment and how to stay out of trouble. After all, he was a likely quarterback candidate for the Rams '90 season.

The school buzzed with a powerful energy during Homecoming week. Goose was more excited then he displayed after being elected as Homecoming King. He beat Vinnie and Ricky, although Ricky later won the senior vote for the 'Most Watchable Walk.' Goose had an unwitting manner that made girls drool behind his back.   He stereotyped the perfect quarterback; good looks, blonde hair, deep blue eyes, a calm mannerism, and he was smart. To top all that, he had the flair to grow hair above his lip.

They were all anxious for game time to arrive and when it did, the Rams seemed to click as a team. Annese gave them a new challenge, setting goals for them to reach by the *half* against **Atherton**. Players continued doing the little things from beginning to end; it was their secret ingredient that set the tone for the game. Montrose scored on every possession during the first half; Kies scored three TD's in the opening quarter alone. Cliff, who still hobbled on his injured knee, added a pair of TD's in the second period. Within a minute after he scored their fifth TD, the Rams intercepted the ball. When the offense prepared to take the field, Annese told them, 'Do not score anymore!'

He specifically looked at Vin and then at Goose, 'No passes, understand?'

They both nodded. Annese looked at Vin, 'Next week at Lake Fenton you can pass all you want. You can even break a school record, but not tonight. They're scouting us and I don't want it on film. Do not pass and do not score, fall down if you need to!'

The Rams were relaxed and Coach Annese let Goose audible as he saw the play develop. The line provided great coverage, giving Goose plenty of time on his reads to make the call and react to what unfolded in front of him. He stepped back, then placed his feet in proper position while his eyes scanned the field. Goose watched Vin cut loose, and couldn't help but notice his spatted cleats. He watched Vin in the locker room when he meticulously positioned the tape, giving his shoes a sharp contrast between the bright white tape and dark black cleats. Vin heard that it made a guy look faster. That was Vinnie, a bit flashier than the rest but had the speed to back it up. He was the Rams *go-to-guy* in the receiving corps. He had hands like glue and was difficult to tackle in a crowd, let alone *see* because of his small stature.

Goose knew Vinnie would be open in about two seconds. He checked his conscience, while listening to the quick debate going on in his head.

We haven't passed all night.
(We were told not to!)
But it was the perfect opportunity.
(We don't want to show Lake Fenton anything for the next week.)
Yeah right! But he didn't hesitate to give Kies and Cliff their 100+ yards for the game. Just go for it. It's Homecoming!

A part of Goose resented that *his stats* always seemed to be the ones getting cut. The quarterback quickly glanced at Coach Annese on the sideline. Coach knew Goose so well, immediately grasping the play exploiting in his quarterback's mind and wildly waved his arms. Annese even jumped up-and-down to get his quarterback's attention, screaming, 'No. Don't pass!'

Goose looked down the field at Vinnie who invitingly waved his arms in the endzone. *Do it Goose! Vinnie's wide open. He's begging you to throw it!* His conscience went to work. The line provided great coverage, giving ample time for Goose to glance back at Coach Annese, this time with defiant eyes. Goose gave in to his rebellious side, in spite of watching Annese throw a fit on the sideline. He couldn't resist and released - *The Bomb.* It was showtime.

It was the only pass of the game, a perfect spiral with teasing hang time that added to Annese's intensity. Vin caught it effortlessly like they did in practice every night. He ran back to Goose and celebrated, like quarterbacks and receivers do after connecting on a successful play. Vin grinned from ear to ear, feeling pretty tall in front of the huge Homecoming crowd.

Mr. Venturino swelled with pride in the stands, after telling his grandson what his daddy just did. He was the man in the stands that glowed with pride after his friends patted him on the back. Dads always did that to each other when their sons ran a good play or placed a good block, as if *they* somehow deserved the credit.

Annese wasn't grinning though. He was furious after Goose kicked the PAT, making the score 41-0. Relaxed and happy, the guys exchanged high-fives when they came off the field, until they reached the sideline. The disappointed look on Coach Annese's face extorted the thrill of it.

Goose didn't understand what the big deal was and thought, *C'mon, it's Homecoming and the game's not even close.* He quickly learned that Coach was pissed when they disobeyed him. The Rams broke the unwritten rule that a team doesn't intentionally run up the score. Coach Annese shared his disappointment in the locker room during the half. His speech was intended for Goose who stayed on the field to participate in the half-time festivities, fulfilling his role as Homecoming King.

Annese pulled Goose aside before the start of the third quarter, sharing his frustration, but his speech landed on deaf ears. All kinds of thoughts ran through Goose's head. *Is Coach pissed at me for being Homecoming King? Like I had anything to do with that. I never signed up for it. I was just elected.*

Goose had an understated confidence about what he felt was right. He shunned recognition and hated the spotlight, but joined in the half-time activities because he felt it was the right thing to do. He was glad he did, and cherished the fun experience he shared with his classmates that created a memory he'd always value. Posing with the attractive Homecoming Queen was part of the honor, and made more sense to Goose than joining his team for a good laugh in the locker room of a 41-0 snoozer. Goose wondered if Annese resented him deep down because he never fully bought 100% into *all* of his ideas. He knew Coach would never admit that Goose pissed him off to no end, because he couldn't get into his head like he could the others. It caused a few pissing matches between a coach and his quarterback, because Goose was every bit as stubborn and competitive as Coach was; he just wasn't as flamboyant.

Apprehension consumed Annese when he lined up with the offensive line on the first series of the second half. All too soon the Rams were in the Wolverines red zone, too close to score. Goose handed off to Kies while a cautious head coach watched. He had an odd feeling they would run it in against his wishes and screamed at Kies, 'Fall down! Fall down!'

Kies easily scored his fourth TD and thought, *I'm not gonna look foolish and trip.* The fans loved it and wanted more. The coaches despised it and wanted less. Again, the team celebrated when the offense came off the field. Kies sensed it would be his final TD, and noticed how the team quickly distanced themselves when Annese approached. 'Do you want to get voted for anything in the Conference? Do you? You can't keep running up the score!'

Kies already had 183 total yards on 16 carries, surpassing 100 yards in the last four games. The tough back felt he was only doing what he'd been trained to do and wasn't about to look stupid by falling down, even if it meant getting pulled.

Kovl loved it when Kies got pulled. As a junior, it was hard for him to shine with extraordinary backs like Kies and Cliff in the backfield. He knew his turn came in '90 when he was a senior and they were long gone. Still, He was all too anxious to prove what he could do whenever he had the chance. With the secondary in, Kovl scored twice for the Rams, helping Montrose claim a '61-0' victory over Atherton.

The coaches were disappointed with their final score, but pleased with their performance, in spite of the confrontations. Players still had to execute and continue to improve, knowing that undefeated Goodrich lurked for the season finale.

Post-season positioning wars were underway, while the Rams entertained a darkhorse playoff hope. Montrose faced eighth ranked Lake Fenton in the Class B Region, and needed several things to happen to thrust them into the top four. While Chesaning led their Region, the Rams could only play their best in preparation of their dream; everything else was out of their hands. So the Rams broke records instead. They amassed eight TD's and 615 yards in total offense. Vin set a school record by catching ten of Gooses' 12 passes for 130 yards. Kies set a rushing record with 217 yards while Cliff rushed for 156, trying to prove that his knee was better. The truth was that it hurt like hell, but he wasn't going to let it stop him.

The Rams hadn't punted since the New Lothrop game, and managed to hold **Lake Fenton** to only nine yards on the ground. Lake Fenton gained 177 yards in the air, but allowed Montrose to intercept five of those passes. But their '48-8' victory over Lake Fenton didn't give Montrose a big head. Annese was furious about their 130 penalty yards and the fact that Rob Fisher got kicked out of the game. 'Fish' punched an opponent in the facemask for something he felt he deserved, and they both got kicked out. The Rams played aggressively, but Annese felt the offensive line should've had enough experience after seven games to eliminate those types of mistakes.

Fish soon discovered the price he'd pay for getting kicked out. Annese made him carry a waterlogged dummy that was so old it had to be leftover from the 70's. He ran three laps around the perimeter of the entire football practice field, including the baseball complex, each night with the weight of a 100 pound waterlogged dummy on his back. One night, Wixson screwed up during practice. Annese told him, 'Give me eight laps!'

Wixson ran with Fish; both absorbed the laughs from their squad after realizing how ridiculous they looked. Wixson wasn't a bad kid by any means, all the guys liked him. The entire senior class liked him enough to vote him as their Class President, but Wix wasn't quite as straight-laced as Coach Annese wanted. He was more of a party guy, full of life and vigor. He had that extraordinary quality of being able to have fun no matter what situation he was in. Wixson worked hard during practice, pulling a prank on someone whenever he could. But on weekends he was the 'good time Charlie' on the team, and missed a few curfews.

Vin knew Wix was already tired from a tough workout, so he ran two laps with him to show his support. It was the least he could do after Wix had stood by him. Vin ran into two nine year-old youth football players on his way back to the school who asked, 'Why is that guy running with a doll on his back?'

Vin turned back to watch his friend, realizing how absurd Wixson actually looked. He bent down to be at their level, 'We call that a dummy. That's what the big guys have to do when they mess up. Coach makes us carry that dummy on our back and think about how to do it the right way.'

They seemed satisfied with his answer and raced off to join their teammates. Vin watched them and thought about his own son, now seven-months old, and wondered if he would play football one day. His son was born January 4th, the very day that Vinnie celebrated his 17th birthday. When he came to school that day, he saw posters on the board, 'Congrats Mini-Vinnie.' Coach Annese teased Vin about having kids that would be older than his own. That seemed strange. Vin had dated the mother for a few years, but now that they had a child, they didn't discuss marriage. They were both too young and worked out a schedule after school and on weekends, to help raise their son.

Coach Annese felt a bit feisty after practice and wanted to play a joke on the senior. He told Vin, 'When Wixson comes in, tell him to go back out and start all over.'

'Coach, you've got to be kidding. He's not in the mood for pranks.'

Annese replied, 'Come on. I'm only joking. Just tell him and act serious when he comes in.'

Vin agreed, but had a bad feeling about it. Back on the field, Wixson's tall stance leaned forward as if someone added a five pound weight after each lap. It made his long youthful body appear like a tired, old man, but he wouldn't quit nor would he cheat. Wixson was determined to prove that his spirit couldn't be crushed by a mere eight laps, but did plenty of gut checks after each round, reaching deep to finish each one. *Credibility builds character.*

He was dragging ass after the fourth lap, but wouldn't stop even though he was on the honor system. He was too mad to quit and finished the final four laps with barely enough energy to walk back to the school. Vin was the only one around by the time Wix finally walked into the locker room, totally exhausted.

Vin didn't know if he could pull it off. 'Hey Wix, Coach was just here looking for you. He said you went too slow and he wants you to start all over.'

Wixson stopped dead in his tracks and looked at Vin. 'Are you serious?'

It was all Vin could do to keep a straight face. 'Yeah. He seemed upset.'

In an instant, Wix became mad at the world. He practiced hard, he didn't cheat, and couldn't believe what he just heard. He quickly became agitated and worked himself into a fury, shouting, 'I quit man. Shit. This is bullshit!'

Annese walked into the locker room at that moment, 'Is there a problem?'

Coach brought out the best in most and the worst in some. Unfortunately for Wix, it wasn't his best. He slammed his sweaty fist against the cold metal locker, too pissed off to even feel the pain. A nerve-racking, eerie feeling started at the base of his spine and crept up the entire length of his back. He started to swear up a storm, even made up a few cuss words of his own while strange noises flew from his mouth. Neither Vin nor Coach dared to laugh or even smirk, especially when he finished his rampage with, 'I quit!'

Annese continued to play along and told Wixson, 'You're going back out there, right now!'

'No way man, I quit!'

Coach realized he had crossed Wixson's breaking point and looked at Vin for support, 'Tell him it's a joke.'

Vin replied, 'He's right Wix, it's all staged. It was just a joke!'

But they already pushed him to the brink. Wixson was so demented and pissed at that moment that his grumbling voice sounded more like a moaning whine, 'I don't care man, I quit!'

Wixson was usually the one pulling the pranks and could usually receive one, but he was too tired and wasn't in the mood to be the blunt of their joke. He was hot and exhausted, and now they humiliated him. Wix grabbed what he needed from his locker, then cast an evil stare Vin's way before storming out of the school. Vin shook his head, feeling like a villain that ratted on a good friend.

Coach sensed Vin's reaction, 'Don't worry. He'll be back tomorrow.'

Vin nodded, 'I know, he loves playing tackle too much to quit!'

Goose silently witnessed the entire scene while standing nearby, with crossed arms and a smirk on his face. He shook his head, confident that Wixson would be back the following day. For a big man, Wix had the softest hands that Goose had ever seen. He was a natural athlete who could catch anything thrown his way, and made it look easy. Goose thought his talents were wasted on the defensive line alone. He thought Wixson would've made a great tight end on the offensive side of the ball. Wixson had fantastic instincts to go with his phenomenal athletic ability, and had a nose for the ball. He was an absolute, 100% team player that always put the team first. It was obvious that Wixson really wanted the team to succeed, above all else.

Wixson liked pranks but always knew when it was time to be serious and get down to business. When Goose looked at Wix on game night, he saw the face of a competitor. Goose remembered a few months back in late spring when Wix convinced him that the Rams would go 9-0. He said, 'We could be better than the '85 Team, which their brothers and cousins played on.

Goose thought, *Just being mentioned in the same breath as the '85 Team was an honor. That class produced some great athletes.* They were the heroes that Wixson, Goose, and the rest of the squad modeled themselves after.

Wixson came back the next day and helped the Rams cruise by **Bendle** with a '41-0' victory. He watched the bone-jarring Chris Kies surpass the 1,000 yard rushing plateau.

The victory set the stage for the last week of the season's 'winner-take-all' battle against undefeated Goodrich, who boasted the League's second best offense and defense. But they were close. Montrose was No.1 after scoring 246 league points, while Goodrich posted 204. The Rams allowed only 34 total opponent points scored, compared to Goodrich who allowed only 47. The Goodrich offense was almost a mirror image of Montrose. Goodrich had two excellent junior running backs that were leading scorers. Their quarterback was very mobile, showing ability to throw on the run, just like Goose. Both were defensive teams as well. The challenging game won the recognition to be broadcasted by Comcast Cable's 'Game of the Week.'

Before the Rams left Thursday's pre-game practice, Coach Annese reminded them of the three goals they established at the beginning of their season: to win the GEC League, go undefeated, and make the playoffs. His uncompromising voice gave them chills. 'If we lose to **Goodrich** we can forget all three!'

Annese talked about taking care of business and taking care of the things they could control. Wixson threw a glance at Vin and thought, *This is the way it should be. The two undefeated teams battling for the championship in the ninth game of the season!*

While the Rams still entertained a dream of making the Michigan High School Athletic Association (MHSAA) playoffs, they needed plenty of outside help to move from ninth place to fourth. It was a slim shot, but enough to provide a glimmer of hope. The Rams could control their first two goals, but unfortunately the third was completely out of their hands. Warner Brothers couldn't have scripted a better ending since Goodrich also had a longshot to make the playoffs. Obviously, more than just the GEC Conference Title was on the line.

Vin could smell Brody's awful T-shirt when he passed his locker. He hadn't washed it all season and the smell disgusted the entire team, but no one messed with superstitions, *no matter what.*

The team felt like heroes when the school lavished them with overflowing spirit at Friday's pep assembly. The Rams prepared to defend their league crown. A win allowed them to be the first team to repeat League Titles since the Rams won in '83, '84 and '85.

Goodrich and Montrose felt untouched by the recent disasters that stormed the U.S. While the west cost dealt with an earthquake that registered 7.1 on the Richter scale, forcing Interstate 880 to pitch and heave, the east coast recovered from Hurricane Hugo that ravaged South Carolina's coast. But life went on in normal fashion for the Goodrich Martians and Montrose Rams. Both felt safe and unaffected in their midwestern location, totally focused on the game of football.

If Goodrich won, Coach Joe Pruchnicki would lead the Martians to their first ever GEC football league crown. It could be the biggest game for Goodrich in 15 years; their entire community jumped on their bandwagon. The Martians had the prevalence of playing on their home field, but that didn't matter. Montrose had won 15 in a row and eight of those were played on the road. Their dedicated fans followed them wherever they played.

Parents realized making the playoffs was a long shot, and anticipated it was the last high school football game. It was difficult to see their season end after witnessing their dedication and hard work. They decided to go out with a bang and organized a caravan. When they met at the school parking lot to decorate their cars and school buses, they left their mark by forming the longest caravan ever in Montrose history. A few parents left early, placing signs along the way to fire up the Rams on the hour-long bus drive to Goodrich. Players weren't allowed to talk once they boarded the bus; Coach wanted them concentrating on the game. The silence only added to their nerves and the butterflies that danced inside them. The buses made the exit off southbound interstate I-75 and rounded the curve onto the high I-475 overpass. Michigan's icy winter months often turned the overpass into a driver's nightmare.

An instant smile formed on the face of Coach Annese. He couldn't take his eyes off of what he saw. When the special teams' bus made the long bend on the overpass, he slowly stood up from the front seat and stared. 'Hey guys, don't say anything. Just turn around and look.'

Curious heads quickly turned as the entire team watched from the bus positioned high above the I-75 traffic. Knots swelled in their throats as their mouths dropped. Junior Al Olah played tackle, but was also the long snapper, so he rode that bus with the special teams and cheerleaders. He let out a long, whispered, 'Wow' as goosebumps danced up his arms.

The luminous glow of glimmering headlights outlined the interstate for three long miles. Hundreds of people formed the caravan to watch the Rams play what could very well be their *final game*. Players couldn't help but sport a grin, which conveniently broke the nervous tension in the air. The warmth from the afterglow planted a special feeling firmly in their memory banks; a sensation that wouldn't easily be forgotten.

Cliff oozed with pride. That moment made every ounce of pain that his knee endured all season worthwhile. Cliff was satisfied in what the Rams had accomplished, but he was determined to fulfill one final goal. He wanted to account for 1,000 yards, but didn't know if he could get it against Goodrich. It was a competitive thing between the backs; Kies had reached the magic mark, Goose was close, and Cliff wanted it.

After warming up, players walked to the locker room for their pregame pep talk. They noticed all of the fans that tailgated. It looked like a college parking lot during a Saturday game. When the Rams made their way back to the football field, they were surprised to find a human tunnel. It started at the entrance gate and extended the entire way to the middle of the field lined with students, parents, neighbors, and fans. Players didn't expect it and had never seen anything like it. People reached out to touch them, cheering their names like they were a popular rock band ready to take the stage for the biggest concert of the year. It created an even greater desire in each of them to perform their best.

One of their key fans was missing. The boisterous Mr. Kies was at work where he was expected to stay the entire night. At least that's what the schedule reflected, but he had other plans when he announced, 'My son's playing in a great game tonight.'

He was disappointed when his boss replied, 'Too bad you have to miss it. You can't have it off.'

Mr. Kies thought to himself, *That son of a gun.* Something mysterious happens to special dads during such moments, forcing them to follow their hearts and bypass any monetary commitment. His son was the leading rusher for the Rams and set an all-time school record for the 'best rushing average.' He knew he would be miserable and never forgive himself if he missed his son's last high school football game. The thought chewed on his mind until he couldn't stand it. *He couldn't forego the game, no matter what the consequences were. He coached that team during little league, when they were only nine. They all grew up in a flash and were about to play their final game. How could he miss it?*

He couldn't concentrate and worked himself into a frenzied state, deciding to put his job on the line. Mr. Kies stood up and firmly announced, 'I'm leaving.'

He knew in his heart that it was the right decision. He didn't have any regrets from the moment he stepped out of the building. His eyes did a double take when he entered Goodrich's field. The sight caused him to stop and stare in total awe. It looked like a heavy snowstorm hovered over the Montrose side of the bleachers, compliments of Vin's mom who distributed bags of shredded paper she saved from work. Mr. Kies found a spot near the other parents and settled in. A nostalgic smile lit his face as he glanced around, feeling the charisma of the night. It felt right to be there.

The game held high stakes for both teams, which explained the enormous turnout. Goodrich started the action by booting a high-hanging punt one-minute into the game. It was already fourth down when Vin positioned himself deep, then fumbled the punt on the Montrose 15 yard line. *Damn.* Goodrich recovered and had great scoring position.

Shit.

Although Vin usually made it look easy, catching punts was more complex than it looked, especially under the bright Friday night lights. He hung his head as he walked the lonely road back to the Montrose sideline. It felt like a death march. He couldn't stand to hear the Goodrich fans cheer so rowdily. It made him feel as if he let the entire town of Montrose down. *Man, this is my senior year. I played two seasons on Varsity and returned so many punts all season. How could I have dropped that one?* He wanted to play football in college and started doubting his own abilities. *Would he buckle under pressure?*

The louder the Goodrich side yelled, the more Vin slithered into his helmet for shelter, treating it like a private sanctuary. He stood at the very end of the sideline, far away from the coaches. From the corner of his eye he saw Coach Annese approach. *Oh shit. Here he comes. I feel bad enough*

and don't need Coach in my face so early in the game. Vin braced himself
for a major butt chewing. But Coach knew that Vin would settle down after
the opening pressure and encouraged him. What a surprise. He told Vin
exactly what he needed to hear at that very moment, 'Don't worry Vin, we'll
get it back.'

One simple sentence that magically converted Vin's fears and self-doubts
into a trusting confidence. All Vin needed to know was that Coach believed
in him. He prepared for what became the game of his life. On the next
series, the defense maintained their reputation for being physically tough.
The Rams were quick getting to the ball and arrived in a bad mood. They
kept Goodrich out of the endzone by stopping a fake field goal attempt on
fourth down. It appeared the defense wanted to win the game even more than
the offense did.

The Rams exchanged punts with the Martians, then Cliff opened up the
scoring with a 74 yard TD run. Cliff was a bruising hard-nosed back who
could do it all. Whether he played back, linebacker, quarterback or kicker he
had tremendous balance to go with his formidable athleticism. Everyone on
the team respected Cliff because of his work ethic, and his history of
consistently producing on game day. He didn't need outside motivation, his
was all intrinsic. Cliff was all about the team and its success.

Tafoya dropped a pass for a first down. It was a roll out over the center of
the line, but simply fell through his hands. It was the only pass he dropped
during his two Varsity seasons. He was their quick go-to-guy for short 10
yard passes. Even before his coaches chewed him out, the disappointed look
on Tafoya's face showed how bad he felt in such an exciting game.

Montrose fumbled on their next series, but recovered on the Goodrich 14
yard line. Goose ran the option to perfection when he tucked the ball, then
slanted 15 yards for their second score. Shortly afterward, Goose threw a 55
yard pass to Vin who made a circus catch behind two Goodrich defenders to
score a third TD. Spectators felt the momentum shift when the Rams went up
21-0 at the end of the first quarter, in front of the shell-shocked Martians.

Cliff continued to press their imposing offense when he took over from
the three, running the conversion in. Goodrich punted again and Wixson
heard Vin call his name. The Goodrich opponent was totally focused on Vin
and didn't even see Wix coming, until he got decked.

Annese decided it was showtime. The offense was thrilled in the huddle
when Goose said, 'Okay guys, it's flea flicker time. Let's make this work.'

They practiced the trick play all week. Vin lined up on one side of the
field and Led, a junior wingback, was on the opposite. Goose flipped Led the
ball who took the reverse then acted like he was running with it. Led watched
Vin use his speed to beat everyone as he sprinted down the field, while
whipping his flashy, spaded cleats. Led threaded a perfect 81 yard strike to
Vin directly in the seam between Goodrich defenders, while the line provided
tough blocks that made it all work. The ecstatic skilled positions celebrated

with their offensive line, while enthused coaches mentally made big plans for Led's next season. The Rams felt on top of the world when they walked off the field, checking the stands. Montrose fans were a big source of energy and shared in the excitement of their big play.

Their performance was nothing short of awesome. They scored 36 points in the span of 11 minutes during the first half alone. The Rams had a quiet confidence all week, concentrating on defending the entire field during practice. They realized Goodrich would show a lot of different looks. Montrose made adjustments early in the game that paid off, then relied on its rugged defense to preserve the victory in the second half.

It was time for special teams to turn it up a notch. Ricky's heart raced when he took his position on the line. *Would it work?* They practiced it all season and never had a chance to use it. They had a good lead and nothing to lose. Vin was the deep receiver who caught the kickoff, then handed off to Cliff while Ricky ran on the outside. Once he got into position Cliff pitched it, Ricky caught it and sprinted, feeling awesome. They didn't score on the play, but made a good return. Ricky couldn't wipe the smile from his face; it was a great way to finish the League.

Annese pulled his seniors out, one-by-one, letting fans acknowledge them. Vin searched the stands for his grandpa and his dad who held his young son. He waved back at the three generations of Venturinos, noticing the delight in their faces. They were even prouder when they learned that Vin was selected as Comcast Cable's 'Player of the Week.' It was a bittersweet moment for Vin. Like his teammates, he never thought about losing all season, but he wasn't ready for it to end. *Not just yet.*

The bulldozing Chris Kies easily spotted his dad sitting next to his mom; they both proudly waved when he made his final exit. As tough as Kies was on the field, he felt his heart fall to his knees. He absorbed his kudos, realizing that he would cherish the memories forever. Kies ended his season as their leading scorer with 15 TD's, and their leading rusher with 1,153 yards, setting an individual season record. His parents overflowed with pride when he received a standing ovation.

Montrose Football meant everything to Cliff at that point in his life. Cliff closed out another brilliant prep career in fine fashion, by shattering another 1,000 yard milestone. He actually did it, two years in a row. He was thrilled yet sad, as if a chunk of his heart was yanked from his chest and left on the football field. Cliff played each game in agony, but felt it was worth every ounce of pain endured. He hugged Coach Annese, then surrendered his emotions. The moment was right and he closed his eyes, letting the tears roll. *He wondered what to say to a man who raised the expectations of his athletes. Who made believers out of non-believers. Who taught him how to carry himself through some tough times, and how to bond with his teammates. Who taught them about life and how to prepare to win. He taught them about pride and how to be successful together, instilling a work ethic they would carry throughout their lives.*

Fans clapped even louder when Goose came off the field. He nodded at the crowd, soaking in the moment. He'd entertained them at the helm for three solid years. Goose served as Annese's quarterback since he started at Montrose. After spending so much time together, they knew each other like brothers. Goose was a quick thinker and Annese helped him develop into an excellent veer quarterback. They came so far together, always settling their differences, and always on the same page. Both held a great deal of respect for the other. Coach Annese shook Goose's hand, already missing the fact that he wouldn't be back next year. He looked Goose directly in the eye and said, 'Good game.'

Kies, Cliff, and Goose all surpassed the 1,000 yard mark in their awesome '89 Season. Many commented that they were the best backfield trio in Montrose history. Kovl anxiously awaited an opportunity to get into the game, and capitalized after scoring a final TD to shutout the Goodrich Martians '43-0' in front of a standing room only crowd.

It was supposed to be a close game, but ended in a shutout. Coach Annese was immensely pleased with his kids and told them, 'This is an incredible accomplishment. You rose to the occasion and played a fantastic ball game. When you dominate opponents as completely as you did, you guys are something special!'

The game meant something unique to all of them, one they would always remember. The atmosphere was unforgettable and touched the essence of their souls. Tafoya took one final look at the guys around him, realizing how unbelievably close they were. Everyone had been out for the team and helped each other. They discovered that it wasn't about individualism. *That's what made it all work.* He had his few moments of glory but didn't feel he was a stand out and didn't need to be. He played on the line and did his job well. Everyone did. They didn't have any weak links. He realized at that moment that the '89 Rams developed something special; far beyond what many high school teams ever experience. Tafoya discovered how far he could push himself. He learned what he could do and wasn't afraid to try. Montrose Football made a difference in his life. He left the program much richer than he started.

Coach Annese talked to the extended group of fans encircling his players in the middle of the field. Montrose proudly accepted the GEC Championship Trophy. Coach publicly thanked the fans for their support of his program. 'I've played high school and college ball and this was the most exciting thing I've ever experienced. The fans were great with their human tunnel, the marching band, and the cheerleaders. This has been a special group of athletes, especially the seniors. They earned everything they have and deserve it. They worked in the off-season and I'm very proud of them.'

The seniors rode the wave of adrenaline for as long as they could. Wixson had one last devilish ploy when he pointed to the cooler and looked at Cliff who nodded back with wide eyes. They did what college and NFL players do on TV. Each grabbed a side of the cooler then ran behind their coach, dumping ice cold water over him, catching Annese totally off-guard. They all laughed while nervously waiting for official news about playoffs. It was a long shot, yet they still felt the bitter taste of disappointment when they didn't make the cut. Neither did Chesaning. Someone suggested the Rams have their own playoff with the Indians and call it the ESPN Dream Season Game.

It was a fun ride and parents, like their sons and coaches, simply didn't want it to end. They wished the playoff point system used a different method, one that rewarded an undefeated team. Parents arrived back at the school before the players did. Dads placed cone-shaped fireworks every 20 feet along the parking lot, and lit them when the buses turned the corner. The celebration served as the grand finale to a terrific season. *What more could they have done?*

The bus ride home should've been a happy one. *It wasn't.* Taking a back seat in the playoff race was flat and disappointing. Ricky felt torn as he stared from the bus window, *We worked so hard and did all we could.*

Players watched from the bus with a bittersweet feeling, impressed that people cared yet felt an embittered emptiness. *Something was missing. Their dream fell one goal short.* Commentaries would be written that the talent on the '89 Montrose Team should've qualified them for a playoff spot. They were stacked three deep and were the Rams first undefeated team. The state playoff point system didn't award them a spot to show what they could accomplish in the post-season. The MHSAA playoffs only had Class A, B, C and D. Perhaps the grumbling made an impact because four additional playoff berths were expanded to include Class AA, BB, CC, and DD.

Annese brought some life to their depressed mood when he paid up his bet. The team placed him in a chair, then gathered around their nervous coach with an electric razor in hand. Players took turns shaving off his thick, dark mustache, as he slowly lost his Tom Selleck look. The head coach hoped that he could trust his squad, yet felt leery after everything he'd put them through. Would they want revenge after he ragged on them to be clean shaven all season, although some sported a shadow of a mustache by the end of practice. Annese knew his lip was dangerously close to the razor in the hands of inexperienced kids and continuously warned them, 'Be careful. Take it easy.'

The '89 Team left their mark by setting eight team records, as well as three individual ones. They outrushed opponents 3,060 to 535 yards. Coach Reinhart's defense was the stingiest in the League, yielding less then five points a game, recorded three shutouts, and gave up a TD or less in three games.

Success meant different things to different people. The team didn't feel completely successful, because they wanted to show what they could do in the playoffs. Three backs surpassed 1,000 yards in the season, while the team averaged 436 yards per game. The GEC League recognized their success and talent by awarding the Rams with ten First Team All-League selections, along with four spots for Honorable Mention.

Still.

They walked away feeling helpless and empty. They felt cheated in spite of being recognized as 'The Greatest Team in Montrose History.' Even with all of the talent they possessed and all of the records they broke, it wasn't enough for a playoff berth. They wondered, *What more could we have done?* Goose sadly hugged his three backs Vinnie, Cliff, and Kies and told them, 'It was an honor to play with you.'

Goose gave Vinnie an extra hug, respecting him in more ways then he voiced. Vin handled the past two seasons like a champ and everything turned out okay. In his moment of sadness, Goose thought of how some guys really get things mixed up. *Some of us think that knocking up a girl makes us a man. Hell, that was the easy part. What makes you a man is taking on the responsibility of raising a child and being a good father and a role model. No one on our team could argue that Vinnie became a man much sooner than the rest of us did.*

Vin's dad was true to his word and produced a highlight film of his son's awesome season. He shipped them to every Division I college he could think of. Vinnie decided on Morehead State in Kentucky.

The Venturinos were a close family who never quit believing in their son. They set a great example of how to make it all work. They gave Vinnie a chance to *follow his dream.*

FLINT JOURNAL PHOTO/Jane Hale

Clockwise from top left: #16 Chris 'Goose' Clolinger, #42 Chris Kies,
#33 Cliff Casteel and #84 Jason Tafoya

3. EFFORT – 1990

**I firmly believe that any man's finest hour is that moment
when he has worked his heart out in a good cause
and lies exhausted on the field of battle, victorious.**

-Vince Lombardi

Al Olah looked over at the love of his life sitting next to him, while driving southbound on I-75. He glanced at her, then at his watch, then back at her, contemplating if he should ask. Would she mind? Maybe they could just drop in for a quarter or two and check it out. They were on their way to a party in Troy, Michigan, not too far from the Silverdome. He suggested the detour then carefully watched her reaction, immediately pleased with her response. After hearing so many stories about Montrose Football she welcomed the idea.

The game was underway when they entered the top level of the 'Dome.' The bright emerald field, the professional lighting, and the crisp sound system made the scene picture perfect. They immediately felt the energy of the Montrose crowd who yelled, 'LET'S GO RAMS' like a lighthouse beckoning them over. Olah introduced her to several of his old teachers and friends. She could instantly tell which guys played football by the radiant expressions on their faces. They stood out above the rest, making it obvious there wasn't any place on earth they'd rather be. Without exchanging any words, the guys thought about the 'what ifs' that prevented them from playing here. A few missed blocks, and those ill-timed fumbles at critical moments, took it all away. Still.

They were the ones who tested the waters, then stepped back and watched the seemingly rippled effect that cascaded. They sensed the uniqueness of being in the Dome together, like some kind of tribal telepathy.

Former players tasted the excitement that rocked the Dome from the moment they arrived. The couple completely lost track of time, forgetting about their party. They were glad they came. Before Olah pushed the metal bar on the exit door, he glanced over his right shoulder for a final look then shook his head in amazement. A happy calmness devoured his body, making him proud that he was a part of something so magical. He cringed as the fixed, heavy, sound of the metal door slammed shut behind him. The impact created an echo that sounded so final, as if giving closure. A slight smile shaped his face as Olah walked away. He honestly felt, in some strange way, that he had left his mark.

Newt looked at Brody as he hung up the hotel phone. 'Can you believe they want us to come down for a drug test?'

Brody sighed heavily, 'Again?'

It wasn't the first time they were *randomly* selected, so they knew the routine. Newt and Brody were intensely dedicated and overly passionate about weightlifting year round. Their intent went beyond having a muscular body. It all came back to football. They wanted to be blatantly strong so they could move mountains next fall. Their dedication placed them a cut above their rivals, rewarding them with larger physiques, but the pestering rumors of steroid use pissed them off. Neither was concerned about passing the test, they just hated the disruption. Brody grabbed the remote, flicking off the TV. 'C'mon, let's get it over with.'

Less than an hour later, they slapped each other a high five, deriving pleasure after proving they worked for every bulging muscle on their youthful bodies. Their clean test results energized them, daring them to make the most of every minute while in the twin cities.

Newt stepped out of the hotel lobby, inhaling a deep breath of crisp June air, while absorbing the variety of smells and unfamiliar sounds of the busy city. He stood by the curb with an easy smile on his face, eagerly gazing at the towering buildings that silhouetted a vista of crisp, blue sky. Brody joined him a few minutes later, allowing Minneapolis to swallow him with its noisy traffic, congested streets, and massive crowds. Minneapolis had a different look and feel than their hometown, which suddenly seemed incredibly petite and exceptionally far away.

The eager pair joined the rest of their powerlifting team who appeared keen, raring to go after their long drive. Most of them only caught a few hours of sleep the night before because they couldn't resist watching the Detroit Pistons win a National Championship. That celebration kept them awake until 1 AM. They gathered three hours later at the school parking lot. Their jokes and laughter kept Reinhart awake during the 14-hour drive from Montrose to Minneapolis. Reinhart scrambled to locate a hotel room, after their contact at the university fell through. He only found one, and crammed twelve teenagers in it; Reinhart graciously volunteered to sleep in the van.

The guys laughed about the strange looks they got on the interstate in their borrowed van from the Baptist Church. A short, longhaired coach drove the extended van, containing a bunch of white, skinhead students who were not singing Alleluia songs. The kids ripped on Coach Reinhart who dished it right back. Friendships developed outside of their traditional roles and shaped amusing memories. The road trip also formed an undetectable bond they regrettably needed to draw on months down the road.

So far the trip felt more like a vacation to Newt, yet held an underlying mission. Like the other powerlifters, he appreciated the hometown locals who supported their car washes and donated funds for their first trip to a National Powerlifting Competition. Now it was up to them to prove what they could do. It was their chance to show just how strong they'd become during the off-season, but that wasn't necessarily their primary objective. It was more or less a stop along the way to their ultimate goal of winning a State Football Championship.

That's how it was if you played Montrose Football, you lived and breathed it all year long. They were somewhat surprised to discover that football wasn't like that at other schools. Montrose players became good friends after they spent so much time together; football brought them even closer.

Montrose was thrilled to place fifth at Nationals. They could have tied for first if one of their competitors hadn't bumped up a weight class, while

Reinhart parked the van. They proudly deposited their mark in the school's trophy case next to their two State Champion Powerlifting trophies. Perhaps it was just a piece of wood and metal to some, but to Newt it represented the team's vigor and strength. It energized him every time he walked past the display, fueling his craving for the '90 football campaign to begin. All Newt wanted to do over the summer was prepare for his senior football season.

One summer afternoon, Newt glanced through his yearbook and naturally thumbed through the football section. He knew that he'd miss those seniors whose funny messages tried to rescue forgotten memories. Katt's message popped out of the page, causing Newt's throat to tighten. No matter how many times he read it, Katt's message caused the same reaction:

> 'Newt:
>> Next year will be our year.
>> We're going to get our shot.
>> We're making up for last year.
>> We're going to win States!'
>
> Katt

His heart thumped madly in his chest, making him conscious of each forceful beat. Those five simple words tugged at his soul, *We're going to win States!* What made them so powerful was the source -- 'Jason Katt,' their most determined and disciplined player. Katt's focused attitude was larger than life. Everyone respected his strong vision of what the '90 Montrose Rams could do. Newt only hoped Katt's words became a reality. Newt sensed that Goose already missed football by the words he wrote; he wasn't ready to join the alumni. *Not yet.* Goose would soon be off to college, bringing an end to the luxury of having a stable quarterback three consecutive years.

Since the starting quarterback position was up for grabs, the coaching staff eyed two experienced J.V. quarterbacks: Corey Crockett, a junior, and Jason Liddell, now a senior. Coach Annese was pleased with the work ethic of both athletes who were locked in the midst of a healthy battle for the quarterback position. Crockett and Led were friends who met faithfully at the school every day throughout the summer to throw passes to each other. Katt and Jerry Kovl joined them, allowing the school to become their home-away-from-home. The boys lifted weights in the mornings, and spent afternoons running football plays or shooting hoops in the school parking lot. Their summer evenings were reserved for playing baseball, which satisfied their need to constantly compete. Led noticed the commitment that Kovl made day-after-day and mentioned it.

Kovl laughed, 'Hey, I only got 240 rushing yards last year.'

They all knew that Kovl respectfully stood in the shadows of Casteel and Kies for an entire season. Kovl patiently watched and learned from them, but he worked hard. They left big shoes to fill and he wanted a chance to show that he could carry the ball. The handsome back was blessed with striking good looks, yet wasn't conceited in the least. His likable personality and trusting eyes persuaded his senior classmates to vote him as their Class Treasurer.

When August finally arrived, the team handled two-a-days with a businesslike atmosphere. They dreaded them at first, then little by little the hard training and discipline created a craving. Everyone had a job to do and goals to accomplish; the team didn't want anyone screwing around. Their seriousness was an indication of how they tackled their upcoming season. The '90 Team had something to prove after a previous undefeated season without a playoff chance. They shared a dream that no one else could see, yet was so alive in all of them they could taste it. *That dream became their driving force.*

The day finally arrived. Newt felt it the moment he opened his eyes; that strange, magnificent feeling of anticipation. He sat on the worn locker room bench, anxiously inserting the pads into the pockets of his white, worn practice pants. He yearned to hit somebody and could hardly wait to get on the practice field to physically smear his friends, just to see how hard he could push them. Once drills started, he felt like a wild, caged animal that was suddenly set free after being trapped for months. Underclassmen felt the sting of a Ron Newton hit. He showed no mercy, causing players to nervously count the positions in line. *Who would be paired against Newt? Who would draw the animal?*

Like Newt, Katt also transformed into a rage during drills, terrifying the hell out of the sophomores. They tried to stay out of his way and cringed when they faced him. Perhaps it was because Katt hit a J.V. player so hard that *his helmet exploded;* at least that's the story the sophomores heard. Katt unconsciously implanted his willpower and intimidating passion into underclassmen, who emulated his motives when they played Varsity. They wanted to be just like Katt, they just didn't want to face him --*yet.*

Ram drills became the necessary evil of football life. Katt and Newt both wanted to face senior Brody Mier. The three of them were the tough honchos who faced practice with an added intensity; and were eager to show they had a lot to prove to the world.

The sideline drill was introduced to the rookies on the first day of pads. Tony Beardsley bought the entire football program from top to bottom, determined to prove his worthiness as an average-sized, offensive sophomore. Beardsley prepared to face a senior defensive tackle as he cut full speed across midfield, ready to tackle him one-on-one. Usually the running back juked his opponent to avoid a head-on collision, but Beardsley was oblivious to that. He just wanted to go full guns to prove what he could do. The senior tackle forcefully plowed into Beardsley, driving him a good ten yards into the chain linked fence. Beardsley didn't know what hit him. Hell, he didn't even know *who he was* at the moment.

The team heard Beardsley belt out a deep 'Yeah' as if he'd won the knockout fight. Then his limp body surrendered itself to the unwelcoming ground. Beardsley collapsed the moment he tried to stand. From his angle on the ground, the 240 pound senior looked gigantic as he towered over him. The senior continued to hover for an exaggerated moment, since his powerful hit attracted everyone's attention. He used the opportunity to vent his frustration about sophomores moving up to Varsity.

Beardsley read it another way. Yeah, he was dazed and confused but his smirk revealed that he earned his initiation, in addition to his concussion. Beardsley found those first few weeks of Varsity practices grueling. Everything was so much faster at this level; he learned to step up quickly to survive. He was used to competition from having three younger brothers; two who were bigger than he was.

In another drill, Led played quarterback and handed off to a running back. His pad got caught in the ruckus, causing him to injure his rotator cuff. Led immediately felt the pain; he had to nurse it back. His injury prevented him from throwing during the rest of two-a-days, so he practiced at flanker while his shoulder recovered. Crockett gladly stepped in and played quarterback -- *with ease.*

The players felt a vim of energy at the end of practice when they gathered around Coach Annese who doled out uniforms. Coach allowed returning players to have first dibs on Varsity jerseys. For some it was a chance to reclaim their number or to pick a lucky one. For others, it was a chance to proudly wear a jersey in honor of a former player or simply give in to their superstitions.

Led yelled out, 'I'll take my old #11 jersey.'

Coach still hadn't decided if Led or Crockett would be his starting quarterback for the '90 Season. Annese glanced at Led and tantalized him. 'You know since the streak began, the starting quarterback always wore #16.'

Led wasn't going to fall for that superstition, 'I still want my number from last year, give me #11.'

Coach Annese threw Led the #11 jersey then grabbed the #16 from the box and threw it to Crockett; 'Congratulations on being the Rams starting quarterback.'

Crockett caught the jersey and proudly held it up while Annese glanced at Led, unsure of his reaction. Coach held his gaze as Led returned the stare, conscious of how he must feel. Led experienced mixed emotions. In a way he felt he earned the starting quarterback position until his shoulder injury, yet he realized that Crockett was an awesome athlete. He honestly believed Crockett solidly qualified for the position, a gifted athlete who later developed into a Division 1 recruit. He also felt, however, that the guys might look up to *him* with added respect since he was a *senior.* His feelings didn't have anything to do with Crockett being the only black athlete on the team. After all, they grew up together as friends and never considered race an issue. That's how it was at Montrose, even with its predominately white student body. Players were teammates as well as friends, regardless of race. Led accepted Annese's decision. He realized that breaking in a junior provided the luxury of having a seasoned quarterback for the '91 Season.

As soon as practice broke up, Led walked over to Crockett and congratulated him. Crockett looked at Led, 'You okay with this man?' Led stood tall and nodded with conviction. Crockett could tell he honestly meant it. Both realized only one starter could be picked. They talked about it over the summer, agreeing to withhold any resentment. With unselfish attitudes, they made a pact to put the team first. One became the quarterback, the other the receiver, just like they'd practiced all summer.

Coach Annese caught up with Led and threw an arm around his good shoulder. Led was a key contributor and Annese didn't want him feeling inferior. Annese had good things in store for Led and planned to use him as a key receiver, defensive back, and on special teams. He explained how powerful the team could be with both of them on the field at the same time. Besides being a football co-captain, Led was the Student Council Vice-President, President of the National Honor Society, and their Valedictorian. Led didn't feel deceived after he nodded and walked away. Instead, he felt important and good about himself and their upcoming season.

Joe Morse, now an assistant coach, felt betrayed after spotting a few players shortly after curfew. The team knew the rules, be home by 10 PM weekdays, and midnight on weekends. It was a simple rule that a few disobeyed and were busted during the annual Montrose Blueberry Festival. The entire team discovered peer pressure at its best -- with gassers. Newt hated running gassers. They all did. No matter how dedicated they were, it pissed them off to receive punishment for something they didn't do. Seniors made grave threats that underclassmen took to heart. By the time they finished running, everyone understood the curfew rule.

The coaches noticed that players hit harder during daily tackling drills than the first day of pads, which was normally the toughest pounding day of the season. Practices became regimented once the team developed a positive attitude. It became their strength. The Rams had been successful the past few years and they felt responsible for keeping that tradition alive.

The linemen tried to break up the seriousness; junior Mike Sullivan was no exception. He rushed to get his quick drink of water with the other linemen when the team moved from their special groups to start team plays. His face was already sunburned and flushed from running, but he didn't care and took a running back's position. This time he picked Kovl. If the slippery back wanted his spot back, he had to wrestle Sullivan, also known as 'Bulldog.' Reinhart dubbed the name on him because he was short and played low to the ground in his tackle and guard positions.

Kovl eyed Bulldog down. They were about the same height but Bulldog had a good 50 pounds on him. He thought, *I must be crazy, but what choice do I have?* He shook his head, took a deep breath, and dove at Bulldog with every ounce of strength he could muster. Bulldog thrived on the drill that allowed a heavy, sweaty lineman to force his weight on a quick, slippery back, claiming the spotlight for a short moment. Coach seemed to encourage the ritual, which eliminated the fear of getting in trouble. Eventually, they all took a shot at wrestling the linemen. While the matches became quite intense, the prank broke up the seriousness of practice.

Eric was the leading rusher when he played on J.V., and found himself somewhat intimidated by the intensity at the Varsity level. He was a determined junior with a lot of heart, who wanted a starting position as a back more than anyone. His dad, Larry Hyde, coached youth football and intentionally arrived early to watch the last 20 minutes of the Varsity practice. For two weeks, he listened to Annese scream at his son, 'Eric Hyde, if you don't start doing what I'm telling you, you'll never see the field.'

Larry never mentioned what he overheard to Eric. His son always worked hard at every sport he played and never appeared to be a slacker. Larry ran into Annese the night before the first game and asked, 'Well Coach, how are we looking for tomorrow night?'

Annese replied, 'I think we'll be okay. I'm going to start Eric.'

Larry threw him a puzzled look. 'You are?'

Coach replied, 'Yeah, I'm going to throw him to the wolves.'

'Well, the way you've been screaming at him I was beginning to think he wasn't cut out for Varsity,' said Larry.

'Yeah, I just like to ride him. I try to push him farther than he thinks he can push himself. I want him to be better.'

Larry realized Annese was the type of coach who made players reach deep inside to find that extra ounce of determination. When he walked away to start his own youth practice, he couldn't help but reminisce about Eric's youth football games. He started helping youth coaches, Ed 'Sonny' Rupperd and Dick Salter, when Eric and his friends were eight years old. Eric drew Sonny, then a recently discharged Marine Sergeant, for his first football coach. Sonny was a young, stocky, burly guy that shocked parents when he habitually screamed at their young sons. The eight-year-olds appeared to thrive on discipline, or he simply scared the living hell out of them and they did whatever he said the moment he spoke.

The young ex-drill sergeant screamed crazy phrases during practice. One night, Larry heard him yell at a lagging kid, 'You're slower than the second coming of Christ.'

The other coaches weren't allowed to swear at the kids and didn't quite know what to think of a former Marine who repeated phrases to eight-year-olds that were strictly meant for boot camp. Sonny only coached a few youth football seasons, then re-enlisted in the Marines. Larry had to laugh when he thought of Eric's first year of football with an ex-drill sergeant as their coach. It had to be part of a master plan to prepare him for the intense Varsity experience under Coach Annese.

Larry moved up each year to coach Eric's youth football team, and knew the other kids like his own. Now he watched them on Varsity and realized just how fast the years flew by. They gained a few and lost a few along the way but most of them had played football together for almost ten years.

The team soon settled into the '90 school year and the daily routine of practice. Coach required them to be in the weight room by 2:30 PM sharp to lift a minimum of three sets of eight. That gave players ten minutes after school to throw on practice clothes (minus their pads), and start clanging metal. It wasn't a problem, *unless they had a girlfriend.*

Newt and Brody were among a few of the players habitually detained after school every day with their girls. Yeah, they were dedicated to the football season but their hormones had minds of their own. They quickly learned that rules about accountability and punctuality were unyielding. Coach Annese's crisp, deep voice sent chills up their spines when it echoed through the locker room sharply at 2:30 PM.

'TEN, NINE, EIGHT . . . ' Chaos and panic immediately consumed players who were still getting dressed in the locker room. They jumped into high gear, frantically searching for clothes. They would rather be almost naked than be late, and made a dead run from the locker room to the weight room, a good 50 feet down the hall. The deep voice of Coach Annese echoed through the corridor while he counted down.

'FIVE, FOUR, THREE...'

Flirty teenage girlfriends lingered around the weight room door, hoping to catch a glimpse of muscular bodies clothed in only socks and a skin-fitting girdle.

The Montrose Rams appeared like typical high school boys . . . until the first game approached. Then, a businesslike, seriousness concealed any form of normalcy, especially for Katt. He went home the night before their first game and painted their annual motto at the top of his bedroom door:

'Another Perfect Season'

He selected the school colors of their first opponent, then carefully painted the Rams first weekly motto in blue and gold:

Birch Run - 'Practice For A Purpose'

Montrose wanted to start their season off right by beating Birch Run on their home turf. They knew Birch Run wanted revenge after a thrilling 10-9 loss to Montrose a year ago. It inspired the Rams to an intense week of practice. They had lofty aspirations heading into the '90 football campaign, backing it with a determined ambition and an incredible buzz for the sport.

The student body generated a heap of noise at Friday's pep assembly, firing up the Rams to host the Panthers. Excitement filled the Montrose football stadium when the visiting Birch Run Panthers met the Rams on the field. Playing on Friday nights for the first time was more exciting than sophomore Brent Baksa ever imagined. He felt the biggest rush when he ran through the hoop. He couldn't conceal his smile and didn't care who noticed. Brent was so excited that he misjudged his jump when the team piled on each other, *and he fell off.* He didn't notice the attention he drew, but his older brother sure did.

Tony Baksa wasn't crazy about his little brother being on Varsity. When he saw him on the ground with a silly grin on his face, it only reinforced his opinion. In his mind, Brent was just his little brother and should be on the J.V. Squad. Brent's J.V. buddies poured over the sophomore from the stands. They watched every move he made, wondering what it felt like to be on the Varsity. They pointed at Brent the moment he hit the ground, laughing so hard that some even snorted. Brent's landing was worth at least a week of mocking!

Crockett knew he had big shoes to fill and couldn't contain his first game jitters in the huddle. His passing and running skills were tops, but his control in the huddle worried the offense. Crockett began to rely on left guard, Tony Baksa, who helped call plays from the huddle. Newt expected the same confidence that Goose maintained in the huddle, and became a little concerned when it appeared that *the line* was becoming the brain of the offense.

The Montrose offense clicked from the get go and helped Corey Lake score two first half TD's. Crockett ran an 82 yard TD with just nine seconds left in the half. It turned into the biggest play of the night, giving the Rams a 20-0 half-time cushion. Lake (a.k.a. 'Lakester') scored his third TD shortly into the third period, bursting 57 yards on a trap over left tackle, Al Olah.

Olah had a great opener and loved when they ran a trap. The guards pulled and blocked on his side of the line. When they called 'Marsha,' Tony Baksa, at left guard, and Olah pulled to the other side of the line, taking out the defensive linebacker and off-tackle at the same time. It worked so well that the Rams ran it over and over. Olah was the biggest guy on the team, although his broad shoulders and slight spare tire didn't make him quite as large as the program stated at 240 pounds.

Olah was a happy-go-lucky type that liked to horse around off the field. His personality got him voted 'The Most Devilish' by his senior classmates, but on the field he took his position pretty serious. He didn't realize just how excited he got each time the play worked until later when he watched game films. It was hard to ignore Olah's celebration after each 'Marsha' play. He jumped up, smacked hands with Baksa, and everyone else that he passed as they exchanged positions.

He celebrated again when Led caught a 55 yard scoring pass late in the third quarter. His line helped the Rams amass 404 rushing yards. Birch Run scored a pair of fourth quarter TD's to close the scoring at '36-12.'

Reinhart's defense played more of a reading style than attack. Newt, Katt, and Brody were three of his five returning starters, all beginning their third year on Varsity. All three were driven and dangerous on their own but together they could be hazardous to opponents. They led the defense when

Montrose extended their unbeaten string to '17' games, tying the school record. Annese was pleased but told them, 'As far as this team is concerned you only have a one-game winning streak and need to take each game as it comes,' which was exactly what the Rams planned to do.

Katt painted the score of their first victory on his bedroom door, then wrote the motto for week two.

Corunna – 'Cut The Crap Out Of The Cavs'

Five miles away, lineman Chris Buffa sat in his bedroom, drawing a picture of a Ram crushing a Cavalier. He zoomed in a bit closer on the Ram and hung it next to the one he drew for their first game. Buffa was an easygoing, fun-loving kid who didn't take things too seriously. But he did get a bit antsy during the idle time before games on Friday nights. He convinced himself the line would do their job and hold Corunna back. He thought about their last encounter in '89 when Corunna was favored to win. Buffa remembered every detail on the first play of the game, when he stood in the endzone and caught a TD pass from Goose. He could still feel the force of the ball when he cupped it to his chest, recalling just how exciting that moment actually was. It was his favorite game of the '89 Season. Buffa could still hear Coach Kitts say, 'That's the best catch I've ever seen!'

Before Buffa walked out of his bedroom he paused and read the poem, *'It's All a State of Mind'*. He didn't know who wrote it, but his sister cut it out back in junior high and taped it on the wall next to the door. Buffa inherited it when he took over her room and never took it down.

A frosty chill pierced through spectators when they entered the Nick Annese Athletic Field, eager to watch the Rams face the Corunna Cavaliers on a cold, wet Friday night. Corunna had a good team and were favored to win. Annese went to his guns, using his gift as an undeclared motivational speaker to awe his Rams. If he ever got tired of coaching, surely he could land a job teaching Dale Carnegie courses. His smooth voice resembled that of sports announcer Mitch Album; his words flowed just as easy.

Newt intently listened as Coach Annese started his speech in his unique theatrical way. He gradually drew them in, then fluctuated his voice to increase the intensity. Newt felt his adrenaline pump double time while his heartbeat tried to stay in sync. When he glanced around the room, he could tell that his teammates experienced the same sensation.

Annese became emotional when he talked about his dad, the legendary Nick Annese, and struck a sensitive cord in most of them. Kovl listened while Coach talked about his dad looking down from heaven to watch them play on the very field named after him. His dad was Corunna's head coach for 27 years, and the athletic director for 31. They were about to play on the same field that Tony Annese played quarterback on during his high school years, before graduating in 1979. That field had history for the Annese family.

Even the toughest linemen released a tear when they heard Coach say; 'My dad never got to see me coach and I want to make him proud tonight.'

Buffa felt his skin crawl. Coach could pump him up in an unbelievable way. It didn't matter *what* he said; it was *how* he said it. Buffa didn't outwardly display his emotions, but what stirred inside of him was a completely different scene. He felt ready to rip someone's head off. Of course, he wouldn't intentionally hurt anyone, but Coach had them all so tanked up that he wanted to hit the hell out of his opponents.

Buffa heard a grunt and glanced over at Newt. Newt could totally release his emotions and provided the emotional presence they all needed. He openly displayed exactly how most of them felt, including Buffa. Coach moved him in a way that caused an unruly, crazed appearance to surface. When Buffa looked at Newt's face his eyes were sealed with tears. Buffa knew right then that Newt had reached his max; he was glad he wasn't facing him that night.

Coach Kitts was obviously moved and whispered to Coach Reinhart, 'This is great stuff. How could anyone not give 100% after hearing that!'

And they would. Motivation obsessed the Rams when they walked out of Corunna's locker room ready to move mountains. So was Corunna. The Cavaliers defended their home turf and stopped the Rams on their first possession, then scored within five minutes of the start. The Rams held steady and battled back. Lake scored on a one yard spurt with ten seconds left in the first quarter, then grabbed the conversion pass to put the Rams ahead. Montrose's high-powered offense took over while a proud coaching staff watched their Rams make their own adjustments during the game.

The Rams recovered a fumble, then Crockett scored the second TD from four yards out. Five plays later, Lake burst up the middle, outraced the defense, and scored, giving the Rams a 23-7 half-time lead. Corunna fans thought the Cavs were climbing back into the contest when they returned the second half kickoff to the 37 yard line, only to be stopped by the Rams. Five plays later, Kovl scored on a four yard TD.

Then disaster struck, and the celebration ceased. Montrose fans watched in silence when their quarterback laid on the field with an injured ankle. They applauded when Crockett finally limped off the field with assistance. Annese felt confident when he motioned for Led to step in. The back-up quarterback appeared poised and comfortable when he led the offense. The Rams didn't skip a beat with Led at the helm. Led's confidence came from believing that he could've easily been the starting quarterback. He now enjoyed the variety of other positions, but his ego thrived knowing he could intervene when needed. Led capped the final score in the fourth with runs of 76 and eight yards to close 43-7. Knowing they had a qualified reserve provided the offensive coaches with peace of mind.

A remarkable running game quickly became the heart and soul of their attack. The Rams were proud of their work and excited that their win set a new Flint area 'longest football winning streak record' with 18 straight wins.

Led, Kovl, and Lake racked up 336 yards, while Newt and senior Rob Fisher led the defense with 15 tackles each.

'Fish' was an average teenage boy who wasn't afraid to speak his mind about something he felt strong about. When he hit the field he turned mean and hot headed, ready to tackle anything that got in his way.

Katt went home after Monday's practice and painted the next motto in black and white:

New Lothrop – 'Protect What Is Ours'

Olah glanced at the eerie, black sky when he jogged to his position on neighboring New Lothrop's windy field. The dark clouds seemed angry as they raced through the sky dumping rain on everything in their path -- including him. He tried to ignore the worst storm ever and disregard the cold, biting rain that sounded like bullets ricocheting off his helmet. It was the perfect setting for a horror film; the type of storm that tested the true loyalty of any diehard fan. The Rams drove 54 yards on five plays before Kovl scored on a 20 yard burst; his first of three TD's for the evening.

Less than a minute later, Montrose cashed in on a fumbled kickoff to score on Lake's 15 yard run. Crockett's ankle was sore but he was back, and dashed over with the two-point conversion to make it 14-0. A fumbled punt gave Montrose possession at the New Lothrop 43. The Rams took advantage and moved the ball down the field, tacking on another first period score by Kovl from the two. Kovl was quick and hard-nosed for his 5'9"-170 pound frame, and became one of the quickest backs that could hit the hole. He scored again in the second.

Fish played tackle during their first two games, but that night Reinhart switched him to defensive end for the first time -- opposite Katt. Both were long, lean, and relatively quick, like a pair of mirrored bookends. Fish liked playing defensive end, a position that became permanent. Katt kept Fish competitive and pushed him without even realizing it. Each wanted to claim credit for quarterback sacks and ragged on each other. Fish joined in the constant trash-talk with the rest of the line who poured it on heavy for the New Lothrop game. They personally knew several opponents who dished it right back. Comments about their sisters pinged back and forth, even if they didn't have one. It was received and returned in fun, while both teams really wanted to cream each other's face in the dirt.

And then it happened. They say the first casualty of war is the truth and for one player it became a reality. Led caught the punt on the right side of the field then ran to his left. He saw a Hornet defender head straight at him when he cut across the field, but the opponent never saw Katt. Katt nailed him with such an extreme intensity, that dads instinctively darted to their feet, aware of the danger of a hard smear. Katt was known for hard hits but that one classified itself as his *most powerful*. It was strong enough to send his opponent flying high in the air. The Hornet appeared lifeless when his head hit the ground, appearing to wait for the rest of his body to catch up. The blow knocked the opponent out cold, while spectators nervously watched for any sign of movement. Some feared it was fatal.

Katt had become fearless, yet was the most likable guy *off* the field. So well liked and responsible that his classmates elected him as their Class President. But on the field he transformed into a fighting machine. Kitts and Reinhart exchanged an unspoken glance with eyebrows raised, while witnessing what easily could have become a high school football casualty. That would have been tragic, not only because of the violent death of a fine young man, but because the anti-football group would've raised the panicked hue, crying they should all burn their pads and play soccer. Coach Kitts broke the silence when he blurted out, 'Remember when Katt was a freshman? He didn't know much about blood or pain then. Hell, he even asked for a band-aid during practice once. Now look at him.'

The sissy freshman had transformed into an intense, fearless, savage senior. His hit became legendary; a blow that was talked about for years to come. It was definitely worthy of a super slow-motion game film highlight that warranted his new hard core nickname -- 'Psycho.'

The injury delayed the game by a good 20 minutes, while the rescue team carefully placed the injured player on a stretcher. The Rams were conditioned to hard-hitting football and loved it, but not to the extreme of seeing an opponent get seriously injured. It felt weird at first to get back in the game, but the Montrose offense remained in sync. The veteran line executed well, displaying a balanced attack between Kovl, Lake, and Led. Led had an outstanding night both running and catching the ball, while Lake added a pair of second half TD's to post a '41-12' victory.

Lake was grateful that Annese and Reinhart converted him from offensive guard to running back. He was strong and worked hard, thriving on the attention that scoring TD's brought him. Lake and Kovl each surpassed 100 rushing yards three games in a row, modeling themselves after Kies and Cliff. But they were becoming a little too focused on stats.

The media called the Montrose quarterback 'Crockett-the-Rocket' after he passed for 84 yards, using Led and Katt as his favorite targets.

Coach Reinhart was disappointed with his defense, even though they held the Hornets to seven first downs. Many only played one way and Coach yelled, 'You need to grow up quick and prove you belong on the field.'

Eric made a mistake and let a player get around and beat him. Annese pulled Eric out of the game, 'I'll start a sophomore over you if you don't shape up.'

Eric talked with his dad about the incident after the game. He was so driven and said, 'Dad, if he tries to start a sophomore, I'll hurt him first.'

His dad knew Eric wouldn't intentionally hurt the underclassman, but realized Coach Annese's message to *never let up*, had seeped into his son's soul. The comment motivated Eric who reached even deeper and played even harder through the next week of practice.

Tony Annese lived for the game of football and the kids. He was the person that Montrose may or may not have been ready for, but reaped the results when his program continued to draw more attention. His knowledge of the game was great, even unbelievable to the team. But his weakness was that he loved the game so well. Annese demanded 100%. His players learned firsthand what *effort* and *commitment* honestly meant. Sometimes he forgot they were still high school kids, and coached them with an aggressive intensity. *Excellence was expected.*

Katt certainly understood what *commitment* meant when he keenly painted week four's motto:

Bentley – 'Together We Will Put It All Together'

After three games, Bentley and Montrose were both undefeated in the GEC League priming local TV stations to interview them. Lake was featured as the Flint area's leading scorer with 54 points, while Bentley had a player in close second.

The Montrose High School Football Team was very businesslike. Their moves were so well rehearsed they became instinctive, yet they continued to show improvement each week. Bentley stopped Montrose on its first drive, but not for long. Kovl, Lake, and Crockett came back to score on six of their next seven drives. Their line stepped up, proving they wouldn't be overpowered. Montrose coaches were impressed that the defense handled Bentley's huge offensive line on a wet field, after recording their first shutout. Newt, Katt, and Brody led the defense when they shut down Bentley's high scorer, holding him to just 46 yards on 11 attempts. Katt proved his aggressive intensity when he blocked a punt, as the Montrose sideline admiringly chanted -- 'Psycho, Psycho.'

Sophomore D'ar Destrampe was moved up at the beginning of the season because of his outstanding athleticism. So far, he only ran plays in and had not handled the ball. It was time to expose him to Varsity level -- D'ar felt ready. He was more than ready when he burst through with a 36 yard run and racked up 65 yards on three carries. Montrose discovered its newest weapon when D'ar scored the final TD for the Rams to end the score '43-0.'

The Rams didn't overly celebrate when they listened to Coach Annese stress, 'We can't become complacent! We have to improve!'

They wanted to constantly improve at becoming a solid football team by the end of the season. Their motto for week five became:

Atherton – 'Together We Will Get Better'

Montrose didn't waste any time when they sacked the Atherton punter in the endzone to gain a 2-0 lead, and set the tone for the game. Baksa lined up at left guard, then stared at his opponent to intimidate him. Baksa noticed a strange expression staring back at him and then it registered -- *FEAR*. He glanced at the other opponents and noticed several other faces held the same expression. Baksa fed off of it, remembering their last contest when the Rams shutout Atherton 61-0. The Wolverines struggled to rebuild their football program, yet Baksa spared no sympathy. He remembered what Coach said earlier, 'Montrose finally cracked into the AP Ratings and were ranked third in their Class BB playoff region.' The top ten teams were ranked, but only the top four advanced to the playoffs. The Rams couldn't let up on any opponent. *No one.*

Katt hauled in Crockett's 28 yard TD strike, then Lake broke loose and scored on a 53 yard run. Corey Crockett scored three TD's and Corey Lake added another to spark the media's new title of the 'Corey-duo.' The Rams played hard the first half and didn't want to become complacent; the lopsided '40-0' rout wasn't good for either team. Newt led the defense with 11 tackles, while Led and Baksa each grabbed an interception before being pulled. Lake added a 20 yard TD that contributed to 425 offensive yards for the Rams.

Barry Gross was one of several sophomores brought up to Varsity, since Atherton didn't have a J.V. team. Gross was thrilled to take the helm at quarterback during the closing quarter and called a 39-veer for his first Varsity debut. Gross faked to his back but kept the ball when he ran around the end. No one was within ten yards. He never imagined the play would be so wide open, and pranced down the sideline toward the endzone. He remembered the threatening words Coach spoke during the half, and was hesitant if he should score. *Did those words apply to sophomores? Should he show Coach Annese what a rookie quarterback could do?*

Gross turned and glanced at Coach Annese, looking for a signal if he should go out-of-bounds or not. He didn't get a reaction either way, and made the decision to score his first Varsity TD -- a 30 yarder. He justified his actions by telling himself, *Coach never actually set a limit on total points during the half.* Gross celebrated in the endzone, but his mood quickly halted when he reached the sideline. Annese didn't want to run the score up any higher; Gross immediately realized that his coach was mad. Gross was unsure of how to react. His victorious spirit was quickly overshadowed by a pissed off head coach, who stood so close in his face that Gross actually counted the hair follicles on his chin. He didn't mean to disappoint his coach, and immediately felt his scarlet face burn as panic consumed him.

The seniors could tell Gross felt bad and ragged on him to lift his spirits. The sophomore did his best to hold his head high, trying to disguise how awful he felt inside. Gross thought, *As low as I feel right now, if I had a chance to do it all over again I wouldn't change a thing.* The memory was worth every minute of the royal butt chewing. His first Varsity TD would always have a special place in his heart. He would never forget the night the Rams defeated Atherton '61-0' for the second consecutive year.

While most of the guys spent their evenings watching Pamela Anderson on Baywatch that weekend, Katt drifted to his room and painted the motto for week six:

Lake Fenton – 'One Game At A Time'

The line looked at Coach Annese as if he was a bit crazy when he asked players to deliberately pinch and hit each other during practice for Lake Fenton. A rivalry had developed between the two teams. Coach wanted it out of their system, so they would resist the urge to retaliate from their last contest. Lake Fenton hosted the Rams on a cold, windy Friday night and caught Montrose off-guard on the very first play of the game. The Blue Devils executed a halfback option that covered 60 yards and ended on the Montrose 10 yard line. The defense didn't allow their opponents to get any closer than the five, and watched Lake Fenton settle for a field goal. Seeing numbers on Lake Fenton's side of the scoreboard frustrated the Rams, after shutting out their last two opponents. Montrose went to work on their next possession by driving 69 yards in five minutes. Kovl scored, giving the Rams a 6-3 lead.

Montrose only needed two plays on their next possession. Crockett passed 25 yards to Led, then scored on his own 24 yard quarterback keeper to end the first quarter. The Blue Devils defense checked the Rams who knew they'd be running gassers for the penalties that Newt and Brody racked up. Brody was a boy in a man's body who had a lot to prove to the world. He could move the line of scrimmage by five to ten yards when he was motivated. Some of his teammates didn't fully understand him, but Brody remained his own person by showing his intensity on the field.

Baksa was known for borderline late hits right before the whistle; that night wasn't any exception. Defenders needed to be on-guard until the whistle blew, because Baksa nailed them if they stood around the pile. That was his style. He became the most exciting lineman to watch. Newt looked at Baksa and said, 'You're the baddest 165 pound headhunter I've ever seen.'

The Rams finally settled into their game. Fans could tell that Crockett felt extremely comfortable at the helm, displaying his great communication with Led. They worked together by signaling each other on the fly. Lake Fenton's defensive back played close on Led. When Led felt he could get around him, he tugged on his facemask; a gesture for Crockett to throw *the Bomb* instead of the planned running play.

Crockett abided and connected with Led on a 36 yard scoring pass, with eight seconds left in the half. It was a huge score for the Rams; Lake's conversion put the Rams up 22-3. But the Rams knew it wasn't cause to celebrate when they left for the intermission. Montrose coaches felt the team didn't execute well, and went livid during the half. Coach pulled the three sophomores aside and ripped into them for playing timidly. He needed them to step up, *now!* D'ar, Beardsley, and Brent felt pretty low when Coach finished with them. It was gut check time. Tony Baksa watched his little brother get reamed and felt caught in the middle. As a big brother it was okay for *him* to pick on Brent but when someone else did, well it just didn't sit right. Baksa felt like he should protect Brent like he did when they were little, but he couldn't do squat to help him at that moment. Brett had to learn how to hang with the big boys if he wanted to play Varsity ball.

Olah lined up next to Buffa in the third row when they took the field for the second half. Olah wasn't a man of strong superstitions, but he stuck to his ritual of having Buffa on his left side, just like they lined up on the field. The squad locked hands, and were led by captains Katt, Led, and Newt in the first two rows. Brody always brought up the rear. *Always.*

The Rams took the field as a different team, playing a stronger second half, but so did the Blue Devils. With seconds left in the third, Lake Fenton intercepted Crockett's pass and returned it 68 yards to score. The scoreboard reflected 22-9, but it was too close for their liking.

Kovl raced 24 yards in the fourth frame to pay dirt for a final TD for the Rams, his eighth for the season. Kovl had 54 points after six games, but Lake still held the title as the area's leading scorer with 90 points. He tacked on the conversion to lock in a '30-9' Montrose victory. But fans could hardly tell which team came out the winner. The Rams didn't celebrate their sub-par victory. Instead, they intently listened as Annese boldly stated; 'Your attitude and overconfidence allowed you to become complacent. You need to come prepared to play every game or else people will do a number on us! If we needed an attitude adjustment, hopefully this game did it. There's a big lesson to be learned in this game. Maybe this will give us a wake-up call.'

Reinhart roared on his defense, 'We became lackadaisical. We had some mental breakdowns tonight and took a step backward! Maybe this was the best thing that could've happened to us!'

They all knew he was referring to the upcoming Goodrich game two weeks away. It would be a rematch of last seasons 'showdown of the unbeatens,' since both teams stood at 6-0 and were expected to square off for the league crown.

Katt went home after the game and prepared for Bendle week. He pulled out the blue and gold paint and wrote:

Bendle – 'If We Won't Be Beat, We Can't Be Beat'

Montrose faced the Bendle Tigers for their Homecoming. Festivities sparked the entire student body as three football players: Katt, Led, and Newt, entertained their nomination for Homecoming King. But thoughts of last week's opening threat haunted the Rams during practice all week.

Mrs. Baksa wasn't about to miss the Homecoming game, especially since both of her sons played on Varsity. Tony was a senior and Brent a sophomore; it was the only year they played football together. She had just been discharged from the hospital after major surgery with orders to stay in bed -- but this was Montrose Football. Parents were overexcited, which sometimes clouded their judgment. She simply didn't want to miss a game and told her sons when they left the house, 'It'll take more than doctor's orders to keep me away.'

Her husband explained the situation to the policeman guarding the stadium entrance gate. He gave them access to park in the endzone, then watched while Mrs. Baksa was positioned in a padded lounge chair in the back of a Chevy pickup. She looked comfortable enough with a huge smile on her face, obviously thrilled to be there. She decided not to tell her physician; what he didn't know wouldn't hurt him. He probably wouldn't understand it anyway, but she knew it was the best therapy available.

While the Homecoming crowd settled into the bleachers, the Rams relaxed in the wrestling room with the galloping hits of Poison. While New Kids on the Block stormed the pop music scene, the mighty Rams needed heavy metal. They wanted hard rocking, violent guitars to pump them up, while they worked into their game head. That is, until Annese entered the room with the ambiance of a commanding officer. They respectfully dimmed the music, giving Coach their undivided attention. He had a way of connecting with everyone in the room. Olah tried to control his emotions while a wild side unrestfully stirred inside. He glanced over at Newt, watching how Annese transformed the linebacker into a beast when he ended his talk, 'We're gonna go out there and show everybody who's the best.'

Crockett proved how dangerous of a quarterback he was after opening the game with two TD passes. Led caught both of them, grabbing one with a jazzy over the shoulder catch in front of 2,000 enthusiastic fans. He had a great game, hauling in six passes for 102 yards.

The Rams fleet-footed quarterback threw a second half TD pass, then eluded a host of Bendle defenders when he criss-crossed the field on a 51 yard scamper for a fourth TD. A 36-0 half-time lead set a festive mood for the Homecoming celebration. Ron Newton didn't head toward the locker room with the rest of the team. Instead, he fulfilled his duties as the '90 Homecoming King by handsomely posing with the Queen.

When the Rams came back for the second half, they diversified their grueling ground game with a quick strike, passing attack to keep Bendle off balance. Annese trusted Crockett to audible off, a privilege he and Led took advantage of. Led ran four yards, then faked towards the sideline when he heard Crockett audible '99' for a nine route. On another play, if the defensive back was far off Led, Crockett audibled a '92' for a two-route, throwing a quick slant pass to Led. The two of them stuck together. If Coach ever questioned a play, Led covered for Crockett. 'Hey, I called it.'

Lake wore receiver gloves when he scored two TD runs, maintaining his status as the Flint Area's leading scorer. He was concerned with performing for his football team and his town, and dreamed about playing pro-football one day. Lake didn't know if he'd ever go that far, but he genuinely wanted to contribute to something he could always be proud of.

The veteran-laden offensive line allowed several players to get in on the action, helping the Rams defeat the Bendle Tigers '55-0.' The shutout stretched their winning streak to '23.' Katt wanted another win, and painted their next motto on his door with a forced determination.

Goodrich – 'The Truly Great Are at Their Greatest When The Challenge Is Great'

The importance of the Goodrich game brought a new level of intensity to all coaches and players. They met on Sunday afternoon to watch game films like they did every weekend, but something was different. *They all felt it.*

The coaches analyzed hours of film, while spouses and girlfriends surrendered their time with them. Goodrich week began with the feel of a teaching session as coaches outlined mistakes, showing who screened and who missed their blocks.

Coach Joe Prunchnicki prepared his Goodrich Martians with the same intensity that Coach Annese prepared his Rams. Both teams worked exceptionally hard, proving how much they wanted the victory. Goodrich wanted revenge from '89, when Montrose prevented the Martians from winning the GEC Title. The undefeated status of both teams made the league contest the biggest game of the season. Montrose averaged 44.1 points per game; Goodrich was close behind with 42.9. Both teams posted three shutouts and permitted six points per game. Goodrich was ranked ninth in Class CC, while the Rams were ranked fourth in Class B. Both communities provided great fan support because the League Title was on the line, or at least a share of it, and more importantly, a state playoff berth. The magnitude of the contest was even larger for the Rams, whose winning streak was an added factor. Goodrich brought buses of students, their pep band, and high expectations when they arrived at the field, 90 minutes before game time.

Eric arrived at the school early in an effort to close the gap and pass the time. He took his equipment out of his locker in the same order that he had all season, carefully placing his pads in his pants. He continued doing everything in the same sequence; he was becoming superstitious. They all were.

It wasn't any different for Lakester. He made sure he wore his lucky Champions Club T-shirt that he earned over a year ago. It was now cut off at the waste, paperthin, and flaunted battle wounds throughout. It was still considered his *lucky shirt;* he wouldn't dare play a game without it. No one wanted to change anything for fear of causing bad luck. No one wanted to risk losing. *No one.*

Fish was just as bad. He wore an old blue and yellow baseball T-shirt under his pads, a ritual he started his freshman year when the shirt was actually big on him. It fit a bit snugger, but was still his lucky T-shirt even though the sleeves were cut out, and the material now held together by threads. Fish wouldn't dream of playing in a game without it. He might go a game or two without washing it, but it couldn't hold a candle to the stench of

Brody's shirt. Nobody's shirt smelled as bad as Brodys. The odor reeked as bad as it did last season; it was plain disgusting.

Buffa continued his ritual of drawing a Ram before the game by enlarging the mascot so only half of it fit on the page. Before he walked out of his bedroom, he glanced at the inspiring poem on his wall and read *'It's All a State of Mind'* one more time.

The Montrose fans formed the longest human tunnel anyone could remember. It started at the back entrance gate, and continued a good 100 feet to the goal post. The Montrose Marching Band extended the tunnel to the middle of the football field. Goodrich students also formed a tunnel as both bands united to play the National Anthem in front of an estimated crowd of 5,000. Spectators felt it was the largest crowd in the history of a Montrose home football game; the Athletic Boosters amply benefited from concessions.

Goodrich players arrived on the field first, while the students that made up the Montrose human tunnel waited patiently. The Rams were in the locker room receiving the most motivating speech any on them had ever heard. Rod Studaker, the public speaking teacher, received a rare invitation to videotape the Goodrich locker room talks; he had no idea of what was in store.

Coach Annese theatrically explained how the entire game came down to *six minutes of live football* when the ball is *actually* in play. That shocked the team after considering the number of hours they worked each week -- *for only six minutes.* Coach Annese addressed the squad with a seriousness in his voice, theatrically delivering his pre-game speech.

> *'Every single time we're in this position we win. Never fail. Every time! EFFORT. The winners of this ball game will give the greatest EFFORT. Six minutes of 'live' football. We run the veer EVERY SINGLE PLAY. From the beginning of the play until the whistle. You're busting your tail. EFFORT!*
>
> *Effort on the sideline. On the line. In the backfield. Effort in everything you do.*
>
> *Six minutes of football and who is the champion? That's what determines it. Effort. Big concentration. Big football games. What happened last year? They were down and they folded. They didn't concentrate. I'll tell you what, that's why we were here July 23, busting our ass. So that we would be prepared for something like this. We're trained, we're ready.*
>
> *SACRIFICE is what we're all about. It's in our hearts. It's in our lifestyles. It's in this football team. It's MONTROSE FOOTBALL. It's 23 in a row. It's two League Championships, going on three. That's what it's about.*

Sacrifice. I want you to know this. You're going to get slapped in the face a thousand times and not get a little bit scared to get slapped in the face again.

You start flinching. You understand that? You get slapped around and you start flinching. You start getting scared. You're not having it upstairs. That's what that's all about!

77 to 7 in two years, Goodrich has played Montrose and got their ass kicked, 77 – 7! That's got to mean one thing to you fellas. That means the first play of the game, you knock them on their ass! On first possession you're not going to let them get a yard.

YOU give the effort. YOU make the sacrifices. YOU go out. YOU get possession. Let's go fellas!

Newt couldn't restrain his emotions as he rocked back and forth; deep grunting noises oozed from his body. The Montrose Rams left the room possessed with a wild emotion, yelling - 'YEAH, LET'S GO. LET'S DO IT BABY!'

Coach Annese stepped in front of Newt as he approached, 'ARE YOU GONNA GET SLAPPED IN THE FACE?'

Before Newt could answer, he felt a hard blow across his right cheek. Spit flurries rushed from Newt's chops, reacting like a deranged dog foaming at the mouth. He instantly reacted by slapping Coach Annese across his face, yelling - 'NO WAY!'

It was the exact reaction Annese sought from Newt. He realized he couldn't slap too many players, but knew it motivated Newt in a big way. Newt felt like a packed grenade ready to explode, which was the result Annese wanted before sending him on the field.

The proud Rams walked two-by-two, with locked hands as they entered the longest human tunnel they ever saw. Their fans stimulated them even more. The captains paused under the goal post then jumped up-and-down to release adrenaline, while waiting for the rest of the team to catch up.

Fish had the flu bug earlier in the day and slept during his lunch period. He didn't want to miss the Goodrich game for anything and talked himself into feeling better. By the time he walked on the field, he completely forgot about being sick. The site of Wixson, and some of his old teammates from the '89 Team standing under the goal post, made his juices flow.

Olah recognized other former teammates donned in street clothes. He knew they would surrender their kid brother for one last chance to play with the Rams. They slapped Olah and grabbed his facemask, 'ARE YOU READY TO KICK SOME ASS?'

Olah was so pumped that he couldn't stand still. When he looked around he saw people everywhere. The stadium was completely packed. Montrose always had a good following, but never before had people come down on the field to wait under the goal post with them. It felt exceptional, different than any other pre-game.

The game didn't start fast enough for the seniors. They couldn't wait to make contact, wanting that first hit. Former players felt it too, and missed it even more. The squad glanced at the huge number of fans in the bleachers and the overflow crowd surrounding the field. The aura refueled their highly inflated emotions. The infectious reaction energized the fans that roared when the Rams broke through the cheerleader's hoop, racing to the Montrose sideline.

Montrose won the toss and elected to kick off to Goodrich. The two unbeaten teams played to a scoreless standoff for the first 12 minutes. Led dove for the ball then grabbed the interception. The defense gave an awesome performance by choking off a pair of first period Goodrich scoring threats. The defense seemed to carry the Rams until the offense got on track. Eric picked-off an interception. His heart thumped when he raced 60 yards to the Goodrich seven. It was a huge break for the Rams that allowed Lake to score three plays later on a one yard run to finally break the scoreless tie. The momentum shift opened the floodgates; Lake, Led, and Kovl kept the scoreboard moving to give the Rams a 20-0 lead at the half.

The Goodrich and Montrose Marching Bands entertained the huge crowd during the intermission. The upbeat scene was a far cry from the serious atmosphere in the locker room, where coaches calmly reviewed key plays and made suggestions. Annese wanted Crockett to stay intense and not let up. In his mind, it was still a close game. Crockett respectfully listened to Coach Annese whose finger poked him in his chest; 'They're going after you. You have 600 yards rushing, which is probably the most of any quarterback in the state. They don't want you carrying the ball!'

Then Coach Annese addressed the rest of his Rams:

'Now listen guys, this is critical. One thing we have prepared for is a 'second half, first possession team.' And we score. Always! One time in two years we didn't score and that was because we didn't concentrate on the first play after half. One time in two years!

Didn't you see it at the end of the first half? They had it written all over them. I Quit! Their coach is over there getting them all fired up again. He's telling them – It's only 20 to nothing. Three touchdowns and we can win this! That's what they're saying. But I'll tell you what. When we score our fourth touchdown, their coach won't be there to fire them up again. I'll tell you what they'll be saying, 'I hate playing Montrose every year. It's the only freaking game we ever lose. It's the only one we lose!'

You stop them and you have the best team. They're going to be the losers with this first possession, second half. That's what it's all about and I hope that's what you work for, because they won't score tonight!'

Newt had a fire in him that he couldn't control. When Coach altered his voice it made him grunt. His shoulders jerked back-and-forth like he was having an epileptic attack. The intensity that Annese delivered in his talks drove Newt absolutely crazy with motivation.

Mr. Studaker was amazed as he watched the stormy reaction through the eyes of his video camera. He thought he had a magic way of pumping up his softball girls, but his style of coaching didn't compare to Annese. This was totally different, but he found it exciting. Unrestricted bewilderment filled the locker room; he felt their energy and their youth. If someone handed the middle-aged man a set of pads and a helmet, he'd eagerly join his students on the field. He watched the overly hyped Rams jump and shout, 'COME ON, LET'S GO!'

Led took the second half kickoff and marched 70 plus yards. They did exactly what Coach told them to. Baksa took his stance at guard and faced his opponent. 'You don't look like you're ready!'

His teammates chuckled at his constant intimidation techniques.

Crockett ran in from 12 yards out early in the third, and banged the final nail in the coffin. Goodrich was a good team with big players, but that night the Rams proved to be mentally tougher, and it demoralized them. Lakester spoke in the huddle, 'Look, they're falling apart. They're not a come from behind team.'

Kovl added a fourth quarter TD followed by Led's interception that he returned for a 35 yard TD, tying the school record for eight interceptions in a season. He mastered his ability to back peddle then go with the play and explode. Led eyed the Goodrich quarterback, watching for any kind of a sign, similar to how he communicated with Crockett. He used his experience from playing those same positions to get a jump on the play and grab the interception. Led caught the attention of Saginaw Valley State University (SVSU) college recruiters who played a big part of his future.

Goodrich averted the shutout in the waning seconds of the game, when a defensive back scooped up a loose ball and scored.

Coach Pruchnicki shook Coach Annese's hand after the game, 'Good luck in the playoffs. We'd like to see you win States. I don't think anyone can stop you.'

When the Rams huddled in the center of the field Annese told the team how proud he was of them for the way they played. 'It was a great win, especially on Parents Night.'

He gave them credit for holding Goodrich to seven first downs and 105 yards. The Rams were obviously happy, but didn't want to over celebrate. Annese reiterated their first goal each year, 'We want to win the GEC and go unbeaten. We want to leave our mark on history. We have some goals beyond the regular season we'd like to achieve. We'll hug after Game 13.'

Without referencing a schedule, they all knew that *Game 13* was the State Championship.

Later, Katt couldn't help but smile when he painted the final score '40-6';
then prepared for their final regular season game against the Hawks.

Hamady – 'There Is No Tomorrow'

Montrose moved into second position with 83 computer playoff points in
Class B, Region 3. They planned to do everything in their power to guard
against a possible letdown. They found it difficult to concentrate during
Hamady week with a playoff date looming on the horizon. A third straight
GEC League Title and a state playoff berth were at stake, if they lost to
Hamady in the final league game.

The Rams were stalled on their first possession, but managed to score
before the first quarter clock expired. Lake scored shortly before the half
ended. Later, the Rams blocked a punt on Hamady's 14 yard line and
Crockett scored.

Hamady threw a pass but D'ar didn't cover his opponent the way Annese
thought he should. D'ar expected to get yelled at, but it was worse than he
ever anticipated. He felt like the scum of the earth when Coach grabbed his
facemask, then lit into the impressionable sophomore as soon as he reached
the sideline. Annese couldn't afford to have D'ar get beat on a pass play,
especially with playoffs looming a week away.

Annese usually got the result he wanted. Some thrived on his techniques
and performed better, while others felt that his yelling intensified their nerves.
D'ar had exceptional talent and Coach knew how to push his buttons, while
grooming him for the post-season. The team thought D'ar handled the
confrontation well, but on the inside he was publicly humiliated. D'ar vowed
to learn from his mistake; he never wanted Coach Annese to openly
downgrade him like that again. *Never.* The message was spoken to D'ar, but
the entire team felt it, and turned the intensity up a few notches. They drove
60 yards in nine plays to score their fourth TD when Lakester took it in.

Hamady made an impressive drive and only needed one yard for a first
down. The defense stiffened, turning the Hawks back on three consecutive
plays on the Montrose nine yard line.

It was time. Annese reached into his bag of tricks for the grand finale of
their 9-0 season. Having the opportunity to run a trick play in practice was
one thing, but executing it in a game secured it as a life-long memory. It was
a blast to catch opponents off-guard, giving the fans an appreciation for the
thrill of the unknown.

Crockett threw a lateral pass to Led, who passed 62 yards to Kovl for a
final TD. Maybe it was a peace offering from Annese that allowed Led to
show off what his arm was still capable of. Kovl raced back to celebrate with
Led, treasuring the moment. Nostalgia set in while they watched the
scoreboard quickly tick away, ending their last regular season game with a
'37-6' final score.

When Led played defensive back in 1991 as an SVSU Cardinal, he looked back on the quarterback decision, realizing that his pre-season shoulder injury was a gift in disguise. It allowed him to gain experience as a receiver, running back, defensive back, punt and kick returner, which launched his college football career.

Lake's two TD's ended his regular season with a total of 20, holding his title of 'Leading Scorer' for the entire Flint area with 134 points.

At the start of their season, Annese worried that losing four superior athletes from the '89 Team would hit their running game hard. But the Montrose system was designed for players to be interchangeable. Crockett, Led, Kovl, and Lake stepped in as their replacements, and wrote their own page in the Montrose grid history books by shattering the 1,000 yard rushing mark; a rare but rewarding position for an offensive coach.

The victory capped off a second straight undefeated football season for the Rams, their third consecutive outright Conference Championship, and extended their winning streak to 25 games. Most importantly, they had a chance to prepare for their second season. They didn't want to just be in the playoffs, they wanted to make an impact.

Montrose prepared to host its first playoff game against the **Lansing Catholic Central (LCC) Cougars,** and treated the post-season as a new season. The entire school buzzed with spirit. LCC tackled the big boys in Class A and B while Montrose played mostly a Class C schedule, which naturally labeled the Rams as *the underdog.*

LCC won a State Title in '85 and appeared in the post-season in 1987. Montrose also made the playoffs in '85 when Detroit Tiger pitcher Scott Aldred quarterbacked the Rams to a stunning victory over Beecher, an inner city Flint school that was favored to win. The Rams played above the hype of Beecher's #5 Courtney Hawkins who later played for Michigan State, the Tampa Bay Buccaneers, and the Pittsburgh Steelers. Andre Rison starred for Beecher the previous year and played wide receiver for Michigan State. His professional career included playing for the Atlanta Falcons, Cleveland Browns, Green Bay Packers, Kansas City Chiefs, and the Oakland Raiders.

Unfortunately, the '85 Rams went on to lose to Marine City during the regional final. The '90 seniors attended that game as sixth graders, and wore their youth football jerseys. They watched their heroes, and dreamed about their future when *they* were the stars that people came to watch.

Their time had arrived.

The Montrose coaching staff planned to take the same approach by executing what they did best. They didn't want players thinking they had to do *something different* in the playoffs. Coach Annese sensed the tension the night before their first playoff game and staged a little surprise. He watched his team spread out on the field to warm-up, dressed in their traditional pre-game uniforms. No one dared to be late the day before a long-awaited playoff game. The squad stretched from a hurdle position as Newt yelled, 'One and Two and Three . . .'

Coach Annese interrupted and yelled, 'All right, who's late for practice?'
Players looked around to determine who was missing. They hated when a
player was late for practice, knowing they would all share in the punishment.
Their view from the ground prevented a good look at the approaching player.
Annese yelled, 'What the hell! He's got the wrong jersey on! DON'T
YOU REALIZE WE'RE PREPARING FOR A PLAYOFF GAME?'

The guys noticed a tall figure haphazardly approaching the field, in a
relaxed casual stroll. Coach Annese continued to yell as the guy walked
closer. The team stopped stretching and stood up for a closer look, then
wanted to laugh.

Led asked Kovl, 'Who is that guy?'

No one recognized his casual walk or his tall frame. He simply didn't
look familiar. To top it off, he donned a white jersey that symbolized an
away game. They looked at his feet and wondered, *Is he wearing brown
cleats without laces, or are they dress shoes?* They looked at his head and
saw a helmet without a facemask and an old pair of practice pants -- with
brown socks. The team couldn't believe that anyone took a playoff pre-game
practice so lightheartedly, and wondered what Coach would do. They
nervously waited for Annese to explode, and didn't understand his reaction.

He laughed. *He actually laughed.*

Players looked at each other, still unsure of how to react, until they
recognized the mystery player as he walked closer. It was Newell -- a tall,
basketball player. Relief gratified them, after realizing it was a set up. The
mystery player kicked a few field goals and even ran through a few plays with
them, providing the perfect stress reliever for their pre-game practice.

Fish went home after school, laid on his bed, and listened to the best of
MegaDeath. *Hello Me-Hello the Real Me,* blared from his boom box, while
the classic heavy metal vengeance pumped him up; a ritual he did before
every Friday night game. He didn't know if he could be any more excited,
and could hardly control the butterflies that plunged in his stomach.

Buffa sat at the kitchen table and ate his traditional pre-game spaghetti
dinner, soaking in every carb. He wore his faded 'Ram Pride' gray T-shirt
that was knotted at the left shoulder to hold it together. Unlike Brody, he
washed his favorite game shirt every week, which had turned paper-thin. It
served him well during his two years on Varsity, but he needed it to last four
more games. He drew his pre-game poster, making the mascot even larger
than the previous week. Now, the Ram practically took up the entire sheet
when he hung it in his room next to the others. Buffa stared at it, and worried
about being the underdog.

When the LCC Cougars and their fans arrived Friday night, they were not
impressed with the Montrose Football Stadium, surrounded by a cinder track
and limited visitor seating. After playing larger schools with nicer stadiums,
they didn't expect the Rams to be much of a challenge, and labeled Montrose
as a hick school.

The Rams eyed their opponents when both teams warmed up on the crisp, fall evening. The Cougars were a huge team, which subconsciously intimidated a few Rams. Kitts shared a glance with Reinhart while they read each other's mind, *We're gonna get slogged!* The same sentiment passed through a few minds of the players, coupled by the enthusiastic noise the 4,000 fans surrounding the field generated. *It was showtime.*

Annese called for a double-pass on the first play of the game, and caught the Cougars off-guard. Crockett passed to Led who didn't see D'ar streak down the sideline wide open, and elected to pass over the middle. The pass was on target to Katt, but LCC made an outstanding play and broke it up.

The Cougars recouped, hammering the ball down the field on an impressive drive of power football. They lit up the score board first on a three yard run, with slightly over a minute left in the first quarter.

It was the first time the Rams were behind in a ball game, since Corunna jumped ahead 7-0 during the second week of the season. LCC played a tough physical game, causing the Rams to execute sloppy the first half; an abnormal position for the Rams. With four minutes left in the first half, Montrose narrowed the gap when Lake burst into the endzone for a three yard score.

LCC had a chance to score again before the half, advancing to the Montrose four, but couldn't get the ball in the endzone. It was fourth and goal with :17 seconds left. Forget the field goal, they wanted six and attempted a pass option to the southwest corner. The ball was in-and-out of the hands of an LCC receiver, who dropped to the ground in agony when he couldn't get a handle on it. It was a lucky break for the Rams, who took over on downs to finish the first half 6-7.

Annese tried to settle his team down during the intermission, since they had lost some of their composure. His Rams played tight, as if they were afraid to make a mistake. Annese spoke about being a second half, first possession team, like he stressed during the Goodrich game. He wanted them attacking when they hit the field.

That's exactly what they did. Led returned the second half kickoff to the Montrose 43. Their momentum flourished early in the second half, when a Cougar defensive back picked-off an errant pass from Crockett and returned it to the 10 yard line. Led was the intended receiver who felt frustrated after losing his footing and slipping, which set up the interception.

The Cougars turned the opportunity into another successful drive, that ended with a TD early in the third. The score was now 6-13. The Rams countered with an outstanding drive that brought the overflow crowd to their feet chanting -- 'LET'S GO RED! LET'S GO RED!'

Crockett called the quarterback keeper, then Lakester ran for a short gain to reach the 41 yard line. Kovl sprinted 59 yards off the straight veer dive, dazzling the crowd with his TD to even the score 13-13.

Kovl's zest to win sparked the defense, which stiffened to hold the Cougars to three plays and out on their next two possessions. D'ar returned the punt to the 45, setting up great field position for the Rams. D'ar brought a new element to the game, -- *finesse,* as he smoothly zigzagged and juked his opponents.

The Rams received a penalty on the play, which shoved them back across midfield. Crockett dropped back to pass on first down, and was flushed out of the pocket to his left before hitting Led for a strike. Led became intently focused, determined to make up for that provoking interception. His persistence carried him 71 yards down the field into the endzone, giving the Rams a 19-13 lead for the first time.

Annese planned to go for the kill and called for an on-side kick following their score, but the Cougars were too quick and recovered. They appeared to be driving for another TD when fate stepped into play. LCC faced a third-and-five from the Montrose 20 yard line, when their quarterback ran a sprint option to his left. But no one was on the receiving end for the Cougars when he pitched the ball.

Katt quickly moved his tall, long-legged body across the field, pouncing on the pigskin like a tiger stalking its prey. He recovered the fumbled option pitch; his efforts made a huge momentum shift. *They all felt it.*

The coaching staff felt a sense of security whenever they were in a bind, because Katt was at defensive end. His intense effort played every down like it was the first down of the game.

The Cougars produced serious threats until Brody sacked their quarterback on a fourth-and-eleven early in the final frame. The Rams showed great poise and concentration when Lakester took off on a 47 yard run off Olah at left tackle, putting the Rams in scoring position. Crockett handed off to Katt on a crucial third-and-eleven counter option pass, which placed the ball at the five yard line. Next play, Crockett took the ball on an option, eluded his tackler, and scampered the final five yards into the endzone, giving the Rams a 25-13 cushion with almost eight minutes left in the game.

The Rams used the entire field to wear down several opponents that played both ways. Their style of offense forced the Cougars to play them from sideline to sideline. LCC fought back and completed two long passes, placing the pigskin inside the Montrose eight yard line. The same opponent that scored both TD's for the Cougars, fumbled on the four yard line. Brody amazingly snuffed their final hopes when he smothered the loose ball.

A Montrose fan thought the coaching staff needed advice when he yelled from the bleachers -- 'TAKE A SAFETY.'

The first down was played, then the second, and the third. After each down the enlightened fan continued to scream, 'TAKE A SAFETY!'

The coaches on the sideline heard a lot more than fans may have realized, but also had their breaking point. On fourth down, Annese couldn't stay quiet any longer, turned around and boisterously yelled at the crowd, 'DOES ANYONE ELSE WANT TO HELP ME COACH THIS GAME?'

The crowd fell silent, like news of an instant death. It only took a fraction of a second for the rowdy fan in the home crowd to realize, *Oh I see what he's*

doing. Good call! The home crowd went wild when the scoring ended with
the Rams ahead, 25-15. Coach Annese couldn't resist the urge to turn around
and wave to the outspoken fan, letting him think that he actually called the
play.

The Rams managed only eight first downs compared to 15 for the
Cougars, but amassed 364 yards in total offense against 199 for LCC. Lake
made his biggest impact all season by running for 168 yards and a TD. He
propelled their momentum and affected field position by making key plays at
key times.

A delighted Coach Annese told his team afterward, 'This was the closest
game we've had all year. I'm proud of how you played tonight. They hit us
early and hit us hard, but you stuck with it and fought back. We were down
twice and you came back both times. You showed tremendous character and
effort. Your attitude was super. Good things happen to good teams. You
came into this ball game thinking you couldn't be beat and you made your
own breaks. You proved to be better conditioned. When it comes to pressure
situations, the team with the greatest character will always come out on top.
This team has an awful lot of character.'

Montrose played true team football. But the Rams were not satisfied with
just making the playoffs, they wanted to advance and gain statewide respect.
Beating a team that played good Class A competition gave the Rams great
pride. They capped a new motto, '32 brothers never die!'

They needed three more wins on their quest to become State Champions.

The Rams prepared to travel south near the Michigan-Ohio border to play
the **Monroe St. Mary Catholic Central Falcons.** It was a perfect matchup,
No.1 in the State against No. 2, only they met in the Regional Championship
Round instead of the State Finals.

Annese told his squad during practice, 'Monroe St. Mary is not a carbon
copy of our team but they are similar. Our two teams are so alike that the
team that makes the fewest mistakes will probably win.'

He reiterated how the Rams took advantage of three Lansing CC turnovers
last week. The Rams didn't play a perfect game, and would need to play
better against Monroe. After watching the LCC game film numerous times,
the coaching staff felt some mistakes were fundamental. Teams had a
tendency to neglect some of the little things when playoffs arrived. When
practice started the following Monday, the Rams took a step backward, and
spent some time on fundamentals.

The coaches followed Son of Swami's column in the Detroit Free Press,
chuckling at his prediction; 'Even Scott Aldred coming out of retirement can't
help Montrose. Catholic Central is so good – CC 26, Montrose 21.' Swami
predicted Montrose within a TD; the Rams considered that a compliment.

The team prepared to leave the school extra early for the long drive to
Monroe. The cheerleaders were great at generating school spirit all season,
but nothing compared to what they did for playoffs. The halls were lined with
students and the band, when the team walked from the locker room to board

the bus. The student tunnel continued to form outside of the school, snaking its way to the chartered bus. Motivation consumed the team as they walked through the celebration. Friends and teachers patted them on the back and cheered, providing the perfect send off. Larry Hyde drove the chartered bus, just like he had during their final youth football games. The cheerleader assigned to Kovl, handed him something as he boarded the bus. Once he found a seat, he unfolded a white handkerchief she made, and smiled at the message written in fabric paint, 'Give It All You Got Jerry - #30.'

The team found a steak house when they arrived in Monroe that offered a choice of chicken, fish, or beef. Eric and Buffa couldn't eat their traditional pre-game spaghetti and Bulldog couldn't order lasagna, a ritual they kept all season long. It gave them a bad feeling; the threesome hoped the change in routine wouldn't jinx the Montrose Rams that night. The bus took the players to the Monroe YMCA to relax and kill more time. The coaches wished they hadn't left the school so early; they had too much time on their hands -- too many idle hours to think about the game.

Having a great football program created substantial support from the small Montrose community. Three additional buses were chartered due to an overwhelming response from the fans. Several school buses formed a caravan for the three-hour drive south on I-75 to Monroe. The rains continued to fall, but the faithful fans didn't allow the lousy weather to dampen their spirits.

Some stopped at a nearby McDonalds and generously received black garbage bags to use as makeshift raincoats. Fans arrived at Monroe's Navarre Field early enough to bombard the team as they deported the chartered bus. Having over 1,000 fans surrounding their bus overwhelmed Kovl. He liked arriving before the fans, and used that time to adjust to the strange surroundings. Kovl needed that time alone to take it all in and prepare his game mind. Brody preferred to be by himself before the game, and wondered where he could go for a moment's peace.

The Falcons won the coin toss and deferred possession of the ball until the second half. The Monroe St. Mary Catholic Central Falcons kicked off to the Montrose Rams on a cold, rainy Friday night. Led subconsciously stretched his fingers, feeling his receiver gloves as he tried to ease his early game jitters. He wore gloves through part of the season, so they felt natural on his hands. Led intently listened for Crockett to call their first play from scrimmage, then concentrated when he ran, turned, and caught Crockett's pass right on cue.

But in a flash the ball slipped through Led's hands.

Damn.

Crockett caught up to Led, 'Hey, shake it off Led. It's early, we'll get it back.'

Crockett was a perfect fit in the Montrose offensive scheme. He possessed the two attributes vital to success at quarterback -- determination and intelligence. Before the night was over, his team relied on both.

The Falcons recovered the fumble on the Montrose 30 yard line. Five plays later, Fish missed his first assignment at defensive end. Monroe scored on a 15 yard run. The extra point failed but Monroe St. Mary Catholic was on the board 0-6 with nearly nine minutes left in the first quarter.

Fish covered the dive back when he should have taken the quarterback. He was pissed at himself for not stopping him. It was the most important game of his life and his brain kept repeating, *I can't believe I just did that.* Tensions mounted and he felt the wrath of his coaches' words, first from Reinhart, then Annese. Neither held back any emotion and royally chewed him out. Fish hung his head, feeling like he deserved every biting word that gushed from their mouths. He guaranteed it would be his only mess up the entire game.

Monroe carried their momentum into the next series and kicked an on-side kick. Lake was the 'up back' on the return team and was caught off-guard when the kick went by him and their deep man. The Falcons recovered and regained the ball on the Montrose 38 yard line. It was a tough break that happened so quickly.

Coach Reinhart fired up his defense when they took the field, determined to stop the Falcons. The Rams forced a fourth down at the 21 yard line, but the Falcons quarterback dropped back and passed 21 yards for a second TD. The score climbed to 0-12.

Coach Annese calmed down his Rams while he tried to build their confidence. The Rams responded in championship style by taking the ensuing kickoff and marching 59 yards in seven plays to Monroe's one yard line. The offense found its rhythm when Kovl earned chunks of real estate in the series and helped the determined Rams narrow the gap. The cold weather didn't give Kovl cause to wear receiver gloves. He liked to wear them during practice, but not in a game. Kovl needed to feel the leather in his hands.

On the other hand, Lake preferred wearing gloves. Who could argue? They helped him become the leading scorer in the entire county. He took them off before the game and handed them to Brent Baksa to hold, then changed his mind after the game got underway. Lake decided he needed them; a decision he'd regret for the rest of his life.

Lake ran a trap up the middle; his mind totally focused on crossing the goal line. Then, it all happened too fast. He felt the ball get stripped from his hands, causing a fumble on the one yard line. The Falcons recovered, forcing the Rams to surrender their scoring opportunity. In a flash, Lake couldn't believe that he dropped the ball. Lake rushed to the sideline to find the trainer. In a panic he held out his receiver gloves and shouted, 'Spray me with stick`em.'

She never saw him so intent and hastily obeyed, totally oblivious of her contribution. The Falcons failed to convert a first down after taking over on the one yard line, then were forced to punt. D'ar gave the Rams another scoring chance early in the second period, when he hauled in the kick at Monroe's 40 then scampered to the 10. But the Rams couldn't punch it in and turned it over on downs. The Montrose defense stiffened for the remainder of the half, while the offense penetrated to Monroe's 18 yard line, but still couldn't score.

Once again, Annese successfully motivated them during the intermission. 'We're moving the ball, we just need to hang on to it!'

The Rams felt confident when they left the locker room at the end of the half; they planned to come out and win.

The Montrose Rams kicked off to the Monroe Falcons to open the second half. The Rams defense took a stand by forcing a punt on their first possession. Newt was always there when the foot hit the ball. He was a key component to the defensive success, taking pride in performing at an optimal level week-after-week, throughout their entire season. He was the heart-and-soul of the defense, their ringleader, whose actions revealed how badly he wanted a victory. It was the most important thing in his life; he gave every ounce of energy he had. *Effort was valued.*

The Rams struck quick on the second play of the following drive. Crockett threw a screen pass over the middle to Led, who outraced the Falcons secondary for a 60 yard TD. The senior standout pulled his team to within six. Their confidence surfaced, as the Rams appeared to take control of the game. Montrose drove down the field for the tying TD with their momentum moving in the right direction, in spite of the cold rain. After reaching the six yard line Olah thought, *We'll take it in sure this time. No problem.* Then he watched in devastation as the pigskin popped free *again,* from Lake's hands, for a Falcon to pounce on. The tying TD turned into a devastating turnover, giving Monroe St. Mary another opportunity to stay in the game.

Lake ran directly to the trainer, demanding that she spray his receiver gloves *again.* They were actually borrowed gloves, since his had lost their tackiness after being worn all season. In desperation, Lake seized the one thing he thought would help him hang on to the ball -- *the sticky spray.* He was completely unaware that the freezing, rainy weather caused an adverse effect, *one that could be devastating.*

Newt asserted his captain responsibilities when he directly approached Annese and firmly stated. 'Will you pull Lake out of the game? He's having a bad night!'

Annese wouldn't pull Lake. 'Hey, Corey was a big part of getting us to this point. He'll get it back. I'm not pulling him!'

Newt respected his coach, although he silently disagreed with him. He didn't want anything to interfere with winning that ball game, or ending their dream. Newt thought, *Lake is my friend, but this is playoffs; one of the most important nights of my life. We sacrificed too much and worked too hard to let anything screw it up. I can't believe Coach won't pull him. What's he waiting for? I would expect to get pulled if I had an off night. There's too much at risk to care about feelings right now!*

The offense that depended on each other all season seemed to break down that night. Lake felt he had a clear shot for the endzone on a 38 veer, but Crockett decided to keep the ball. Disaster struck again later in the series when Montrose fumbled at the 46 yard line, surrendering the recovery to junior Falcon Cory Gildersleeve.

Newt wanted to win so badly that it terrified him. The loyalty, the pride, the will to succeed had been drilled into him for three Varsity seasons. It was what the Rams worked so hard for. Panic gnawed at his stomach; it never occurred to him that they wouldn't accomplish their dream. He had to do something and went to Coach Annese after Lake's third fumble. Newt begged from the depths of his soul, 'Coach, please take Lake out. He can't hang on to the ball tonight!'

Olah was under the same opinion. Later, he'll wish that he treated Lake better, but during that game it meant too much. Lake was the high scorer for the entire county, running over Olah's side the entire season. The twosome formed the left side. They weren't even considered 'the strong side,' but Olah's large frame made a shield for Lake to run through all season; *but not that night.*

Coach Annese followed his own instinct and kept Lake in. His season stats included 21 TD's and eight conversions, backed with an awesome rushing attack of 1,241 yards. Maybe Annese wanted to stick with the plays that got the Rams there. Perhaps he wanted a chance for Lake to save face and become the hero. He still had confidence in his star back, feeling sure it couldn't happen again.

Words of encouragement echoed from the Montrose stands, 'Come on boys, get it back!'

The game continued to be a nightmare for Lake. It was a night different from all others. He never felt totally in the zone, no matter how hard he tried. It began during warm-ups when it started to rain, and the cold temperature teetered at freezing point. The ball became hard for him to hold on to, resulting in his worst performance all season. He struggled with his concentration and felt his technique break down; then the human element of trying too hard came into play. It was unbelievable. He felt his frustration increase after each fumble, which was so uncharacteristic of him. Lake reached the point where he couldn't think straight anymore. *What the hell was happening? I only fumbled once the entire season. The entire season! This is totally unbelievable. I can't believe this keeps happening to me!*

Things continued to go badly for Montrose. Statistically, the Rams dominated, holding the Falcons to 65 yards the entire second half and only two first downs. If the Rams could just hang on to the ball they knew they could pull out a win.

Eric's frustration mirrored the sentiments of the entire Montrose defense. Their unyielding will to win kept them going, in spite of their fumbles. They were still in the game; only one touchdown away from keeping their dream alive. The Montrose defense played extremely hard to stop Monroe only to have the offense give it up. It became mortifying, but no one would quit.

Eric told Buffa, 'We're dominating the game, yet we're still losing.'

Buffa played linebacker and felt confident that the Rams would pull it off. Long before he grew into a Varsity lineman, he dreamed about a State Championship; it was still within their reach.

Fish thought, *For sure we'll get it in this time. Things went wrong all night. We just need one little break, just one more chance to score and we win.*

Montrose played like they had a tomorrow, but in the playoffs -- tomorrow didn't exist. In the final seven minutes of play, the Rams fumbled again on Monroe's 40 yard line. Once again Gildersleeve recovered. The opponent didn't realize that his future path intertwines with the Montrose Rams several years down the road.

The Rams were down 6-12 when they got possession back. *It wasn't over yet.* Montrose never gave up. They were still within one TD, with hardly any time left on the clock. *Could they take it in?*

Annese called for Crockett to launch *The Bomb,* trusting they could pull it off. In a final unrelenting quest to tie the ball game, the Montrose quarterback lofted a desperate Hail Mary pass to the endzone. Crockett's right fingers extended as he completed his follow through, then watched the ball sail into the endzone. It seemed to hang in the air, suspended in time, along with the hopes and dreams of the entire squad. He watched with eager eyes, hoping one of his favorite targets would be celebrating with him in a few seconds. Hundreds of eyes followed its trancelike motion, while holding their breath and silently praying, *Catch it. Please catch it.*

Monroe's Gildersleeve capped a phenomenal defensive night when he batted the ball away on a final heroic play, just as the dreaded flat sound of the buzzer sounded. It echoed through the stadium like the solitary sound of *Taps* being played at a funeral, squashing their dream of a state crown.

Newt couldn't believe it. It was hard to grasp that it was over. His exhausted body fell to the ground; a look of horror secured his face when he screamed, 'NO!' Devastation crushed him as he squatted in the middle of the field. The cold rain that slapped his face shielded his tears. He couldn't hide his disappointment; it felt like his world just ended. Newt couldn't believe it ended like that. *Not like that!*

It didn't matter that he led the defense with 17 tackles, giving him 135 for the season. He didn't feel very brilliant at that moment, and fought to control the wrenching feeling that tore at his gut. Hurt or healthy, he gave his best for three years. But wasn't ready for it to be over. *Not yet.*

The loss not only ended his high school football career; it also ended the closeness they shared as a football family. The daily contact with his teammates and coaches filled a huge void left by the loss of his father, and he knew his life would never be the same.

He lifted weights with Coach Reinhart for years and they were close. Reinhart helped him make decisions at an early age, and deal with the hardships that life handed him. Coach Annese taught Newt how to set goals and what effort and commitment were all about. He taught him how to win and be successful and not want second place, which made their final loss even more difficult. Down the road, he realized that football taught him many lessons about life, while preparing him to survive the tough times that he faced.

Newt looked around at his fellow brothers whose tear-lined cheeks made him swallow hard. The dreary scene forced the knot in his throat to tighten; he'd never seen any of his friends so distraught. Their disappointment ran deep. They all wanted a State Championship more than anything; being left with a shattered memory was extremely difficult.

Led joined Newt on the field. It didn't matter that he scored their only TD or caught five passes for 96 yards. He was the Rams most skilled and talented athlete, and was Crockett's primary receiver as well as an outstanding back. They dominated the game but couldn't put it away when they needed to. Their efforts didn't advance them to the Pontiac Silverdome on November 23rd. They would not accomplish their quest for the Dome, leaving them with the emptiest feeling most had ever experienced.

Katt's intense efforts contributed nine tackles. He played with a fierce intensity, proving he was the type of defensive end that opponents hated to face. Katt played with everything he had to give, but three fumbles in the final quarter tore the Rams down. It was difficult to deal with the fact that their dream was over.

Kovl was extremely quiet and didn't immediately speak, unsure of how to respond. His eyes shifted from the strong leaders, to the rest of his teammates as he analyzed their reactions. Some were so emotionally distraught they couldn't hold back sobs, while others looked thoroughly pissed off. He saw Chris Buffa cry his eyes out. The easygoing linebacker never thought they would lose and when they did, he simply wasn't prepared. *None of them were. Surrendering defeat was tough.*

Kovl felt numb, like he was in a daze watching everyone around him. It all seemed to end too quickly. He carried the ball 14 times for 109 yards. He felt frustrated that their offense had moved the ball the entire game, running plays the same way they had all season. They just couldn't put it in the endzone that night; he only wished he could've scored at least one TD for his team.

Montrose held the spotlight of owning the state's longest winning streak at '26' games. They had been dealt their first loss since the `88 Chesaning game. If they could have held on to the ball, they would have beaten the No.1 ranked team, and paved their way to the Dome. *It wasn't their destiny.*

Coach Annese gathered his team in the middle of the field, and thanked them for their efforts. 'I've never been prouder of a group of kids. You are champions. I take full responsibility for this loss. It was a coach's loss, not your loss. Our goal was to be State Champions. We should have been in a position to do that, but we took it away from ourselves. The best team doesn't win all the time. We took this game away from ourselves and we have to accept that. We can't fumble the ball within the five yard line and expect to win a championship game. We just didn't get it done when we had to get it done. We gave it a shot and tried to prove we were the best team in the State in Class B. I think we did it by our actions, if not on the scoreboard. You never quit. You kept fighting to the end.'

Coach Annese publicly accepted the blame for his team's loss. Perhaps that made it easier on Lake. There were several things that went wrong; he was afraid of Lake becoming a scapegoat. Annese wanted the team to remember what Corey Lake accomplished as their leading scorer with 1,241 rushing yards and 21 TD's for the season.

Even though Lake was in a state of devastation, he found admiration for Coach Annese. He knew how important that game was to his coach, yet he remained positive, never doubting their ability to win the game. Coach never placed blame on anyone on the team - only himself. *That showed class.*

Men of muscle usually try to be rough and conceal their emotions, but that loss made even the toughest ones break down. They discovered that being macho wasn't important anymore. They couldn't hide their disappointment; it was simply too overwhelming -- *too final.* Their pride was deeply wounded. Fans sensed their grief as they witnessed the dreadful misfortune crash in front of their eyes. They patiently waited for the Montrose players to exit the field, before starting the three-hour drive home.

Players held their heads high when they marched toward the goal post, leaving a piece of their soul on the muddy field of Monroe St. Mary. By the time they reached the goal post, it seemed like the dam burst. Most couldn't contain their emotions any longer. It wasn't supposed to end like that! On top of their frustration everyone was wet, muddy, and chilled. Some wanted to shower, others just wanted to get the hell out of there. They took a vote and decided to change before boarding the buses for the long drive home.

Olah stood under the steamy mist, with one thought on his mind. *What could he have done differently to change the outcome? Then it hit him – it was his cleats. It had to be.* His shoes had the rubber cleats built in, and he wondered if it would have made a difference had he worn different cleats. Monroe's field was so muddy that he had a hard time keeping his footing, and missed a few blocks early in the game.

Bulldog had developed a strong passion for the game. He couldn't remember ever being so upset about anything in his life. He felt nauseous ever since that dreaded buzzer sounded, and finally walked off by himself and hurled. The lineman couldn't stand to watch his teammates, especially the seniors, cry like babies in the distant locker room.

The blood, sweat, and chunks of turf that adorned their rumpled uniforms dripped slowly to the floor, adding to the mosaic of stains on the cracked concrete. With each sob the boys lost a bit of their childhood, and some would say, gained a morsel of manhood.

Bulldog approached Coach Annese in the locker room after the game and made a promise. 'We'll be back next year.'

Annese stared back at Bulldog. He heard the conviction in the lineman's voice and saw it in his face. He knew Bulldog meant what he said; one of his '91 captains just stepped up.

The team, now showered and dry, walked to their warm bus for the long journey home. They didn't feel comfortable when they approached the faithful Montrose students, patiently waiting by the team bus. Fans felt chilled after waiting so long in the rain, displaying a true act of friendship. Tears started again once players approached their friends and parents. No one felt too proud to show his true emotions. It was difficult to see strong, macho teenagers experience such a tough time. The scene created a painful high school memory that none of them would ever forget. It was the senior's last gridiron contest; an unforgettable loss that was hard pressed to find a lesson in.

Wixson, from the '89 Team, listened to the game in the parking lot during a wedding reception a few hours away. He felt as frustrated and drained as his former teammates. Like Wixson, Vinnie faithfully followed Montrose Football during his first year at Morehead State. Vinnie constantly talked about the Montrose Rams, and convinced two of his college teammates to make the drive to the Monroe game. It was a long, quiet ride home from the Ohio-Michigan border to Kentucky. Vinnie didn't say one word the entire way. He only thought about his former teammates and the hell they must be experiencing. His heart ached for his friend Corey Lake.

Lake boarded the bus and plopped down next to Newt for the long ride home. He finally broke the silence. 'I don't understand why I couldn't hang on to the ball.'

They played a good team that tackled well, but he honestly felt Montrose possessed the caliber of a State Championship team. For whatever reason, the Rams were not meant to win that game. Lake felt Montrose could play Monroe and beat them nine out of ten times, they just had a bad night. Many champion teams had a bad game. Lake knew it took 11 players to make an offense, but felt they would've won the game if he had performed better. He tried to make sense out of everything that happened that night; it was a bizarre game that would forever be embedded in his memory.

Newt didn't want to talk to Lake; he didn't want to even look at him. He closed his eyes and placed his throbbing brow on the cold metal bar from the seat in front of him. Newt stayed in that position for the duration of the endless trip, while the question echoed through his head, *Why did it happen?*

It was the topic that no one had an answer to. He felt numb and miserable as the sour taste of failure burned in his throat on the long bus ride home. It put a huge dent in their pride and made Newt wonder, *What lesson are we suppose to learn from this? Was it to teach us that no matter what happens in life, we have to pick ourselves up and move on?* He didn't know, and he couldn't seem to think straight.

For most of them, it was the lowest point they had ever reached in their young lives. They listened to the stifling silence of the humming of the bus, which made the three-hour ride seem even longer, especially for the seniors. After they had been on the road for an hour, a scuffle broke out in the back of the bus between Brody and some underclassmen.

Led stood up and sternly yelled, 'Sit down and shut up!'

They all settled down, listening to the motion of the subdued bus the remainder of the ride home; each lost in his own misery. D'ar was overwhelmed at what he'd just experienced. He studied their playbook, and had memorized every play backward and forward. He knew he benefited from his exposure to Varsity level football, but nothing prepared him for that ending. Dealing with the extreme emotion his heroes displayed that night, etched a desire deep in his soul to make the most of his remaining two years.

It was extremely late when the bus pulled into the abandoned school parking lot. The J.V. players unloaded the wet raincoats off the bus, before heaping them into a pile in the tiny office. Later, the exhausted coaches came in and used the wet pile as a makeshift bed. Annese, Reinhart, Kitts, Persails, and Morse threw themselves on that pile and stared at the ceiling in silence.

Kitts finally breathed out a slow and solemn, 'Wow!'

The painted concrete walls could not absorb the wetness from the coats or the ache from their hearts. They laid on that pile of damp raincoats and talked about the game until 2:30 AM. One of them kept saying, 'We had it. We had our chance so many times.'

They talked about their heartbreaking loss in a Regional Championship Game to a team they dominated in every statistic of the game -- *including fumbles.* Borrowing a phrase from Dickens, 'It was the best of times, it was the worst of times.' They couldn't understand how their Rams turned the ball over five times, or how their senior standout fumbled twice in the endzone for undisputed touchdowns. At that time, the coaching staff was still unaware of how much stick'em was sprayed on Lake's gloves.

The results of the game didn't make sense to any of them. *It never would.* Monroe scored on the first two possessions . . . and that was it. Montrose felt like they kicked the snot out of Monroe the rest of the game, yet they still lost. They honestly felt the Rams were better than Monroe St. Mary and should have won. They couldn't believe their chance for a State Championship slipped through their hands. It just slipped through their hands.

Lake woke up Saturday morning and wished it was all a bad dream; *but it wasn't.* He could only blame himself, as he felt their dream slither away. It was only the beginning of many dreadful, surreal dreams. In some, he found himself disguised as another player in an effort to get another chance. In others, he had the opportunity to play the game again, with a happier ending.

He wanted to win a State Championship just as bad, or more, than anyone on his team. Lake operated in survival mode with his ego out front all year.

Monroe gave him a sharp blow and he felt like his world came crashing down around him. He had a tough home life; football filled a huge void from certain things that were lacking. Like his teammates, no one knew how to handle a loss of that magnitude, as they painfully discovered that they were human. Lake still had plans to play college football and hoped that recruiters looked at his entire season, not just his last game. He thought about it over and over. If he had one thing in his young life that he could change, it would be to replay the Monroe game. That game haunted him for many years. He wondered if the person who created the phrase, 'It's just a game,' ever played under similar conditions.

The Monroe contest was a lesson in life. In the game of *highs and lows* it was classified as an *all-time-low* that he needed to overcome.

Most of the team had two sleepless nights, unaware that the Monroe game would haunt them for years to come. A gnawing ache severed the pit of their gut whenever they heard the word 'Monroe.' Time does heal, and the sharp pain settled into a dull ache, but at the time their wounds felt raw.

Coaches hoped their disappointment didn't overshadow their accomplishments. Once their pain eased, players realized they set nine team records and two individual season records. They gained over 4,592 yards for the season, averaging 417 yards per game. Ten of them made First Team All-League.

Some teammates brought their anguish with them when they returned to school by throwing Butterfinger candy bars in front of Lake in the hallway. Other students blamed him by intentionally dropping their books in a theatrical move to mock him. Several teammates wouldn't even speak to Lake on Monday, or the rest of the school year for that matter. It all took a mental toll on Lake. He finally asked Katt, 'How come the guys won't talk to me?'

Katt was totally honest with Lake. 'Hey, a lot of the guys are having problems with what happened that last game. You have to understand that it's not necessarily their fault. They have to deal with it in their own way. By not talking to you, may be the best way.'

Lake wished they could move forward and not look back. He didn't lose that game single-handedly, but soon became the scapegoat, discovering that friendships are tested over time. He wondered if they would ever be able to forgive him, or if their disappointment would linger permanently throughout their lives.

Lake felt responsible for the loss to Monroe for many years. Memories of that game grabbed at his heart, tearing deep to the pit of his gut. No matter how much he wanted to, he couldn't change what happened and needed to live with it.

After school the following Monday, Coach Kitts stopped in the weight room to watch players. Just eleven months earlier the Rams dedicated themselves, under the leadership of an incredible young coach, to a strict regimen of weight training. Coach Reinhart, a former National Bench-Press

Champion, combined his expertise with the motivational skill of Coach Annese to create an orgy of powerlifting. It seemed the room was filled with young men every day, from the end of one football season to the beginning of the next. It became such a ritual that sometimes over fifty boys lifted at once. The program spilled over to the gridiron, where the Rams of Montrose Hill-McCloy High began a decade of domination.

They lifted with a fierce intensity that was therapeutic for the seniors who took out their frustration on the machines. Katt, Led, Kovl, Lake, Newton, Olah, Buffa, Baksa, Fish, and Brody had to accept that high school football was over for them. They all went on to college where six of them played football.

Their spirit was tested. The juniors were thankful they had one more year to accomplish their dream. A promise was made to the seniors to do their best and make the most of their last year, vowing to not end their grand finale with a loss. Starting that day, the juniors worked their butts off to prepare for the '91 Season. They went the extra mile, pledging they would never have a repeat of what happened against Monroe St. Mary. They would play as hard as they could -- *every down, every game.* They set goals to go undefeated so they could make the playoffs. It was the start of an obsession that possessed them, driving them into the '91 Season.

The Rams would be a young team in '91. Coaches realized when a team lacked exceptional talent, but contained a strong human spirit, they'd be hard to beat. Something very special transpired in the weight room that Monday. All of the hurt and pain developed into a special team unity. Not all teams are blessed with that type of rapport.

Magical things happen when a team possesses it.

TRI-COUNTY CITIZEN PHOTO
#40 Ron Newton after Playoff loss to Monroe St. Mary Catholic

FLINT JOURNAL PHOTO/Randy Belinsky
From left: Brody Mier, Ron Newton, and Jason Katt

4. OBSTACLES – 1991

Success is to be measured not so much
by the position that one has reached in life
as by the obstacles
which he has overcome trying to succeed.

-Booker T. Washington

His eyes focused on the lineman, critiquing every move that #95 made. He watched the huge tackle sack the quarterback, then celebrate his huge hit like he was on top of the world. The thrill of a sack shot through his veins, carrying an honesty for a well-deserved adrenaline rush. He reminisced about his days playing tackle, figuring that he would've done the same thing, only he was a smidgen shorter and wore #79. They were seven years apart, yet he felt connected to the lineman in a mysterious way.

Would the obsession ever leave? He hoped not. He knew that he couldn't stop until he developed a program that played for a championship. He felt one step closer to his goal every day of his life. Maybe people thought he was crazy, but he loved to work with football players and watch them succeed in achieving their dreams. He never lost his love for the game. It would take a hell of a lot of desire, knowledge, and luck to win the big one. But when all three components united, the world would be a better place – at least for 48 minutes. Call it fate. Call it destiny. Whatever it was, he would be ready when his turn came. From the time he was a teenager, that all-consuming desire never left him. He hoped it never would. It was more than a strong feeling; it was a burning passion that smoldered within, like a perpetual flame.

The excited lineman on the field was totally unaware that his actions restored the invisible torch, and passed it back to a former player, now a coach. The torch was intangible to measure, but its worth was as bonafide as a family heirloom handed down from one generation to the next. The transient torch sparked a passion that the young coach still had for this crazy game. It reaffirmed that he was still on the right track, doing what he needed to do. Sullivan would continue working with young people to build a passion, not just for the game of football . . . but for the game of life.

Eric felt terrified. His body shook uncontrollably as beads of sweat formed on his forehead. The distress in Bulldog's voice alarmed him. 'Don't look at it Eric. Just don't look down.'

Even though his head felt like a box of rocks, he found the strength to lift it and look for himself. *Oh shit!*

He felt the weight of his head plop down on the muddy field and closed his eyes. *This couldn't be happening.* His foot appeared to be turned *totally around.* Eric opened his eyes to check if he was actually lying on his stomach or his back. He tried to recall the play, but everything rapidly turned fuzzy. He remembered hearing an unfamiliar pop, and feared that something really bad had just happened. *It had.* He soon learned that both major bones in his leg were broken; his ligaments seemed to be the only thing keeping his foot attached to his leg.

Eric slowly opened his eyes. He knew Bulldog was lying out of his teeth when he said, 'You're gonna be fine.'

The truth was that Bulldog could hardly keep himself from hurling after he looked at Eric's foot pointing in the opposite direction. It reminded him of the time he spitefully manhandled the leg on his sister's doll when he was a kid. But this was real. He could tell Eric's pain was excruciating as he watched his friend go into shock. That tackle did him in.

The thought of pins holding his bones together didn't appeal to Eric in the least. Eric became one happy football player when the orthopedic surgeon told him a leg cast would help his bones grow correctly; he could avoid the dreaded surgery. The doctor warned him that he would naturally want to limp on his leg once his cast came off. But there would be no chance of that with Coach Annese around. Coach followed Eric between classes and wouldn't let him baby it. He wanted Eric to walk on his injured leg to make it stronger. Eric was impressed that Coach Annese did that for him; after all, he was only a freshman at the time.

That was three seasons ago, but Eric still remembered that painful ending to his Freshmen Season. His broken bone almost convinced him to give up football, but he came back and had a good sophomore year. Then came that damned Monroe St. Mary game, which ended his junior season with a totally different kind of pain. He was so young to have experienced such deep pain; both physical and emotional. The Monroe loss still haunted all of them like a bad dream. They simply couldn't forget it or put it to rest. It drove them to finish each set of reps no matter how sore they were.

Eric glanced around the crowded weight room, enjoying the familiar clang of steel hitting steel, while grunts gushed from the mouths of his teammates. They thrived on challenging each other, pushing it to the max.

Normally, when the snow melted in Michigan it was time to gear up for baseball season. It was the sport football jocks played when spring and summer rolled around. Eric fit that mold. He played little league baseball from the time he was six through his J.V. Season, but he needed to make a change. No matter how much he enjoyed baseball, football was his first love. He only had one season left to accomplish his dream. Eric searched his soul, discovering that he had never felt so adamant about completing a goal.

It gnawed at him for months; now he realized what he needed to do. He took his new captain role seriously, wanting to be as strong as possible for his senior season. When he told his teammates about his decision to give up baseball and focus on weightlifting, he was surprised that several joined him. They were unmistakably committed to the promise they made to the '90 seniors and planned to work especially hard to make the playoffs in '91. They all knew that powerlifting competitions would make them even stronger. It was a part of their mission to become State Football Champions, even it if meant giving up baseball.

Naturally, Eric assumed Coach Annese would support his idea, but was caught off-guard by his response. 'I'm pleased that you plan to increase your weightlifting workout Eric, but you'll have to work it in after track practice.'

'Track? I've never ran track!'

Coach expected the puzzled look on Eric's face. 'That's right, we need to work on your speed during the off-season. Welcome to the track team. Go tell Bowen and Crockett to be at track practice tomorrow after school.'

The baseball team started to lose talented players when Annese used his influence as the track coach to convince his backs to become sprinters, instead of base runners. He wanted to see how fast his backs really were. Scott Bowen sat next to Eric during the track meeting, browsing through a handout containing quotes from famous football coaches about winning attitudes, goals, and becoming champions. Both felt the subtle undertow of football preparation which was fine by them, but they wondered if the diehard track guys resented it.

It seemed football had become the base that everything else compared to. Bowen proved he was the second fastest guy on the team, second only to Crockett. Track tapped into abilities Bowen didn't realize he even possessed, giving him added confidence. He placed second in the league meet in both the 200m and 100m behind Crockett. Their relay team, which happened to be all football players, placed first. Bowen looked down at the medal he won at the league award ceremony and said to Eric, 'This just doesn't seem right. I worked my butt off all season in football to win a league medal. I ran one race and got the same medal.'

About the time track season ended, the Montrose School District found itself in financial trouble, and prepared to ask the community to approve 4.7 mills. The millage failed to pass twice in 1989. School buses were discontinued and students heard rumors about splitting the high school with neighboring communities. Football players teamed up with the cheerleaders and the student body to hold a pep rally. The local TV crew broadcasted the school assembly on the evening news. The students in the bleachers were divided into sections that chanted, 'DON'T - CLOSE - OUR SCHOOL!'

Katt was geared up for graduation, but couldn't walk away knowing the future of his high school was in shambles. He grabbed the microphone in an effort to make one last difference before he left. 'We need to do something about this. This ticket will not pass by itself. I don't want my friends to be shipped off and play sports for different schools. If this is the end of Montrose Football, THEN THAT'S PATHETIC! Go home and ask your parents and your neighbors to support Montrose Schools and VOTE FOR THIS MILLAGE!'

His speech excited the kids who anxiously cheered even louder. Bulldog was even more vested, and was seriously concerned about the millage. He wanted to play Montrose Football his senior year. He organized students and football players to actively campaign and participate in a parade planned for the downtown area.

Katt and Sullivan organized their friends to go door-to-door and beg people to vote yes on the millage. They held rallies in the streets to raise awareness and generate support. Students canvassed the phone book hours before the polls closed, encouraging the community to vote. They pulled together to provide rides, doing everything they could to help it pass.

It did.

Montrose Football was still alive and kicking. Now Newt and Led could move on and play football at Saginaw Valley State University (SVSU). Corey Lake could play for Grand Valley State and Katt could take his football scholarship and play for Hillsdale College.

But Katt wasn't expecting what awaited him at Hillsdale. The skilled quarterback from Monroe St. Mary Catholic was now his teammate, along with a huge tackle from Lansing Catholic Central. Katt mumbled under his breath the first few times he faced the Monroe player during practice. To balance his frustration, Katt ripped on the Lansing Catholic teammate, since he helped stop their playoff dream. His new college quarterback could humble Katt with one simple word . . . 'Monroe.'

Katt eventually worked through his frustration and became good friends with his rival. They learned to trust each other and even traded their high school football jerseys. His former opponent actually helped Katt work through the Monroe loss and confided that Montrose should've won that game. The two friends wondered if Montrose and Monroe would have a rematch for the State Title in 1991.

The Rams hosted their first veer camp during the summer of '91. In order to win a fourth straight GEC championship, Annese felt his team needed to mature quickly. He told his Rams before the camp started, 'We need to realize what it takes to be successful. We've had good teams as role models the past couple of years and I hope it rubs off. We have a lot of people to replace. This year will test our ability as a program. We're going to find out if we can lose a lot of kids and still be competitive. We'll find out whether we're one of those programs that rebuilds or reloads.'

The new program at Montrose experienced success and started to get attention. Opponents hated to lose to the Rams, yet respected their program. Bowen worked with a group of guards at a summer camp when he overheard Coach Annese lead another drill 30 yards away. The intensity in his coach's voice caused an aggressive reaction that took Bowen by surprise, forcing him to step it up a notch. Bowen pulled on the very next drill, forcefully knocking a Bendle player on his back. The dazed player sluggishly stood up and respectfully told Bowen, 'Hey, good hit.'

Bendle was in a rebuilding year and was one of eight schools that attended the camp. Eric was at another station, but caught the entire scene. He was impressed to be a part of a team that received that level of respect from an opposing school.

Sunday afternoons during the summer were reserved for Air Force football. Ex-players formed an alumni team and challenged the current high school kids. Annese always joined the alumni team and didn't cut any player any slack. He led by example and ran every play, every down. If the alumni fell behind in points, Coach shamed them into playing longer. After playing

90 minutes in nearly 100 degree heat, Annese said, 'I gave you a chance, now you give me a chance.' *Determination was admired.*

They had too much respect to quit, no matter how physically tired or sweaty they were. They knew if Coach could compete at that level, they'd better be able to. Players ranged in age from 14 – 21, and everyone ran and passed the ball. Not just the star jocks, but the kids who hardly played. The linemen, who rarely touched the ball, found themselves in the best shape of their lives. Coach didn't cut the bigger linemen any slack throughout the summer, which resulted in the big guys staying in shape. They were strong and fit. Annese implemented the '50 Mile Club' as an added incentive, which encouraged players to run during the off-season. He managed to get linemen to run distance. The same guys who complained about running a gasser, attempted to run 50 miles for a measly T-shirt . . . and the measurement of pride that accompanied it.

Traditionally, their quarterback had been a team captain. Crockett was a great leader on the field, but Coach wanted to strengthen the leadership influence in the weight room. He asked the players to elect an additional captain. A committed captain was needed in the weight room, who could motivate his teammates to work hard during the off-season. If someone wasn't doing his workout, the captain was expected to take care of it.

Bulldog was the obvious leader, after he helped the Powerlifting Team become State Champions for two consecutive years. His commitment helped the team compete at Nationals in Florida -- a memorable trip with 14 kids, two coaches, and 1200 miles in a motorhome.

After conditioning started, players voted for yet another captain to make their program even stronger. The highest votes ended in a tie between Eric Hyde, Scott Powell, and John Diem. John felt he was just an easygoing, hard working, run of the mill type of guy, who was surprised to win the vote. He led by example; the guys knew how hard he worked. His new title made him determined to work even harder. Coach decided to let all three become co-captains. They were responsible for the guys in their positions. Annese handed each captain a letter that outlined his expectations:

> *Being chosen as captain is a great honor, but an even greater responsibility. You are expected to be a hard worker, a great motivator, an excellent communicator, and a fabulous leader. Your role is very similar and as important as the coach. In fact, you must consider yourself as a coaching assistant. In many situations, you can have a greater impact on the future of the program than the coach can. If you don't take your job as captain seriously, it could hurt our program for many years to come.*

Bulldog and Eric soon discovered firsthand what a captain's responsibility involved. They took a drive to the tressel, an abandoned bridge located north of Montrose. The tressel had a bad reputation of hosting wild parties where kids from different schools gathered and typically drank too much alcohol before the fights started. It simply wasn't a good place to be, especially on the weekends. Several accidents had occurred through the years; some ending tragically.

The captains found themselves in an awkward position. Eric and Bulldog tried to ignore the knots in their stomach as they parked the car and approached the group. Neither wanted to go, but felt it was his duty. Bulldog wondered why *his* stomach felt so anxious. 'This stinks. If anyone's there, *they* should be the ones who feel guilty, not us.'

Eric agreed. No one wanted to rat on a teammate, but players had to learn to be accountable. They all signed a commitment during their first football meeting stating that they would *not* drink alcohol, take drugs, or use tobacco. Both breathed a sigh of relief when they found only a few players harmlessly standing around a campfire, who willingly left with the captains.

Breaking in green freshmen was much more interesting. On the first day of conditioning, Bulldog looked like a drill sergeant eyeing a batch of fresh recruits. Chris Wingo caught his eye. His huge size instantly labeled him as a lineman. Wingo didn't even want to come, but couldn't back out when his classmates came to his house to pick him up. 'C'mon, you're coming with us.'

They were anxious rookies ready to be drafted into the Montrose Football tradition. Three years later, they became the `94 Varsity Rams, but needed Wingo, the biggest guy in their class, to be a part of their Freshmen Team.

The group of freshmen arrived to their first practice in typical freshmen style . . . *late,* but soon learned about accountability. Wingo watched players run 360's, full sprints around the football field. Wingo was a typical lineman, already bigger than most and hated to run. He watched one of the bigger senior players vomit then throw it at some guys and wondered, *What in the world have I got myself into?*

The disgusting senior player soon discovered that he didn't have what it took to endure the Montrose Football regimen, and quit before the season really started. Wingo was hooked by then, along with the other incoming freshmen. They listened in awe to the convincing head coach. 'Participating in this football program will be one of the most memorable experiences you will have in your life.'

Little did they know then, how true those words became.

Before school started, players learned about a new 'Pay to Play' program that required a one-time $75 fee. Even though the fee covered all sports for a year, coaches were concerned the fee would reduce the number of players coming out. *It didn't.* It actually increased with 32 players on Varsity, 22 on J.V., and enough freshmen to field a complete schedule.

Sean Unangst transferred to Montrose after Christmas of his junior year. Once he heard the buzz about Montrose Football, he wanted to be a part of it. He was an experienced soccer player, having played since the second grade, including three years on Varsity. Sean was a quiet type but made friends quickly once he started working out in the weight room. He hadn't played football since eighth grade and looked forward to the season. He felt confident that he could kick and wondered, *How hard could this be with someone holding the ball?*

As a senior rookie, Sean didn't know quite what to expect on his first day. Those first practices were tough. He tried to learn how to hit somebody without getting all of his 150 pounds knocked down at the same time. He knew his muscles would adjust if he could just get through two-a-days. Bulldog heard Sean mention that he could kick, so he held the ball and watched him boot it. His kicks confirmed it, and the challenge was on.

Sean was one of three guys who tried out for the kicker position. The threesome started from the 10 yard line, then added five yards after each round. Tony Beardsley got eliminated, but Crockett and Sean continued to kick from the 25. Crockett missed a few, so Sean became the PAT kicker. Bearsdley became the punter, since his foot was the only one that actually fit the special kicking shoe, and Crockett became the kickoff guy.

Bulldog recruited players to come to his house and bail hay between two-a-days. Some came because they wanted a new adventure, others because it was something to do. Whatever their reason, their youthful energy helped them endure an all day workout, passing the time until their first game.

Eric tried a new strategy for their home opener against **Byron** by hanging a Monroe St. Mary Catholic Central T-shirt in the locker room. He met two Monroe players at a pre-season camp at EMU and traded T-shirts. Initially, Eric felt that he should hate the Monroe guys, but after hanging out with them the first few days, he discovered they were pretty cool and became friends. Eric thought displaying the T-shirt would provide added motivation to win their first game. Instead, it became a scapegoat for their stifled anger. Seniors couldn't resist tearing it when they walked by. *Revenge felt sweet.*

Later, Eric walked by the T-shirt and couldn't believe how damaged it was. It wasn't the reaction he had expected, but he knew it raised their intensity level by the number of holes it now displayed.

Sean was told that whatever he did before the first game, he had to repeat before every game. He kept his plans to go to the mall after school with two other players for pizza from the food court. They stopped at each other's house on the way home to pick up their clothes before heading to the school, a ritual they repeated every Friday night.

Sean found a spot on the mat in the dark wrestling room with his teammates, who relaxed to the heavy acoustical jams of AC/DC. The music soaked under his skin, pumping him up in a wild way. He felt thrilled to be a part of the team and thought, *This scene is so different from anything I ever did before soccer games.*

Back in Black became their favorite. Players closed their eyes and thought about their first opponent -- Byron. Less than fifty feet away, a nervous head coach sat in his miniature, cluttered coach's office unsure of what to expect. The chances of going undefeated in '91 would be a challenge. The Rams graduated nine seniors that were First-Team All-League selections. Crockett was his only returning starter from that potent offense. The entire offensive line and three star running backs had to be replaced. He only hoped the seed was planted in the 16 returning lettermen and five starting defensive players.

Coach Reinhart entered the dark room first and turned on the lights, 'Let's go guys, listen up.'

The music was instantly cut and a serious mood engulfed the room. All eyes and ears focused when Coach Annese spoke. 'Tonight's a big night, the first game of the season. We've developed a good tradition and you need to live up to the expectations you've set for yourselves. You made a big commitment the last time you wore these uniforms. You've worked hard in the off-season in preparation for tonight. It all starts right here! Right now! We're not a major contender yet. We have to prove it on the field.'

Two of their captains led them on the field, then stopped under the goal post. Crockett and Bulldog looked at the bleachers, engulfed by the energy and vigor of the huge crowd. After two spectacular seasons, and anxious for a new one, the Montrose community came out in huge numbers to support its football team.

The warm September air rendered something special as the aroma of buttery popcorn mixed with the crispness of a fall evening. It said good-bye to summer and hello to football. It also held an intriguing wonder about their new opponents. The Byron Eagles made their first appearance in the GEC League after having played in the Mid-State Athletic Conference. With only one loss in two years, the Rams didn't know what to expect from their newest opponent.

Troy Andrews was pumped to be on the field after earning a spot on special teams. Determined to make the most of this chance, he grew anxious when Coach spoke before the kickoff team took the field. 'Now somebody go down there and put your hat on the ball and cause a fumble!'

Troy found his position, hardly able to control his adrenaline while he listened for the opening whistle. He literally took the direct words of Coach Annese and threw a tough hit, causing Byron to fumble. He couldn't contain his grin when the Rams lit up the scoreboard four plays later. Troy discovered that he already loved Varsity football

Sean took deep breaths before he kicked his right leg upward several times. While he stretched both his muscles and his nerves, he took another deep breath from the sideline. Trying to calm his first game jitters he told himself, *Act like you've done this a hundred times. Quit making a big deal about it. Just ignore everyone in the stands. Go out there and kick it!*

He took the field with the rest of the PAT gang, then marked off his steps. A final glance at D'ar signified that he was in position, ready to set the ball. Sean nodded that he was ready, then watched while the ball was hiked. D'ar's quick reflexes caught it then set it perfectly, just like they'd practiced for weeks. Sean was in motion, totally focused on the position of his steps, and didn't notice that his tackle went the wrong way and didn't block his guy.

Sean was caught off-guard . . . everything happened so fast. He wanted to make a good impression on his first PAT, but before he could audible he got hacked hard and thought, *I never took a blow like that in soccer.* Bulldog helped him up, 'Welcome to Varsity Football.'

D'ar gave Sean a supporting glance while they listened to the tackle get chewed out. Later in the half, D'ar generated some excitement when he picked-up a first down on a fake punt that led to Crockett's second TD. It gave the Rams a 14-0 cushion. Byron's first mistake led to a poor first half, which forced them to punt three times and rack up 30 penalty yards.

Bowen proved how exceptionally quick he was at guard. He could be across the line of scrimmage before his opposing tackle even moved. The coaches actually pegged him as a running back after discovering his speed during track. But Bowen didn't want to be the center of attention. He liked using his quickness at guard and didn't want to worry about fumbling the ball. Bowen didn't need the glory of handling the ball or scoring touchdowns; he just wanted to hit somebody.

D'ar caught Crockett's short pass then rambled 30 yards for a third quarter TD, igniting the crowd. Byron scored from one yard out late in the third, but in the fourth all they could manage was a fumble, a punt, a loss of downs, and an interception.

Coach Roger Bashor's Eagles pursued the ball well, making it tough for the Rams to get loose around them. The Rams finally broke a big play with just over six minutes left in the game. Crockett ran around the right side for 35 yards to score the final TD ending the game '28-7.'

When the team gathered on Sunday to watch their first game film of the season, they felt like unwanted stepchildren. Criticism was dispensed by the handfuls. Even the most dedicated juniors experienced how much quicker Varsity level was. Tackle Vaughn Paxton seemed to become the scapegoat. He listened while they picked on him for being 'lazy' and 'not quick enough' on the line. Vaughn played along and tried to act tough, but it bothered him when the team labeled the film, *Vaughn on Vacation.* Vaughn was a quiet-natured guy; the biggest guy on the team at 240 pounds. He loved to talk, but quickly learned that excuses went on deaf ears. He felt compelled to step up real quick and made up his mind right then. *No one would laugh at Vaughn Paxton again!*

D'ar had a great game, but the junior remained quiet and humble, while absorbing the criticism being dished out. The Rams observed just how green they were. They had penalties, fumbled too many times, and put themselves in harms way more than once. The defense didn't look all that bad, but the offense didn't move the ball very consistently. They paid for it during practice.

Game two fell on Friday the 13th when the Rams faced the powerful **Chesaning Indians.** The two teams hadn't met since 1988 -- the contest held big stakes. The Detroit Free Press ranked Montrose *first* in the State in Class B and Chesaning *second* in Class BB.

Chesaning won their season opener and planned to defend their eighth straight MMB League Championship, while Montrose held the GEC Championship for three consecutive years. Chesaning appeared loaded, while Montrose appeared to be down compared to their past two seasons.

Players already developed superstitions for Friday night pre-game rituals. Barry Gross went home after school and ate spaghetti, then went downstairs, put his pads on, and jammed to AC/DC.

Bulldog drove home after school, grinning the moment he opened the back door. The alluring aroma of garlic bread and cheesy lasagna stirred his senses. It was a tradition that his mom started a year ago. She never questioned her son's superstition, just agreed to her end of the bargain to have lasagna ready on Fridays by 2:45 PM.

D'ar teased the lineman, 'How can you eat such heavy food before a game?'

The 215 pound lineman only laughed. When you bench 385 pounds they don't tease for long. The second part of Bulldog's ritual was to buy a 16 ounce Coke in a cup of ice at Mr. G's. He drove through town twice while Hank Williams Jr. vibrated from his cassette; a tradition he started in '90 and needed to continue. Bulldog liked to arrive at the school early to bridge the idle time before the game. After putting his shoulder pads on, he grabbed his cup of ice and found his usual spot in the dark wrestling room. He closed his eyes as the music switched to rock, and became lost in the crashing chords of AC/DC.

Vaughn's house was located directly across the street from the football field. His living room had a close view of the south goal post. When he walked into the street to make the short hike to the school, Tim Follett stopped his car. 'Hey Vaughn, want a lift?'

Vaughn shook his head, 'No Thanks. You gave me one last week and I played awful.'

They both laughed and mutually agreed to ignore the first game tradition rule.

No one wanted to miss the Chesaning game, especially Led and Newt who were now roommates at SVSU. They were paying their dues as college freshmen on the Cardinal's football team. Led earned a spot on special teams. The rookie was supposed to stay on campus Friday night to watch a movie with his new teammates and relax before Saturday's game. Even as exciting as it was to play college football, the former players felt the magnetic pull to come home on Friday night to support the Montrose Rams. Led did something he normally wouldn't do, and lied to his new coach. It was just a small lie about his grandparents being in town (which was true), but he neglected to mention his plans to attend the Montrose-Chesaning football game.

Led and Newt made the 45 minute drive back to Montrose and waited for Ricky Diem (a teammate from the '89 Team), to pick them up. The threesome headed south on Seymour Road toward M-57 when Led said, 'Hey, take the back way and avoid the traffic heading to Chesaning.'

They wanted to arrive early and watch the Rams warm-up. After they backtracked to Farrand Road, they headed north a mile to Lake Road, parallel to M-57. Led sat in the passenger's side of Rick's GrandAm as they headed west on the bumpy, gravel road. Led was too hot and started to take his coat off, as they approached the intersection of Lake and Duffield. He slid his right sleeve off, then unhooked his seat belt to take out the left. In that brief moment, before he had a chance to latch his seat belt, a northbound driver approached the country crossing, ignoring the stop sign. Led glanced up just as they reached the intersection. His eyes widened and his heart rate exploded seconds before the driver's side of the GrandAm got blind-sided.

The impact forced the frame on the driver's door partially open, throwing Led's body crossways to the driver's side, then jammed his head between the frame and the door. The impact knocked him out cold; he was totally unaware of the mess he was in. It all happened so fast, without warning. Ricky was in a daze after his head hit the steering wheel. Newt was alone in the back seat and felt his body take a strong jerk from the impact. He was a little groggy himself, but the strong linebacker managed to climb over the seat and escape from the passenger side window.

Shit.

He tried to think straight as the adrenaline rush caused his heart to race even faster. He jumped up and ran away from the wreck, circling the car in a panic. *Oh man, tell me this isn't happening.*

Newt looked at two of his closest friends. *Just a minute ago they were talking and laughing and now look at them!* He tried to help Led but his head was wedged. He yelled at his unconscious friend, 'LED, WAKE-UP!'

He yelled at Ricky, who was pinned between Led and the steering wheel, 'Are you okay? Are you okay Rick? Led? Can you guys even hear me?'

Ricky managed a faint 'Help us.'

Newt was their only hope; he tried to focus so he could think straight. He looked at Ricky, 'What do we do man? Led is messed up!'

Newt didn't know if Led was even still alive, and Ricky seemed totally helpless. 'I'll get you out Led. I'll get you out buddy. Just hang in there.'

Newt was strong but Ricky wondered, *Could he possibly move the frame?* It could have been a feature from the TV series, *That's Incredible*, when average human beings performed abnormal tasks in emergency situations that saved lives. A higher power must've looked over the former Rams that night. Newt couldn't explain how he suddenly possessed incredible strength and was able to pull back the car's steel frame to relieve Led's jammed head.

Time stood still.

Seconds felt like hours until the emergency crews arrived. Newt monitored his unconscious friend, while the rescue squad worked on all three of them. Led wasn't moving and looked as pale as a Michigander in February. Newt thought he was dead. Just three months earlier, Led stood at the podium during commencement as their class valedictorian, appearing larger than life. It was too early for his life to end. The EMT's attached neck braces to all three of the boys, then loaded them on stretchers and rushed them to the hospital. The piercing shrill of the ambulance siren shot an alarming sensation through Newt's body. *So much for making it to the Chesaning game!*

Police surveyed the accident, wondering how Newt ever possessed the incredible strength that normally required the Jaws of Life. The men on the rescue squad were also local football fans. They stood vigil and guarded the endzone on Friday nights, hoping their services were not required. The grown men were shaken to see former football heroes injured, and silently prayed for a speedy recovery.

It didn't take long for the alarming news to travel to Chesaning's football field. Montrose fans located girlfriends and family members who rushed to the hospital; those left behind had a difficult time concentrating on the game.

The Rams on the field were unaware of the accident while they intently listened to Coach Annese build up the rivalry. 'Chesaning didn't play us the last two years because they thought Montrose couldn't compete with them anymore. You'll be walking around ten years from now and run into these same Chesaning players. Do you want THEM to rub it in your face? DO YOU? Or . . . do you want to show THEM what YOU can do!'

The Rams came unglued when they took the field; their adrenaline flowed like wild fire. Coach kept them alive after Chesaning scored half way through the opening quarter. Montrose countered and marched 62 yards before Beardsley scored on a one yard plunge in the waning seconds of the first.

Sean felt the pressure to make the PAT; he tried to control his nerves. He thought about the comments from guys in the locker room, *If we beat Chesaning, we'll be in the playoffs for sure.* It only intensified his pressure. Sean felt it was all up to him, and realized extra points could make or break a close game. When he ran on the field his brain repeated, *Oh man,* realizing he needed to calm down. He closed his eyes and tuned everything out; *the crowd, the band, and the fact that the last time we played Chesaning - we lost.* Sean only concentrated on the hike, then the set until his foot firmly met leather. It felt *on* as soon as the ball left his foot, his eyes cautiously trailed the piece of leather as it soared toward the goal post. His parents held their breath in the stands. Sean waited until both refs raised their striped arms upright before he breathed a sigh of relief and thought, *I did it!*

The Rams went ahead 7-6, but Chesaning regained the lead halfway through the second period. Scott Powell was still learning the linebacker position against a tough team. He became frustrated after failing to intercept a pass that he thought he had. During the series Coach Destrampe yelled to Annese, 'I don't think Powell's ready yet, give me Troy.'

Powell greatly improved at the position and earned the name of 'Silent Killer,' but that night junior Troy Andrews made his debut beyond special teams. Troy's heart raced when Coach D called his name. He tried not to panic while listening to his inner voice attempt to convince him. *You wanted more action, now here's your chance. You practiced this position. You know it well. You're ready.*

Spectators watched two totally different offenses and defenses battle it out. Both teams showed why they had dominated their respective leagues for so long by having gutsy comebacks after each play.

It was junior Rob Schlicht's second game as the Rams center. 'Schlichster' tried to block out the roaring crowd while ignoring the accelerated heart rate throbbing in his throat. He tried to focus on the snap . . . and thought he saw movement. The center felt that he had to go, and nervously snapped the ball on the count of 'one' instead of 'two' and missed the nose guard.

The local broadcaster gave Schlichster the benefit of the doubt when he announced, 'Maybe he was trying to throw Chesaning offside.'

But Crockett knew better; so did the coaches. Montrose barely managed to get the first down before Crockett came unglued. He slapped Schlichster's helmet in their next huddle; a common reaction after anyone screwed up. His leadership abilities made him look like he was the coach on the field instead of the quarterback. Schlichster gave Crockett his full attention when he yelled, 'Get outta here! Just get outta here!'

Schlichster got the quarterback's message loud and clear. They all did. Crockett built fear into the soul of each player; he expected them to play at a certain caliber. The experience he gained as a quarterback in `90 was valuable, and caught the eye of a few Division I scouts. The offense respected their quarterback, but relied on him more then they should to make the big plays.

Crockett led the Rams on an 80 yard drive that covered 14 plays. It was time to release *The Bomb,* which Crockett threw to his favorite target – D'ar. It was a little off, forcing D'ar to make a diving catch that the Indians argued was a trap.

The call was overruled. The All-State Quarterback snuck in from a yard out with only seconds remaining in the half. John Diem grabbed the conversion to put the Rams back on top with a 15-12 half-time edge.

The game was dangerously close, triggering everyone to be on pins and needles. The coaching staff felt sick after learning about the accident during the intermission. The bond they developed with former players was still very strong. Just a week earlier, Led and Newt confided how much they missed Montrose Football. They both liked college ball but missed the closeness between coaches and players and the honesty their brotherhood held. It was different at the next level and they had to adjust. Their new teammates seemed to play an underlying game of cutthroat when they competed for positions. Montrose Football became even more special once they were no longer an active part of it.

Now coaches wondered, *What would happen to them?* Annese and Reinhart felt like surrogate fathers to both Led and Newt, and prayed they made it through. Like worried parents, coaches wanted good things to happen to the kids they attempted to mold and motivate. The coaches realized it would be even harder to focus on the game and decided to inform players about the accident afterward. With only a three point lead, the Rams had enough on their minds.

Annese looked at his exhausted team in the locker room. He expected a tough game, probably the toughest the Rams would face during the regular season. The fatigued line was exhausted and needed the intermission to rest. Bulldog felt like the Rams couldn't stop the Indians, but it was a two-way street. While he rested, the lineman got a brain wave for the second half.

Bulldog started talking crazy stuff on the line. Both teams quickly began shooting names back and forth about their mammas and their sisters. It eased the pressure of the game for the line, until Bulldog topped it off with his next move. He created a distraction by forcing himself to vomit just as the ball was snapped. Football always gave him a nervous stomach; hurling had become the lineman's trademark. His opponent looked up just as Bulldog popped him with the aftermath of his distraction, or *was that lasagna smeared on his uniform?* Whatever it was . . . it was gross. The successful distraction made Bulldog chuckle on his way to the huddle. *Yeah, that was a good one!*

Chesaning used its depth of running seven backs to keep their energy fresh. It was an emotional tug-of-war, a good old-fashioned dogfight. Neither team scored during the third quarter. Eric tried so hard to turn it around when he intercepted a pass, but he couldn't hold on. He regretted it even more when Chesaning muscled in from the four in the final stanza to move ahead 15-18.

The Rams were dead tired when Annese repeatedly told them, 'Just suck it up fellas. We're not done yet.'

The undiscouraged Rams moved 66 yards on 10 plays. They ran the veer on the opposite side that Scott Bowen played. Crockett watched Bowen run across to the linebacker, then push him the entire way to the endzone. Crockett jumped Bowen in the next huddle, 'What the hell are you doing?'

D'ar was determined to score regardless of his torn quad that he pulled during two-a-days. Because he never gave it sufficient time to heal, it took its toll when the Indians tried to wear him down. D'ar took advantage of the huge hole the line made when he sprinted in from 11 yards out. Sean felt confident when he took the field and successfully kicked the PAT. With just over three minutes left in the game, Montrose was up 22-18. Everyone wondered, *Could the Rams keep the lead?*

Chesaning returned the punt, then drove the ball on the inside, gaining three yards at a time. They were on the 50 yard line when Bulldog looked at the scoreboard. *Ninety seconds.* That was an eternity to a lineman in a close game. Crazy, murmured sounds no longer came from the linemen, only labored breathing between brief gaps in the quarterback's cadence. Strong grunts of sheer determination followed before the bump-and-grind of contact, causing both teams to fight with everything they had left, trying to wear each other down.

They battled all night long, keeping the game close and within reach. Twelve plays and 70 yards later, the Indians thought they were in. After a controversial call, the officials said Chesaning was stopped at the one foot line. Coach Sager was furious and called an offensive timeout for Chesaning with :30 seconds left. The defense supported each other in the huddle. Bulldog thought about their 26 game-winning streak. *I don't want to lose this game. I can't let former players down. How could I face them if we lost? I have to stop them. I have to!'*

They lined backed up, patiently waiting for the snap. The Rams proved they were disciplined. Just as they extensively rehearsed, no one moved early. Chesaning called a second timeout as they played mind games with the Rams. They refocused during the huddle, determined to hold Chesaning with total commitment. The united Rams heard Troy yell, 'No one will go offside. No one will quit!'

When their huddle broke up, Bulldog glanced at the clock again. *Thirty seconds.* The lineman tuned out the noise from the screaming fans, and focused on Chesaning's quarterback instead. When his voice called out the play, Bulldog tried to ignore the pressure of his heavy heartbeat as he crouched on the line. Everything seemed to roll out in slow motion. He drove his head forward as sweat flew from his beat red face. The Indians ran a bootleg, but got stopped by the Rams when Alan McDonald turned him outside then Gross smashed him for a loss on the 12 yard line.

Chesaning had :15 seconds left and one more timeout. Everyone wondered, *Could the Rams hold them one last time?*

A fatigued Montrose defense grasped hands when they huddled, united in a critical moment. Bulldog tried to catch his breath and get a pulse on their attitude as he shifted his deep blue eyes from one sweaty face to another. He gained confidence from the determination stained on their faces. At that moment, he knew the Rams had the strength for a final goal line stand. Bulldog found his place on the line, took a deep breath, then listened.

The play broke out and the stubborn Montrose defense stepped up. Gross felt his rapid heart rate increase as the moment intensified. He never took his eyes off the ball and started to cover his tight end, while closely watching the quarterback. He acted like he was going to run it, but Gross followed his gut reaction and ran as fast as he could. Just when the quarterback faked a handoff to the back and planned to run up the gut, Gross made a game-winning sack on the two yard line to keep their 27 game winning streak alive . . . *by two yards.*

A jampile formed near the endzone toward the sideline with Eric on the bottom. Eric and Beardsley felt the weight of the pile increase as it grew. Bowen played tackle on the last play and tripped an Indian player before he got stepped on, then fell on the pile. Bowen looked down at Beardsleys' bulging eyes then heard him yell, 'GET OFF ME!'

Bowen tried to push himself off, but couldn't move due to the crushing weight of so many bodies piled on top. The Rams on the sideline watched the scoreboard tick down . . . three . . . two . . . one . . . BUZZ.

Ecstatic Montrose coaches rushed the field. Annese grabbed Gross and jumped in celebration. Reinhart excitedly grabbed Scott Powell by his facemask. Their heads collided in the commotion and broke his glasses, which cut his forehead and splattered blood down his face. Coach was so elated that he didn't feel any pain, even though the cut required stitches. It was worth it.

Moaning rose from the pile. Coach Keith Williams feared the jampile was becoming dangerous and started peeling players off. He wasn't concerned about anyone taking cheap shots, but was worried about the guys on the bottom. They were all bushed and couldn't move very fast. Coach Williams pulled Bowen off Beardsley, then finally reached Eric at the bottom of the pile. Each player felt like dead weight. Their limp, exhausted bodies were too tired to move, but they were thrilled that Montrose came out the winner in the non-league dogfight.

True athletes have an unspoken mutual respect for each other after such a physical battle. When both teams lined up to shake hands, it was difficult to tell which team actually won. The hard-hitting game coupled by the grueling heat, made it too draining to celebrate.

A very happy and relieved Coach Annese huddled his team together in the middle of the field, complimenting them for not knowing the word *quit.* They were too dog-tired to talk for long so Annese kept it short. 'This was a classic. It was like two heavyweight boxers battling in the center of the ring …Tradition vs. Tradition … a great battle! It seemed almost fitting that it took the clock to run out to stop one of us.'

Fatigued Rams kept their tradition by walking two-by-two with hands locked, from the middle of the field through the goal post. They continued their march to the team bus. Eric walked with John Diem who usually wasn't very vocal. But that night he couldn't stop talking. 'This is unbelievable; this is just the greatest feeling in the world.'

The level of emotion was difficult to hide or ignore. Their legs felt like rubber, causing them to drop like wounded soldiers when they reached the team bus. Eric's dad searched the numbers on the battlefield until he found his fatigued son -- #33. He expected Eric to be elated, but his son had depleted every ounce of energy. 'Dad, I'm so glad it's over. I couldn't take one more step. I just couldn't go.'

The Rams didn't feel very glorious as they laid on their backs, allowing weariness to seep into their drenched jerseys. They felt even more drained after learning about the pre-game accident. That bus ride home was filled with strange and confusing emotions, as the dark night absorbed everything that happened. The news about the accident downplayed the thrill of their close victory. The seniors were tight with their injured friends, and felt apprehensive about their outcome. They were all young and felt immortal;

accidents and death were topics they never thought about. The horrible realization that someone they personally knew could die haunted them, while they silently prayed for Led, Newt, and Ricky.

Later that night, Newt was released from the hospital with a neck brace. Ricky left with a bruised body but Led had to stay until Sunday. Like Newt, he had to wear a neck brace for two weeks. The threesome appeared to come out without too much physical damage, but the accident made a significant emotional impact on their college careers. Football hopes were dismantled when SVSU gave Led a medical red-shirt. It was more extreme for Newt, whose back would never be the same. He couldn't give football 100%; just lifting weights was extremely painful. Even though he appeared to fare the best from the accident, it sadly brought an end to his college football career.

Schlichster paid for missing that critical count at practice on Monday; his teammates provoked him to be the first to finish every drill. The center felt numb halfway through practice, but kept going when the team set up for the next drill. They worked on his reaction time until it became second nature. Every time they ran the drill, Schlichster snapped the ball. Defenders were already in the gap before he snapped, making him work twice as hard to block them. No one cut him any slack as one fresh player after another went against him. Schlichster pushed himself like never before, drawing energy from their hard core tactics. He was a proud, bruised and sweaty lineman who didn't need to score points. He only wanted to hike the ball, block on cue, and hit somebody. When he felt like he couldn't go anymore, his subconscious repeated the words of Coach Annese, *You can be the best center Montrose ever had.* His inner voice continued to repeat the phrase, allowing the thought to become his personal goal.

Coach Annese praised them after practice for playing so tough against Chesaning. He always made an effort to acknowledge one player who stood out. That time, he threw the football to Sean. 'If you hadn't made the extra points we could've lost the game.'

Sean soaked in the praise and wondered if anyone recognized just how nervous he was during that game. He tested himself under pressure . . .*and he passed.*

Montrose didn't want any more close games. It created intensity when they took the field against **Lake Fenton**. Crockett looked like a one man wrecking crew after he booted the ball on kickoff, then made the tackle when the Blue Devils ran it back. Unfortunately, Crockett looked like the one who got smashed in the process. The impact flipped him in the air before thrusting him hard against the ground. Crockett didn't appear to be knocked out for any amount of time, so the intensity of his collision went unnoticed by the coaches, who sent him on the field with the offense.

The strange looks from his teammates didn't register in the quarterback's mind, as they reacted to his off-the-wall comments in the huddle. Crockett was 7 for 15 passing and managed to handoff to D'ar, Eric, and Beardsley. But Eric thought something was strange when Crockett gave him a quick nod, like he always did after calling a play in the huddle, except that time he never called the play. He just nodded.

Coach Annese didn't realize how foggy Crockett was, until he went the wrong way on a few plays. But when he took the field with the defense, Annese realized that his head got rattled on the opening kickoff, and pulled him out.

When the coaches analyzed the game film afterwards, they noticed how Crockett's body went limp, appearing to lose control when he flipped in the air; a good indication of a concussion. The coaches wondered how he pulled off the game as good as he did. Crockett was more experienced than in '90; the extra time he devoted during the off-season developed his skills. He already displayed great ability and made good decisions. Even when he was in a fog, he managed to help the Rams to a '36-6' victory over Lake Fenton.

Varsity players wondered who the brave soul was that showboated in the endzone at the **New Lothrop** J.V. game. They discovered it was Eddie Howell. Varsity players looked at each other and laughed. 'Man Beardsley, you better tell your little brother about the rules. If Coach Annese saw us do that, we'd be in deep shit!'

As if on queue, their head coach appeared from the press box, then stomped from one bleacher to the next. The hollow echo between each step displayed just how pissed off he really was. Annese found Eddie on the sideline and, in his own theatrical way, chewed on him in front of everyone. Players were given a 'Code of Conduct' at the start of the season that explained unacceptable behavior. The Varsity could laugh when it happened to underclassmen, because they knew the entire J.V. Team would run gassers for it. Under their laughter, the squad comprehended the message, and would think twice before they showboated in the endzone.

A few of the Varsity players didn't think twice about pulling a prank on the Hornets. Crockett, Bulldog, and Scott Powell decided to sneak over to New Lothrop's field and have some fun. They nailed wooden crosses in various places on the field, assuming the strong Catholic community might find it amusing.

They didn't.

Montrose wondered what to expect from the New Lothrop Hornets since they had a new coaching staff. Annese warned his Varsity to keep their guard up. New Lothrop's first year head coach played football with both Annese and Reinhart at Alma College. Egos were on the line.

The Rams made a couple of early turnovers, but once they settled in, they dominated by scoring in every quarter. Crockett and Hyde starred for the Rams on offense, while Powell and Bulldog led the way on defense. They kept their coaches' egos in check by claiming a '40-6' victory.

The Rams were anxious to take on **Goodrich,** who had just lost to Byron. Their loss ended the showdown hype between the unbeatens for a fourth year. Annese didn't want his Rams becoming overconfident after the newspapers favored Montrose as the 'best in the GEC League.' They were only half way through the season; he wanted the Rams playing for first place.

Jeff Klopf tried to dodge the team's midnight curfew over the weekend, but the J.V. quarterback was busted. On Monday, the J.V. Coaches offered the team two options: the entire J.V. Team could run gassers with Jeff and let him play on Thursday, or Jeff could absorb his punishment alone and not play at all. The J.V. Team chose *not* to run. Jeff couldn't hide his disappointment when his teammates confessed, 'Don't take it personal Jeff, we just hate running gassers.'

It wasn't worth it, even at the expense of losing their first string quarterback. Jeff lived for football and felt awful that he wouldn't be able to play in the Goodrich J.V. game.

Disaster appeared to strike on the Varsity practice field, changing the game plan. Crockett went down hard on his ankle and didn't get up. Annese realized the severity of Crockett's injury, and felt doubtful that he'd be ready by Friday. Goodrich was hungry to beat Montrose and create a three-way tie for first place. Montrose beat Goodrich the last nine seasons, and only allowed two TD's during the past four years. Goodrich wanted revenge. Annese knew Goodrich would take full advantage of their quarterback's key injury, especially since Crockett was the League's highest scorer.

Montrose needed a quick back-up plan since Crockett would be hard to replace. Led was off to college and the Varsity didn't have an experienced reserve. Annese approached the J.V. coaches, informing them of Crockett's ankle. Coach watched Jeff at practice for awhile then announced, 'I want Jeff to train with the Varsity in case Crockett isn't ready by Friday.'

It placed the J.V. Coaches in an awkward position since Jeff was ineligible for missing curfew. It wasn't a school rule that was violated; it was a football rule that the coaches took seriously. If they agreed, Annese would break the very rule that he developed. So the J.V. Coaches compromised. Varsity could have Jeff on one condition -- the *entire* Varsity ran the gassers that the J.V. Team vetoed.

Coach Annese wouldn't even consider it. The master of psychology had a hunch that Jeff would already have his hands full trying to be accepted as a sophomore quarterback – the only sophomore on the team. He knew asking his Varsity to run additional gassers after the extra hard practices wouldn't fly. The team was in a predicament so he used his judgment as the head coach and made an exception. Annese overruled, but not without reparation.

Jeff wanted to crawl in a hole by the time Coach Annese finished his lecture about breaking curfew. Coach made Jeff feel so low for doing something so stupid, then turned around and built him up like he was the most important person in the world. Jeff concealed his emotions in front of everyone, but he really wanted to scream -- *Wow. Here's my chance to play starting quarterback on Varsity!* He was thrilled for his lucky break and didn't mind running his gassers - *alone.*

Schlichster practiced snapping the ball to Jeff, but didn't feel confident in their handoff. Jeff grabbed the ball differently than Crockett. Schlichster became frustrated when he hit his fingers on the release and caused fumbles. Jeff pulled out faster, throwing the center's timing off. Annese needed the twosome to gel quickly and tighten up their exchange by Friday. Coach made them stay an extra 30 minutes to practice the snap, over and over, until they adjusted to each other.

Coach Annese brought Crockett home that night to keep his ankle iced. Several Division I colleges had their eye on the Montrose starting quarterback, who didn't have a clear focus of what he wanted to do after football. The quarterback was full of life, but handled it on a day-by-day basis. He needed more structure. Annese knew Crockett had the natural talent, so he exercised his position as a coach to personally go that extra mile to help him maximize it. Crockett had a rough home life, even though his mom tried her best. He often got involved in things he shouldn't, bringing inner city life to their small, rural town.

Annese often brought Crockett to his home during his senior year. The quarterback felt comfortable there and enjoyed the attention. Chris Annese was a smart career woman. Players thought that she maintained a coolness to some, but she had simply outgrown high school jocks and their boyish tactics. She had a finance degree and was the school's business manager. No one could label her as unsupportive. She did a lot of work behind the scenes to contribute to the team's success, which included nursing sprained ankles. Crockett appreciated that she iced his ankle throughout the night, in an effort to keep the swelling down.

Annese asked Bulldog to spend time with Crockett on the weekends to keep him away from temptations. Bulldog made sure Crockett got home safely and stayed out of trouble. Crockett and Bulldog had been friends since Bulldog moved to Montrose in the second grade. Crockett told him on the very first day of school, 'I'll be your best friend.'

Bulldog went home and told his mom; 'He's dark. Is that okay?'

She smiled, 'Of course son.'

Crockett had become a familiar face at the Sullivan home through the years. Now Bulldog was able to repay the favor years later when Crockett needed someone.

After five years, Annese had long grown into the head coach position. He realized that his job intertwined with the personal lives of his players. Even though Montrose was a typical, small midwestern town, it had its share of dysfunctional families that created victims out of otherwise normal teenagers. The majority of his players came from typical families with two working parents; the ones that didn't needed him in a different way. Coach Annese fulfilled the father role they lacked at home; he became the person they sought advice from. Whatever their story was, he did what he could to help them deal with their situation. He helped kids that came from divorced families, had deceased fathers, dads with drinking problems, or mean stepfathers. Even kids from traditional families experienced emotional roller coasters from typical girlfriend or academic problems. Outside influences always seemed to linger around the locker room. It didn't take Annese long to realize that his job went far beyond coaching the game of football.

While Crockett slept on Annese's couch, Coach sat at his kitchen table writing a letter to boost Jeff's confidence. Annese knew his back-up quarterback had great potential, but he needed to prepare Jeff mentally. The pressures at the Varsity level would be different from what he was used to.

Coach found Jeff before school started on Thursday, and handed him the letter. Jeff took a seat in his first class, then anxiously opened the envelope, unsure of what to expect. He read the top of the paper, which listed the run and pass plays he routinely used on J.V.

PLAYS FOR KLOPF

RUN	PASS
38 & 39 veer	sprint 805 and 905
38 & 39 load	boot 807 and 907
36 & 37 wham	216 – 5-7 throwback
42 & 43 trap	117 – 5-7 throwback
12 & 13	200 screen middle
12 & 13 iso	200 screen left
12 & 13 opp.	
18 & 19 lead	
18 & 19 chopper	
16 & 17 C.T.	

* HOW YOU WILL LEAD US TO VICTORY *

1) Stay within yourself: You are very capable of running all these plays with perfect execution. That is why we spend all summer working on these plays. Be yourself and we will win.

2) Confidence: You can look at this situation and react in two ways. A loser would worry about failing and hope he doesn't 'screw up'. A winner would take advantage of this opportunity, realizing that he has prepared diligently for this chance and would prove to everyone he is a winner. I believe you are a WINNER.

3) Minimize Mistakes. You should have a goal that you will not commit a turnover. Our quarterback this year has yet to achieve this goal. When you do make a mistake, respond positively. Do not dwell on it. Be perfect on the next play.

4) Have Fun. I'm looking forward to this situation with enthusiasm. I am very confident that you will do tremendously well. I have had all-conference quarterbacks three seasons in a row and I honestly believe that you are the best quarterback I've ever had.

Let the Jeff Klopf era begin!

Each time Jeff read the letter, he felt an excited wave of self-assurance. He read the last sentence over and over. What a compliment. Especially since he might fill the shoes of the likes of Corey Crockett who was All-State in '90 and Goose who had a tremendous three-year stretch.

Concentrating on classes all day became difficult. Jeff continued to read his letter over and over, wanting to believe all of it. By the end of the day he had the letter memorized, word for word. Pre-game butterflies kicked in and Jeff wondered, *Could I really do this tomorrow night?*

The team ran through plays during their pre-game practice. Jeff was at the helm; Crockett was on the sideline. Whenever the play didn't go as planned, Jeff recited the letter in his head, reassuring his confidence to jump back in. He didn't want to blow his chance. He hardly slept at all that Thursday night, thinking about Friday's game.

Neither did Eric. He felt so terrible when his alarm blared Friday morning, he'd forgotten it was game day. He pulled the warm blankets over his chilled body and rolled over. His entire body ached. After a few minutes he realized it was Goodrich day, which only made him feel worse. He forced his weak body to stand up and walk around the room, trying to convince himself that he wasn't sick or dizzy. It didn't help. Without a doubt, the flu had the best of him. Eric barely had the strength to stumble back to the comforts of his own bed, where he could sleep a few more hours and still be eligible to play. It was his only option at the time, so he closed his eyes and hoped for a quick recovery.

Hours later, Eric still felt very weak but managed to drag himself through the last half of school. He wasn't about to let the flu interfere with the Goodrich game. *No way.* Eric went home after school and slept some more, in an attempt to tame his fever. His mom made his standing Friday night spaghetti supper, but Eric didn't have an appetite. In spite of his pigheaded superstition, the slight thought of eating spaghetti made him nauseous. He settled for dry toast instead. The last time he missed eating spaghetti before a game was 'Monroe;' he hoped it wasn't a premonition of what the night could bring.

His dad took one look at Eric and didn't think his son could even make the hour bus ride to Goodrich, let alone play. But something magical happened when players donned the red and black; making them forget about sickness, injuries, or any of their personal problems. Only one thing rested on their mind . . . *winning.*

Jeff's stomach turned somersaults when he looked out of the bus window. The entire ride to Goodrich, the young quarterback felt the weight of the world on his shoulders. He couldn't remember the last time he felt so anxious about anything. Jeff went through the motions as the team completed pre-game stretches, trying to mentally prepare himself. He noticed that Crockett dressed for the game, but was told it was 'for show only,' to keep Goodrich off-guard.

The entire team lacked confidence with Jeff at the helm; they were used to following Crockett's lead. In their eyes, Jeff was just a sophomore. Contrary to the rest of the team, Jeff actually felt self-assured by game time. He only needed to prove it to the team. On the first play of the game, Jeff ran a 38 veer. He earned a small morsel of confidence after gaining 10 yards, but the rest of the team didn't feel it and Montrose surrendered the down. With just over two minutes left in the opening quarter, Goodrich scored on a one yard run. The Rams were pissed when the scoreboard flaunted 'Visitors 0 -- Home 8.' They sputtered without Crockett at the helm, which increased Jeff's nervousness. He did a respectable job leading the team for a 61 yard gain on the ground and passed for 11. But the offense didn't block well and the defense looked flat. Their lack of confidence in Jeff became obvious to everyone. Annese felt outright disappointed in all of them. His Rams looked like a different team.

Jeff recognized the squad's reluctance to trust him, and repeated the words from the letter. Maybe he felt more confident than the shakiness in his voice revealed. Bowen sensed the uncertainty from the guys on the line. When the huddle broke up, he told the rookie quarterback, 'C'mon Jeff, calm down.'

The foggy weather blew a cool mist that sprinkled a chill over the spectators. Players concentrated so intensely on the close game, that the damp weather went unnoticed. One of the coaches noticed how sweaty and pasty Eric looked in the huddle. When he returned to the sideline, he yelled, 'Eric looks like he's dead out there.'

The head coach yelled back, 'Leave him alone, he's got the flu.'

Annese approached Crockett on the sideline, 'How's that ankle feeling?'

'I'm ready to give it a shot Coach.'

Crockett iced and rested his ankle most of the week and wanted to play. He felt ready. As if someone flipped a switch, the Rams stepped up their level of play the moment Crockett stepped on the field. Players didn't even realize the transition; they were simply conditioned to respond to him. Crockett had an unspoken expectation for all of them to perform at a higher level. If they didn't, he was in their face.

With seconds left in the half, Crockett led them on a 38 yard drive, then snuck in from the one. Beardsley's two-point conversion tied the game 8-8 at the intermission. The Rams were relieved to be on the board, but were not excited about their half-time meeting. Scott Powell felt his heart race when they walked to the locker room. He knew they were going to get their butts chewed out. *They did.*

Crockett started the second half, allowing his senior leadership to spark the offense. He snuck in again from a yard out just as the third quarter ended. Eric completely forgot about the flu when he used a burst of energy to bolt through the endzone for the two-point conversion. The Rams went up 16-8.

Montrose dominated the second half under Crockett's emotional leadership, and prevented Goodrich from getting a first down. Crockett was great at concealing the football. He faked a handoff to D'ar, then fleeted down the sideline as his long legs made great strides. He totally faked out the officials who followed D'ar, not Crockett, and blew the whistle when the play stopped. D'ar jumped up and pointed at Crockett in the endzone, 'He's got the ball!'

Schlichster looked up from his ground view and saw Crockett in the endzone frantically waving his arms with the ball held high. 'Hey, I'm over here. I just scored!'

It was too late. The referee openly botched that call when his inadvertent whistle stopped the play. The embarrassed official listened to a rowdy, displeased Montrose crowd uttering their two cents about 'his eyesight' and how 'he should pay attention' to the game. Needless to say, Annese came unglued. The score was too close to give up a TD.

Goodrich moved the ball down the field when D'ar spurted through and grabbed an interception to stop their drive at the 30. It was a huge play for the Rams, which Crockett capitalized with a game-winning TD. Eric scored another to seal a very important '23-8' win on the road.

Jeff joined the Varsity on Sunday to critique the game film. When the team watched Jeff on film, they realized that *he* didn't play bad at all; *they* did. The squad rightfully felt embarrassed that they didn't step up and work as a team, and discovered they didn't give their back-up quarterback a fair chance.

After films, Jeff prepared to go outside with the team to run through a few drills and take a few laps. Coach Annese grabbed his arm, 'Hey Jeff, what are you doing? You don't need to run with the Varsity, you're going back to J.V. this week.'

Jeff sat in the abandoned locker room after the team went outside, trying not to pout. The longer he sat, the more he fumed. He felt used and unappreciated. *How could the coaches move me up like that, then just expect me to go back down because Crockett could play?* The longer he brewed, the crazier he became. Without even thinking he grabbed a practice jersey, pulled it over his head and marched to the field. He found Coach Annese and bravely looked him directly in the eyes, 'You moved me up to Varsity and I'm staying here, even if I'm just a back-up.'

It was a strong approach that certainly caught the attention of the head coach. Annese paused as he looked at the sophomore. *That took a lot of guts.* Coach wasn't used to players telling him what to do, although he secretly appreciated Jeff's spunk. The Varsity needed a back-up quarterback so he decided to let Jeff stay.

Jeff sensed an added element of excitement among the players. He couldn't pinpoint whether it was because Crockett was back, or if they were geared up for Homecoming week against **Hamady**. Bulldog, Scott Powell, and Corey Crockett were the Homecoming King candidates. Bulldog walked through a kaleidoscope of crepe paper streamers when he entered his bedroom the night before the Hamady game. He found posters that displayed his name and football number along with a decorated pillow. Ahhh, the cheerleaders struck and the attention felt good. The cheerleaders repeated the scene at the homes of Powell and Crockett to set the stage for Homecoming.

The voting was extremely close among the three candidates, but the crown for the '91 Homecoming King went to Corey Crockett. He was a fun guy, who was obviously liked by his classmates. His visible prospect as a Division I quarterback gave Crockett added recognition.

Trainer Matt Noble taped Crockett's ankle like he had every week, then laughed when Crockett autographed it. 'Hey Matt, this is gonna be worth some dough when I go big time!'

While the team prepared for the game, excitement filled the small community who watched the Homecoming parade exhibit the beautiful Queen candidates through the small town. Fans settled in their seats and watched D'ar score a pair of first quarter TD's. D'ar's reflexes responded so quickly that he often soared over opponents when he ran; it was the reason he held the Champion Club's record for jumpovers. Coach Annese was afraid D'ar would get injured, and repeatedly told him to stop jumping. But D'ar continued to leap over opponents until he finally landed on his head. Coach Annese was deeply concerned that his star back was injured when he joined the team physician, Dr. Alton, on the field. Relieved that D'ar was conscious, Coach voiced his thoughts while looking at him with concern. 'You jumping bastard!'

D'ar opened his eyes and looked at Coach Annese then forced a grin. 'You sure have a strange way of showing how much you care!'

Before the team doctor and trainer helped D'ar off the field, they exchanged a look that conveyed how much Coach really did care.

That game was much smoother when Crockett and Eric added TD's to produce a 21-0 first quarter lead. Beardsley and Troy led the Montrose defense that only allowed three first downs the entire game. Jeff gained more experience as the signal caller during the second half, leading the Rams to a '49-6' Homecoming victory. Sean added a dimension of excitement when he booted seven extra points, setting a new school record for the 'most PAT's in a single game.'

The Rams 6-0 record pushed them to the #2 spot in the state football Class B polls, but Montrose wouldn't earn many computer points for that victory. It could, however, hurt them. The coaches started to worry about a playoff berth, since Montrose played a predominately Class CC schedule. Even if they went undefeated, they needed some help to qualify. Unfortunately, Atherton was the Rams next opponent, who only had one victory for the entire season and wouldn't provide many computer points.

Annese didn't expect a threat against **Atherton** and moved three sophomores up to gain some Varsity experience. Sean wanted to play in the Atherton game but faced a dilemma - *Geometry*. He was a good student, but trying to find the volume of a pyramid was easier said than done. It wasn't that he didn't try, he and Geometry just didn't click. He needed to pass his test with a minimum of a B to raise his grade point and remain eligible to play in the Atherton game. Sean studied. He felt that he did his best and was anxious to find out his grade. But he couldn't hide his disappointment after he saw the big red 'C' at the top of his test. The disheartened kicker approached Coach Annese. Coach talked to the Geometry teacher, pointing out that Sean did put the effort in and had improved. But the teacher wouldn't budge or offer extra credit to compensate. Sean was out of luck and extremely frustrated after setting a school record the previous week. His kicking foot would have to take a break during the Atherton game. He could dress, but was stuck on the sideline, and it tore him up.

Crockett opened the scoring against Atherton with a 20 yard keeper, then threw to D'ar for the conversion. Later, Crockett handed off to Eric who scored two second quarter TD's. Then disaster struck again. Not only did Crockett have another ankle injury, their standout receiver, D'ar, separated his shoulder. A hush fell over the concerned crowd when both star players headed to the emergency sports medicine clinic.

Montrose was up 22-0 at the intermission, but it appeared that Atherton kicked the crap out of them. The offense had difficulty moving the ball in their normal fashion. Coach Annese stormed into the locker room during the half and angrily kicked a water bottle. The innocent bottle traveled airborne, attacking Nate Leeseberg. The sophomore lineman wanted to laugh out loud after getting drenched, but he wasn't stupid. Coach definitely had the squad's attention when he prepared them for a tough second half, using a vocabulary that prevented the rookie sophomores from disguising their shocked faces.

A different team returned. Eric and Beardsley carried the offensive load, while the defense turned in a stonewall performance. They only allowed two rushing yards and 61 passing. Beardsley scored the final TD, then Jeff made the conversion to nab a '30-0' win.

The Rams knew it was an ugly win when they gathered midfield after the game to listen to Coach Reinhart. 'We aren't going to beat people by just showing up! This might be the best thing for us. It will give us an opportunity to refocus. We have to continue to improve!'

The team expected a royal butt chewing from Coach Annese, and found it odd that he didn't give one. The team actually felt they deserved to be punished, yet were relieved when they boarded the bus.

And then it happened. Players knew they were doomed the moment Coach Annese stepped aboard the bus and told the sophomores, 'Get off and ride with the cheerleaders!'

Sean felt his heart race directly before the goosebumps broke out, sending a cold shiver up his arms. The harsh words gushing from Coach Annese made them all feel absolutely terrible for their performance. The bus fell completely silent except for the droning sound of the motor. The quiet 45 minute trip gave Coach Annese time for his blood to alter from simmering to scorching. He stood up before the bus even came to a complete stop near the locker room entrance door. 'Meet me in the wrestling room – NOW!'

That had never happened before. The team didn't know quite what to expect, but had a feeling they wouldn't be meeting their girlfriends that night. Coach stormed in a few minutes later, pushing the TV/VCR stand, then forcefully jammed the game film in. He was so pissed that he couldn't even wait until Sunday to review the game. Annese reviewed each mistake, play-by-play. The team stayed for two hours, while Coach provided immediate feedback, critiquing every last mistake. He wanted them to think about what they did wrong over the entire weekend.

John Diem listened when Coach yelled, 'We weren't going for the jugular! We weren't going for the kill -- for the knock out punch -- like last year's team!'

It seemed they were constantly compared to the `90 Team. By the time he finished going berserk, Coach rekindled their desire to not only finish the League undefeated, but to play exceptional football. Only two weeks remained before playoffs. They had to play better to be prepared for a shot. Everyone wanted to accomplish their dream by picking up the post-season where they left off with Monroe. But they needed to get it together 'with or without Crockett.'

Once again, Crockett didn't give his ankle ample time to heal between injuries. He iced it throughout the weekend, and was able to bounce back to practice for **Bentley** week. Bentley only had one loss coming into the contest and could be a threat. A loss could set up a tie with Byron for the League Title. Eric was one of 18 seniors who wanted more than *a share* of the GEC League Title; he wanted to win it outright.

Eric backed his desire by intercepting a pass that he returned for a 50 yard TD. The senior leader played his best game of the season, determined to end both of his Varsity Seasons undefeated. Crockett and D'ar were on the field, helping Eric form a trio that led the offensive drive. The offensive line followed suit; together they racked up 400 rushing yards. Crockett scored four TD's and D'ar added 90 rushing yards, while they both played through their injuries.

Bulldog was just as determined and took a stance when five Bentley opponents charged him. The only thing he knew to do in that split second, that could allow them to score, was to throw a cross body. It was a simple reaction that allowed him to take out all five guys on the block. D'ar still got tackled, and Bulldog got a 15 yard penalty for hitting below the waist. But it was worth it and became his contribution to the highlight film; a classic block that linemen lived for. The Bentley coach was so upset that he actually came on the field, ticked at Bulldog. If he didn't swear at the lineman he sure came close. Bulldog felt he deserved every biting word. The other linemen tried not to laugh at the scene, knowing the entire team would run gassers for that penalty.

Bentley played hard by grabbing two interceptions. They caused Montrose to fumble five times; luckily the Rams only lost one. Penalties slowed down and frustrated the Rams during the first half. Coach Annese addressed those issues during his half-time talk and discussed their mental mistakes.

During the second half, Montrose came out and played their best football offensively. The defense stood strong and held Bentley to 46 yards and only four first downs. The '43-6' win clinched at least a share of the GEC Title, but the Rams wouldn't celebrate. *Not yet.* They felt good about the win yet remained even-keel, playing out their season one game at a time. The Rams walked off the field in business like fashion, they way they did after every game.

The Rams prepared for **Bendle**. Seniors hauled underclassmen through the mud after their pre-game practice, making sure to punish the ones that were routinely late. An uneasy feeling haunted the team that entire week; worried it could be their final game. Even if they finished with a perfect season, the computer point system could deny them a spot like it did in '89. That thought lingered in the back of their minds, like an anxious patient waiting to hear if he had cancer. The coaching staff tried to prime them for the worst case scenario by not getting their playoff hopes up, and be surprised if they got in.

Bulldog wondered, *How could we not get our playoff hopes up?* It had been their prime motivation for an entire year. He dressed Friday morning with a feeling of excitement and intensity. For the first time in a long time he couldn't wait to get out of bed and get to school. After grabbing breakfast in a gulp, he was off. Every teammate he passed in the school halls seemed to sense the same apprehension and excitement that he did. It was their moment. No matter what the outcome was, it was their day and they seized it. They worked as hard as any team could have. A victory would leave them '9 and 0.' The squad honestly felt that should earn them a state playoff spot. *Think positive and it will happen.*

The entire school buzzed. Even students and teachers who didn't seem overly interested in football talked about their chances. The community learned about the promise they made to the '90 Team, and also felt they earned a ticket to the post-season. Signs popped up throughout the town, displaying the fans support.

Bulldog felt they were ready. Everything was set; they just needed one more victory. He maintained his pre-game ritual after school and ate a plate of hearty lasagna promptly at 2:45 PM, cut from the same position from the same pan. *Always,* Mrs. Sullivan watched her son with an ache in her heart, realizing it could very well be the last time she fixed his pre-game meal. Bulldogs' parents enjoyed watching him play football all through school and felt a sadness that it was close to ending.

Bulldog drove around the town exactly three times while Hank Williams Jr. blared from his tape deck. He wore the same socks, T-shirt, and underwear that he wore every game. By now, his T-shirt resembled Swiss cheese, containing more holes than fabric. He could barely keep it on, but he wouldn't dare play in a game without it.

The team met at the school at 4:30 PM, like any other game day. Bulldog felt his senses become more intense as he looked around the locker room, memorizing minor details about players: where they stood and what they did to prepare for the game. He wondered, *What if tonight really ended up being my last game? Would it be the last time I'd ever dress as a Montrose Football player?* He pushed the uncomfortable thought aside and decided to hope for the best.

A teammate came in and held up a newspaper, 'Hey guys, USA Today says we're ranked 16th in the nation.'

Bulldog's brain took in the statement but he didn't really want to hear it. It didn't matter that they were ranked in the *nation*, they still needed a win, and some luck. They were held by fate and the state's playoff point system. Fate didn't care if they were ranked #1 in the nation, neither did the computer point system. Montrose needed to focus on beating Bendle; the rest was out of their hands. In the quietness of the room, Bulldog saw the fire in the eyes of his teammates. In that defining moment, he knew the squad wanted to win as much as he did.

The bus contained an eerie ambiance as players stared out of the windows, wondering what the outcome would bring. Montrose Football had become such a component of their daily lives. Eric thought about football, this fatuous game that taught him so much about life. It was difficult to even try and imagine a day without football and the brotherhood that accompanied it.

Bulldog sat behind Coach Annese on the bus. As a team captain he felt that he needed to ask, 'Hey Coach, be honest with me. What kind of chance do we have for playoffs?'

Coach turned around and faced his captain, 'Let's just see what happens.'

He didn't want to discourage them or jeopardize their ability to play their final League game like they had a post-season to look forward to.

The Montrose Rams focused on keeping their winning streak alive at 33 consecutive games and still held the fifth position in Class B, Region 3. But only the top four teams get an invitation to the post-season. Someone in the four seeded teams had to lose. The trouble was, they were all very good. The post-season looked pretty bleak, but the Rams hung on to the thought that anything could happen to change the odds during the course of a game.

The Rams went through their pre-game warm-up exercises after arriving at Bendle's field. Coach Annese captivated each one of them with an awesome pre-game speech. Sean thought it was the best one he had ever given. Coach realized how hard they all worked since the `90 Season ended; they wanted to be prepared for the `91 playoffs. He remembered their powerful promise to complete what the `90 Team didn't. 'This is your last League game and very possibly your last football game. For many of you, it could very well be the last time you'll ever put on a pair of pads. We can't control the point system, as unfair as it seems to us right now. We can't control all of the other teams that need to lose tonight in order for us to get in. All we can do right now is go out on that field, play our hardest, AND WIN

THIS FOOTBALL GAME! It's the only piece we have control over. It's the only piece!'

Coach Annese got through to every one of them, especially the seniors. Sean's heart pounded so hard that the roof of his mouth throbbed, as did Powell and Bowen. The rush of determination made them all want to rip someone apart when they took the field.

Bulldog dug his cleats into the ground as he eyed his opponent on the first play. He knew his battle was 75% over when he saw that his opponent was smaller. He couldn't resist and called 'Kitty, Kitty,' the code word he gave his linebacker to alert him of the kind of opponent he faced.

When the play began, Bulldog saw Bendle's back come straight for the hole. He stepped up and nailed him for a three yard loss. With that hit, he knew the Rams would not be denied. His enthusiasm spread to the rest of the line, as Bowen and the others joined in.

Beardsley managed to do stunts on defense that Coach Reinhart never called. He did crazy things that caused fumbles; it seemed something good always came out of it. When Bendle called a trap, the Rams were on them fast. *Everything clicked during that game.*

D'ar and Crockett were healthy and started the scoring when D'ar took the handoff, then scored a first quarter TD. Eric ran for two second quarter TD's, then caught a 20 yard pass from Crockett in the third. Crockett added two TD's of his own, while Sean added four PAT's to lock in a '34-8' victory.

Sean missed one of five PAT's. His disappointment grew after learning that he could've tied a state record. The sting of his absence in the Atherton game bit him again. Had he been eligible to play in the Atherton game, he would've broken the state record for sure. What an honor that would've been. But Sean still left his mark in the record books at Montrose Hill-McCloy High, when he kicked seven PAT's in a single game. It was the only school record set in '91.

Bendle's victory extended their regular season winning streak to 34 games and four straight GEC League Championships. Few people suspected the Rams would go unbeaten in '91, considering their inexperience at the start of the season. But they did it. Crockett geared away from their traditional ground game by completing 13 passes for 173 yards and a TD. He finished the season as the area's top scorer with 106 points and 17 TD's.

Even when things appeared to go well . . . *they didn't.* The Rams huddled in the middle of the field after the game to listen to Coach Annese. 'I asked you guys to win tonight and you did. We've been together as a team over the last year and had a tremendous season. You guys better celebrate. You just won the GEC Championship!'

Coach Annese told some of the juniors to pick up the seniors and carry them off the field. Schlichster threw Scott Powell over his shoulder and was almost to the end of the field before he realized the rest of the team decided to parade under the goal post. Schlicht was strong, but carrying a football player on his shoulders after playing an entire game was exhausting. But he managed to catch up.

The Rams were happy to be GEC League Champs, yet felt let down when they walked away. The realization set in. The seniors understood why Coach told them to celebrate; yet they hung on to any minuscule of a possibility for a post-season. They nervously watched their coaches from a distance while scouts contacted them. Each passing minute only increased their heartache. It didn't look good.

Former Ram Noel Dean, now in his first year as Bendle's head coach, was in high school when the '83 Rams went 8-1 and barely missed the playoffs. He remembered how torn his team was after coming up short.

The Rams loaded the buses for the 45-minute drive home, ignoring the raunchy smell of sweat that lingered heavy on the stuffy bus. Bulldog sat next to Coach Annese. Hearing his voice quiver while making calls from a cell phone seemed odd; Coach was always in control. Bulldog thought, *'Hmmm, that's not a good sign.'*

Honking cars in a crowded parking lot greeted the bus. The Montrose fans were always there to greet them. The small town hadn't experienced much business growth, but their fans grew by leaps and bounds.

Montrose was a typical small midwestern town where people cared about one another, greeted each other at the local post office, and enjoyed visiting at football games. It's a town where locals gather at Dee's Bakery for a cup of coffee and a chance to catch up on the latest news. Not always for the sake of gossip, but for a genuine caring about what happened to people they knew. The owner let the volunteer firemen in the back door during the early hours of their shift. He enjoyed the company amidst the wonderful smell of freshly baked dough. The town often got caught up in small town politics, but came together to support its football team. Football helped the town forget about their differences and brought them together.

Players deporting the bus didn't look like a team that just won the GEC League Championship. Parents realized their dreams and completely understood their desolate faces and dreary moods. Any other school in the League would have been thrilled to change places, but anyone associated with Montrose Football knew they fell short of a much bigger dream. Parents witnessed their dedication, while making their own personal family sacrifices. Schedules had been rearranged to meet football commitments, while summer vacations were postponed so players could lift everyday.

Parents provided pizza and pop for the team. It served as a cure when they were young, but would it work for heartbroken teenagers? They soon discovered that not even their favorite pizza eased their sadness.

Three of the four teams ahead of Montrose had won, yet the hopeful Rams held on to a slim possibility that the last team in the top four would report a loss. It wasn't completely over when Coach Annese announced, 'You need to be respectful. Go meet with your parents and eat some pizza. I'll come down and let you know as soon as I find out.'

The team stared at him as if he were crazy. *How could they eat pizza and socialize at a time like this?* They gathered outside of the coach's office to wait for the final call. The wait seemed endless while players nervously glanced at each other with hopeful, yet frightened, expressions. The disappointed look on Coach Annese's face provided an uneasy feeling when he stepped out of his office. His whispered voice cracked when he looked at the team with wet eyes. 'It's over fellas.'

Swallowing that bitter pill was difficult. It became even harder after realizing just how close Montrose came to getting in. Milan narrowly won by 15-14 over Willow Run to clinch a berth along with Millington, Monroe St. Mary Catholic Central, and Lansing Catholic Central. Milan's one point victory kept the Montrose Rams out of the post-season.

A crestfallen Coach was truly heartbroken once he regained his composure. 'I know you wanted a chance to redeem yourselves. It feels like someone stole that opportunity. I only hope that you can reflect on what you've accomplished this season because you achieved a great deal when you consider all the new players we started with.'

Missing the playoffs for the second time in three seasons, despite posting undefeated records, left players in tears. Many of the seniors started to breakdown when they thought of how hard they had worked for *an entire year*. It felt like someone slashed open their chests and ripped out their hearts with uncaring bare hands. The '91 team felt they had earned their fair shot, but someone stole their opportunity.

The coaches hugged the squad, then teammates hugged each other. They told the seniors how much they meant. Everyone felt hollow and empty; wanting a playoff shot with every fiber of their being. Their pain was real.

Bowen got caught up in the camaraderie and hugged D'ar, 'I love you like a brother.'

D'ar was quiet by nature but the entire scene choked him up. He was thankful he had one more year, yet felt the ache of the seniors. It was over for them.

Players reacted differently. Some slammed their fists into lockers or walls to release their frustration. It felt so unfair! Their outburst carried on for ten minutes until Coach Annese suggested they attend the celebration.

He watched his group of young men experience one of the saddest days of their lives. They felt cheated and wished someone could repair the unfairness, but it couldn't be fixed. They appreciated the efforts of their parents, but no one felt like celebrating or eating – not even pizza. Instead, they felt like they were forced to walk to the guillotine; ten minutes just wasn't enough time to regain their composure. *Injustice was torture.*

Parents felt helpless while they tried to make the best of a bad situation. They patiently lined both sides of the long hallway that connected the locker room to the cafeteria. Players found it difficult to walk past them. It was tough to face anyone, but seeing the ones that cared about them the most, made it twice as hard.

Eric felt like he was in a daze on a dead man's walk. He felt so empty inside when his parents hugged him. Other parents tried pumping some life into them when they shook their hands. 'You had a great season.'

Coach Annese, and his brother Steve, came down to the cafeteria where the group gathered. Coach knew how hard they took the news and felt responsible to build on the *positives* rather than the *negatives*. He had a gift for taking a painful situation and immediately turning it around. The team sat in the cafeteria for two hours, while Coach Annese went around the room recalling their accomplishments. He wanted them to realize that what *they achieved* was far more important than what *they didn't*. Coach roasted them, praised them, and helped them remember the good times. He made them laugh again.

Sean glanced at his teammates and thought about what they had experienced. He honestly wished he had moved to Montrose three years earlier and played all four years of high school football instead of soccer. That said a mouthful because Sean loved soccer. He didn't have as many memories as his teammates, but he did have one awesome year with them. They all knew what their jobs were and where the boundaries stood. He had grown in ways that he never imagined and felt they were all united -- like a family. Everyone stuck up for each other.

Coach talked about their future using VanHalen's words -- *Dream another dream, this dream is over.* It was a song that became forever etched in the '91 highlight film.

When Coach Annese finally plopped down in his own bed later that night, he wished he had brought all of them home with him. While dealing with his own emptiness, he still worried about *them*. They were 17 and 18 year-old kids who just experienced one of the most difficult disappointments of their lives. He only hoped they would handle it without doing anything foolish.

Eric and John walked out to the football field together one final time. They sat in the cold bleachers and talked for awhile then fell silent, each lost in his own thoughts. Eric learned so much from his football experience and felt fortunate to have been a part of the tradition. When he looked at the field he thought about Coach Annese and Coach Reinhart and all of his high school coaches. Not only did they teach him about succeeding in the game of football, they taught him about succeeding in the game of life. He knew he would go on and play college football and become a teacher. One day, he would coach and have his own team. Maybe he would fulfill his dream through them.

The empty ache wouldn't go away; he wished they were celebrating tonight. Instead, their mood felt miserably subtle. Both watched their breath form white pillows of clouds from the cold, night air that encouraged them to go home and get some rest.

Bulldog went to the locker room, turned on the shower, then sat on the floor of the steamy stall in deep thought. He had a quiet moment or two crouched in that position. *How could it be over?* 'Over' was such a difficult word to understand and even harder to react to. They worked as hard as they could and did everything expected of them. At that moment, life felt so unfair. The hot water ran for a good 20 minutes, hammering against his head. He only hoped it washed his exhaustion down the drain, along with his sorrow. Bulldog took the rejection personal after he lifted every single day for an entire year. Now, he couldn't fulfill the promise he made. The steamy water that slid down his cheeks disguised his tears. Somehow that made crying easier. Bulldog was thankful that most of the guys were gone by the time he finished; he had the entire locker room to himself.

Troubles seemed to loom larger than life on a still night. Bulldog dressed then started to walk toward his car, but he didn't feel like going home. *Not just yet.* Instead, he jumped the football fence and walked out to the middle of the field and sat Indian style on the 50 yard line. The field felt like a comforting haven, a soothing buffer from the unfairness of the world. The dark evening sky was quiet and still, as if bestowing a peace offering. Bulldog took a deep breath and focused on the fact that they just won the GEC League Championship. He went from feeling on top of the world to enduring one of his lowest points, all in the same night.

The lineman closed his eyes to breathe the unique smell of the dewy grass, yet felt nothing but emptiness. Bulldog realized he had a shot at playing college football and had his entire future ahead of him. He reminisced about the many good memories he had on the very field he sat on; that's when it hit him. He wasn't ready for them to become memories. *Not just yet.*

Another teammate thought he was alone when he stumbled over the fence then climbed the bleachers. Bulldog heard the commotion and realized that one of his buddies had turned to the bottle for comfort. Bulldog ran from the center of the field to the top of the bleachers to talk to his friend who yelled out threats. His senses were obviously dulled by the alcohol, causing Bulldog to wonder, *Is he suicidal? Would he really jump from the top of the bleachers?*

His friend yelled, 'Man, we could've been State Champions. We worked our asses off this year. Is this what we get? It's not fair. Life's not fair. Maybe if I jump, it will get their attention and they'll change their stupid point system.'

Bulldog remained calm, 'Hey, sometimes things happen for a reason. We don't always understand what that reason is when we're in the middle of it.'

They both felt they had a shot at the Title. To sweeten the pot, Monroe was in their region and considered the favorite. The stage was set, but the Rams were not a part of the cast. It would've been the perfect opportunity to settle the score from last year -- to finalize their promise. Bulldog felt anxious when he agreed with his friend, but tried to remain calm. They talked for a while longer. Bulldog found himself repeating a lot of the things that Coach Annese said earlier. They both found comfort in saying, 'We did all we could. It was totally out of our hands!'

His teammate finally calmed down so Bulldog drove him home. He sobered up enough to realize what Bulldog had done and thanked him. When he got out of the car he looked at Bulldog, 'Maybe you should think about coaching.'

Bulldog smiled and thought, 'No, I still want to play.'

The experience was never mentioned again. They both realized how that painful night could have ended in a real tragedy. Several teammates turned to alcohol that dark, Friday night. Guys that abided by the rules and didn't drink all year wondered what the hell all their hard work was for. What good did it do? Drinking seemed to dull the sharpness of their disappointment, at least temporarily. Bulldog put his energy into a different format. He visited Coach Annese bright and early the following morning. 'Coach, we have to do something. I started to write a letter to the MHSAA. They have to change this point system. It isn't fair. Can't they see it? Do we have any options?'

Coach Annese saw the anguish in Bulldog's face and invited him in. His own downcast mood matched Bulldog's. Coach had spent his morning on the phone gathering playoff information. Bulldog became furious when he learned how the regions were divided. 'You mean to tell me that two undefeated teams in our region won't get in, yet two teams in weaker regions with several losses made it?'

It didn't make sense to either of them. They finished with an 84.4 point advantage, which was higher than their total from `90 when they were second in their Region and hosted a first round game. But in `91, they sat at home, out of the running.

The cutoff for Class 'B' school status was 502 students. It was the exact number of students at Montrose, making them the smallest Class B school in the state. The Rams finished with a playoff point average higher than most of the 16 teams that qualified for the post-season. They ended up in a tough region in spite of being ranked No. 1 in Class B by the Detroit Free Press and No. 2 rated by the Associated Press. They outscored GEC opponents 353 to 47 and averaged 35.3 points per game, yielding a meager 5.8 points a game.

The goal of the MHSAA, when they implemented their new system in 1990, was to put all 9-0 teams and most of the 8-1 teams into the post-season. The MHSAA split each class in two, creating eight classes instead of four. It allowed for twice as many playoff qualifiers, but only four teams from each region qualified. If one region was overloaded with good teams, somebody got the proverbial shaft; that's what happened to Montrose.

They felt that the MHSAA needed to wake-up to make the playoff system fairer, allowing 'any 9-0 team' to have a shot in the playoffs; that's how other states did it. Annese's biggest complaint was the way the regions were set up. Montrose was tenth overall, but only fifth in its region. He wanted to see the regions dismantled, and the top 16 teams in each class taken with no regard to regional standings. Another problem Montrose faced in 1991 was being a Class B school that played in an all Class C League, losing valuable playoff points. Dropping out of one league and joining another was not a simple task.

Other sports had to be considered and bigger schools feared losing computer points to a smaller school. The regions didn't make total sense to the team if the intent was to keep travel to a minimum. The Rams didn't understand how Frankenmuth, another Class B school 30 minutes away, wasn't in their region yet Monroe, two hours away, and Lansing Catholic, one hour away, were.

It seemed their only option was to submit Bulldog's letter. Bulldog spent the rest of the weekend composing and rewriting his letter, giving special meaning to each word. It felt therapeutic even though he realized nothing would change the outcome. But it would be worthwhile if he prevented future teams from experiencing a similar heartache. Writing down his thoughts helped him vent his frustration and deal with his grief. He contacted one of his favorite teachers, Mrs. Nelson, to proof it.

Mrs. Nelson had several football players in her class and personally felt their pain. She couldn't hold back her tears once she read Bulldog's letter. She could tell how he poured his heart into his writing and spent hours preparing it. His efforts made her proud. She gladly worked with Bulldog to check his grammar and polish the final copy. Doing something constructive helped Bulldog feel better, instead of brooding about their bad luck like the other guys.

A few players never made it to school on Monday. They didn't feel like facing anyone. Coach Annese called a team meeting after school, and requested the squad turn in their uniforms. It was a depressing scene, another reality check that their season was actually over.

Coach Annese read Bulldog's letter at the end of the meeting. When his voice choked, players sensed how difficult it was for Coach to read. The incident made the bite of each heartfelt word sting even deeper. Most of the squad sat with their heads down, staring at the floor while intently listening to each truthful, yet painful word:

11-14-91

Mr. Roberts:

I feel compelled to write you and share one of the most miserable things that has ever happened to me. I hope that you can try to understand the pain and suffering involved in this situation so that changes can be made to insure that similar events never occur again.

My name is Mike Sullivan and I am a proud member of the 1991 Montrose Hill-McCloy Varsity football team. Why am I proud? Well, I was taught early in my life, and constantly reinforced, that if you put forth a lot of effort and commitment toward something, then eventually you will be rewarded. Well, Mr. Roberts, my teammates and I have not been rewarded. We spent from November 9, 1990 until Friday, November 1, 1991 working diligently preparing to represent Montrose Hill-McCloy High School in the 1991 Michigan High School Football Playoffs. Mr. Roberts, when I use the word 'commitment', I do not use it lightly. You see, on November 9, 1990, we lost in the second round of the playoffs. We performed miserably, and we were very disappointed. I was a junior at that time, and my teammates and I decided we would be back. We promised this to our coaches, our parents, our friends, and most importantly, ourselves.

The word 'commitment' became more than just a term, but rather a way of life.
We began lifting weights every weekday (I do mean every weekday), preparing for the
next opportunity imaginable to 'live our dream.' Our players didn't drink alcohol nor
do drugs'; we ate things that would help us become stronger, we followed a strict
curfew regarding when we would be in bed for the evening. We simply put football
before any other thing in our lives except academics. We ached for the opportunity to
show the state of Michigan how great one can become if they aspire to be great.

Mr. Roberts, Friday, November 1, 1991, was a day that I will never forget. My
mind and my body were in such utter turmoil that it is still difficult to express how I
felt. We had just defeated another opponent to complete the regular season with a
perfect 9-0 record. We won the League Championship and I'm certain that everyone
felt tremendous gratification in our accomplishments. Coach Annese threatened us,
"You had better celebrate." But we didn't.

We couldn't. We instinctively knew what Coach Annese was saying. He was
trying to tell us that this could have been the last time we would play football together
again. "How could this be?" I kept asking myself. We spent every day in the weight
room this summer preparing for our dream. We have won 34 regular season games
in a row. Mr. Roberts, we arrived back at the school (we played away) and we
anxiously awaited our fate. Surely, something will go our way, I felt. Coach Annese
will walk into the locker room with a smile and say, 'See you on the practice field
Monday.' But, when he walked in to speak with us, there was a tear in his eye. We
knew it was over. We knew that we would never be able to 'live our dream.'

Mr. Roberts, on Friday night our team cried, hugged, and told one another how
much we loved each other. We had just defeated Burton-Bendle 34-8, completed
another perfect season, and we all felt miserable. There was pain in my teammates'
eyes, distress on their faces and our hearts had been broken. We shouldn't have had
to feel this way. IT JUST WASN'T FAIR!!

Today is Monday, November 4th, 1991. It is 28 degrees outside and there is a
thin layer of snow on the ground. What I would give to have the opportunity to
practice today for the playoffs. I have a Detroit Free Press sitting in front of me. It
says that in Class B, Region I, Menominee will make the playoffs with a 5-4 record.
Five wins and four losses; they made the playoffs winning only one more game than
they lost, and they get to practice today. Standish-Sterling has a common opponent
with us (they play them a game apart). You should check the results, Mr. Roberts.
You may defend your regional format and say that no system is flawless. Well, when a
team from Monroe, a team from Albion, a team from Millington, and a team from
Lansing are in the same region, what purpose do regions serve? Last year, we played
in Monroe for the Regional Championship. I didn't know where I was, but someone
said I was minutes from the Ohio border. I just don't understand why certain teams
are fortunate to be in a weak region and we were so unfortunate to be in a strong one.
It just isn't fair. My teammates and I SHOULD be practicing for the playoffs today.

Mr. Roberts, I am very proud to be a member of the 1991 Montrose Hill-McCloy
Varsity football team. We have accomplished a lot and I am aware of that fact. But,
for my teammates and myself, there is something missing. An emptiness that will live
with us for the rest of our lives.

We did everything in our power to 'live our dream' but something failed us.
Someone told me that it was your association's system that did this to us. I know that
nothing can be done to heal our broken hearts, but PLEASE don't let this happen to
any high school football player again. All that is left for the seniors of the 1991
Montrose Hill-McCloy football team are memories of the greatest time of our lives.
Or better yet, what could have been the greatest time of our lives.

Sincerely,

Michael Sullivan,
Montrose Ram Football Captain

Players appreciated how accurately their captain described exactly how each of them felt. Suddenly, they didn't feel so alone, and drew strength from his words. The letter inspired the juniors, who found themselves repeating the same promise to the seniors. They would work hard the entire year, and do everything in their control to make the state playoffs in `92. The moment Coach dismissed them, they headed to the weight room. Each jumped up to touch the word 'Champion' above the doorway. Within minutes, metal slammed in the weight room. No quitters were in that room as the invisible torch was passed once again.

Bulldog attached a paragraph to his letter, before addressing it to several newspapers. He ended the article by stating that those in support should contact the MHSAA. Bulldog learned that every year a few teams end up with an undefeated season and don't make the playoffs. He received calls from all over the state in support of his letter, and continued to get calls each year when teams found themselves in the same unfortunate situation.

School wasn't the same for the seniors after football season, but their journey continued, and so did their will. Before they played football, half of the guys on the team were just classmates. Now they were connected -- *like brothers*. The seniors displayed their true character by continuing to lift weights after football season, getting stronger each week. Bowen and Bulldog set an example for the underclassmen by leading the Powerlifting Team to a fourth straight State Title. They topped it off with a National Title in St. Louis, Missouri. Coach Reinhart ran the powerlifting program and Coach Annese flew along on that trip to help fifteen competitors place at Nationals; claiming seven first places.

The three captains each accepted college football scholarships. Crockett took his prestigious All-State award and headed off to the University of Hawaii, Eric accepted one at Adrian, and Bulldog planned to attend Northwestern Iowa.

Coach Annese handed Bulldog a letter shortly before he gave the commencement speech as President of his senior class. Bulldog treasured each word, swallowing hard as he read:

Bulldog:

I wanted to take the opportunity to express my sincere gratitude to you as a leader, a student, and a friend. I am writing only one letter to anybody who played for me this year and obviously it is to you.

You have meant so very much to our football program. It is sometimes difficult to find players that you can use as examples for future teams, but I know I'll be talking about Mike Sullivan for years to come. Regardless of where I am in five years, I'll be telling my team about this great captain I had that was the engineer in constructing an undefeated season. I'll talk about how you made people become motivated to succeed, how you were like a second coach, and how you believed so strongly in what we were trying to teach.

However, your memory will be with me forever.

Just important as your contributions to the football program are your contributions to me individually. I have learned a lot from you by observing your actions. You have been a very dear friend to me, someone that I love very much! You are a 'winner' Mike, in every sense of the word. My life had been changed in a very positive way because of you. I know time will pass and we will lose the regular contact that we've experienced the last five years.

I know you'll make me proud at Northwestern Iowa, regardless of your success on the gridiron. I'll always be proud of you because you are one of the greatest people I have ever had the pleasure of knowing. I'll miss you.

Love,

Coach Annese

By the following August, Bulldog teamed up with Joe Morse, from the `88 Team, as a freshman football coach. They both attended SVSU in pursuit of teaching degrees. Bulldog became Coach Sullivan. The young coach knew that he made the right decision the very first time he stood on the sideline. No longer would he wear #79, but he felt completely at home chewing on a cold, metal whistle. *Coaching was where he belonged.*

TRI-COUNTY CITIZEN PHOTO

#16 Corey Crockett, quarterback and #10 Barry Gross

TRI-COUNTY CITIZEN PHOTO

1992 National Championship Powerlifting Team

5. PREPARATION - 1992

There are no secrets to success.
It is the result of preparation, hard work and learning from failure.

-Colin L. Powell

He watched the poised quarterback gradually work his way into the pocket, while his steady eyes searched for an open receiver. Everyone was guarded so he snugly tucked the ball under his left armpit, like he'd done so many times. He quickly searched for a hole then ran, lunging forward to gain more yards than anyone expected.

D'ar joined the thousands of roaring spectators who shrieked with pleasure and wondered, 'Can they possibly feel as excited as I do?' He still couldn't believe they were actually in the Dome!

The instant replay lured his eyes, like a magnetic force drawing him in. He focused his gaze at the huge screen in the upper deck then watched #16 repeat the play. His face held a grin, as if he'd just watched a rerun of the best scene from his favorite movie. Strange feelings stirred inside as he watched the quarterback, #16, who seemed a little stockier, bulkier than he remembered. He even ran with a different cadence, a different confidence.

D'ar unhurriedly shook his head to get a grip, realizing #16 wasn't Jeff, 'his' quarterback, but instead his little brother Teddy.

A different senior in a different time who was living 'his' dream.

D'ar had dreamed about playing in the Dome since the eighth grade. His heart still raced when he remembered the energy of the crowd that very first time he entered the Pontiac Silverdome. The strapping force embedded itself around his heart like a blood-sucking parasite -- and never released. He stood next to his dad, a head shorter since he hadn't hit his growth spurt yet. D'ar impatiently peeked through the mob of people standing around the upper deck. He inched his way through an opening in the crowd . . . then he saw it. His heart fluttered, forcing him to inhale several times to catch his breath. The world stood still while he fixed his deep blue eyes on the bright green turf a hundred yards below. He stood motionless as if the football gods had cast a spell over him; a sort of unexplained hex that grew into a burning desire during his football career.

That was five years ago. If he closed his eyes he could still picture himself carrying the ball, while dodging opponents as he easily skimmed across the spongy turf, in the place they called the Dome. D'ar thought about it constantly, wanting it more than anything. D'ar felt ready to play his first football game as a senior, but didn't want to think of it as the beginning to an end. It was his third year on Varsity. He felt an urgency to have a happier ending than the '90 and '91 Seasons. Somehow he had to conquer that invisible demon. *He had to.*

D'ar felt anxious when he drove home from his first football meeting. After opening the front door, he charged the steps three-by-three, reaching the second story in no time. He dropped his worn, black gym bag on his bedroom floor then gazed straight ahead. His serious reflection met his stare as he glanced at the weekly motto he'd written on his round, antique mirror. Normally he'd peek in on his younger sister down the hall. They shared a closeness that parents only hoped a brother and sister developed. But that night she had to wait; D'ar had an important football assignment to complete.

Just a few hours earlier, after their pre-game practice, he sat next to his teammates, listening to Coach Annese reiterate their goals. Of course they wanted to beat their first opponent and go undefeated, but the team was rightfully skeptical to think beyond the regular season. *But they did.*

Coach dangled the carrot the moment he mentioned 'winning a State Championship.' Those precious words would not be mentioned again, but lingered in the private thoughts of the entire team and staff. It was the reason they didn't cheat on drills. It became their ammunition to do things every day to improve. It was also the reason Coach asked each one of them to write a season quote that would drive them to accomplish their dreams for the '92 Season.

D'ar fell back on his bed, staring at the ceiling. *How do you describe something that means so much into one phrase?* His memory of the Dome seeped into his brain. It became his greatest dream; everything else was just a step along the way. He wrestled with phrases from motivational posters and cheers he heard at pep rallies. But he needed something catchy like Nike's 'Just Do It' . . . and then it hit him. The moment the thought flashed in his head, he knew it was the one. He jumped up in search of a marker. D'ar carefully drew three simple-yet-precious words on a poster -- *LIVE THE DREAM.* Three easy words that could change his season . . . *and his life.*

He stood on his twin bed and taped the poster to the ceiling directly above his pillow, where he could stare at it every night before the evening stole his thoughts. He wanted *LIVE THE DREAM* to greet him the moment dawn cracked through his window every morning. That was how D'ar wanted to end his senior season.

A few miles away, Troy Andrews lay on his bed, staring at his poster -- *TO LIVE THE DREAM TAKES ALL YOUR HEART.* Like D'ar, it hung directly above his bed where it served as a constant reinforcement. That powerful phrase seemed to sum up the consensus of the entire team. *Dreams are powerful.*

Schlichtster earned respect from his teammates when he took charge of the linemen over the summer. He held a practice every Wednesday, and taught the incoming freshmen and J.V. about commitment. The early season practice was considered legal as long as a coach wasn't present. He took pride in his responsibility as a captain and monitored the weight room activity throughout the summer, keeping tabs on all no shows. They could expect a phone call and had better had a good excuse. His efforts resulted in only six unexcused linemen absences during the entire ten-month off-season. It meant that the Varsity only had to run six gassers once the season started; that in itself was worth his effort.

Players didn't always make it to church on Sundays, but they seldom missed Air Force football. It was as much a part of Sunday afternoons as Major League Baseball and BBQ chicken. Schlichtster added a new twist for the linemen by persuaded them to play *tackle* instead of *touch* like the skilled positions. The close-knit group of seniors played football every day throughout the summer, counting down the days until their season started. They endured the profound August heat that made the dog days of summer physically grueling and emotionally draining. The 12 seniors thought two-a-days might be easier since they were in shape, but didn't realize that Annese stepped up his program. Coach quickly recognized their combined talents and worked them harder than usual to tap their potential.

Junior Jeff Klopf practiced with them day-in and day-out. He knew he had big shoes to fill and felt the pressure to uphold the outstanding quarterback tradition. Some local football followers were not convinced that Jeff was the right athlete, and questioned his leadership skills after witnessing the '91 Team's lack of confidence in him. Annese felt confident in Jeff's skills and encouraged his dedication, working with him one-on-one during the off-season. The new quarterback worked on his passing and ball-handling skills, logging at least two-hours each day. Jeff spent hours studying plays, and to thoroughly understand it, learned how to get a grip on the offense. Coach helped his quarterback believe that he could handle the task. Jeff was anxious to show the progress he had made since his sophomore season.

It was the Thursday before their first game. The squad ran through a light practice on the football field with their game gear on. They had already warmed-up and rehearsed their keys for the week, going through all of the special team positions - Kicking, Punting, and the PAT. The PAT team set up on the two yard line and practiced. Barry Gross held the ball while Tim Unangst and D'ar kicked several times, working rearward for a bigger challenge. Coach sent Vince Carmichael behind the goal post to retrieve the balls.

Vince was a short, kind of chubby kid who wore glasses and had a way of making people laugh. It was the only year he played Montrose Football. He wasn't the most athletic kid on the field, but he sure enjoyed the camaraderie the guys provided. Vince took his spot behind the goal post and caught kicks while providing comic relief. He watched Unangst attempt a long field goal, which he shanked to the left like a soccer ball. It sailed wide and wasn't even close to the goal post, slamming into the scoreboard 30 feet away. Vince ran over and picked-up the ball then cocked his arm back to throw it. Instead, his arms flailed in a panic. He threw the ball up in the air like he was trying to hit something. He ran around in a circle like a wild man whose pants were on fire, then threw his helmet off, followed by his shoulder pads.

Gross stopped what he was doing and joined the rest of the team who laughed like crazy, wondering, *What the hell is going on with Vince?* Jeff thought he was having a first-time-ever seizure and rushed over to his friend. 'Vince, what's the matter?'

He forced out, 'BEES!'

Jeff dragged his friend by the shoulder pads, pulling him away from the swarm of bees like a fireman rescuing a victim from a burning building. The ball jarred a nest of hornets when it hit the scoreboard. Once it landed, the bees formed an attack on the first thing in site -- Vince.

The coaching staff immediately thought about Coach Destrampe who previously had a near death experience from a bee sting. Reinhart turned to tell Coach D to run then vociferously laughed as the assistant coach raced in the opposite direction. At age 36, Coach D didn't need another near death experience.

Jeff breathed a sigh of relief once he discovered that his friend wasn't in any medical danger. D'ar joined in, relieved that his dad was out of harms way. They all hit the ground, laughing at the hilarious scene they had created.

Jeff looked out for his friend Vince. He appreciated the way he endured every practice, in spite of hardly seeing any playing time. He realized how much his buddy thrived on the discipline Coach Annese expected from every one on the team. In a way, Coach Annese substituted the missing father figure in his friend's life. Jeff looked out for his fatherless friends. He was close with his dad, who spent so much time with Jeff and his younger brothers that he couldn't imagine not having a dad around. He extended an invitation earlier in the season for Vince to move in with the Klopf family. Jeff's parents were strong football supporters. His two younger brothers gave his friend someone to pick on; although five males under one household was almost too much testosterone for Jeff's mom.

Jeff was extremely nervous before their first game. Unlike his linebackers who shoveled in pasta, he didn't dare eat a thing. Jeff knew it would make him feel sick; he didn't need to deal with that on top of his trembling, shaky nerves. Tony Beardsley sensed Jeff's tension and stepped up. The blonde-haired captain had an easygoing smile. He grabbed Jeff's right shoulder during their pre-game warm-up. 'Jeff, you're gonna have a good game tonight. You're gonna be a good one.'

'Thanks,' was all the junior quarterback could manage. It was exactly what he needed to hear and carried more weight coming from a senior. Jeff only hoped that Beardsley was sincere and not just blowing smoke. Jeff used self-talk to build his confidence. *You can do this. You're prepared. You've studied the playbook inside out. You've done your homework and practiced as hard as anyone. Just control these game time nerves and you'll be fine.*

Coach Annese told his squad that **Byron** was on the warpath to knock Montrose out early, since the Rams had provided their only league loss in '91. He expected Byron to be even better, but felt his Rams were ready for them. Annese was extremely anxious to turn Jeff and D'ar loose in a game situation.

Schlichtster wanted to make the most of his senior year and started a new tradition; one he intended to carry throughout the entire season. He woke up early Friday morning and shaved his head entirely bald, except for a 4-inch letter 'B' engraved in the back. The 'B' represented Byron, their first opponent. He proudly dressed in a shirt and tie like the rest of his teammates, eager to attend school on their first game day.

Byron meant business when they took the opening kickoff and drove to the Montrose 15, but then fumbled. The Rams however, gave up their possession after senior Brad Barnett fumbled the ball. Barnett was so frustrated at himself that he took off his helmet and kicked the ground. They all felt the pressure they placed on themselves, including the head coach.

Annese got caught up in opening game jitters when he approached Barnett. Harsh words robotically flew from his mouth that weren't meant for the virgin ears of the young, innocent water boys. Coach unintentionally slapped Barnett's unprotected head in the process, catching both of them off-guard. Barnett gave Coach his utmost attention. He realized the blow was harmless, hurting his pride much more than his head. Unplanned or not, slapping was off-limits. It was the forbidden taboo between coaches and players. To make matters worse, the scene took place on the Montrose sideline directly in front of the fans, obviously raising a few eyebrows. A female school board member became outraged after she personally witnessed the incident and planned to escalate it.

Did it help the Rams or add to their tension? It was hard to tell. The Rams appeared tight when Byron got the ball back and moved it dangerously close to the goal line. They were within three yards from scoring, but wouldn't if Troy could help it. He ignited everyone when he sacked the quarterback. It generated a turning point that stopped Byron from scoring on the series. The momentum shift coerced the crowd to feel the excitement as the Rams came into their own. D'ar ignited them with a dazzling 72 yard punt return. He finished the '91 Season as a junior, racking up 1,380 all-purpose yards, in spite of limited rotation in his elbow. The coaches called plays that worked with his handicapped elbow, often requiring D'ar to switch the ball to carry it.

D'ar had injured his elbow back in the eighth grade after reaching for a hockey stick during gym class. The weight of a classmate fell on his elbow. Since then, he actually felt loose bone chips and heard them grind when he repositioned it before shooting a basketball. It was gross. After a few unsuccessful years of being treated for tendonitis, he found an orthopedic specialist who discovered the exact damage.

Would D'ar undergo the consequences to correct it? The recovery time, after they cut his elbow open, would cost D'ar his senior football season. As far as D'ar was concerned, that wasn't an option. No way would he forgo his senior season. *No way.* Thankfully, he found a surgeon who understood the dreams of an athlete and offered him a second alternative -- experimental surgery. He scoped D'ar's elbow and removed the bone chips, which allowed the bone to calcify and blood to circulate the joint again.

After playing with broken fingers, a cracked jaw, torn quads, severe bruises, and recurring shoulder injuries, D'ar felt like a new kid. He never even told his coaches about most of his injuries; he feared being labeled as a *wimp.* Although Coach didn't make players practice quite as hard when they were genuinely injured. D'ar felt alive again against Byron. It felt great to be healthy and carry the ball, not thinking about his limited elbow rotation. It no longer hurt and he ran like Forrest Gump without leg braces.

Later, Jeff broke through a huge hole made by Schlichtster and scored an eight yard TD. Schlichtster was an integral part of their unit, perhaps more than the center realized.

D'ar kicked the PAT and it seemed he never let go of the ball. Five minutes later, it was back in his hands and he returned it to the 34 yard line. Jeff plunged over from three yards out, then added another TD on a keeper, using his quick speed to fly 37 yards to give the Rams a 21-0 lead at the half.

Annese kept them pumped during half-time. He felt they could play a good second half once they got their composure. The Rams already showed they were fierce competitors with strong leaders who could work as a team.

Jeff connected with D'ar for a showy 41 yard TD, giving the crowd a preview of what they could accomplish in 1992. Together they were poetry in motion, making it look effortless and exciting. The coaches anticipated that Byron would be their toughest league competitor; a lopsided '42-6' victory wasn't expected. As the staff followed the team off the field, Annese mentioned to Reinhart how the '92 Rams reminded him of the '90 Team. Reinhart agreed as they walked away with a strong feeling about the rest of the season. *First goal down.*

Jeff's parents beamed Saturday morning when they opened the sports section and read the caption in big, bold letters, 'COREY WHO? MONTROSE QUARTERBACK SCORED 5 TD's!' Maybe the title was a way for the media to relinquish some of the doubt they planted in the minds of their readers after losing Division I recruit Corey Crockett. Whatever it was, Jeff's parents couldn't be prouder and were pleased their son had a good start. Jeff had a career in one night considering that he also passed for a TD, ran for a two-point conversion, and passed for a second. The Klopfs hadn't developed the hard core shell that quarterback parents needed, but they would as the years went by and watched all three of their sons become quarterbacks for the Rams. They tried not to dwell on a few negative pre-season comments about Jeff's inexperience, and hoped fans gave him a chance.

Jeff was a natural runner and had finished third in the 100 meter dash in the league track meet just three months earlier. Last night he showed his speed when he ran down the field instead of around it. Jeff read the article and couldn't hide his smile when he read it again. His mom watched a frown spill over his face and asked, 'What's wrong?'

'I feel guilty getting all of the attention. They don't say anything about the line.'

Jeff knew it took all of them to work together to make things happen. He wanted to have a powerful year and didn't want his line feeling shafted after their first game. He needed them and was glad that Beardsley's name was mentioned for his 12 solo tackles and seven assists. Jeff sat the paper down, as he remembered the confident words Beardsley spoke before the game.

Then he laughed at what he said afterward. 'Damn Jeff, you scored more touchdowns in our first game than I scored all last season!'

The following school day, Annese confronted the female who had accused him of abusing his position. The team overheard their Coach's voice at full throttle, 'We're playing football here, not girls volleyball.'

She backed down. She was only doing what she thought was required of her position, then decided to drop the issue.

Annese felt bad about the incident and came up with a plan to smooth it out, in his own way. He asked Barnett to come into his office before practice, then taped an autographed tracing of his handprint on his helmet. He told Barnett, 'Hey, why don't you wear it through practice?'

Barnett was a good natured athlete with skinny calves who always had good hair cuts. He accepted the peace offering from his coach with a laugh.

The team realized their coach wasn't Bobby Knight. It was simply the result of a heated moment that they later laughed about. Players respected their coach, who led without fear and wouldn't back down. He held a mysterious control over them, but they willingly abided by his rules and shared a common goal. His toughness was appreciated because he wasn't afraid to show that he genuinely cared about them and their future. As far as the team was concerned, the issue was dropped.

The Rams had more important things to focus on while they prepared for **Chesaning**. The state polls ranked the Chesaning Indians No.1 and the Montrose Rams No.2. Although the contest was their only non-league game, both schools fell in the same Class B playoff division and could meet again in the post-season, making the stakes even greater.

Barnett and senior linemen Vaughn Paxton routinely ate their mouthpieces and required new ones by Friday. Both were so tense during Chesaning week that they destroyed them by Wednesday.

Gross read too many newspaper articles during the week. The media had a field day playing up the contest as 'the toughest each may face all season.' Memories of last year's 20-18 cliffhanger remained fresh in the minds of both teams. Gross knew that if he played for Chesaning he would want revenge in a fierce way, intensifying his anxiety level.

Gross became extremely nervous whenever he thought about the upcoming Chesaning game. The senior tight end was a good student, President of the National Honor Society, Vice-President of his Senior Class, and considered a levelheaded guy. By Friday, he was a nervous wreck. Concentrating on his studies was extremely difficult. Gross was a quiet leader and found that football made him a more outgoing person. It also made him jumpy, so he held his arm under the table during wood shop class. He felt like a patient with Parkinson's disease and didn't want anyone to see him shake. After all, he was a captain and needed to be in control. He tried to calm himself down with constant deep breaths before slowly raising his arm above the table. Each time he tried, it shook so badly that he quickly moved it back. He wondered if school would ever end so they could play the bloody game and get it over with!

Gross wasn't alone in his jumpy restlessness. Nate Leeseberg, a junior tackle, experienced a severe migraine during pre-game practice on Thursday. Schlichtster watched Nate stop the play then grab his head while his knees hit the hard ground. Nate's nerves caused another migraine during school on Friday, just hours before the game. His 205 pound body was strong, but a migraine could bring him to his knees in a heartbeat. He contributed it to a severe case of pre-Chesaning nerves and wondered, *will 7 PM ever arrive?*

Troy went home after school and stared at his poster, *TO LIVE THE DREAM TAKES ALL YOUR HEART.* He couldn't stand the tension any more and walked up to the school three hours early, then paced a path in the empty, dimly lit halls. The shiny floors reflected the twirling football in his hands while he threw it up and caught it, over and over, until enough time had passed to head for the locker room. Most of the team came up early and sat in the dark stillness of the wrestling room, tossing a football around with nothing on their minds -- except beating Chesaning.

Eric Hyde came home to watch the Rams after his first football game at Adrian College. He just couldn't miss the Chesaning-Montrose game, but felt like a fish out of water sitting in the bleachers. It was incredibly strange and he felt jealous not to be on the field dressed as a Ram. He was thankful his football career hadn't ended with high school and now found the college level very different. His new teammates didn't know each other that well, yet he felt disappointed in their commitment to team goals. Their work ethic shocked him and he felt like it wasn't as good as what he had experienced through Montrose Football. His parents experienced a similar, bizarre feeling when Eric ran on the field at Adrian College for the first time, proudly wearing yellow and black instead of the familiar red and black he'd worn for ten years.

The crowd anxiously watched the Montrose Rams proudly enter the field, with the flavor of a military squad. A friend of Coach Annese came to watch a Montrose game for the first time. He stood next to Annese when the nervous Rams walked in front of them. Annese's friend watched in disbelief as Tony Beardsley vomited through his helmet. The regimented Beardsley never missed a step, emulating a Marine in procession. Annese's friend couldn't believe the level of discipline displayed from a high school player. Needless to say, it made an incredible impression on the observer who couldn't help but mention it to Annese.

Not only did Tony Beardsley have a severe case of nerves, he had a few kidney stones thrown in for good measure. He was an aggressive, solid football player on both sides of the ball who wouldn't admit when he was hurt. Stingers got the best of him more than once, but he wouldn't come out of the game. He didn't want to miss a play. Beardsley led the Rams in tackles during '91 as a junior and was an integral part of the Montrose defense. Nothing could prevent him from facing Chesaning -- not even kidney stones.

Game time finally arrived. The Indians and the Rams held each other at bay as an exciting, scoreless 18 minutes passed. Montrose lost two first-half fumbles then made up for them when they intercepted two passes. Barnett ignored his throbbing finger during the game. He broke it during practice and had Dr. Alton pad it up. The officials checked it before the game and gave clearance for him to play. Good thing, because Barnett wouldn't let a broken finger keep him out of that game.

Schlichtster faced a short, strong, quick Chesaning opponent. He remembered him from their last contest when the guy set a record for number of tackles in a game. The opponent was unaware that he had played mind games with Schlichtster all week. Schlichtster wasn't about to let his opponent set any more records. *Not on his shift.*

Chesaning continued to pound up the middle. Finally, Beardsley had a chance to spark the defense when he recovered a fumble on the 35 yard line.

Gross was a lean athlete with a narrow chin and a great smile; a trait that got him voted 'Best Smile' by his senior classmates. But he wasn't smiling at the moment; a look of serious concern painted his face. 'C'mon guys, we got it back now let's take it in.'

Annese saw a difference in his Rams when their fear transformed into confidence. He could tell they wanted more when he faced them in the huddle. Barnett felt the intensity of his Coach's conviction by the way he looked each of them directly in the eye. Troy felt his motivation seep under his skin while he listened to every word; Annese had them all eating from his hand. They honestly believed they could accomplish everything Coach told them they were capable of. The Rams left that huddle determined to score on the possession. D'ar caught Jeff's pass then made an impressionable run to the five yard line. Jeff connected with Gross for a three yard toss in the endzone, putting the Rams on the scoreboard.

Shortly after, D'ar took a pitch from Jeff, rolled left, then connected with junior Eddie Howell. Ed used his strength to break a tackle, got behind the secondary, then raced to the endzone for an awesome 72 yard score. Jeff ran a reverse on the conversion, giving the Rams a 14-0 half-time lead.

Tony Beardsley and Eddie were step-brothers. The bond they shared as a team joined them even closer as brothers. Their parents stood proudly in the stands, enjoying their sons' contributions. They had a third son on Varsity, sophomore Jason Beardsley, and a younger son that played youth football. As if that wasn't enough, their only daughter dated D'ar. Their washing machine never sat idle with gobs of practice clothes that stunk like curdled milk, if they didn't get washed right away. The boys were responsible for doing their own laundry, a wise decision from a busy mom. The Beardsley household was hectic during football season, but there was no place on earth they'd rather be on Friday nights.

During the half, Coach spoke with strong belief, persuading each of them how to go out and score on their first possession. He had a way of making them believe in themselves . . . and that's exactly what they did. The Rams took the second half kickoff and marched into scoring position.

The Rams found themselves in a fourth-and-short and decided to take a chance. They didn't get rattled, but gained confidence from each other. They relied on guys like Vaughn, the strongest Montrose lineman, who could bench 360 pounds, squat 520, and dead lift 515. He was a guy you wanted on your side of the line. Vaughn bought time for the skilled positions, enabling D'ar to take the pitch then connect with Gross on a 14 yard TD strike. Jeff hit Troy for the two-point conversion, allowing the Rams to breathe a bit easier with a 22-0 lead.

Once Montrose relaxed, they scored two final quarter TD's and accounted for 415 total yards and 38 points. They didn't appear nervous or fidgety in their huddles; everyone just did his job. Reinhart was pleased with how his defense played. They held their positions and worked together to hold a talented team like Chesaning to only eight points.

The Rams were off to a good start by holding their first two opponents to one TD. Newspapers called D'ar 'A One-Man Wrecking Crew' and 'D'ar the Destroyer' after he caught two TD's and ran for one against visiting **Lake Fenton**. The senior flanker easily displayed his wide range of skills, using his elusive style to dart, cut, and outrun defenders. D'ar was quiet by nature, yet was driven far more than the average athlete. He had the rare combination of raw talent and the heart of a lion to back it up.

Just when the offense lined up to get set in their stance, Jeff jumped up and casually jogged over near Gross at tight end. He appeared to be telling Gross what to do when Annese started to yell at his quarterback. It looked to the fans that Jeff didn't hear his coach. Annese yelled again then jumped, theatrically waving his hands from the sideline. Jeff stood up and shrugged his shoulders, appearing to be puzzled.

Why would his coach interrupt him now? Jeff obeyed and swiftly approached the sideline, shrugging his shoulders with raised palms, looking totally confused to the crowd.

Lake Fenton's defense had to wonder, *What the heck are the Rams doing?* They expected the official to call a delay of game penalty against Montrose. Suddenly, Schlichtster hiked the ball to D'ar at flanker and the offense provided terrific blocking. In the blink of an eye, Jeff jolted down the sideline. D'ar utilized his halfback option to loft a 44 yard TD pass to his quarterback in the endzone. *It worked.*

The officials were alerted prior to their trick play and raised their striped arms to confirm the TD. Being on the other end of a scoring pass produced a big jolt of adrenaline for Jeff. It was stirring to be a part of a trick play. A rush of excitement jolted D'ar when he sprinted to the endzone. Jeff felt totally ridiculous when the offense rehearsed the play during practice, wondering if they'd ever use it. He celebrated with D'ar, 'I'm so glad you got a good pass off, or I would've felt stupid!'

'Hey, I wouldn't let you down.'

It was one of those trick plays a team could only get away with once. They called it 'Confusion.' It instantly became a classic that younger players talked about for years. Youth football coaches shook their heads, wondering if Annese laid awake at night inventing trick plays. One could bet they made mental plans to try it out with their youth football teams. The scorekeepers in the booth also shook their heads, and couldn't help but grin as they punched in the score. It was the perfect Tony Annese trick play and the crowd loved it. Montrose Football was exciting. Spectators never knew what to expect next. Some felt a twinge of guilt for doubting their intentions seconds earlier. The '92 Rams were becoming an entertaining group that possessed an element of surprise, which brought fans back week-after-week.

The Lake Fenton Blue Devils didn't laugh, but felt foolish after getting sucked into the theatrics. They had a few tricks of their own, which only frustrated the Rams who tried to avoid getting wrapped up in the negative things occurring on the field. An annoyed Annese threw his black ball cap down a few times during that game; a ritual he ensued whenever he was totally pissed off. The coaching staff wondered why they weren't playing with the same intensity and drive they showed against Chesaning; unaware of another battle underway on the field.

B.J. Dean was a fit, dark-haired sophomore who already had the massive frame of a serious bodybuilder. He had an extremely intimidating way of standing over his opponents after he tackled them. The sophomore led the defense with 11 tackles and a fumble recovery.

Beardsley also worked hard. He didn't want to be outshined by a sophomore and made 10 tackles, an interception, and scored two TD's to boot. D'ar stacked up 291 of their 528 offensive yards. Montrose forced the Blue Devils to punt six times and made 23 first downs to beat Lake Fenton '38-17.'

The stats looked impressive, but the post-game was anything but. The Rams appeared to be the beaten up team when they undressed in the locker room. The Blue Devils were obviously pissed after the confusion play and resorted to dirty play. When the helmets came off several players' faces displayed long, jagged, facial scratches. Beardsley's mouth was sore from opponents reaching inside his helmet and digging with their fingernails. D'ar's knee throbbed from an opponent intentionally twisting it.

A reporter wouldn't hear any sounds of celebration or find any big heads in the quiet locker room that night. Although the Rams did many things right, they also did several things wrong. Coach Annese was displeased with the 105 penalty yards that resulted in two TD's being called back. The Rams fumbled six times; three occurred on their first five possessions during the long 2-1/2 hour game that produced some strange calls from officials.

Annese pulled his hat down tighter, a gesture he often did when he was mad. His voice echoed, 'It's not a lot of fun when you're making a lot of mistakes! Good teams make good plays and for us to be a good team we have to play better. You have to get it up every single week in this game. This team has to mentally prepare for that. One of our strengths in this program is to prepare every single day and not just on Fridays! A championship caliber team cannot expect to make that many mistakes and succeed!'

Annese detested penalties. The greatest remedy was to shell out gassers during practice. The results produced improvement when Montrose visited **New Lothrop** during week four. The Rams talked about coming out with a fast start to make up for the previous week.

The media called Jeff and D'ar 'Lethal Weapons II,' after they stood in the spotlight with a '48-14' victory over the Hornets. Jeff threw four TD's to D'ar before the first half ended. He broke the record that had been held by former Ram and Detroit Tiger pitcher Scott Aldred; a record of three that was set during the Rams '85 Season. The tough line bought Jeff ample time to sit in the pocket and throw a tight spiral. Jeff and D'ar mastered their timing, developing that special connection between a quarterback and a back. When they put the ball in his hands, D'ar made things happen by scoring another TD in the second half.

Tim Unangst was both nervous and excited when he kicked extra points. His foot warmed-up and stayed on target to kick six PAT's. Unangst was a junior, Sean's younger brother, who proudly upheld his brother's tradition as an accurate kicker for the Rams.

Unknown to the upper classmen, two opposing sophomores had a different type of battle taking place on the field. B.J. Dean found it strange to play against Hornet Steve Whorf. Steve had been his best friend all through school until they lost touch after Whorf moved to New Lothrop in 1990. They both proved their allegiance to their teams when Whorf made New Lothrop's last TD, while B.J. racked up six tackles, two behind Barnett. When the team lined up at the end of the game, the twosome exchanged a hug. Both were obviously happy to see each other. They were still friends who left the battle on the field.

Afterward, the New Lothrop coach told Annese that he hoped Montrose could get in the playoffs, and have a chance to show just how good they were. Montrose had some super athletes and Scott Cousineau felt they had an opportunity to go far in the post-season.

The Associated Press weekly poll ranked Montrose No.2 behind top-ranked Marysville. It pleased the Rams to be ranked above No.5 Monroe St. Mary. However, the AP poll didn't mean squat if the MHSAA's point system denied them an invitation. The enrollment at Montrose High barely pushed them into Class B again, which was when the point system failed them. The Rams chose not to dwell on that possibility, fearful it would bring them down. They focused on their second goal – to win the League – and channeled their energy while preparing to face unbeaten **Goodrich**.

Montrose High buzzed with the anticipated excitement of Homecoming week. Students dressed in themes for Backward Day, Farmer and Western Day, the 50's, and Opposite Sex Day, but Friday was reserved for the sacred Red and Black Day. Beardsley, Gross, Barnett, D'ar, Troy, and Brent were selected as the King's court.

Goodrich spectators read another article in the Flint Journal about D'ar; his talents were constantly emphasized in the newspapers. They watched the athletic build of #41 catch passes while he warmed-up with the other receivers. Naturally, they assumed someone of his caliber only had football on his mind and didn't notice how he searched the stands for his girlfriend. She hadn't taken her eyes off him and waved the moment he looked her way. D'ar waved back, his helmet camouflaged his smile. It was a part of his pre-game ritual that satisfied his weekly superstition and positioned him in the right frame of mind. D'ar was an exceptional athlete on the field, but was a typical 17 year-old kid when it came to hormones. Satisfied that he found her, he felt ready to focus on Goodrich.

Coach Annese didn't talk about it much, but players read about Nick Annese in the Flint Journal. Their coach had a chance to beat his father's 38 game winning streak. Even at their young age, they had enough wisdom to realize what a rarity that was and became even more determined to make it happen. If Coach Annese hadn't realized their effort, he soon would. His Rams scored on every one of their first half possessions. D'ar led the attack with three scores on jaunts of 31, 10, and 31 yards and racked up 105 yards in the first quarter alone. D'ar was hard to key in on and ran with an intensity that excited the entire crowd. He ran so hard that he grunted with each step, a signal Troy used to time his blocks.

Things were going so well that the team wondered why three players were kicked out. The field got heated on the second series of the game. Barnett and Alan MacDonald, along with a Goodrich opponent, wrestled for a fumble after the second series. All three of them hungrily fought for possession. An official thought they were all too aggressive and kicked all three of them out of the game. Annese was furious about the decision and did his best to reason with the officials, but to no avail.

It was a conditioned reaction to assertively chase the ball and not give up until it was in their hands. Barnett found his game after he racked up five tackles; he couldn't believe the official's call. His frustration increased by the minute when he stood fixed on the sideline, where he would be anchored for the rest of this game as well as the next. Barnett simply couldn't understand why the official kicked them out; neither could the huge Homecoming crowd.

Tony Beardsley tried to calm Barnett down. It was Beardsley's day; he was crowned Homecoming King and scored the next two TD's on a pair of four yard treks giving the Rams a 33-7 lead. Montrose worked hard to hold Goodrich down, but allowed the Martians to score two second half TD's. D'ar made a seven-yard dash to the endzone in the fourth and tacked on the two point conversion. Unangst booted three PAT's during the first half to make a final score of '41-19.'

The '92 Rams made coaching fun because they were experienced, smart, and learned quickly. They studied plays and knew exactly where to go. When the offensive coach ran a play in, four Rams could change spots without any handholding. D'ar racked up a dazzling 168 rushing yards and four TD's in 11 carries before he left the game. He continued to prove that he was capable of producing those numbers every week. If Goodrich keyed only on D'ar or Jeff, Beardsley would sneak up on them.

Goodrich Coach Pruchnicki gave his team a lot of credit for not giving up; they played with pride and dignity. Goodrich prepared for the contest with high hopes of finally ending Montrose's hex, then became stunned after the first quarter.

The Rams were on a quest to win one more GEC Title. Coach Annese proudly told them, 'We've cleared five hurdles after tonight, we can't afford to trip. We wanted to play well early and we're pleased that we did that and minimized our turnovers.' He commended the offensive line, 'You came out and asserted yourselves early in the game. Now we have to work on improving each and every week.'

The win marked the 39th regular season win for Coach Tony Annese. He surpassed his father's record, from 1957-62, when he coached at New Lothrop High School. He followed in his father's footsteps exactly 30 years later, although he felt his accomplishment did not make them equal by any stretch of the imagination.

Tony Annese made his mind up in the fifth grade that he would be a football coach. Nick Annese was one of the state's all-time greats, coaching at New Lothrop and Corunna winning a total of 12 League Titles. Tony and his three brothers were within a year in age and all played football, taking turns being the ball boy at Corunna during their youth. Now, Tony's brothers made time to help at practices and scouted upcoming opponents.

The Annese brothers felt that Tony would be the one that stepped into their father's shoes. He had the same great relationship with his players that his dad did. He learned his work ethic and competitiveness from his dad. Nick Annese had open-heart surgery when Tony was only nine years old, then died in 1982 while Tony was a junior at Alma College. Nick Annese never had the chance to see his son coach, although he knew one day Tony would.

Coach Bob Hayes was squeezed in-between Nick and Tony Annese. Hayes coached at New Lothrop after Nick Annese left, then moved to Montrose and built a powerhouse football program for 19 years before Tony arrived. He observed several similarities and felt Tony was trained to be the ultimate football coach, learning from his dad's example.

Tony Annese developed a trust in his coaching staff. He showed his confidence when he let them call plays after wanting to run the show himself for the first five years.

Annese asked Jeff and D'ar to stick around after practice to work with the youth football kids; neither expected the reaction they received. After they demonstrated a few handoffs and worked on a few plays, Jeff felt kids touch his shoulders. D'ar saw their faces light up when he paid attention to them. The two Varsity stars were moved by the response, and realized they were ranked as heroes in the eyes of the young boys.

The Rams wrapped up the League by beating **Hamady** '43–14,' then defeated **Atherton** '59-13.' Jeff and D'ar entertained their fans. Their moves were so well rehearsed they felt instinctive. The multi-talented D'ar Destrampe continued to attack the record books by tying the six-touchdown single game record set by Cliff Casteel in 1988. The record was set against Bentley. When it came to the Bentley Bulldogs, Annese wasn't pleased that his defense allowed a season high 326 yards. He screamed at them. 'WE CAN'T AFFORD TO GIVE UP THAT MANY YARDS AND MAKE ANY KIND OF IMPACT IN THE PLAYOFFS!'

It instigated a tough week of practice. The Rams worked hard on their tackling drills. Coach wanted them sharp and prepared for playoffs. The team tried to regain faith in the MHSAA point system when computer rankings positioned Montrose in the fourth spot with one regular season game remaining. However, that system failed them twice and they could lose their position and still not make the playoffs in spite of being ranked No.1 or remaining undefeated. Another win could possibly move them into third place to face the No.2 ranked team -- DeWitt. The coaching staff opted to think positive and prepared early. Instead of practicing Bendle's offense, the Rams learned DeWitts. They even wrote 'DeWitt' on the scout team practice jerseys. The coaching staff made sure the Rams were not overconfident, and preached how they had to beat Bendle or their playoff shot was as good as over.

Before the last league game, Coach Destrampe drove through a fast food restaurant to buy his son a chicken sandwich. D'ar couldn't handle eating a greasy burger on game day. A chicken sandwich had been his ritual before every game. It worked all season and he wasn't about to change his pre-game routine. After D'ar ate his sandwich, he went upstairs to the comforts of his bed, closed his eyes, and ran through plays. He wore his favorite black T-shirt with its ripped off sleeves, that he got from a Michigan State football camp. D'ar always arrived at the school's wrestling room way ahead of schedule. He liked to have plenty of time to fall asleep while Metallica's hard-rockin' hits blared from a boom box. It was the same Metallica tape that he listened to since his sophomore year with the '90 Team. He tied his shoes while he sat in the same spot on the wrestling mat in the dark room . . . *tradition.*

While D'ar slept to relax, Troy took a shower, put on his favorite game T-shirt then walked the school halls. He always carried a football and threw it to himself while his thoughts focused on the game.

Guys that needed edgier head banging music gathered in the locker room to jam to the psychotic noise of metal giants Pantera and MegaDeth. When game time approached, they all migrated to the still darkness of the wrestling room until the coaches came in and said it was time to go. Sitting in the dark with the rest of the team was Brent Baksa's favorite part of his Friday pregame; it helped him screw his game head on.

Most players and coaches were abnormally superstitious about their pregame rituals; no one wanted to change any part of their routine for fear it would jinx their season. D'ar's grossest superstition was that he wouldn't let anyone wash his football girdle. It reeked so badly that his mom refused to let him bring it home. The disgusting odor became more concentrated each week and smelled like three-day old rotten meat. The stench forced his locker buddies to hold their breath while they dressed, but no one complained. It worked for Brody Mier of the '90 Team and now it worked for D'ar. If that's what it took to keep him performing, they would hold their breath and put up with it. *Superstitions were sacred.*

The Rams executed with skill and confidence when they scored against **Bendle** on Jeff's 27 yard TD three minutes into the game. The Rams were obviously pumped about their optimistic chance to play in the post-season. The crowd got excited after Jeff connected with Eddie three minutes later on a 10 yard pass in the corner of the endzone.

In the second quarter, D'ar caught an awesome over-the-shoulder catch from Jeff then streaked down the sideline to score his first of four TD's. It was poetry in motion at its purest level. D'ar gave the Montrose Rams multiple dimensions, allowing the coaches to design the offense around his skills. They were impressed when he took plays beyond their original design; beyond what defenses could stop. The coaches knew without D'ar they would be limited in what they could do. He used his balance in a deceptive way to throw off defenders. D'ar found the openings while his effortless moves awarded him center stage whenever he had the ball. The Rams positioned him in the backfield running splits and slots. His TD's gave him 29 for the season, breaking a 24-year school record held by Jerry Maitland.

He absolutely loved the game, but didn't allow his accomplishments to give him a big head. D'ar hated when he fumbled or screwed up; he always looked for ways to improve. He was an extremely good-looking yet humble guy who always acknowledged his linemen. They were big thick guys who blocked the secondary and made big holes for him. Like Jeff, he regretted that they never received the spotlight or made the paper. It was a two-way street though. The line worked as a team and loved blocking for D'ar, who got results and made their jobs worthwhile. The linemen referred to him in a unique way, 'D'ar was just . . . *D'ar.*'

He was an exceptional kid with an extraordinary name. His parents saw the movie, *The Three Musketeers* shortly before his birth, and decided to name him D'artagnan after the fourth Musketeer. He inherited his speed and agility from his parents who were both outstanding athletes during their high school years at Montrose. Both played basketball and were sprinters in track; his mom was on the Girls Track State Champion Team. Each parent played football; his petite mom was the high scorer during the Homecoming powder puff football game her junior year. An unexpected appendix attack hindered her senior year plans, while she begged the surgeon to discharge her from the hospital. The female seniors missed her speed; without her -- *they lost.*

The coaches tried sophomore Shawn Yuncker at D'ar's position. He was stockier than D'ar but just as determined, with the strength of an ox. Yuncker made an impression with a final quarter TD. Unangst kicked six PAT's, one shy of his brother Sean's record, to close the shutout '47-0.'

Bendle was glad to get on the bus and head out of town after the Rams sacked their quarterback three times for minus 20 yards, and forced them to punt seven times. Montrose clinched the GEC League Title outright and claimed another undefeated season. The question on everyone's mind was, *Would they hold their playoff spot in the top four seats?* The Rams nervously held their breath after the game, while facing their moment of truth. Everything they prepared for and dreamed of rested on fate, and less than one percentage of a point. The team tossed and turned throughout the night. Phone calls were made first thing Saturday morning. *The Rams made it. They were in.*

Montrose held the No.3 spot with 75.439 points, squeaking past Millington with 74.875. The Rams celebrated their playoff berth and League Title by shaving their heads. Schlichtster was glad that his teammates joined in his hairless ritual. He was true to his pledge by engraving each opposing school's initial in the back of his head with the little hair that managed to pop out each week. But the joke turned on them when the eight players who earned All-League honors had their pictures taken with shaved heads. They all resembled bald cancer patients undergoing chemotherapy. Sports readers had to wonder, *What was in the water in northern Genesee County?*

Playoffs were all about emotion. It was hard for players to describe the excitement of the preparation. The entire town buzzed with energy when the Rams got their post-season ticket punched. It didn't matter that **Dewitt** was favored to win, or that Montrose was included in the region labeled as the toughest Class B in the state. All that mattered was that *they were in.* The Rams had to beat all of them to accomplish their dream.

The Rams proved what they could do locally after four straight 9-0 seasons, a 43-game regular-season-winning streak, and five straight GEC League Titles. But they wanted to send a message to the rest of the state and put an old story to rest. Annese had the opportune year to prove his program, since he sported one of the best teams in his six-year stint at Montrose. A smiling Coach Annese told the press, 'We're not only playing Dewitt this week, we're playing to the minds of several doubting Thomases who are skeptical of our heavy Class C schedule. We want to have a good showing in the playoffs to prove to people we're one of the top quality programs in the state of Michigan.'

After a tough first day of post-season practice, a few linemen felt the raw ache in the voice of their former teammate Mike Sullivan. His voice relived the pain of playoff denial. After coaching the Freshmen Team, he was available to help the Varsity in anyway he could. He started by channeling a year full of vented, anguished playoff denial to increase the desire in the '92 Rams. The former lineman wanted the team to appreciate the honor of having a shot at a State Championship. He reiterated what it meant to the '91 seniors and what they would give to be in their shoes. Sullivan defended their vow to the '90 Team to make up for their unfortunate playoff loss to Monroe St. Mary. 'We never had a chance to redeem ourselves, but *you* can. If you can't find a reason in your hearts to do it for yourselves, then do it for past teams.'

Not one person on the team lacked desire. They wanted a State Championship just as much as anyone before them had. Seniors witnessed firsthand the depressing scene of the Monroe locker room. They were young, impressionable sophomores then; unable to erase the heartbreaking ending of the '90 Season. It sliced a deep wound in their young hearts leaving a lasting impression that most would never forget. It became a life defining moment that still haunted them. Seeing their heroes openly suffer the hardest experience of their young lives, while tough coaches exposed their sensitive side was immensely disturbing. They unexpectedly learned in that gloomy locker room, that it was acceptable to cry. The toughest of them did. Once they released the knots in their throats, they didn't feel ashamed to show how much it meant. No one dared to laugh.

They lost a part of their boyhood while they sat on the worn benches in Monroe's stuffy locker room that night. It was an experience that embedded itself in their permanent memory. If they could press a rewind button to erase that painful scene, they would've pushed it a long time ago. It only reinforced their desire to have a different ending in '92. They would never take their shot for granted. They were a goal driven team with extraordinary talent and desire to continue their quest for the Dome; even if they were *the underdog* coming in. Coach planned a different tactic in his pre-game speech. He debated whether to share an anonymous letter he received days before their first playoff game, then decided to read it at the last minute. His voice choked while reading sections of the letter about his dad. The team knew Coach felt personally attacked:

> '. . . *Montrose accomplished a lot of things but was never able to conquer the battle in the big games. You have a lot of talent and speed and have built a great program, but will you be a team that chokes under pressure? You may have broken your dad's record, but do you have what it takes to fill his shoes? Do you think you could ever live up to what your dad did?* '

The squad was left with a desire to play even harder. Players knew how much Coach Annese's dad meant to him and were willing to do whatever they could to advance. Brent could hardly sit still and was over anxious to hit someone. Schlichtster kept his head down during the entire speech, trying to get a handle on the emotions that tore through his chest cavity. He felt tears stream down his face while he listened to Coach Annese. Finally, he couldn't stand it anymore and slowly raised his head. The speech moved every fiber of his being; he didn't care if anyone saw how emotional he was. After sheepishly glancing around the room, he noticed that he wasn't alone. Moist eyes everywhere, confirming how Coach had touched their hearts. But their mood was far from wimpy. That speech reached into the core of their souls, rousing an overpowering spirit. Like someone flipped a switch, their emotions rotated from sensitive to brutally oppressive when they jumped up and shouted, 'LET'S GO. LET'S KICK THEIR ASS!'

Coach Annese got to them. They couldn't be any more prepared; except for D'ar. Coach Annese's voice provided a backdrop as he closed his eyes and visualized running plays in his mind. He pictured himself catching the pitch, searching for a hole, then breaking through as fast as he could. That was how D'ar prepared himself. Eddie Howell sat by D'ar and picked-up his quiet, psyche up approach. It didn't matter what method the team used to screw their game head on, the seniors knew that no one would stop them once they took the field. *No one.*

Montrose grew leery of DeWitt's huge front line after heavily scouting them and planned to use their physical strength and quickness. Annese raised their expectations and moved their minds to a higher level of competition. He helped them believe they could win. Annese created a burning desire in each of them to go on that field and beat DeWitt.

It didn't matter that DeWitt had the home team advantage on a biting cold, Friday night. DeWitt Memorial Stadium offered the appearance of a small college field, and was a great complex to host a playoff game. Fans felt the contagious excitement surrounding the field as both teams warmed-up. The stakes were set. The winner went on, the loser went home. Neither team wanted to lose.

It wasn't snowing but temperatures were below freezing on the early November evening. Enthusiastic fans bundled in layers of clothing; some even donned snowmobile suits before joining the crowd of 5,000 spectators. Fans watched their Rams, whose shoulder pads carried the pride of their school and their town, when they marched toward the field.

Both teams had several weapons. Montrose fans were anxious to see the DeWitt version of D'ar when the two All-State candidates faced each other. As D'ar warmed-up pre-game, he wondered if he could run after a tackler fell on him during the Bendle game, injuring his hip. He went to physical therapy every day for a week and nursed his hip, hoping he could run by Friday night. No way would D'ar miss a playoff game; not even with two broken legs.

DeWitt won the coin toss and deferred to the second half. The Rams didn't waste any time and worked together to score on their first possession. D'ar broke free off tackle to complete a 50 yard sprint just five plays into the game. He already found his zone and totally blocked out his hip injury. His mom watched from the bleachers and noticed a change in D'ar's reaction after he scored. Usually he considerately flipped the ball back to the official, *but not that night.* He actually jumped up and celebrated. It was the first time D'ar ever showed emotion after he scored. She felt confident that something special was about to happen. Barnett and Troy always reached D'ar first. Usually they didn't talk, just extended an arm to help him up or slap his helmet or give a nod. That game was different. It was big. It was playoffs and the Rams just drew first blood.

Tim Unangst tried to calm his heart rate down since it was his first playoff PAT. He walked his steps back then focused on D'ar's hands while he waited for the snap. D'ar started to set the ball, but it fell off the tee just as Unangst approached. He decided to go for it anyway, but his kick wasn't even close. His dropped shoulders and bent neck proved how extremely disappointed Unangst was.

Montrose cheered anyway, since D'ar's TD marked the first time an opponent scored against DeWitt in the first quarter. The Rams planned to catch DeWitt off-guard with an on-side kick, but the Panthers were too quick and obtained possession. The Panthers drove 52 yards to score from one yard out to take a 6-7 lead. They celebrated while their distinctive scoreboard shot an awesome blaze of fire that lit up the dark sky, feeding the frenzy of the crazed playoff crowd.

The Montrose offense came right back and marched 67 yards in five plays. Excellent blocking allowed D'ar to score on a 21 yard run with a minute left in the first. Unangst wanted to make up for this first kick. He thought it was good, but the extra point failed for the second time. The crowd noise overshadowed his displeasure when the scoreboard reflected 12-7.

Montrose stopped the Panthers on downs then fumbled deep in their own territory early in the second quarter. DeWitt took advantage of their prime field position. Three plays later Beardsley thought he deflected the pass, but DeWitt got it off and scored from 15 yards out to take a 12-14 lead.

It was a dogfight. The persistent Rams fought back when they took the ensuing kickoff and drove to DeWitt's four yard line. The referee spotted it dangerously close, summoning the chain gang to confirm. The disappointed Rams missed an emotional first down by inches on fourth down. D'ar out gained the entire DeWitt Team by 36 yards after racking up 150 yards on 14 carries during the first half. Even with their gallant effort, the Rams trailed at half-time for the first time all season.

Gross was thrilled to be a part of the playoffs, yet felt helpless and frustrated when he sat on the bench during the half. How ironic that he tore his ACL during their least competitive game of the season. It only added salt to the wound and made his knee throb even more. Gross annoyingly told his replacement, over and over, how he would give anything to be able to play.

Montrose was only down by two points. It was still anyone's game when both teams prepared for the second half face-off. Reinhart calmed his defense and reviewed where they broke down. The tone in Annese's voice held their attention. 'We have to stop their big plays! It's critical that we stop DeWitt's first possession of the second half. We need to set the tone for this game. We need to show them who wants it more!'

They drew confidence from the certainty in his voice; he spoke with conviction and assured them they could win this ball game. He didn't yell at them, blame them, or appear upset. He just motivated them until they felt the hair on the back of their necks stand up. The squad was ready to face the second half battle. The defense halted DeWitt's first possession, gaining confidence after realizing the powerful DeWitt Panthers could be stopped. Their faith increased when Jeff broke through the secondary on a keeper, then raced for a 45 yard TD midway through the third quarter. The Rams tried to make up for the lost PAT's, but DeWitt stopped their two-point conversion attempt. Montrose led 18-14.

The lead changed hands five times during the game, giving the impression that whoever had the ball last would come out the winner. DeWitt had a critical chance for the go-ahead score from the Rams three and everyone wondered, *Could the Rams hold the Panthers at goal line?*

The Rams blended every ounce of strength their bodies had left, determined to deny DeWitt their glory. In the huddle, Schlichtster looked at the anxious faces of his line. He stared at Chris Wingo. *Yeah, he was a sophomore who stood 6'4 and weighed 260 pounds, but did he want it bad enough?* He studied Adam Stiverson, another sophomore lineman who was a strong, powerful weightlifter. To his right stood B.J. Dean, their third sophomore, who generated high tackles week after week, second only to Tony Beardsley. *The underclassmen played side-by-side with them all season, but were they as hungry as he was? As the rest of the seniors? Did they have enough Montrose Football in them to know what was riding on this play?*

Then he heard Stiverson grunt, which reinforced his uncertainty. He noticed B.J.'s clenched jaw, and how Wingo's nostrils expanded like a raging bull. It was then that Schlichtster realized that all three were hooked. The sophomores were now a committed part of them. Schlichtster felt confident that they were all one unit who trusted each other. He took a deep breath when the huddle broke. In that brief defining moment, the Rams became unbreakable.

They did it. They actually stopped DeWitt's commanding offense at goal line, successfully shutting them down for the second time in Montrose territory. A metamorphosis instantly transpired in the Rams that united and strengthened them; reinforcing their bond as brothers even deeper. *They felt unstoppable.*

An aggressive battle ensued when both teams laid everything on the line. Each needed the victory. Each tried to prove they wanted it more. Montrose drove to the DeWitt 19 yard line when adversity hit. A fumble recovery followed a five yard penalty for a minus one yard loss. To add salt to the wound, Jeff was sacked for a minus 10 yards, leaving them at the 35 on third and 26. Jeff maintained his composure on a last second audible when he dropped back to look for the tight end up the middle. When the corner faded up the middle, Jeff lofted a precisely timed aerial, hitting D'ar in stride for a picture-perfect 35 yard TD. Everyone knew it was a nine-route to D'ar, yet he still flat-outran his opponent, strolling untouched into the endzone. Troy was the first to reach D'ar and greeted him with extended arms. But D'ar jumped so high that he flew over Troy's shoulders and smacked the ground, before landing on his injured hip.

After the play Coach asked D'ar, 'Hey, how's that hip holding up?'

D'ar surprisingly realized that he blocked out any indication of pain during the entire game. He couldn't believe that he didn't think about the ache in his hip after the painful week he had.

Jeff and D'ar became a razzle-dazzle duo by connecting for four TD's and 299 combined yards against DeWitt. Unangst tacked on the extra point, allowing the Rams to breathe a sigh of relief with a final score of '25-14.'

Montrose fans went nuts when Jeff picked-off a pass in the final two minutes of the game, crushing DeWitt's final comeback hope. The Rams didn't expect to have that well of a game. The squad absorbed the roaring noise from their fans as they soaked in the excitement of the moment.

The offense played their best game. The defense would never forget how they held Dewitt at goal -- twice. The Montrose Rams left Dewitt thrilled for a chance to prove they belonged in the post-season party. DeWitt continued to earn their respect on the bus ride home after Rams sensed how bruised their bodies felt. DeWitt had to be the hardest hitting team Montrose had ever faced.

Troy let his sore body heal over the weekend, then faced a welcoming fresh snow that covered the practice field. He lined up with the rest of the defense for the sled drill. Troy was first in line to pop it, but the entire sled spun around like bald tires on an icy road, causing the entire team to burst into laughter. They tried to fire out one at a time, but the sled slid all over -- so they united. Whenever Reinhart yelled, 'HIT AND DRIVE' they all pounced on it.

The '92 Season encountered a gamut of weather. They practiced in the extreme heat, they practiced when it hailed and poured buckets, they practiced in freezing temperatures, but no one ever remembered practicing in the snow. Mother Nature blessed them with a blizzard earlier in the day, making for an unusual yet fun practice.

The laughter soon ended when they got down to business to prepare for round two against the **Millington** Cardinals and their high powered offense. Millington's quarterback was a Division I prospect who connected for over 1,800 yards and 19 TD's, while their veteran backfield combined with their quarterback for over 3,000 rushing yards.

The coaches prepared more hours than they cared to add up. D'ar tagged along with his dad after practice to watch more game films at the Annese house. D'ar listened when Chris Annese handed the phone to Coach and introduced a former player calling from college. D'ar heard the calm voice of his coach speak into the phone, 'Just tell him you don't want to drink because your dad was an alcoholic.'

It amazed D'ar to learn how many former players still called their old coach for advice. It made him appreciate the relationship he had with his dad, yet made him realize that coaches filled that void for a lot of guys.

Reinhart realized that the defense hadn't faced a team with such a balanced attack. They durability of the scout team was constantly tested during the long, tough practices of Millington week. Players reached the locker room physically exhausted every single night, but the elevated morale kept them going. After all, it was the second round of playoffs.

Coach D brought videos of their youth football games to watch the night before the Millington game. The team spread out in the wrestling room to remember their youth at laugh at themselves. They easily recognized players, and discovered that many had developed their own style as early as eight years old. It helped them realize how far they'd come and how clumsy and uncoordinated they once were. Nostalgia set in for the twelve seniors that played football together for ten years. It was the perfect thing to do the night before the Millington game, reinforcing the fact that no one wanted football to come to an end. *Not yet.*

The seniors reminisced about meeting behind D'ar's house to play football and baseball year round since elementary school. Beardsley moved to Montrose in the sixth grade and thought he was pretty fast, until he raced D'ar. Beardsley felt he was no contest for the sprinter then, and was still amazed at how fast D'ar still ran six years later.

Coach D didn't want D'ar playing organized youth football until the sixth-grade, but taught him the fundamentals in his own backyard. It prevented D'ar from experiencing the burn out factor by playing organized sports too early. Coach D showed him how to take a handoff, how to run a curl and even had his wife hold the ball so D'ar could practice kicking. He worked hard with D'ar yet made it fun, while establishing his own coaching style in the process.

Coach D became sentimental as he watched the film, realizing how fast those six years went. He thoroughly enjoyed coaching his son and his friends and knew he would surely miss that special group of kids.

The larger-than-life seniors seemed quiet when they left the school that night, feeling even more determined to keep their playoff dream alive. The squad wanted their journey to last as long as it could, *at least two more weeks.*

More than the casual fan took notice of Montrose Football. Excitement filled Montrose on Saturday as cheerleaders and parents decorated the town. They wanted to send a message to the visiting Cardinals when they entered 'Ram Country.' A powerful sense of community existed, providing Montrose residents with a proud feeling of belonging to something very special.

Millington Cardinal fans were just as loyal and also provided a huge crowd. Both teams had playoff experience but neither had ever advanced to the semifinals. Both teams were hungry to become Regional Champions. On that cold Saturday afternoon, one of them would finally break that barrier and advance to the next round.

The Rams planned to control the ball as much as possible to keep it away from powerful Millington, away from the hands of their awesome quarterback.

Montrose was off to a rocky start. On their first possession, Jeff's pass glazed off the fingertips of the intended receiver and was intercepted. That wasn't part of the game plan. The Cardinals answered by scoring on a 14 yard TD strike after marching 78 yards on the first play of the second quarter. B.J. was pissed at himself. He easily made tackles all year and felt he earned his linebacker position as a sophomore, but he tripped on the slippery, muddy field and missed his tackle. A good PAT lit up the scoreboard 0-7 in Millington's favor.

Following the kickoff, the focused Rams came right back on the first down. Jeff ran the option around left end then darted 65 yards to score. It became a chess game between coaches, causing fans to wonder, *What would the next move be? Tim Unangst was a safe bet for the extra point or would Annese go for the lead?*

The game was young and Annese wanted to send a strong message. The line blocked like they had no tomorrow, allowing Jeff to swiftly run the conversion in. The Rams went ahead 8-7. It was Millington's move. The Cardinal wide receiver tried to haul in a high pass on the sideline when disaster struck. The wire that outlined the field was intended to divide the playing field from the fans, not to cause injury. But the Cardinal slammed into the thin wire and injured his ribs, forcing Millington to quickly change their game plan.

The Rams drove down the field 66 yards on their next possession, then lost yardage on a clipping penalty. The fans were spellbound on the next play after watching D'ar amazingly get past five defenders, break three tackles, then use a spin move to avoid the safety. D'ar had a distinctive running style that defined him as a superstar for Montrose Football. Future players appreciated what he had accomplished years down the road. His strength and courage set him apart from the others when he deceptively cut and used his balance to throw off defenders. Even his teammates thought he was down after he took on half of the Cardinal defense by himself. But he bounced back like the Energizer Bunny; he kept going and going until he scored.

Check.

The crowd went nuts as soon as the points were scored, but the ball popped loose seconds later. D'ar was physically drained after his corporal run yet managed to jump on the pigskin, determined not to surrender it. The linemen laughed at his reaction then shook their heads with pride. They may have been *ox-strong,* but D'ar was unstoppable because he was *heart-strong.* His determination served as a source of inspiration to all of them.

Similar runs throughout the year made opposing coaches realize they couldn't stop D'ar. Instead, they did their best to contain him to minimize the damage. D'ar had the unique ability to see the field, allowing his keen football sense to read the defense. He saw holes open before the play entirely unfolded and was quick enough to charge through. Defenders found it hard to bring him down, which only pissed some of them off. Some opponents spit in his face, hoping D'ar would retaliate and warrant a personal foul. D'ar's humble fashion tried to rise above it, but he had his breaking point. Barnett and Beardsley knew where D'ar's fine line was and stood close by, like body guards ready to divert him.

Troy caught a 12 yard pass then broke loose into the secondary for a 40 yard run. He tried a juke move and ran into the defender that had chased him from behind. He laughed at himself and later told D'ar, 'Somehow, you make that look so much easier.'

When D'ar scored 216 points in '92, the paper called him a 'Scoring Machine.' They referred to him as an *individual* at the top of a chart that outscored 24 *entire teams* from the Flint area. Only 17 area teams outscored D'ar and eight of them made the playoffs. *He was amazing.*

Coach Annese felt his Rams settle down once they were on the scoreboard and added some pizzazz to the game. Jeff pitched to D'ar on fourth down. He artfully dodged opponents while Jeff fleetingly ran to the endzone, just in time to catch D'ar's 41 yard 'transcontinental' TD pass. Jeff could barely see #41 through the mud on Dar's jersey, but he couldn't hide his smile when he raced to the endzone to celebrate their 21-7 lead. Others joined in, leaving muddy smears after they hugged. Jeff and D'ar were an irresistible force, even when they traded positions. The team only practiced that play four times, but had complete trust in each other. They felt confident they could pull it off if everyone did his job.

That was how the '92 Team operated. Some had their differences outside of football but when they stepped on the field, they pulled together as one unit. Unlike some other teams who appeared to be individualistic, the '92 Team focused on team results. Coach Annese constantly stressed how important the entire team was. He didn't want them getting lost in the media's constant attention to Jeff and D'ar, the touchdown tandem that had entertained fans all season.

Millington had a chance to get back in the contest on a drive before the intermission, but had their march stalled when MacDonald attempted to sack the Cardinal quarterback. The Ram end had difficulty bringing the quarterback down, but wouldn't give up. In a desperate measure MacDonald grabbed whatever body part he could and wouldn't let go. In the speed of the tackle, the end didn't realize that he grabbed his privates but he wasn't about to let go, even if it meant dragging the pants of his opponent partially down in the process. MacDonald's efforts proved to be a big sequence for the Rams who couldn't stop laughing at the scene. He was determined and fearless; traits that fed his future love of skydiving. McDonald got credit for the sack, along with a new nickname – Psycho that received years of jeering once his move became a highlight film classic.

Montrose took the second half kickoff and marched down the field, determined to score. The line clicked on all cylinders when it made a big hole up the seam for D'ar to punch through and score a 12 yard run. He brought to Montrose Football what Michael Jordan was to basketball. The Rams were up 27-7.

Check.

The Rams knew their home field was in horrible shape; the shoddiest it had been the entire season. The ragged midfield became even muddier during the second half, making it difficult for players to get their footing. Millington wasn't prepared to play on a slippery field, but neither were the Rams. D'ar agreed that midfield stunk and restricted his speed, so he ran to the outside using the grass for traction whenever he could. Both teams dubbed it the 'Mud Bowl.' Broadcasters commented on how the game exhibited 'real football' and joked about starting the tractor pulls and mud wrestling events.

Annese had previously worked with a group of local men, mostly youth coaches and dads, to form a football club. Their main objective was to improve the stadium. The group now understood Annese's desire to raise funds to rebuild the football field. After witnessing the horrendous Mud Bowl, they undoubtedly gave their support

Montrose ignored the mud and ran a flea-flicker pitch-pass that allowed D'ar to hit Eddie on a 12 yard aerial with two minutes left in the third. An over-excited Barnett reached Eddie first and celebrated by head-butting him. Barnett knocked Eddie over and almost knocked him out as the Rams continued to move the chains. It only frustrated Millington who saw their playoff dream slip away.

Annese called for Tim Follet to run a play. Follett panicked, afraid his swollen thumb would cause him to fumble. He had caught his hand between two helmets during the first quarter but didn't think it was broken. It began to swell and turned a funny color, but he thought he was fine -- until half-time. He took a leak and could hardly tie his football pants with one hand. He didn't want to be a wimp and complain, but decided to show his swollen thumb to Eddie. He took one look, 'Dang Follett. Show this to Coach.'

As much as it throbbed, Follett replied, 'No way Ed, just help me and promise not to say anything.'

Eddie was true to his word and didn't rat on Follett. As he looked at his friend, he wished he had spared him that awkward moment. Follett sheepishly held up his swollen thumb to Coach who only shook his head with mixed emotions. In the back of his mind, he wondered if he prepared them to be too tough at times.

The Cardinals added a six yard TD run in the final frame, but it wasn't enough. The kings of the Tri-Valley East Division took their men off the board and left the final score '35-14.'

Checkmate.

The '92 Rams jumped and screamed, hugging everyone in sight. They were thrilled to pass their shiny Class B Regional Championship trophy around. Players handled it with admiration and proudly kissed it, embracing the moment. They accepted the challenge of being the first Montrose Team to reach the state semifinals. The victory felt like a double win to Vaughn, since Montrose beat Millington in powerlifting after the Cardinals had dominated the sport for so long. The Rams were 11-0, the most wins in a season by any team in the school's storied history. They rejoiced, yet held back part of their jubilation.

They wanted more.

The days were getting shorter as mid-November approached. Daylight savings time promoted practices to end at dusk while the Rams prepared to face their toughest competitor yet -- **Marysville**. Intensity and pressure increased with every game, so did their quest for the Dome. It felt within their grasp; they were only *one game away* from their dream.

Schlichtster left school on Monday after an exhausting practice. On his way home, he collided with a vehicle hauling a trailer without lights. Later, he wondered if his tiredness had impacted his reaction. *Could I have prevented that crash?*

Word about the accident spread quickly to his teammates and coaches. Patrons at the local bowling alley even heard about his accident before his parents were notified. Schlichtster found the ambulance ride a bit scary, as well as his E.R. experience, but what frightened him even more was the thought of missing the Marysville game.

The hospital admitted Schlichtster, then woke him every few hours throughout the night to check the impact of his concussion. He couldn't recall the ambulance ride and wondered where he was in the middle of the night.

The team worried if their key snapper would be able to play in their semifinal game. Schlichtster was an extremely physical player and his presence would certainly be missed. He thought he was healing quickly and tried to explain the importance of his upcoming semifinal game to his neurosurgeon. The doctor told him, 'Don't get your hopes up. You can't play.'

The news pierced Schlichtster's heart with the same compelling force of a bullet. He didn't want to consider not being able to play in the semifinals. *Didn't they know what this meant? This was not just a Friday night football game; this was 'playoff semifinals' and he was their center. No way would he be denied of his chance to play. No way.*

Schlichtster called Coach Annese and Coach Reinhart when he got home to update them on his condition. To make his life even more complicated, he flunked a test the following day. The accident interfered with his study time. He soon discovered that eligibility rules didn't bend, not even for accidents and state semifinals. In this teacher's mind it was black and white. If he wanted to play on Saturday, he had to pass the test.

Schlichtster's eyes brightened once the team doctor examined him after school. He had made progress and was given a glimmer of hope. He might be able to play on Saturday and thought, *Whoo-hoo, things just might work out.* Schlichtster came back to the practice field and watched from the sideline, while his teammates endured a long practice. He stayed the entire time to prevent being replaced or counted out. After a long day, Schlichtster forced himself to concentrate and forget about the upcoming game. He studied for hours late Wednesday night, determined to pass the test. *He had to.*

Schlichtster took the test for the second time on Thursday, then visited the team doctor after school. The doctor checked his eyes and agreed to allow the center to practice lightly the rest of the week under two conditions: wear a special foam ProCap on his helmet and return on Friday for a final check. He borrowed a ProCap from Joe Heystek who had experienced several concussions during the `92 Season. Schlichtster felt physically exhausted from an intense practice and barely slept; he was too worried about his test results.

He anxiously approached his teacher before the first bell rang on Friday morning. 'Well, did I pass?'

A smile quickly parted his lips and he breathed a sigh of relief. Schlichtster left the room with a skip in his walk and yelled, 'Marysville, here I come!'

The school buzzed with excitement throughout the week while the Rams prepared to face perennial powerhouse Marysville. Streamers hung from hallway ceilings amongst players' decorated lockers. The Rams continued their unrelented quest for the Dome while they studied Marysville and industriously prepared to meet them.

D'ar was extremely quiet when he went home after practice and chose to be alone in his upstairs bedroom. He could barely see his own reflection in the mirror because of each weekly motto surrounding it. He slowly read each one, then grabbed a black marker and wrote the motto for Marysville in the dead center, 'THE DOME OR HOME!' His room didn't contain any signs of heroism, even though his name and pictures were constantly featured in the newspapers. Those were quietly tucked away in a scrapbook his mom dutifully kept. D'ar didn't focus on what he'd already accomplished, instead he concentrated on their unfinished business. They needed a semifinal win in order to achieve their final goal. If they didn't win tomorrow, it would be his last high school football game.

He fell back on his bed and stared at the ceiling poster that he made before the season even started. The tape under the far right corner no longer stuck, causing the edge to roll up, but he could easily read the words, *LIVE THE DREAM.* D'ar wanted to experience his ultimate dream of earning his chance to play in the Silverdome. He envisioned running plays over-and-over in his mind, causing him to become restless, so he visited his sister's room. 'Hey Shaunne, come downstairs with me.'

The `91 highlight tape was still in the VCR when he picked-up the remote before taking his favorite spot in the rocking chair. As the rock music blared from the tape, his sister plopped on the couch, faithfully watching it with him like she had every pre-game night. Shaunne discovered that D'ar didn't want her to talk, he just needed her presence while he slowly rocked in the chair until he became lost in the music. He was in his zone while he watched his team and focused on what he needed to do. She was proud to be D'ar's sister and loved watching him play, and didn't mind getting lost in the shadows of his fame. She tried to be a good sport, but viewing the same highlight tape in total silence week-after-week bored her. Between her dad coaching and her brother playing, Shaunne possessed an understanding of football superstitions and avoided upsetting either of them. She did her part.

It was exciting to be a part of the offense. The Flint Journal printed D'ar and Jeff's picture with the caption, 'The Wizard and the Touchdown Makers.' The rapport that Jeff and D'ar developed allowed the touchdown tandem to account for 52 TD's and more than 5,000 total offense yards coming into the Marysville game. The Rams realized how hard it had been to get that far, and wanted to do something special with their chance. Their story was one of preparation, perseverance, and the sacrifices they constantly made to reach the semis, to become State Champions.

Coach Annese called the MHSAA after being told they were scheduled to play at the 8,000 seat Memorial Stadium in Port Huron. He understood that regional playoff games would be held on neutral turf in a stadium large enough to handle the anticipated crowd. He questioned how they considered Port Huron as a neutral site when it was located five miles from Marysville, yet 80 miles east of Montrose.

It didn't take a rocket scientist to realize that displeasure still existed about Bulldog's letter from a year ago. Montrose fans would travel the distance, no matter how far. That wasn't the issue, but the disadvantage of an unnecessary long bus drive infuriated him.

When the Rams watched game film, they realized that Marysville was a better team than anyone else they had faced. Their polished program challenged the Rams. Marysville had made the playoffs seven times in the last 12 years. They read about Coach Walt Braun who was the third-winningest coach in Michigan history after 27 years as head coach. To a bunch of high school kids that seemed ancient. They laughed when a teammate imitated Coach Braun walking with a cane.

Mixed emotions consumed J.V. Coach Jamie Kitts when he watched his alma mater. He was an All-State Viking for Marysville during his high school years. Kitts had nothing but respect for Coach Braun, who'd taught him so many things that he now used as a coach.

The Rams studied the Vikings wing-T ground game which had 16 strong senior starters on the two-platoon squad; eight on the wing-T offense and eight on the 5-2 defense. Annese told his team, 'Walt Braun is the master of the wing-T in Michigan. That's their trademark. They have a great ability to execute the wing-T and they're about as deceptive as they come.'

Annese knew both teams would be quick and strong and felt that whoever had the ability to control the ball game would win. He prepared his Rams and raised the stakes, while increasing their belief in themselves. The Rams were a small school from a small town with a big dream. Thousands of enthusiastic fans supported their dream, and faithfully made the two-hour drive to Port Huron's Memorial Stadium. Parents hauled cars full of red and black balloons that were released on kickoff, then joined more than 6,000 overly excited Marysville and Montrose fans in the stands.

Things didn't start out right for Montrose. The Rams moved the ball down the field when a controversial call was made against them, ending their first drive. Jeff went back to pass from the Viking's 30 and was hit by a Marysville linebacker. The ball was batted into the air, fell to the ground, and was picked-up by Marysville for a 46 yard return to the Montrose 14. The controversy rested on whether Jeff's arm was moving forward for an attempted pass. Annese thought he was throwing the ball, but Coach Braun thought it was a fumble. Dedicated fans on both sides supported their head coach. Annese defended the official's decision. It was a tough way to start the game. Montrose didn't want Marysville to gain the momentum.

The Montrose coaching staff couldn't help but wonder, *Would this turn into another Monroe?* The Rams turned the ball over on downs four plays later, then Marysville took a 0-14 lead after a 68 yard Viking drive. Marysville was extremely quick yet it was uncharacteristic of the Rams to break down in a game, especially so early. They were both football smart and academically smart, and wouldn't quit.

The Rams were down by two, but they were not out. They battled back. D'ar came around the left end and sprinted 43 yards to the goal line, with all he had to give, and scored.

Unangst felt good the moment he booted the PAT. He kicked it high like he always did, but a 40-mph wind caught the ball and sent it straight up. His heart sank to his feet when he watched it come straight back down. The game was too close for that to happen and he wished he could have done it over. He would have kicked it lower so the wind wouldn't have caught it. Disappointing eyes glanced at the scoreboard, 6-14, hoping it wouldn't come back to haunt them.

Coach Reinhart watched Dr. Alton shine a light in Schlichtster's eyes. The doctor monitored his concussion when he came off the field after their first two series. Schlichtster still didn't remember the ambulance ride, but he did feel the impact of his concussion. He wouldn't say anything though. That game was too important to complain.

Reinhart approached Schlichster, 'Can you play defense?'

He looked at his defensive coach, 'I'm ready Coach!'

Nothing would hold him back. Before playoffs, he only played offense, then started both ways after the competition heated up. The Rams needed his 210 pounds at defensive tackle, but his parents became disturbed as they watched from the bleachers. They didn't appreciate his health being placed on the line -- Domeward bound or not.

Follett's parents felt a similar reaction at the beginning of the game after watching the Marysville team doctor cut their son's cast off his broken thumb. The sports medicine clinic confirmed that Follett's bone was broken near his wrist after the Millington game. His heart sunk to his knees when he watched them cast his hand, but he quickly recovered after being told, 'This type of cast will be soft enough to play.' Follett practiced all week, carefully protecting his thumb that extended from his cast. Before the Marysville game started, the referee felt that the cast was too hard and could be used as a weapon. If Follett wanted to play, the cast had to come off. Follet immediately raised his arm. 'Then cut it off!'

They did. The doctor taped a pad over the broken bone and gave him an 'Okay to play;' but it really wasn't. Follett's thumb was pretty swollen and the tape job felt painful against the swelling. He tried to ignore it, but it was a distraction that prevented him from totally focusing on playing his best game.

Like the Schlichts, the Folletts realized the level of commitment their sons gave to avoid making it their final game. Nothing they said to protect their injuries would change that. Their sons would play above the pain.

The deafening crowd couldn't hear the cracking sound of helmets while opposing linemen battled. Schlichster's ProCap made him stick out like a sore thumb. His helmet was bigger than anyone else's on the team; the ProCap barely stretched over it. The coaching staff ordered a special helmet for him at the start of the season to facilitate the size of this head. The impact from contact forced the ProCap loose from his helmet, sending it airborne before hitting the ground. Two Rams responded like they were trained and pounced on the piece of foam as if it were a fumble. Schlichtster finally had enough of the cap popping off and hurled it to the sideline like a frisbee. It was a breezy day. The wind floated the cap almost the entire way to the sideline, giving the reserves a good laugh.

But they weren't laughing on the field. All season long, opponents had difficulty finding a formula that worked against the powerfully elusive D'ar, but the Vikings had. They keyed on D'ar the entire game, compelling the offensive coaches to resort to other weapons. Tony Beardsley was a tough guy with a nose for the ball, who racked up 19 combined tackles against the strong Vikings. He led the Rams for high tackles in `91 and `92, an effort that earned him All-State honors. In spite of his animal attack on defense, he didn't have the records like D'ar did on offense. Beardsley felt D'ar had a better chance at getting past the Vikings and often changed plays in the huddle. Whenever Annese called a '43-trap' or '30-veer', Beardsley switched positions. 'You run it D'ar, just run it.'

D'ar was so close to breaking loose numerous times when his final opponent grabbed his ankle. The Vikings wanted to use a net as their team strategy to defend D'ar. They thought they could contain him by having two linebackers press him in. Marysville spared no mercy while tackling D'ar; his body felt abused. His willpower pushed him harder than any game he had ever played. D'ar became the only back to successfully break 100 yards against the mighty Marysville Vikings.

The Rams discovered how hard it was to win a football game against such a talented, well-disciplined team. Most of the Rams played two ways the entire game against a larger team with enough talent for fresh reserves. The Rams played hard and tried to ignore their fatigue. They had enough heart to refuel their determination, allowing them to play even harder, in spite of their injuries. The coaching staff intensely pushed the Rams all week, requiring them to execute a hard-hitting, physical practice. They may have drained their two-way starters; a strategy they would need to change.

Vaughn couldn't believe how fast the game was going. Marysville obviously scouted Montrose well and knew their book. Vaughn wondered, *Why aren't we using the new things we practiced all week?* Instead, they stuck with their bread and butter, but Marysville knew how to stop it. Vaughn thought, *The Rams are more solid across the board compared to Marysville. Yeah, they had a few standouts, but their defensive line is scrawny. We should be ahead by now!*

Then D'ar shot up the middle from six yards out with three minutes left in the game. It was his 36th TD of the season and gave the Rams a chance to tie the game with a conversion. The thunderous cheers from the crowd echoed throughout the stadium, making it difficult for the Rams to hear Jeff's voice. The Rams were called on a motion penalty and lost five yards. Then, the two-point conversion failed. Instead of a tied ball game, the Rams trailed 12-14. Unangst dropped his head on the sideline and wished more than anything that he would've made his first PAT. *Damn.*

The Rams tried an on-side kick, but Marysville expected it and recovered. The only hope the Rams had was to get the ball back with 90 precious seconds remaining in the game. Coach Annese screamed at the top of his lungs, 'LET THEM SCORE! LET THEM SCORE!'

The Rams didn't have any timeouts left and Marysville executed a no huddle offense. Beardsley couldn't hear his coach, but was determined not to go down without a fight. He tackled his opponent hard on the next play with everything he had.

Coach Annese was extremely frustrated when his players couldn't hear him. He dramatically plunged to the ground on his knees, yelling at the top of his lungs, 'LET THEM SCORE!'

The ruckus from the crowd was nosier than ever. Despite the howling fans and the music from the bands, Beardsley thought he heard Annese and wondered, *Is Coach losing it?* The Rams had never been in that situation. Everything happened so fast, while valuable seconds ticked off the scoreboard. Beardsley was momentarily deafened by the noise, but screamed back at his Coach in a questioning voice, mouthing one word -- 'WHAT?'

The stadium didn't have a track surrounding the field. Players felt like the fans were directly on top of them. The huge crowd let out a mammoth supportive roar and cheered so loud that players couldn't hear anything. A few players on the sideline turned around, motioning their hands downward to silence them. But Montrose fans misunderstood the gesture and yelled even louder, hindering the Rams from comprehending the plan.

Annese hollered, begging -- 'LET THEM SCORE!'

Valuable seconds were lost by the time the Rams finally got the message. It took a few more seconds to register what their coach had asked them to do. Annese would've received the same reaction if he handed them a gun and said, 'Shoot your family dog.' Players expected the game could get hairy, but no one ever imagined surrendering a TD. Troy was irritated, but did what he was told and stood with his long arms at his side. He was peeved as he watched the Viking run past him, untouched, *and score.* Troy watched Marysville celebrate their 16 yard *gimmie* and thought, *This just isn't right.* It was by far the hardest play the Rams ever ran. Brent, Troy, and Follett stared at each other in disbelief, shaking their heads.

Unbelievable.

They were smart kids, all members of the National Honor Society but this didn't make any sense to them. Marysville jumped ahead 12-20.

The Rams listened to victory shouts blare from the opposite side of the field. Annese inspired his squad to attack with every ounce of fight they had left. They just needed some blind luck and a failed conversion. If Marysville scored the conversion, the game was as good as over. Every Ram on the sideline joined those on the field and silently prayed while mouthing the words, 'STOP THEM!'

The entire squad thought, *Thank God -- Marysville didn't score!*

Was it fate? Was it destiny? The Rams had one final chance to tie the game. The bad news was that instead of having `90' seconds on the clock as Annese originally planned, the Rams were down to 33 critical seconds. They needed to take advantage of every precious one. *Could they do it?*

A pass interference call aided the Rams while they prepared for a desperate final trick play – *the Transcontinental.* It worked once. The Rams hoped that Marysville hadn't watched the Millington game. Even if they did, desperate times called for desperate measures. With one chance and only seconds left, the Rams brushed any element of fear aside. D'ar positioned himself near the east sideline behind the end. The Rams quickly lined up. Schlichtster felt a rapid rush of adrenaline when he snapped the ball to Jeff, who threw a lateral to D'ar, just as they rehearsed. The line shifted to the west sideline with Jeff located behind them like they did for a screen. D'ar threw a flawless pass to Jeff who caught it and followed the wall down the sideline, while valuable seconds ticked away.

The crowd rose to their feet. All eyes were on Jeff who sprinted with everything he had. Jeff totally focused on the endzone, the corridor to their dream. Jeff wanted to cross that goal line more than anything he ever wanted in this entire life; so did every Ram that blocked for him. They were a team in motion, working together. Everything seemed to be going their way. Jeff made it to the 40, the 30, the 25, and before he reached the 20 yard line, disaster struck. Jeff was tackled.

Without any time to reflect on what happened, Jeff quickly glanced at the scoreboard. Only five seconds remained and the Rams didn't have any timeouts left. *Shit.*

Their backup plan was a no-huddle offense, then spike the ball to buy one more play. Jeff tried to control the influence of sudden panic as he watched Schlichtster desperately getting the Rams in position. They scrambled while trying to avoid the heavy, gloomy feeling that slithered up their spine, propelling a cold chill. They were almost lined up, while the Montrose quarterback and center yelled commands.

Everything seemed to move in slow motion. Jeff looked like a distressed victim in an old black and white Alfred Hitchcock movie. Nothing seemed normal. Without even looking, Jeff sensed the scoreboard rapidly ticking down while his heart crushed in his chest. He tried to ignore the panic; he never considered that the Rams would lose.

Then he heard it. The blasted sound of that awful buzzer. And just like that, it was over.

Over.

They only needed *one more second;* just one more snap. Instead, the game slipped away from them. It just slipped away while the empty, flat sound of the buzzer blasted the stadium, flickering out a very important dream. The Rams fell to their knees; the life instantly drained from them.

The Marysville side of the stadium looked like pandemonium with people jumping and shouting in jubilation. *They were going to the Dome.* The Montrose side appeared to be attending a funeral. As much as the Montrose players didn't want to leave the field, their fans didn't want to abandon the bleachers. No one wanted it to be over and stood in silence, while they witnessed a heartbreaking ending to an incredible season. Players tried to hold back their grief until they were through shaking hands with the Marysville Team, but they couldn't. Their tears fell prematurely and they were too grief stricken to even care.

D'ar felt devastated. He never quit or cheated or worked so hard at anything in his entire life, only to be disappointed. He looked at Barnett and felt his own voice break. 'How could it end like this?'

Barnett slowly shook his head. He didn't have any answers. The look on his face was just as disturbing.

D'ar finished his senior season with 2,940 incredible yards, scoring 36 TD's for 228 points. Even setting five school records couldn't ease his pain. His efforts earned him AP All-State Special Mention honors. He was the first Montrose player picked to both the Detroit Free Press and Detroit News 'Dream Team.' He played in the All-State Game and was listed in USA Today's Honorable Mention, with the elite of the country. His teammates voted him their 'Most Valuable Player' and he went on to play five years of football for SVSU. He made a phenomenal mark as a Montrose Football legend, but none of that mattered to him at that moment. All he could focus on was that he didn't get to *Live his Dream.*

The coaching staff gathered the Rams in the middle of the field, trying to be strong, while hiding their own raw disappointment. Coach Annese told them, 'I'm so proud of you guys. You played your hearts out. You were the first Class 'B' Regional Championship Team Montrose ever had. You need to feel good about that.'

His words provided some comfort but they all realized that wasn't their goal. They were a picture of grief. The anguish on their faces made Annese feel their sorrow when he looked at them. Speeches usually flowed effortlessly from his mouth, but he found himself searching for the right words to say. Words couldn't soothe their aching pain or his own. Giving up their dream was too excruciating for all of them.

The game happened so fast and was so close. They were not prepared for the outcome. Schlichtster looked down at the ground. He couldn't believe it was over. Gross felt like his world just came to an end. Troy played a tough game and led the team in tackles, but having their dream shattered after they came so close left him devastated. Brent just wanted to crawl into the ground and die. He was their Valedictorian and voted, 'The Most Likely to Succeed.' But at the moment, he didn't feel smart or successful. He only felt defeated. His favorite memory of Montrose Football was winning. Surrendering hurt like hell after they fought so hard. *They came so close.*

The Rams locked hands in their traditional two-by-two stance and walked down the center of the field under the north goal post one final time. They still couldn't believe it was over. Their season ended one week too soon. The team dreaded the walk in front of the bleachers to get to the team room at the south end of the field. They were too tormented to hide their emotions. Parents and friends proudly stood in the bleachers and clapped when they passed. Each parent closely examined their son and saw a tear stained face under his helmet. They realized firsthand what sacrifices were made and shared their pain. It was rare to see their sons so aghast and sob so heavily; the scene broke their hearts, leaving them hollow.

Jim Beardsley hugged his son Tony, feeling every ounce of his pain. Tony felt that his dad was probably the biggest fan Montrose had with three sons on the team. Tony hugged him back, appreciating the comfort and reassurance of a father's hug. His support made Tony feel like his dad believed in him more than anyone. His dad was such a huge influence in his life and he never missed a game. Tony couldn't remember ever crying so hard when he glanced around at his friends. They were such a close-knit group of guys. He felt like a character cast in the saddest ending. He couldn't imagine their season being any better than it was, other than winning the State Title. He knew he had the best of both worlds, playing with his friends and his younger brothers Eddie and Jason. Jason was a giant who stood 6'6" and couldn't stand to see his older brother so tore up. He hugged Tony and consoled him, telling him that he loved him. It was something the brothers rarely said, and they cried together.

Players leaned against the brick building as uncontrollable sobs escaped. They weren't ready to face anyone but each other, and tried to absorb what just happened. *How would anyone outside this team even begin to comprehend what we're feeling?* The coaches saw reporters approach and tried to corral them inside the building. The seniors didn't want to enter, feeling like prisoners about to face the electric chair. They simply didn't want to receive the final sentence – the tough farewell. They had experienced that scene before, only now they were the seniors. This was *their* year and the barrenness was happening to *them*. They simply did not want to repeat that sad memory.

Coach Annese looked around and would forever remember the greatness in that room. He started the difficult procession, then the assistant coaches followed suit. Each sucked up their own disappointment and told each senior how much they meant, and what made coaching each one of them special. They shamelessly cried together. *Finality was painful.*

The colossal emotions that stirred inside Brent caught him off-guard. After playing Varsity three years, he thought he would be somewhat conditioned to a final farewell. He wasn't. It had the same sadness of saying good-bye at the funeral of someone you loved. *It hurt that much.* Coach Annese pushed him to work harder than he ever thought he could. He helped Brent develop a dedication, a work ethic that he would take to college and later use to become a teacher and football coach. He stared at Coach Annese and wondered, *How do you thank someone for that?*

A loss wasn't supposed to happen. They prepared for months together and ran the gauntlet. Troy took a deep breath and felt totally drained when he struggled to convince himself that he would get through this. A quick look at his teammates confirmed his belief that a deep bond existed amongst them. They would forever be connected by that game, that season, and he wondered, *How do you say good-bye after enduring four years of blood and sweat from physically exhausting two-a-days and tough practices with the same guys?*

Even Vaughn was choked up. He was usually like Cliff on Cheers, having a comment and an answer for everything. Vaughn was the guy on the team who was never lost for words. His classmates voted him as 'The Most Talkative' person in their class, but he wasn't at that moment. Even Vaughn couldn't begin to express the sadness that consumed him.

Tim Unangst dealt with his own sadness. His kicks were successful all season, except for that day. He couldn't help but wonder if he had made that first kick, if that one single point could have changed the entire outcome.

Underclassmen, allowed to dress for the game, painfully followed in succession and made their way down the gloomy senior line. Even though they felt closer to some than others, all seniors won their respect as they invisibly planted a seed of desire to continue their quest.

Junior Chadd Patterson experienced one of the most difficult times of his young life while he stood in that depressing locker room. He felt such a sense of family when he told the seniors good-bye. It was difficult to see them so torn up.

Caught up in a game of trauma and dignity, the distraught seniors didn't notice the torch being passed. Just as the '90 Team influenced them as sophomores, the '94 Team was now hooked. The young players glanced at each other with uncomfortable expressions, unsure of what to say to their heroes. They felt like intruders at a private funeral. Their stares formed a silent oath that promised each other that *their* senior year would have a different ending.

Jeff cried right along with the best of them, feeling guilty for not leading them to the Dome. *Damn.* They came so close -- *just one game away.* They all accepted him as their quarterback and helped him orchestrate the offense to perfection. Jeff set two individual season game records for most passes and yardage in a game. He didn't dare mention how thankful he was to have one more year, but he already knew he would be lost without them -- *especially D'ar.*

Maybe next week or even next month the seniors would be able to put life in a better perspective, but that day it felt like the end of the world. Coach knew their wounds would heal over time. One day they would realize how much they had actually accomplished. They broke six team school records and seven individual ones. Their blood, sweat, and tears formed a bond that would last a lifetime. The '92 Rams would be remembered as one of the greatest teams in the history of Montrose Football. It wasn't their ultimate goal, but one day they would feel proud about who they were.

Annese and Reinhart went outside to talk to the press. Coach Destrampe was alone with the seniors. He personally knew that group of kids and struggled to say good-bye. Emotions clutched deeply around his heart, far beyond what a coach normally felt. His only son just played his last high school football game. Even though D'ar had a phenomenal season, his dad knew how much he prepared to accomplish his dream of playing in the Dome. Coach D's experience of raising teenagers provided him with a special maturity and patience to deal with high school kids. His rapport earned their utmost respect. Coach D wondered how he could tell each of them how he felt, when he couldn't even speak above the swollen lump in his own throat. He soon discovered that they didn't need him to speak, they only needed a firm hold from someone who felt the honesty of their pain.

Sunday's newspaper displayed a large, color photograph on the front page of the sports section. A large bold title stated, 'RAMS BROUGHT TO KNEES.' The photo featured a grief-stricken head coach on his knees pleading with his Rams to let Marysville score in the final minute. The moment Troy saw the photo, he knew Coach Annese would be furious. *He was.*

Another newspaper photo zoomed in on Jeff and captured the controversial pass call. The Rams felt more deflated once they saw Jeff's hand in forward motion, his thumb and fingers pointing downward, which signified to them that Jeff had gotten the pass off. They couldn't help but wonder, *What if the official had seen what this picture revealed instead of ruling it a fumble?* The entire outcome of the game could have changed, and they would be at practice today, instead of feeling like they were going to a funeral. The prized photo was enlarged and inserted as the last page in the '92 highlight book. Every time they looked at their highlight book or watched their highlight film, they wondered, *What if?*

Their playoff exposure helped Montrose Football gain recognition. It also opened the door for Annese to work with college recruiters for his players. D'ar, Barnett, Beardsley, and Schlichtster went on to play for SVSU. Gross and Brent joined Eric Hyde to play for Adrian College and Troy played for Michigan Tech. University.

The coaches knew time would diminish their painful feelings. It echoed a distant happiness of a great point in their young lives. The coaches cherished the memories of that special group of young men. Their accomplishments became the baseline that future teams would be measured against. They were a talented group of friends who executed any play given to them.

The coaching staff wrote a letter to the 1992 Montrose Rams, recognizing the people who enriched their lives.

'This is our sixth year at Montrose High School. During that span of time we have had some tremendous players and great teams. We can honestly say, however, that we have never been associated with a better group of young men. This team, above all others, recognized the importance of dedication, teamwork, and unselfishness.

We are very proud of you. Certainly your accomplishments on the field exceeded any other team in our rich football history. But, what really sets you apart from all others was your fabulous attitude toward all the demands the coaching staff presented.

We've never felt so upset to see a season end as we did this season. Sometimes, in our own selfish thoughts, we are sad to see you go on to greater challenges. We are so thankful that you allowed us to share in your successes. We know that you will be 'winners' in the future. You are permanently part of the Montrose Football family and are welcomed at anytime to stop in.

We love you.'

Sincerely,

The Coaching Staff

The seniors moped around for a few days then decided to make Coach Annese a senior video to capture their sense of brotherhood. They realized that they were a part of a super program, which had a positive effect on their school and community. Tony Annese would go on and coach hundreds of other players during his career, but they wanted him to remember the `92 seniors as the first Regional Class B Football Team. They shared his love of the game and accomplished so much together, coming so close. The seniors wondered, *Did Coach realize the impression he made on them, or how he provided a dream that would steer their lives forever?*

Coach brought them together and taught them what true teamwork was all about. He pulled out their best and pushed them to perform beyond their own expectations. He helped them take command of their life. They would never forget him.

Most of the `92 Team made the two-hour drive to the Pontiac Silverdome the following week. D'ar and Troy stood with the others in the lower deck endzone, also known as the Bittersweet Sea. Its flotsam was a colorful current of Varsity jackets ebbing and flowing with each game. They stood amongst other players from other tournaments, who felt they lost because of 'that bad call' or 'that lucky bounce.' It was a spot where players spoke in hushed tones, where there wasn't any yelling or cheering. It was unintentionally valued as a religious experience by the defeated players. Here they sat quietly, a vanquished lot. Only at the half did they venture for food or go to the restroom. They were sea dwellers who were only a matter of minutes or seconds from standing on the very field before them. It gave them respectful pause, as if at any moment they would awake from their terrible nightmare only to find themselves in the tunnel ready to take the field, wondering how they could be anywhere else.

The forlorn Rams stood there during the entire game, sadly watching as Marysville claimed the Class B State Championship, defeating Kingsford 21-12. D'ar stood side-by-side with his somber teammates, whose pale faces and blank expressions watched Marysville receive the State Championship Trophy. D'ar couldn't begin to explain the raw ache he felt in his heart; an ache that drilled through the root of his soul.

Could anyone possibly understand the torture he felt as he watched Marysville live his dream?

FLINT JOURNAL PHOTO / Jack Gruber
Quarterback Jeff Klopf #16 congratulates D'ar #41 after TD in playoffs

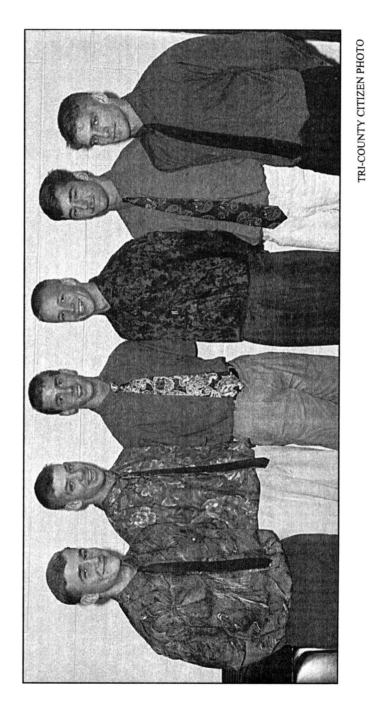

King Candidates (from left): Brent Baksa, Troy Andrews, Barry Gross, Tony Beardsley, Brad Barnett and D'ar Destrampe

6. TEAMWORK - 1993

The way a team plays as a whole determines its success.
You may have the greatest bunch of individual stars in the world,
but if they don't play together,
the club won't be worth a dime.

-Babe Ruth

The Rams ignited their momentum when they marched 92 yards in 10 plays. The quarterback threw two first down passes on the drive. On the next play, he faked then bolted 39 yards up the middle. He saw himself run on the Dome's big screen as the camera zoomed in. Peeking at the big screen to check if an opponent was close on his heels, seemed like cheating. Hopefully, it wouldn't matter as he listened to his own body grunt from sprinting so fast. He felt on top of the world, positive that he could outrun anyone at that moment.

His eyes found the screen again as he watched himself run on the turf. The crowd's voice exploded giving him a surge of energy, while his adrenaline kicked into overdrive. His legs glided smoothly across the spongy turf as if on automatic pilot. It truly was the greatest feeling he could ever remember; yet he still doubted the reality of it. 'If this is a dream, it sure feels genuine and real and I don't ever want to wake-up.'

The camera crew strategically filmed players from several different angles. The one that patrolled the sideline made Klopf look like a pro on Monday Night Football. His parents and two brothers focused on the close up shots after Teddy scored a TD, near the end of the first quarter. Their hearts overflowed with pride.

His brother Bobby thought, 'We deserve to be here. It's about time!'

Jeff on the other hand, didn't feel the same indisputable pride. Instead, it felt more like a sense of jealously or maybe it was sheer resentment in its purest form. Whatever it was, it didn't seem fair to Jeff and he wondered, 'How could it turn out this way, after I worked so hard for so long?'

B.J. Dean focused his eyes on the hard wood floor as he nervously paced the area behind his teammates. He glanced over at Chadd Patterson who sat Indian style on the floor holding his head, as if meditating would help. B.J. and Chadd both placed first, and hoped their contribution provided enough team points to capture a national trophy. The Montrose Powerlifting Team won Nationals a year ago in St. Louis, Missouri. They wanted to do it again. Chadd's eyes shifted toward the rest of his teammates that were sprawled on the floor in various positions, silently, but anxiously, awaiting the results.

Who would win the 'National Powerlifting Title?' The Montrose Rams really wanted it, as well as many other schools from all over the nation, including Bendle. Bendle's strong team provided stiff competition; they desperately wanted to beat Montrose. A powerlifting championship gave them a legitimate shot. Montrose knew the scores were close, maybe too close, as they patiently waited in a Chicago gym. Finally, the head judge called for everyone's attention, while anxious competitors looked his way.

One school jumped in elation, but it wasn't Montrose. The coaches watched the long faces on their kids who failed to hide their disappointment. They worked too hard not to. It started with their New Year's resolution to be in the weight room at 6:00 AM, to avoid interfering with wrestling and basketball practices. The Rams were a dedicated group. The '92 seniors needed to redeem themselves after Marysville. If they couldn't win States in football, they would attempt a National Powerlifting Title. They couldn't let the champion in them wither and die.

Coach Reinhart ran the powerlifting program. He realized the scores would be close, but he didn't realize how close. He watched Mike Sullivan recalculate the points as he leaned over his shoulder, feeling confident that a mistake had been made. They approached the judge's table and politely asked them to compare scores. The judges willingly recalculated, discovering that an error had been made. Feeling somewhat embarrassed, the officials recalled the trophy and presented it to the elated Montrose Team.

Their hard work paid off, allowing the powerlifters to taste the sweetness of a 'National Title,' while Bendle savored revenge. It tapered the edge off not winning a State Championship Football Title. They experienced an all-time high after their flight to Michigan then eagerly placed their national prize into the school's trophy case. *Tenacity was rewarded.*

Winning Nationals became a great incentive, bridging the gap between the off-season and the '93 Football Season. The guys were anxious for football to begin. Two dedicated linemen, Nate and B.J., continued the unspoken rule that team gassers accrued over the summer for weight room no shows.

Linemen loved to hit people; they hated to run gassers. Two-a-days were hard enough to endure in the August heat without the extra running. B.J. and Nate took it upon themselves to monitor anyone that didn't log his weightlifting workout during the summer, and called them. Nate was a dedicated senior, B.J. an experienced junior. The '92 Season left both of them with a burning desire to achieve more.

June marked the start of summer vacation. A time for most school kids to relax or find a summer job. For Mike Sullivan it meant election time, as he ran for a spot on the Montrose School Board. His victory at age 19 made him the youngest candidate ever elected. Sullivan demonstrated his maturity and leadership abilities to his teachers, classmates, and their parents throughout his high school career. People trusted Sullivan and felt he provided a closer understanding of the students' needs. Sullivan's leadership abilities sprawled over to his role as an assistant football coach. He, along with Joe Morse, took their coaching jobs seriously. They realized how much the game of football had taught them about life. Both enjoyed the closeness between players and coaches and wanted to drill the same work ethic that they were taught. It all started in the weight room.

Weights slammed and voices grunted as sweaty boys pushed their bodies to complete their reps in the foul smelling weight room. The hard-hitting chords of AC/DC blared from a boom box on the floor, when Steve Head walked through the back door of the weight room for the first time. His heart accelerated, feeling like it skipped a beat. He instantly liked what he saw as he followed his cousin, Tim Unangst, through the maze of weights.

Montrose Football had been the topic of conversation whenever the cousins were together. Unangst, the star kicker for the Rams, carried the tradition that his brother Sean started when he kicked for the `90 and `91 Teams. It was a tradition that his youngest brother, Tommy, planned to continue. The Unangst family moved to Montrose two and-a-half years earlier, and the boys were glad they had. Tim Unangst was sandwiched between an older brother and a younger one. He was the smallest guy on the team, got along with everyone, and made friends fast. Fast enough that his senior class voted him as their 'Most Friendliest Student.'

Unangst had been a soccer player before he moved to Montrose his sophomore year. But he didn't have the inbred killer football instinct that most of his teammates developed through youth football. Being the skinniest guy on the team, he padded the scales to weigh 150 pounds that the roster claimed he weighed. But hitting wasn't his favorite past time. Unangst was a laid back, funny kid who goofed around in practice. He made fun of the fact that he got killed in certain drills, but didn't take it too gravely. Unangst was their kicker, an important assignment that he did take seriously.

Steve had almost 100 pounds on his little cousin, towering over him by five inches. Needless to say, Steve turned a few heads when he walked in. No one recognized the big blonde kid, but instantly pegged him as a lineman. Steve surveyed the amount of equipment in the weight room and the number of guys that worked out. Every machine had someone lifting, while spotters screamed out challenges. Working out suddenly formed a new meaning. Steve felt a sudden urge to hang out with these guys; they made it look fun. He wanted to belong to a program that won the past five GEC League Championships. Steve felt like he fit in. Montrose became his first choice.

The Head family currently lived in Grand Blanc, and planned to relocate to either Montrose or neighboring Clio. Steve's dad was the head baseball coach at SVSU and wanted a closer drive. The two towns were less than ten miles apart, divided by Interstate 75. The academic programs in both schools satisfied Mr. Head, allowing sports to become the deciding factor. Montrose had a stronger football program, and provided his sons with an opportunity to play sports with their cousins. But he felt Clio had a stronger baseball program, the sport that he loved.

Steve used his older big brother influence to persuade Scott to choose Montrose. He brought Scott to the school in an effort to convince him. B.J. showed the Heads around, introduced them to some of the players, then to Coach Annese. The Heads instantly liked Annese and asked if they could try out for the team. Steve was a junior, and had only played one year of football at Grand Blanc High School. Scott was only a freshman. Coach Annese liked their size, but didn't promise them anything. He told the big boys, 'Your first step is to get in the weight room and firm up some of that baby fat.'

The Head brothers were excited and convinced their dad to find a home in Montrose, instead of Clio. Steve and Scott anxiously joined their new teammates, finding them restless to hit somebody on the first day of pads. A haze of fog swallowed the squad as they stepped outside of the school one early August morning to run a warm-up lap. The team could barely see the guys that ran just an arms length away. Nate's neon orange socks served as a guiding light through the fog. A sophomore player fell behind, getting lost in the dense fog; a premonition of their season.

Ben Maviglia was a senior, and hoped the Rams had a good season. It was his first season back since his freshman year. Montrose Football had received so much hype that he didn't want to look back after graduation, and regret that he forfeited his chance. But Coach had a subtle way of welcoming him back. Maviglia was the only tight end at a passing league camp in Alma. After playing five games in the steamy, summer heat, he discovered that Annese didn't give him much of a break. Since Maviglia was a quiet, shy young man, he didn't speak up. He felt glad to be back in the saddle and endured every play. But after two hours, he felt more like a wet noodle. Physical exhaustion helped him sleep like a baby the entire way home. But it was a good tired, that left him wondering if Coach Annese handed him a silent payback for his two-year absence.

Annese had been blessed with an uncommon luxury of a third year Varsity quarterback. Jeff made 16 TD's and earned a Class B All-State Honorable Mention in '92; and he had speed. Just three months earlier, he used his speed to become a Class C State finalist in the 100-meter dash.

Jeff's younger brother, Bobby, had a tremendous season as the J.V. quarterback. Bobby didn't especially like playing second fiddle to his older brother. Facing off with Jeff often got complicated because they couldn't leave it on the practice field; they had to ride home together. Bobby never told his brother, but he secretly wished that Jeff would get injured so that *he* could be the starting Varsity quarterback.

Getting injured was the last thing on Jeff's mind when the '93 season started. He was the only First Team All-League gridder back from the '92 squad, and realized how different '93 was. He longed to see D'ar at the end of his passes, and felt like the '92 seniors had abandoned him.

Like the coaches, Jeff also worried about leadership; a trait that was vital to a football team. Jeff wanted to lead by example, not with his voice. He silently wondered, *Who would step up? What if nobody did?*

Physically, the '93 Rams had the tools for a decent season, but seemed to lack the intensity and emotion for the game that previous teams showed. The Rams went from a senior dominated team, to a team that was relatively inexperienced. They lost two All-Staters, seven first team players, and three second-team All-Leaguers.

When Jeff opened his locker, he thought about the goals that he made for the season. He glanced at the laminated copy of *The Winning Pledge* that he taped inside of his locker door. Jeff felt the lump form in his throat as he read it again. He honestly meant every word on the page. The realization began to sink in, he was starting his third and final season of Montrose Football.

I, Jeff Klopf, will enthusiastically commit to making myself a better football player this summer. I will also dedicate myself to help the team achieve the goals we have established in every way I can. Therefore, I willingly make the following WINNING pledge:

Weights – I pledge that I will lift weights every weekday throughout the summer. If I am unable to lift, I will inform the coach that I will be absent and the reasons why.

Individual skills – I pledge that I will work on the individual skills which are specific to my football position. I will encourage the coach to help me master those skills necessary in making me a better football player.

No alcohol, drugs, or tobacco – I pledge that I will not use alcohol, drugs, or tobacco this summer. I will also stop teammates from indulging in alcohol, drugs, or tobacco.

I make these pledges in order to maintain, throughout the summer, the peak mental and physical conditioning that is necessary to achieve a successful season in the fall.

He signed the pledge, along with Coach Annese. Every player did. But Jeff felt that he was special to Coach Annese; he could tell by the way that Coach handled him. Coach didn't yell at him or hang him out to dry, like he did some players on scout team offense. Maybe he just understood Jeff, after spending so much one-on-one time working with him. It was weird. Jeff had been close with his dad, who supported his love of football in every way that he could. With two younger brothers at home, Jeff didn't lack male companionship, but he had a different type of closeness with his coach. Coach made Jeff feel like he was a great quarterback. He drew out the best in Jeff, without rattling his cage. Coach didn't scream in his face, earning Jeff's utmost respect in the process. Jeff would do anything that Coach asked of him.

After losing 18 players to graduation, the coaches realized they had plenty of work to do. The '92 Team left big shoes to fill with a glittering 11-1 record, posting the best mark ever by a Montrose Football Team. Their winning tradition ignited enthusiasm when 35 players formed the '93 Varsity, the highest count yet. The coaches were glad to see the high numbers of anxious players come out, but feared the lack of Varsity experience would impair them. At least they had something to build on.

Coach Annese worked tirelessly as he started his seventh year. He had enjoyed the building process up to this point, but worried about the future of the '93 Team. Practices were demanding, but everyone knew what to expect. The coaches made sure that the team got the message. After the first two weeks of practice, Coach addressed his Rams: 'We can't rely on tradition. You have got to do things on your own. You need a better understanding of what got us here in the past. We have to reestablish the work ethic.'

Injuries started to plague the Rams early. Coach had high hopes for junior Shawn Yuncker who had been a J.V. stand out. Yuncker banged his knee against a player at veer camp, then twisted it during a defensive back drill. His knee injury was serious and kept him out of the first four games of the season, throwing a monkey wrench in their offensive plans. Before the team even practiced with pads, another junior, Jeff Lange, broke his hand on the first day of two-a-days. A third junior, Tim Leeseberg, came to his first Varsity season with four stitches in his right hand. His injury was caused by an accident that happened outside of football, putting a glitch in his chance to make the offense or the defense. All three juniors felt extremely disappointed. They looked forward to playing for the Varsity and hung around until they healed.

The coaches moved three hard working sophomores up to finalize the Varsity that only had 13 seniors, but 22 very impressionable juniors. The underclassmen were totally committed to the Montrose Football program, and would do whatever their coaches requested. A few seniors felt shafted that sophomores replaced them. They had paid their dues after waiting in the shadows of a very talented '92 Team; they wanted *their* shot.

Chadd Patterson couldn't wait for football practice to start; it was the reason he looked forward to fall. After experiencing the teamwork and closeness of the '92 Team, he wanted the guys to pick-up where they left off. Instead, he sensed a different attitude after he saw individuality forming on the very first session of two-a-days. Chadd didn't feel like the '93 Team was off to a good start. Some guys acted like they were the stars of the team before the season even started. He mentioned it to B.J. and surprised himself when he said, 'I think it would be best if I just quit the team.'

Chadd's bold move caught his teammates off-guard, since he was pegged as the polite, quiet one. If a complete stranger met Chadd on the street he wouldn't think he was a tough guy, but get him in a drill and he could throw a mean hit. Chadd's muscular body confirmed that he worked out faithfully. He proved that he was the strongest in his weight class as a national powerlifter. He wanted a starting position his senior year. The squad knew that Chadd would run through a brick wall if a coach asked him to.

Coach Annese found Chadd sitting in the bleachers after their morning practice. 'Hey Chadd, B.J. mentioned you're not coming back. You know you're a bigger part of this team then you may realize.'

Coach sat on the bleachers next to Chadd. They talked for a long time. Coach didn't want any quitters on the team, but needed to get to the core of the problem; especially for someone as dedicated as Chadd. He convinced the senior to come back to the afternoon practice and continue to work hard. Coach had a way of making each player feel important, like he was a major component of the team. 'The younger guys will learn from your example and

the seniors will pick-up on your commitment. Hopefully, it all falls into
place.'

The Montrose coaches had an early confidence in their line. Wingo, B.J.,
and Adam Stiverson returned as juniors, after gaining valuable experience at
the Varsity level. All three had earned All-League accolades as sophomores.
That held promise, and the fact that the rest of the J.V. Team had a successful
season. It seemed the only thing lacking was senior leadership.

The '93 senior class was sandwiched between two classes that were close
and talented, which created a different attitude between them. Jeff and Eddie
Howell hung around together, and were very talented senior athletes. They
were the popular guys, but each had a quiet demeanor. Eddie didn't play a lot
of football as a junior, and didn't feel comfortable stepping up as a leader.

Annese appointed B.J. as a captain; a position he traditionally reserved for
seniors with strong leadership abilities. He struggled with appointing a
junior, but B.J. had a year of valuable Varsity experience. Coach felt
confident that B.J. possessed the characteristics that he looked-for in a leader.
B.J. felt honored, yet apprehensive, about how the seniors would react. Nate
accepted him without any regrets. In Nate's mind, B.J. had already proven
himself on the field with 109 Varsity defensive tackles under his belt. Nate
felt that B.J. deserved the captain's honor, and voiced his opinion to the other
seniors.

B.J. reached out to sophomore Joe Rizk; they bonded quickly as friends.
The new captain wanted the rookie to feel the anticipation of football season.
One clear, August evening, they made plans to camp out on the field. Both
welcomed the smell of dewy grass while they ran plays for hours under a
moonlit sky. Their energy was abundant, until they dodged an unexpected
spotlight from a patrol car that made rounds near the school. The cops
spotted a shadow on the field, and stopped to investigate. Once they
discovered a domed tent set up in the far endzone, they yelled for the boys to
come out. Rizk stepped out from the shadows. He looked at B.J. with wide
eyes, fearing they would get busted for trespassing. The cops strutted their
authority before they questioned the busted duo. They quickly recognized
their innocent anxiousness for football season to begin, and decided to let
them stay. Both boys breathed a sigh of relief after the cops returned to the
squad car, wondering if they appreciated their big dreams for the '93 Season.

But the '93 Rams lacked team unity in a fierce way. The seniors were
friends, and the juniors were friends, but the two classes didn't hang out after
practice, with the exception of three sets of brothers. They didn't have a
choice: Nate and Tim Leeseberg; Jeff and Bobby Klopf; and step-brothers
Jason Beardsley and Eddie Howell. A junior player broke his arm during
practice, which didn't concern the seniors. Their mentality was to smear each
other and feel great when they put a hard lick on someone. They all wanted a
spot on the first team, figuring if a player got injured, there were plenty of
others to take his place.

The juniors listened when Coach Kitts borrowed a phrase from the Marines -- 'You are the few, the proud.' He felt it fit them and their status in school. As a teacher and coach, he tried to appeal to their sense of self-worth and pride. Players were usually outnumbered, but had a chance to be role models, standing above the rest of the guys in the school who just talked big stuff. Kitts sensed a pool of doubt develop between the classes, as if the juniors doubted their senior teammates. They didn't verbalize it but he wanted to pull them back together, to get them to see that they were the chosen few. Not only to make them proud but become their identity, the very fiber of who they were, or about to become. The juniors were already close friends, but they needed to gel with the seniors, and they needed to clot real soon.

Tempers flared and heated words exchanged, while players fought for positions during Ram drills. The one thing they all had in common was that they wanted starting positions. Someone challenged, the other accepted and before they knew it, practice moved inside to the wrestling mats. The scene was familiar to the many wrestlers on the football team. They had confronted each other for years on the mat, which often turned into a battlefield. The mat was where they braved the dare, testing each other to resolve their challenge. They completely disregarded the break between two-a-day practices and let the wrestling mat become the true contest. *Who wanted it more?* A good fight seemed natural between brothers, so Jeff and Bobby were the first to go at it. Both wanted the quarterback position, but it soon became obvious that neither had ever wrestled. Bobby was bigger boned than his older brother, and used his extra weight to out muscle Jeff, while his fellow juniors cheered him on.

Jason Beardsley was the joker on the team, always goofing around with the guys. He jumped at the chance to face his stepbrother, Eddie, on the mat. Their coordination quickly showed that basketball, not wrestling, was the winter sport they played. Ed's quick body tried to dodge his brother who stood 6'6", weighing 215 pounds. Jason and Ed become brothers back in kindergarten and knew each other extremely well. Jason dominated Ed in size, but Eddie had quicker reflexes to outmaneuver his big lug of a brother. Ed wasn't too worried about Jason, he knew that his brother was a big teddy bear under his massive height. The coaches tried to push Jason to become a stud football player, because he was so much bigger than everyone else. Or maybe it was because his older brother, Tony Beardsley, was such a good football player. But Jason didn't have his older brother's killer instinct. The coaches often made an example out of him, but it didn't bother Jason. He was popular with his senior class, using his quick wit to make his peers look pretty stupid when he wanted to. He didn't lack confidence in the least, and was voted as the 'Most Outgoing Senior.' Basketball was Jason's main sport.

Somehow, Tim Leeseberg found himself in competition with his brother Nate, and wasn't sure why. They didn't even play the same position. Nate played center and tackle; Tim wanted the end position. But Tim found himself in a one-on-one match when the two joined in the brotherly custom; the match everyone wanted to see.

The original intent of the challenge took a twist from who *wanted* the position to who was the *strongest* brother. For a split second Tim thought, *if I beat him, Nate would be pissed. Nate didn't like to take crap from anyone, especially if they screwed around during practice and he had to run gassers.* Nate hit players hard on any given play, sending a message to knock it off. He had tasted success with the '92 Team and wanted it back. But Tim soon forgot about his brother's easygoing side once Nate lifted him over his head, then dropped him on the mat. Tim discovered that Nate still ruled.

The coaches were determined to bring the '93 Team closer together and constantly stressed. 'You're all brothers and need to look out for each other!'

A new muscle drill was added to mix up practice and generate team harmony. Guys drove their vehicles to the back parking lot near the weight room door, hidden behind the school. Players were organized in groups of three then were timed as they pushed a vehicle around a makeshift course in the parking lot, while one of them steered. The guys accepted the challenge and aggressively competed against each other. The three largest linemen were grouped together and assigned to a Chevette. The combined weight of Nate, Wingo, and Stiverson totaled 720 pounds, allowing them to easily push the Chevette. The scene revealed the back to basics flavor of a Rocky movie, when he ran through heavy snow, uphill, carrying added weight. The squad realized that the three linemen didn't understand how fast they were moving the Chevette, which was headed straight toward Coach Annese. B.J. yelled to the onlookers, 'Jump on the car to add some weight!'

Nate was paired with Stiverson and Bobby Klopf on his next round. Bobby was strong, but moving the Chevette without the assistance of Wingo's 295 pounds was tougher, giving them a greater appreciation of Wingo's strength. Wingo was an easygoing guy, huge, but easygoing, until someone flirted with his girlfriend. His neck looked bigger than some of the guys' thighs, and got lost between his head and his shoulders. His presence earned him 'strong man points' when the team left practice, exhausted from their physical workout. The new drill was a refreshing break after hitting the sled.

If the sled could talk it would share a few stories of its own. Coach Kitts jumped on it when players began a defensive drill. Kitts lost his balance as players fiercely drove the sled, causing him to slip. Players couldn't stop their momentum when the sled ran over Kitt's right shin. Immense pain abruptly shot up his right leg. Kitts thought he would die, but refused to show his pain. His male ego kicked in. He sucked it up and went about his business, with watery eyes. A few players laughed out loud after discovering that nothing was broken. Coach Kitts silently racked up tough guy points from the guys when he overheard, 'God, that had to hurt!'

Kitt's toughness soon disappeared after he got away, and glanced at his new war wound. Just looking at it made his shin throb. It reminded him of the time Coach Persails caught his hand in the old sled; the one that looked like it came over on the Mayflower. The kids were taking hits when it ripped a quarter-sized chunk of flesh out of his hand. Coach 'P' bled like a stuck pig and soon ran out of places to wipe blood. He tried to act like nothing happened and said, 'Awe, no big deal.' But it hurt like hell.

Reinhart randomly dropped the football throughout practice. Linemen were required to instantly jump on it or the entire line had to do extra ups-and-downs. It was a drill that increased their reflexes, forcing them to pay constant attention. Players often repeated the drill between classes, while peers dodged burly guys scrambling in the middle of the hall.

The team showed promise. They created a new tradition by sending a freshman to retrieve the 'deviated combobulator' from the equipment room. The freshman eagerly tried to abide by not screwing up or looking foolish, but didn't have the foggiest idea of what to look for. The rookie returned empty handed, with only a confused look upon his face. B.J. asked, 'You couldn't find it? It looks just like a 'right handed blocking module.' The seniors got a kick out of their own originality, feeling that they creatively instigated a new tradition for freshmen orientation, a clean form of hazing.

Nate, their new starting center, had to snap the ball a hundred times for quarterback brothers Jeff and Bobby. The center got a refreshing break when he filled in at wide receiver after the snap to catch passes. Nate got a kick out of Bobby who broke up the monotony with creative cadences like, 'Big Mac, double fry on two.'

Montrose exploded after scoring five TD's in the first period. It allowed several players to get a taste of their season opener against the **Hamady Hawks**. Jeff and Eddie each scored two, Chadd scored from four yards out, and Persails came up with a safety. Even Jeff's little brother Bobby got his shot at quarterback in the second half, connecting with receivers for two TD's. Tim Unangst booted seven PAT kicks, while senior Joe Heystek held them to make a final score of '51-12.'

With so many studs on the '92 Team, Heystek didn't see a lot of field time as a junior. He hoped for more time his senior year. His 6'2" tall frame sported 165 pounds, and he was good enough to play many different positions, but wasn't the best at any particular one. Heystek felt like the perennial back-up that loved to be a part of Montrose Football, but it wasn't his only focus. Heystek was a member of the National Honor Society. He figured out early that it wasn't only about what you accomplished in high school. Football had been a fun step along his path, but he knew it wasn't his future. He planned to get an engineering degree; a career that could provide a reliable future. But when he stepped on the field on Friday nights, and heard the vociferous crowd scream, he couldn't deny the awesome rush. The Rams winning tradition made him proud. It eased the load of the weights he was forced to lift during the summer. Friday nights made it all worthwhile.

Coach gathered his team in the middle of the field afterward. 'This was smooth sailing tonight, but we've got a tough week ahead. We need to get ready for **Chesaning** starting now. They'll be a tough opponent and you can't think that next week will be the same easy time. Two years ago, we were fortunate to get a win over there. You can bet they're gunning for us.'

The cold weather didn't seem to bother fans that lined the fence around Chesaning's field. They anxiously waited for the game to start, totally unaware of what they were about to witness.

The Rams caught the Indians off-guard when Jeff connected with Eddie on a 17 yard TD within the first six minutes of the game. Six minutes later, they connected again on a 47 yard pass. Unangst kicked both extra points to give the Rams a 14-0 first quarter lead.

At the start of the second quarter, Eddie was in the right spot at the right time. He picked-off a Chesaning pass in the flat, then raced 47 yards to score. Jeff connected on a six yard TD pass, hitting Eddie again for another score in the final minute of the first half.

The Rams scored on five of six possessions, dominating the first half 33-0. Reinhart and Annese felt they had the flavor of the '92 semifinal team. Annese opened his intermission speech with, 'This was the best half I've seen.'

Chesaning Coach Bob Sager was in the opposite locker room. Whatever he said to his Chesaning Indians during the half, completely turned the Indians around. They caught Montrose off-guard when Chesaning hauled in their opening kickoff. The Indians burst through a seam, rambled 89 yards on the very first play, and scored.

Before the Rams realized what happened, the Indians stopped them, then connected on a nine yard scoring pass to make the score 33-14. Coach Annese was concerned about the momentum shift. He convinced Nate that it was perfect football weather, in spite of the freezing temperature. His center needed to totally concentrate on the game, not on the wintry climate.

The Chesaning Indians were so hot the second half that they didn't notice the weather when the fourth quarter started. The Indians scored on a two yard run within the first two minutes. Their successful PAT made the score 33-21, which was too close for the Rams. Five minutes later, the Indians took the momentum from the Rams when they darted 50 yards to score, putting the game within six points.

Unbelievable.

The Rams didn't know what hit them. It was only the second game of the season, and they were still trying to establish leadership. B.J. stepped into the huddle thinking, *Wow, we have the potential to lose this game.* He was still shocked that a senior hadn't stepped up, but felt he needed to encourage the Rams. In previous jams, senior players like D'ar and Tony, always took control of the game. B.J. waited for Jeff and Eddie to step into the leadership role. They were both star players who played a tremendous first half. But like B.J., they were conditioned to focus on their job, and depended on others for that leadership responsibility. So B.J. kept fighting, because the guys needed him to. The coaches could only do so much; leadership was needed in the huddle. B.J. sucked up any inferiority he had and told his squad, 'It's just us now. We're the Varsity; those guys aren't here anymore.'

B.J. tried to pump the Rams up, but didn't feel comfortable. His pep talk must have helped, because the Rams stopped Chesaning's conversion attempt. The Indians had another chance late in the fourth quarter, but an interception preserved the win for Montrose. The Rams hung on, making it through the strangest game any of them had ever played. They protected their precious 45 game streak with a '33-27' win. Montrose felt the commanding pressure of the streak, wanting to extend it, not collapse it. Each year of the streak represented a link in a chain. Each connection was equally important, joining it to the next season. No one wanted to be responsible to unfasten the sacred six-year winning streak. *Humiliation was appalling.*

No one had ever seen Coach Annese so upset. He wouldn't even talk to the team after the game, breaking his own tradition that he implemented seven years ago. He was infuriated when he yelled, 'JUST GET ON THE BUS!'

They obeyed, then sat, and waited . . . and waited, feeling the air grow thicker by the minute. The bus was uncomfortably quiet, prolonging the sick feeling in their gut. Nate knew a royal ass chewing was headed their way; the long anticipation only made it worse.

Coach Annese finished his press interviews, publicly praising Coach Sager, his staff and players, '...for coming back and showing a lot of character, the kind of character Montrose lacked in the second half.'

The prolonged wait on the stuffy bus played on their minds. The stench of their own foul-smelling sweat became overwhelming, causing several players to crack the bus windows for relief. Eddie couldn't enjoy the fact that he scored four touchdowns or caught five passes. It didn't matter that Montrose chalked up 343 yards compared to 172 for the Chesaning Indians. In the eyes of their coaches, they only played half of a game. The scoreboard said they won. The crowd cheered afterward so it must be so, but it sure didn't feel like a victory. It felt more like a royal ass kicking. Nate felt like Rocky after his fight with Apollo Creed. *It's hard to feel like a winner when your eyes are swollen shut, everything hurts including your pride, and you wake-up in ICU.*

While anxious players dolefully waited on the bus, Yuncker waited in recovery. He was knocked out during the entire game and missed the ugly win. The Rams obviously missed their key back. Maybe Yuncker should be thankful, but he wasn't. It was noon when the orthopedic surgeon started to operate on his right knee. Yuncker thought he'd be done in plenty of time to make it to the game, sporting crutches or sitting in a wheelchair.

He was wrong. When his sleepy eyes finally opened from his post-op state, he focused for a second before realizing that it was Friday night. He immediately asked, 'Can we go to the game?'

His mom only laughed, 'Shawn, it's 9 PM.'

Yuncker settled for a recap on the evening news, and was stunned.

He wasn't the only one shocked. A humiliated and astonished coach boarded the quiet team bus, unable to hold back his frustration and screamed. 'Roll up the windows!'

Nate immediately felt the prickly needles work their way up both of his arms before they rushed down his spine. Coach's harsh lecture was meant for players' ears only. The sharp penetration of his words lingered in Nate's head all night long. 'HOW IN THE HELL CAN YOU BE UP 33-0 AT HALF AND LET A TEAM COME BACK AND SCORE 27 POINTS AND ALMOST TAKE IT AWAY FROM YOU? HOW CAN YOU LET THAT HAPPEN?'

Annese definitely had their undivided attention. His uncomfortable pause lasted for an eternity. 'TONIGHT WAS A WAKE-UP CALL. IT'S PROBABLY THE BEST THING THAT COULD HAPPEN TO US BECAUSE NONE OF YOU REALIZE WHAT IT TAKES TO BECOME A CHAMPION! YOU HAVEN'T SHOWN THE CHARACTER OF PREVIOUS TEAMS HERE. YOU CAN'T EXPECT TO PLAY THIS WAY AND BE CHAMPIONS!'

His intimidating words turned hula-hoops in their stomachs. The added hot air steamed up the bus windows, which made driving dangerous. The bus driver peered through a small opening in the windshield as she attempted to exit the school parking lot. She pressed the brakes as the bus approached a gate. The tension was so thick on the bus that her stomach was also in tight knots. The last thing she wanted to do was interrupt a coach in the middle of dishing out an ass chewing, but what choice did she have? She had to speak up. She had never felt so uncomfortable in her life when she bravely forced out the words, 'Coach, the gate is locked.'

Annese wanted nothing more than to get the hell out of town, and abruptly responded without thinking, 'Then break it down!'

Her eyes widened. *Was he serious?* She didn't know him that well and tried to disguise the crack in her voice, 'I can't do that.'

Coach realized his frustration had the best of him. He grabbed the cold metal bar at the front of the bus before he insisted, 'Just let me off.'

When his left foot hit the ground, he turned around. 'Pick me up at the main road!'

Players shamefully watched their coach stomp away until he disappeared into the night, like an eerie scene from the Twilight Zone. Shit. It felt like a living nightmare and they wanted to wake-up and change the outcome. They never saw Coach so mad, as they silently looked at each other with wide eyes, feeling totally responsible for his aggravation.

The motor hummed, as if droning out their turbulent heartbeats. Even the warm bus couldn't stop the chill that flowed through their cold bodies. That 30-minute ride home felt like the longest bus ride they ever made.

Every practice after the Chesaning game was extreme. The coaches made adjustments and constantly yelled. 'We're looking for some tough hitters who want to play football!'

They found them. The team acted thankful for the wake-up call, realizing that winning doesn't simply happen because of tradition. The coaches stressed fundamentals, focusing on the little things like how to stay on their block and come off the ball low. The linebackers and quarterbacks focused more on their steps as the Rams prepared to face the **Bentley Bulldogs.**

Cheese, the oldest Leeseberg, called his brothers from Northwood University the night before the Bentley game. 'Hey guys, we started something – don't end it.'

Cheese always called the night before Nate and Tim's game, but that time his words held a slight threat. Nate appreciated that his oldest brother was on the team that started the streak. He usually found his words encouraging, but that particular call left a nasty taste in Nate's mouth. Cheese thrived at college level football, but he never dismissed that his high school football years were still special to him. The six-year streak stemmed from his senior year, symbolizing a very meaningful time in his life. It was a chapter that he wasn't ready to close just yet. *Neither was Nate.*

B.J. didn't feel threatened to play Bentley after Coach Annese's pre-game speech. Bentley wasn't a threat in previous years and he never thought about losing to them. But the Rams were a young team. They didn't realize that they had to be 'up' for every game, because the opposition longed to knock them off their pedestal.

The Montrose coaches feared that too many players lived in a comfort zone, thinking they could ride the season on their reputation. Bentley had another game plan in mind. The Bulldogs had the talent to be a threat, especially after Chesaning's second half explosion against Montrose, which only encouraged Bentley.

Bentley's kicker got on the scoreboard first with a 25 yard field goal. Unangst felt a little pressure then answered the challenge with a 26 yard field goal to close the first quarter with a tie. The hard-hitting teams continued to stop each other, turning the game into a battle between the kickers. Bentley got into position and kicked a 36 yard field goal, taking a 3-6 first-half lead.

Steve sat in the locker room during the half, reliving the same threatening feelings that he felt during the Chesaning game. It didn't feel good and left him wondering if he was responsible for the Rams bad luck. *I convinced my family to move to Montrose and was so proud to become a Ram. Now, for the second week in a row, we performed with the poorest start the Montrose Rams experienced in years. Am I the one who jinxed the team?* He felt the chill shoot up his arms when Coach started talking.

Annese could be extremely intimidating when he was humiliated. He literally screamed at Stiverson for his missed tackles, 'You're a muscle bound pussy who should play as a defensive back instead of a lineman!'

The head coach understood the emotion of the game and shot the lineman's adrenaline completely off the charts. His goal was to light a fire under Stiverson, the strongest lineman in the League. Players wanted to laugh at his choice of words directed at Stiverson, their national powerlifter who squatted 600 pounds and deadlifted 580 pounds. They wondered, *Who dared to call Stiverson a pussy?* About that time Annese turned around, glaring at them. He grabbed a water bottle and threw it. 'Oh yeah, it's real funny.'

A dead silence swallowed the room. The uncomfortable stillness caused wide-eyed players to exchange unspoken glances, just as the bottle struck Nate. It collapsed, sending water everywhere and left Nate wondering, *How come I always manage to get hit with the water bottle?*

The mood in the room instantly changed, as if Coach snapped his fingers and placed a trance over them. No one dared to laugh as a rigid chill blanketed the silent room, becoming dissonantly still as fear immobilized the squad.

Nate could tell by the way that the veins extended in B.J.'s neck, that he was furious. If the first half wasn't a wake-up call, he didn't know what was. Previous Rams took significant pride building the streak, and now they were in a position to jeopardize it. B.J. didn't want their streak to end. No one did, except their opponents. B.J. knew they could pull it off, if they could just settle down long enough to get things rolling. For the second week in a row, B.J. waited for the senior leadership that never surfaced. He forced himself to step up and provide the guidance that was obviously absent.

The Bentley Bulldogs took the field with a renewed determination. A victory over the Rams felt within reach. *They wanted it.* The Bulldogs claimed control, extending their lead to 3-12 by the end of the third quarter, scoring on a one yard run. The Rams responded heroically to this rare bit of adversity, scoring on back-to-back drives in the fourth quarter, taking the lead. Jeff darted seven yards to score seconds into the fourth. Unangst made sure that his PAT was good, narrowing the deficit to 10-12.

The Montrose offense sure missed Yuncker, who was still recovering from knee surgery. The coaches made adjustments, shifting Eddie from wide receiver to running back. In a last ditch effort to score, they also tried Chadd, B.J., and a few others in Yuncker's position. Their desperateness became apparent.

B.J. didn't have the finesse of a running back but he was quick, strong, and could muscle in from six yards out. With five minutes left in the game, the Rams finally took their first lead. Being in the spotlight was a rare treat for the Rams guard. But B.J. didn't allow his embarrassment to diminish his excitement when he slipped and fell after celebrating in the endzone. He cherished the righteous moment, since it marked the only TD he ever scored during his high school career.

Eddie tacked on the two-point conversion, giving the Rams a hard-sought 18-12 lead. Their nervous fans were somewhat in shock of how the game played out. They screamed 'DEFENSE' at the top of their lungs whenever Bentley had the ball, and shared the enthusiasm after the Rams scored. Montrose fans had grown comfortable being in the driver's seat with large leads. The neck-to-neck, nail-biting games made them extremely uncomfortable. The clock seemed to move in extra slow motion during the last minute of the game, while fans hoped to hold onto their small lead.

It was difficult for Tim Leeseberg to watch his teammates fight the battle from the sideline. He had earned a spot on special teams, but couldn't seem to land a permanent spot on the offense or the defense. He grew frustrated as he watched the Rams fall apart, but encouraged them from the sideline.

B.J. and Stiverson were two of only three players that went both ways during the entire game. The physical and emotional strain started to wear on them. They couldn't believe an undaunted Bentley marched the length of the field, knotting the contest at 18-18 when Coach TerHarr's son connected on a 22 yard scoring strike. The Rams found themselves between a rock and a hard spot, and Bentley planned to go for the jugular. The Bulldogs had a chance to win the nail-biting game in regulation with a good PAT. A successful kick meant the end of the Montrose six-year winning streak.

Bentley's kicker was a shining star that night after making two field goals and a TD. The place kicker for the Bulldogs focused while the ball was snapped, his quarterback served as the holder. He placed the ball then felt the pressure from the kicker's foot sail high toward the uprights. Opposing fans stood side-by-side in the bleachers, spellbound, focusing on the path of the ball. A few hearts stopped on the Montrose side. Time barely moved, causing a matter of seconds to feel like ¾ of an eternity. From where the Bentley kicker and his holder stood, they thought he nailed the extra point. The twosome believed that the Bentley Bulldogs just made history, and blissfully celebrated with their teammates, while the Bentley fans cheered ecstatically.

The visitor's side of the bleachers stood motionless, shocked. Montrose fans felt their stomachs turn sour. Some even appeared terror-stricken, as if they just witnessed a terrible car accident. They watched Bentley celebrate under the belief that they just broke the mighty six-year winning streak. The Montrose community took pride in their winning streak, feeling an abrupt sadness that it was suddenly over. While others thought that Bentley's kick was *wide right* and the Montrose streak remained unharmed. The ball sailed so high that it appeared *centered* to some; it all depended on their angle.

Suddenly, the Montrose bench came alive as God and blind luck seemed to be on their side. Both of the officials, who were positioned directly under the outside of each goal post, saw it differently. One held his arms up to signify a good kick; the other motioned it sailed right. The final decision was that -- *it was off.* Bentley's Coach Cal TerHaar respected the official that made the call, and didn't argue. He later stated with class, 'The official said it was wide and I guess it's wide.'

The Montrose streak was still alive – by a matter of inches on a missed extra point. But it wasn't over yet, the game was tied. On to overtime. The pressure was enough to make some fans leave their seats and pace. Even adults who didn't have kids on the team felt the need to hurl; that's how caught up the town had become in their precious streak. It made adult fans a nervous wreck. They couldn't imagine what the team felt like.

It was stressful enough for the Rams on the field; maybe even more frustrating for those summoned to the sideline. Maviglia stood with the others, feeling like a sitting duck. It could end for them at any minute, and he couldn't do a damn thing about it.

Each team had four chances to score from the 10 yard line. The coaches remembered the last time that Montrose went into overtime. That game ended in a heartbreaking 20-18 loss to Lake Fenton in 1987. That was Annese and Reinhart's first year coaching, and neither wanted to repeat that scene.

It was nerve racking to go into overtime against a team Montrose felt they should have controlled the entire game. For the second week in a row, the Rams fell apart on the field and couldn't grasp why. The players valued the Montrose football tradition, and wanted a win more than others may have realized. Montrose had first crack to score. Coach Annese spoke with conviction when he looked each one of them directly in the eye, 'We WILL win this ball game.'

Eddie was their go-to guy. The confidence in Annese's voice seeped through their skin as the timeout ended. Coach gave his quarterback a final pat on his shoulder, 'I know you can do it Jeff.'

The Rams pulled themselves together, playing as one unit. The line blocked on third-and-one. Eddie caught a seven yard slant pass from Jeff, then ran two yards to score, exactly as planned.

It was up to Tim Unangst to kick the extra point. He felt the weight of the world rest on his small, but strong shoulders. Never before had the Rams been in this position; the streak intensified the weight. Unangst watched the familiar scene in college games all the time, but now it was up to 'him' to win the game. The gnawing question ran through his mind, while he warmed-up his leg with practice kicks. *What if I miss? The whole streak could end right now if I miss.* Just minutes earlier while they were in their huddle, he heard someone ask Coach, 'What if we get a bad snap? What's our back-up plan?'

Coach stared long and deep at Unangst, 'Don't worry, Unangst will make it.' *Conviction generated confidence.*

Unangst walked three steps back and two steps over then repeated the confident voice of Coach Annese, 'Don't worry, Unangst will make it.'

Unangst totally focused on the hands of his holder, Heystek. The kicker's peripheral vision watched as he took the snap, placing the ball exactly where he needed it. Unangst walked off his steps, took a deep breath and booted it. He felt his leg follow through as his eyes anxiously traced its path. It felt right on, but he watched it float through the silent air until it centered itself between the goal post. His eyes nervously drifted down to the officials, and he watched until they both lifted their striped arms. The kicker exhaled a deep sigh, before glancing at the scoreboard to confirm the numbers actually changed to 25–18.

Heystek was the first to reach Unangst and celebrated. Unangst felt relieved, almost too numb to rejoice as his teammates pounced on him. He blew out the rest of his nervous air, feeling relieved that he made it. Unangst made every point they had asked him to, now it was up to fate and their defense. He couldn't help but wonder, *Would Bentley score? If they did, would they go for a conversion and win?*

Bentley had a chance to send shock waves through the GEC League, with a possible second chance to break the precious streak. The Bulldogs were determined to score. But the uncoward, rejuvenated Montrose defense became dangerous when they bonded together like super glue. Reinhart's defense placed heavy pressure on the Bulldogs, causing two incomplete passes. A Montrose penalty left the Bulldogs with a third down at the five yard line. Bentley's quarterback ran to his right on an option play, pitching the ball.

Chadd closely watched how the Bulldogs lined up. It was a play they had practiced all week, and it looked familiar to him. Chadd watched the quarterback pitch the ball, then followed his instinct as he ran between the quarterback and the running back. He knocked the pigskin loose and watched it thrust upward. Chadd positioned himself underneath. The moment it was within his grasp, he intercepted the pitch. He ran as fast as he could in the opposite direction, until his own teammates mauled him. Chadd had saved the nail-biting game. His interception kept their streak alive and breathing; his teammates couldn't thank him enough. Annese hugged Chadd on the field, then watched him soak in every moment of heroism.

Nate grabbed him, 'Chadd, how did you know the ball was going there?'

'I just had this feeling he was gonna pitch it again and I went for it.'

Annese was emotionally drained yet elated, and celebrated with the team. He flashed back to their pre-season when Chadd wanted to quit, and was glad that he stuck it out. Chadd enjoyed the well deserved spotlight. It became a moment that embedded itself into Chadd's memory -- forever. *Fate was cherished.*

The Montrose squad on the sideline charged the field, hugging in celebration, as relief oozed from their bodies. B.J. glanced over at Coach Annese who appeared to be very happy as he celebrated with the team. B.J. was a bit worried after the previous week and thought, *Okay cool, Coach doesn't seem too upset.* The Rams were thankful to walk away with a win, after fighting an ensuing battle during the entire game.

B.J. relaxed as the Rams exchanged a well-deserved respectful handshake with the Bentley Bulldogs. Heystek made eye contact when he shook hands with the opposing quarterback. Both were the PAT holders. A year later, they became fraternity brothers and had endless discussions about 'the kick.' They also became good friends. Heystek understood why Bentley's quarterback couldn't let go of that game; he truly believed that their kick was good.

The Rams gathered in the middle of the field, and discovered that Coach Annese was not the least bit happy. His smile had quickly faded; screams instantly followed. Tim Leeseberg focused his eyes on a blade of grass to avoid eye contact with anyone. But no one could possibly tune out what came next. Coach was rightfully pissed at each one of them, and they felt every cutting word from the royal butt chewing. The entire squad felt like a pile of worthless scum, whether they played or not, as they listened in silence with their heads hung low.

Coach Annese was so mad that spit flew from his mouth. 'If this game didn't scare you, and if you didn't get a wake-up call last week against Chesaning, you sure better have one now. Either we use this to become a better team or we'll be searching for W's!'

Even with their credentials, it was quite possible the best team didn't come out on top that night. A humbled Coach Annese told the press, 'Bentley out did us in every area of the game, including coaching. They defended us like nobody else had. We were very, very lucky and very, very fortunate. We got outplayed tonight by a better Bentley team. From my vantagepoint, it was very, very close. If we lost, we would have been very, very hurt, because it hasn't happened in a long time. It will happen eventually. It could be next week or next year or in two years, but one day it will happen.'

They all felt relieved that it didn't happen that night. The Rams rode home in silence on the stuffy Montrose bus, wondering if the rest of their season would become a challenge. Nate couldn't stand the silence and vented his aggravation when he yelled like a wild man. He played hard on the line and was pissed; he didn't want another call from this older brother. They all shared his frustration. The '93 Rams worked hard, cared about football, and had the same dreams and desires of previous teams. They just needed to gel. They realized that no matter how consistent a team got, someone could always play better on any given Friday.

After two near losses in a row, the Rams had lost their confidence. B.J. thought, *This is gonna be a doozy of a year. We need to pull something together here real quick.* He couldn't pinpoint exactly where the problem was. Jeff was a great quarterback and Eddie was really good at posting numbers every game. They had a blue-collar defense that worked hard and loved to hit. He realized that even good teams could lose ball games, what was important was how fast that they came back. He honestly felt the Rams had the talent to be a good team. They were young and needed to quickly figure out how they all fit together. *Teamwork was lacking.*

Coach wasn't about to let the past two games beat them. He forced their internal fight to emerge. The Rams expected to run laps during **Bendle** week as punishment for screwing up, fumbling, and going offside. Their expectations came true. Players felt like they deserved every last lap after showing their recent vulnerability. The coaching staff sensed an unspoken doubt of the squad's ability to accomplish their team goals. So they built their confidence, yet kept them hungry.

Bendle was undefeated when they prepared to host Montrose during week four. Nate felt the chill pierce through his body when Coach Annese ended his pre-game talk and scolded. 'If last week didn't scare you, let this week scare you. If this week doesn't scare you, then you better hand in your uniform!'

Coach made eye contact with Eddie, Jeff, and B.J. He wanted them emotionally charged for the game and wondered if he got through. By the eager looks on their faces, he sensed they felt the attack of his words. The Rams felt ready to take a stand when they entered the stadium.

B.J. felt strange when he looked across the field and faced his brother, Noel Dean, Bendle's head coach. His mom also felt the awkwardness, but faithfully sat on the Montrose side. She clanged her cowbell while yelling for Montrose, yet silently cheered for Bendle. *She couldn't lose.*

All four of B.J.'s brothers were football captains during their stretch at Montrose, but none of them had to face a brother as an opposing coach. Needless to say, it added a little spice to Sunday dinner conversations. Noel built a strong program at Bendle, yet was still proud of his youngest brother, crediting B.J. as the 'Most Athletic Dean.'

Noel was a Montrose football standout himself who starred on the 1985 Team that advanced to the state Class B Semifinals. Noel's assistant, Jeff Setzke, was also a Montrose football standout that set school records in 1981 for 'most interceptions' in a single game and in a season. Their football heritage derived from being a Montrose Ram, but their loyalties now stood with the Bendle Tigers. Bendle wanted their shot at the Rams after Montrose barely escaped their last two opponents. The Tigers knew it was a matter of time before the streak would break; it couldn't last forever. *Nothing does.*

Bendle and Montrose competed neck-to-neck in powerlifting. They spotted for each other and several became friends. But this was football; friendships were left in the gym.

The Rams thought they were in for another battle when Bendle scored with 6:34 left in the first half, cutting the Rams lead to 12-6. It reminded Chadd of the Bentley game, making him even more determined. Rizk recaptured their momentum when he returned the kickoff to Bendle's six yard line, then scored on the next possession. The Rams gained confidence when they scored numerous times, ruining Bendle's Homecoming with a final score of '32-6.' The Rams finally started to come around as a team; the long awaited gel finally took shape.

Every single team that the Rams faced entered the contest undefeated, including **Byron.** The Eagles had only lost three times in their last 30 regular season games; each time the Rams did the honors. *Byron wanted revenge.*

The contest was on. Jeff showed his seasoned skills when he ran for three TD's and passed for six, leading a balanced attack. Jeff watched Eddie slump over, obviously frustrated after he dropped a 20 yard pass, and another possible four yard TD pass during two first quarter drives. Annese saw him hang his head when the Rams couldn't score in the endzone. He talked to Ed in the huddle between quarters. 'That's going to happen to the best of receivers. Just pick it up Ed, you're going to win this game for us!'

It was a brief conversation between a coach and a player at his lowest point. Two simple sentences that told Ed exactly what he needed to hear, in order to make a strong come back.

Yuncker was over anxious to finally play his first game since his knee surgery. Throughout the game he continued to nervously ask teammates in the huddle, 'Where am I supposed to go?'

His squad couldn't believe how much he'd forgotten while he stood on the sideline all season, but gladly filled in their star running back.

Chadd was also back from a separated shoulder and couldn't wait to get some action. He wasn't expected to be back, but his doctor didn't realize his strong determination or just how strong powerlifting had made him. Chadd sat out the first quarter, then felt a burst of energy when Byron ran four plays on his side. He stopped them all four times. Chadd played so aggressively at strong safety that he received two pass interference calls. He managed to calm himself down and control his anxiousness; it felt great to be back on the field.

The Eagles put up a fight, creating a scoreless game with 3:13 left in the first half. Annese wanted to score before half and resorted to his bag of tricks. Running back, Joe Rizk, took a lateral pass from Jeff, then hit Eddie wide open for a 34 yard TD strike. Rizk was only 5'5" and had a decent arm, after playing as the freshman quarterback a year ago. Rizk ran to the endzone to celebrate with Eddie and the rest of the Rams, who were thrilled to implement a play they had just learned a few days ago.

Eddie thought that the strength shoes he bought during the off-season paid off. The platform shoes looked really strange and the guys laughed at him, but Ed shared them with anyone who wanted to work out. Ed was dedicated, loyal, and easy to get along with. The guys enjoyed being around him. They designed a pulley system, with a 30 yard bungie cord attached that pulled him. All of the sprints and jump drills that Ed did throughout the summer seemed to help him perform better. He felt stronger and appeared quicker and more agile. Ed played cornerback on defense and recovered a Byron fumble that snuffed their final scoring threat. The possession set up the Rams final TD with five minutes left, locking in a tough '14-0' win.

Somewhere during the past five weeks, the Montrose Rams learned to like each other and started to play together as a real team. They gained character and started doing everything right as their season rolled on.

Montrose celebrated Homecoming and scored at will against **Atherton**. Seniors Jeff, Eddie, Chadd, and Heystek soaked in the fun of being Homecoming King candidates. Eddie, and his charming smile, won the final honors. Ed helped Jeff score early in the game. Then Jeff scored on a keeper, hitting his favorite target, Eddie, on an 18 yard TD. Eddie worked hard, proving that he was their go-to-guy for the big plays.

Then adversity hit on fourth and long. Annese didn't want Atherton to get the first down, and boastfully sent Jeff in at defensive end. He wanted Jeff's quick speed to run down their quarterback. Seconds before Atherton took the handoff, Linda Klopf's intuition warned her that something bad was about to happen to her oldest son. Her sixth sense forced her to yell from her spot at the fence, 'Jeff, watch out!'

Jeff made the tackle and everyone cheered. But the noise soon halted when Jeff didn't get up, as if the pro golf tour just held up the quiet sign. Time stood still while Linda Klopf held her breath, waiting for Jeff to move. Jeff's dad filmed from the sideline and immediately turned off his camera, then joined the trainers on the field. His stomach knotted when he glanced at Jeff; he didn't like what he saw. His three boys were his life, and he closely guided their football careers.

Annese realized it was a stupid move as he headed toward Jeff on the field. He heard some Montrose fans 'boo' him after he risked their quarterback in a non-critical situation. He originally planned to start Bobby at quarterback and play Jeff in the backfield. Annese stared down at his quarterback who was in severe pain. He had developed a special relationship with Jeff over the past three years, and learned how to work with his quarterback. He handled Jeff with a different approach. Annese didn't yell at Jeff; that tactic didn't work with him, and they learned to effectively communicate. Jeff had high hopes of playing Division I football. Now he faced the possibility of missing the rest of his senior season.

Damn. Annese wished he could rewind the play and start over.

Bobby watched as his brother lay injured on the field. He felt a nagging guilt seep under his skin for earlier wishing that Jeff would get hurt so that he could start. He didn't mean it literally; it was just his male ego talking. He was both nervous and excited, his stomach churned, he wanted to hurl. Bobby watched as his parents left the game to take Jeff to the hospital. He almost felt relieved knowing they would miss his first shot at the Varsity helm.

Annese was grateful that he had another Klopf in the reserves when he approached Bobby. 'Okay, we need you.'

Bobby appeared calm to the offense, trying to conceal a bad case of nerves that took him by surprise. He attempted a few passes but found that he stiffly aimed the ball, like it was attached to a string. It made him look like he'd never thrown a pass before. Annese was upset and called a timeout; he certainly didn't expect that result from Bobby.

'What the hell's going on? Just throw the damn ball Bobby. You're the quarterback!'

'I know. But I've never done this before, Jeff is supposed to do this.'

'Bobby, you've been throwing the ball your entire life. Just get out there and throw it. It's not any different!'

Annese brought the nervous quarterback to the state he needed to be in. Bobby eased his concentration, relaxed his arm, and focused on the plays instead. After he felt comfortable in his new quarterback role, he wished that his parents were around to see him.

The Klopfs were a dedicated football family who centered their lives around Montrose Football. They constantly stretched their grocery budget to feed the entire team on Sunday during film review, starting a new tradition that future parents continued.

Jeff's grandpa was in a wheelchair, but that didn't stop him from attending every game to watch his grandsons, including the youngest -- Teddy. He was only a seventh grader who tried to emulate the moves of his older brothers during his youth football games.

Homecoming held a moment of anticipation. It appeared that the Rams had the game locked in, but the student body grew anxious about the announcement of the Homecoming Queen. The Marching Band performed an entertaining, yet competitive, half-time show of 'Les Miserables.' Eddie stayed on the field to fulfill his reign as Homecoming King, pulling off his helmet when he posed with the newly selected Queen. An easy smile formed on his face, as strands of blonde hair stuck to his sweaty forehead. His dark green Michigan State T-shirt peeked through the neckline of his black Montrose jersey, sporting a bold red #21 outlined with a thick white border. Ed's favorite green T-shirt, with its cut off sleeves, became the only enlarged color photo in the yearbook; a permanent tribute to his ritual of never playing in a game without it.

Ed joined his teammates in the locker room just in time to hear the ending of an impressionable Annese half-time speech. 'Forget that you're up by 42 points. You still need to give 100%, no matter what. No matter how big the lead is. If you're going to do something you must give a 100 percent, a 100 percent of the time.'

Nate sat in the smelly locker room mesmerized by his speech. That particular talk, which didn't even pertain to a close game, helped Nate through a difficult experience five years later. Nate trained at the Police Academy and found his body trying to survive the ultimate test. He reached the point of being physically exhausted, facing that moment when a man questioned if he had what it took to endure the rest of the program. Nate's brain debated his physical abilities as he witnessed other candidates drop out. It was then that Nate recalled the half-time talk from the '93 season. He heard Coach Annese's voice say, 'No matter what, you must give 100 percent, 100 percent of the time. You never know if you can do it until you try!'

For 16 weeks Nate relied on everything he learned from playing Montrose Football. It helped him endure the vigorous program as the Academy tested his mental and physical limits. Three candidates dropped out on the very first day of training. It was a hundred times worse than two-a-day football practices. Candidates were told daily, 'You're not welcome here – go home!'

Nate related the physical hard work while he pushed his large body to its max. He credited his commitment to his high school football training to finish something that he started. And like football, he wouldn't quit. He discovered that the game of football prepared him to endure the Academy for his career as a police officer.

The Rams took the field during the second half, tacking on three more TD's under Bobby's lead. Annese was proud of Bobby's ability to step in and perform. He decided to add some spice to the game and sent in a mock play, then stood with Reinhart on the sideline to enjoy the reaction.

The squad huddled around Bobby who asked the player to repeat the play. Bobby knew the playbook inside out, after rehearsing every single play with his brother, but he didn't recognize that one. Frustrated, he looked up at his teammates and asked, 'What the heck is that?'

They all shrugged their shoulders. Bobby's head poked up from the huddle as he yelled to Coach Annese on the sideline, 'What play?'

The coaches got their laugh then Annese yelled back, '38 Veer.' They were proud of their Rams who amassed 428 yards in total offense on Homecoming night. Tim Unangst kicked eight extra points. He almost had nine, but his final kick was blocked. His older brother Sean watched from the stands, proud of his little brother who broke his school record. One thing Unangst enjoyed even more than a new record, was a chance to get dirty when Coach put him in as a defensive back. The star kicker actually got to hit somebody.

The Rams had plenty to celebrate after being ranked top in their region, and fifth in the state for Class CC, but they also had plenty to worry about. Jeff, their star quarterback, had separated his shoulder. Stiverson, a key lineman, was injured. A player had a hernia, a knee injury plagued another, while another player received a fractured wrist. The Rams had never had so many injuries during a game. It simply didn't stack up, since they played an opponent with a 1-4 record that the Rams beat '62-0.'

The **Lake Fenton Blue Devils** used a new tactic against the Rams. Their linemen faced the Rams with painted faces in designs similar to the rock group Kiss, only they used their school colors - blue and white. The Blue Devils wanted to appear fierce when they laid on the trash-talk, 'Yeah I got this guy, he'll be easy.'

'Okay, I'll take this one, he'll be easy too!'

Their purpose was to distract the Montrose linemen. They were successful at first, since the Rams had not seen that approach before and gave the Blue Devils credit for their originality. But they weren't sidetracked for long. Yuncker proved that he was back in football mode when he scored a TD in each quarter. He demonstrated that he was a sledgehammer when he rushed for more than 100 yards during the second consecutive week. He shared the points with Eddie after returning a fumble for a TD, and Rizk exploded 24 yards for another. Unangst kicked three PAT's. Eddie ran for a conversion, giving the Rams a '41-17' win and setting their winning streak at 50 games.

Heystek played free safety, but received a concussion during the game. During practice, he was required to wear a special helmet that contained a thick rubber pad around it. A wide receiver for the Buffalo Bills had to wear the same thing, which made the helmet weigh five pounds heavier. Assistant Coach Keith Williams made aluminum antennas and taped them to Heystek's helmet. Williams nicknamed him 'Gazoo,' after the little green man from The Flintstones. It took the edge off a tough week of practice, and gave the Rams a laugh as they prepared to face **New Lothrop.**

The town of New Lothrop loved their Hornets who were still undefeated as week eight approached. Even though it wasn't playoffs, it was cause for celebration. The neighboring town was a big rival of the Rams. The town sent their Hornets off with a parade, escorted by local ambulance and fire departments. New Lothrop's head coach, Scott Cousineau, was touched by their support. He waved to the fans that lined Main Street as the bus headed out of town. It was the supportive send off the Hornets needed to face the unbeaten Rams, and his old college teammates, Annese and Reinhart.

The Rams were plagued by injuries and worried about facing New Lothrop. Montrose felt the pressure to keep their winning streak alive. Since the streak started, the Rams managed to score 1,775 points, allowing only 368 points against. The streak had endured three presidents (Reagan, Bush and Clinton).

A wild first period opened when the Hornets and the Rams both scored within the first two minutes of the game. The Hornets came to Montrose believing that they could win, and sacrificed everything to stop their inside game. But the Hornets couldn't contain the Rams outside speed when the Klopf brothers teamed up. Jeff played as a running back, taking the pigskin from his younger brother Bobby, and was glad to play after sitting out for a week. But Jeff openly admitted that it wasn't the same. He missed being in control of the offense that the quarterback position gave him.

Coach D felt proud that he had a hand in Jeff's new role. He laughed to himself when he pictured Annese saying, 'Jeff's yours now. He can still run, but you've got to teach him to be a receiver, *starting now!'*

B.J. was sore as he walked into the huddle. 'We're going to have to play all four quarters of hard football guys. If we let up at all, we'll be in trouble.'

Maviglia played his best game ever. He usually only played on the kickoff team and had made several tackles, but that night he also saw action at tight end. The Rams had depth that year; Maviglia was in the top ten of the big guys on the team. He was easygoing, fit right in, and even adopted his own sacredness for Friday night rituals. He wore his Tweety Bird boxer shorts every Friday, since that's what he wore the first game. He went to Subway with Ryan VanGorder after school every Friday, ordering a club sandwich. *Every Friday.* He didn't want to be responsible for breaking their streak. Their rituals seemed so normal at the time; that's how paranoid the entire team had become.

B.J. faced his old buddy, Steve Whorf, throughout the game. A year ago, they both played Varsity as sophomores. Whorf won their personal battle when he hit B.J. extremely hard on the last play; obviously leaving any sign of friendship off the field. Whorf showed a lot of guts and character, leaving B.J. with a bittersweet feeling. B.J. was somewhat upset that he didn't wreck Whorf, yet felt proud that one of his best friends came out cocked and loaded against the Rams.

The Hornets led twice during the first half, giving the Rams horrible flashbacks of the Bentley game . . . *and overtime.* That alone was an incentive for Montrose to pull ahead during the second half, claiming their '35-19' victory.

That win took teamwork. The Rams felt their unity growing stronger as they faced **Goodrich** in the snow for their final league game. Bobby threw a pass to Jeff, who hauled in a 38 yard strike for the first TD of the game. Jeff's shoulder injury hindered his ability to throw, but transformed him into a multi-dimensional threat when the Rams used his exceptional speed at running back and wide receiver.

Unangst booted his first of five PAT's then watched Bobby score to close the end of the first period. Yuncker proved what a workhorse he was when he plowed over early in the second. Bobby connected with Eddie for his 14th TD of the season. It gave Eddie 96 points for the regular season; the second highest in the Flint area. Bobby connected with Rizk for a score, then turned the controls over to J.V. quarterback, Shane Schlorf, for a taste of Varsity action.

Everyone was glad to see Rizk on the field after the scare he'd given them. They thought he had a form of cancer and patiently waited for his test results. Normally, the guys teased a friend whose neck was so swollen that it looked like he swallowed a distorted baseball, but Rizk had them all worried.

What were the odds of chewing on a blade of grass, a thin, dark green piece of vegetation, and swallow a parasite? That was Rizk's final prognosis. It wasn't a tumor. It wasn't cancer. It was a parasite that latched itself inside Rizk's neck, becoming infected. Coach Annese was relieved that it was something treatable, and was anxious to use Rizk at his fullest potential.

Montrose closed their regular season with a '35-0' shutout over Goodrich, their third for the season, keeping their winning streak alive with 52 wins. The Montrose defense held strong by allowing only 11 points per game, overcoming the adversity they faced earlier in the season.

The Rams celebrated their undefeated season, happy to claim their sixth consecutive GEC League Championship. But they didn't celebrate long and studied **Reese's** game film, anxious to begin their second season.

An early Michigan snow covered the practice field, forcing them inside. The coaches didn't want to take a chance on anymore injuries for the post-season. The indoor practice allowed the gym to come alive with a renewed excitement, while players practiced for playoffs. Montrose school's enrollment placed them in Class CC division, where the computer point system didn't obstruct them as a state playoff qualifier. The Rams finished No.1 in their region, and would host the Reese Rockets during the first round.

Playoff fever sent an emotional current through the entire town. The Rockets and the Rams breathed in Michigan's fresh, wintry air that left their lungs numb, while they warmed-up in front of a standing room only crowd on a cold, Friday night. Nothing compared to playoffs. The Rams felt it the moment they ran through the hoop, especially Maviglia.

It was Maviglia's first playoff game. He was so excited when he jumped over the base of the hoop that he ran directly into Rece Davis, a local sportscaster, jarring his camera. It became Maviglia's claim to fame, as well as his only tackle of the game. The blooper secured him a spot on the highlight film.

It didn't take long to warm-up the home crowd when Annese reached into his bag of tricks. He took advantage of the Klopf brothers' skills on the very first offensive play of the game.

Bobby threw a short pass behind the line of scrimmage to Jeff. Jeff launched a 64 yard TD pass to Eddie who was wide-open and scored. The fans loved the theatrics of their opening play, totally unaware that the Rams had just practiced it a few hours earlier. After studying game film, Annese thought it could work. He had the team rehearse it in the gym after the pep assembly. His hunch was right. *Spontaneity was exciting.*

Reese came right back and scored with a 28 yard crossing pattern on the first play of the second quarter. Reese's PAT drifted wide right while Unangst kicked a good one, giving the Rams a 7-6 lead. Rizk raced down the field on the ensuing kickoff, making it to Reese's 40 before Bobby's pass was picked-off on the series.

The defense hit the Rockets hard, protecting their four yard line. It caused a fumble, which prevented Reese from taking the lead. Annese ran through plays in his head, deciding to exercise his option of alternating his quarterbacks. The Klopf brothers did a great job, but Jeff was a little quicker than Bobby was. Annese hoped that it threw off the Reese's timing. Annese prepared his offense to take the field and called for Jeff. 'Is your arm good enough to throw?'

Jeff stared at his coach like he was on another planet. *Did he forget about my long, opening pass?*

Annese was so focused that he drew a blank for a second, then they both laughed at his lapse in memory.

Jeff led the Rams on a 97 yard drive, trying to eat up the entire six minutes left in the half. The next laugh was on Jeff after he called a 43 trap, then got sacked when he ran a 42 trap. His parents cautiously watched, waiting for him to get up. It was Jeff's first game back at quarterback in four weeks, and they worried about another shoulder injury.

The Montrose quarterback popped up with a youthful energy, shaking it off as he walked back to the huddle. Nate looked at him, 'Sorry Jeff, but I know I blocked the right way.'

Nate watched his quarterback's expression through his own facemask, feeling relieved when Jeff responded. 'OOPS, my mistake.'

There was a lot to like about Jeff, especially his ability to admit his own mistakes. They all laughed in the huddle, watching Jeff lick his fingers like he always did. A confidence spread through the huddle when their quarterback said, 'Okay, I'll make it up to you guys on this play.'

Jeff called a quarterback keeper and sprinted ten yards to the front corner of the endzone. The only way to avoid contact with his opponent was to jump airborne for the final three yards. With one second left in the half, Jeff stretched the ball into the endzone while his body landed sideways. It was an awesome move, showing Jeff's tremendous effort and athletic ability that some compared to a college athlete. It was a move that underclassmen rehashed years later. Unangst's extra point was good, giving the Rams a 14-6 lead, worthy of their standing ovation.

Shane was moved up to play on the kickoff team. He hung his head when he missed a tackle and thought. *God, I'm going to get screamed at.* He watched as Reese returned the kick 89 yards for what appeared to be a TD, and felt relieved when a clipping penalty called it back.

Reese came back and scored on a 72 yard reverse, tacked on the two-point conversion, then tied the game at 14-14 half way through the third. Montrose went ahead 20-14 on a five yard run. Reese answered three plays later by catching a short pass, then outlegged Montrose defenders for 60 yards to make it a 20-20 ball game.

How much more excitement could anyone take? The offense and defense worked equally hard. B.J. spearheaded the defense with 15 tackles, and was helped by Stiverson who enjoyed his first game back after his mid-season injury. Eddie blocked an opponent, realizing that he injured his neck the moment that it happened. Ed was out of commission.

Coach D implemented hand signals after getting burned by the loud crowd noise during the `92 playoffs. It worked out well with the defense during the season. They watched Coach D form a tree and double fire, but their favorite sign was stud, which made them laugh whenever Coach D grabbed his sac.

Montrose planned to drive up the middle, eating up the clock after consuming an eight-minute drive. The Rams were in field goal range and could go ahead, but they had already given up three TD's on big plays. Annese didn't want to give Reese the ball with good field position and five minutes left on the clock. Instead, he made a gutsy call to keep his offense on the field and go for the down.

Reese showed how much they also wanted the playoff win by denying the Rams the down. They took over on their own four yard line, working out of their own endzone. But the defense showed their character by forcing two incomplete passes and a one yard run before kicking a short punt.

The Montrose offense worked together when Jeff made a tremendous third down, keeping their drive alive. Yuncker took the handoff on the next play, as Jeff watched his back bully through the Reese's tough defense. Yuncker looked like a ball rebounding in a pinball machine when he bounced off a pair of defenders. He steadied himself, before spinning away from the clutches of another. His determination plowed him into the endzone for the game winning TD. Yuncker played hard when he had the ball in his hands, but off the field he was a happy-go-lucky kid, who sported a contagious grin. He had something to grin about as he listened to the great roar of the crowd celebrating their first playoff victory over Reese '27-20.' He knew it could've easily gone the other way.

The Rams hosted **Orchard Lake St. Marys** next, a team that polls considered being in the top three in 'any' class in Michigan. Annese participated in a newspaper interview, with other local coaches, in which they agreed in theory why the Genesee County area proved so poorly in the state football playoffs, yet successfully dominated statewide in girls' and boys' basketball, volleyball, wrestling, and track. Holy Rosary won the lone football Class D State Championship back in 1977, the year most of the juniors were born.

Competing with the well-supported Catholic schools for football was difficult. Annese referred to the Detroit and Grand Rapids areas, as well as the west side of the state, that had more parochial schools and a bigger population to draw from. The result built a more successful parochial program, that attracted other players who wanted to be a part of their football dynasty. At the time, six Catholic schools won State Titles the past three years. Detroit DePorres and Brother Rice owned 12 State Titles between them, and Catholic schools won 10 other State Titles.

Area coaches felt per capita, that the Flint area had more good football players than any other system around with the Big 9 League as good as it had ever been. Flint Beecher, Carman-Ainsworth, Kearsley, Powers, Montrose and Oxford represented the area in past playoffs. As more teams made the playoffs, they hoped that one year, one of the area teams would bust loose.

The coaches tried to make the '93 Rams feel like they belonged there. Yuncker felt the excitement the moment he walked into the wrestling room that Friday night, to watch a movie with his teammates. The coaches wanted to ensure everyone was healthy and accounted for, while trying to take their mind off Saturday's big game. Coach D picked-up the popular movie *'Hoosiers.'* He hoped that the Rams related to being the underdog. Montrose was also a small but determined high school team who dreamed of accomplishing big things for their town, whose pride and joy was their football team.

The coaches handed each player a letter before they went home, suggesting they read it before going to bed. Eddie sat on his bed and opened the envelope, then felt his heart race as he read the words:

Dear Ram:

Saturday, November 14th will be the very last time that the seniors will ever play on our football field. It is my sincere hope that you will reflect on all the wonderful times you and your teammates have spent together playing football in Montrose.

How fitting that your last game on this field will occur on a Saturday afternoon. I'm sure it seems like such a short time ago you were playing for the munchkins, middle-weights, or heavy-weights on this very field on Saturday afternoons. What a unique opportunity to have the most important game you have ever participated in filled with such nostalgia.

Your parents, your coaches, and the Montrose community recall how you played every game like it was the biggest game of your life. You were only eight or ten or twelve years old, but it seemed like you were playing big-time football games in front of tremendously large crowds. Well, tomorrow is the biggest game of your life and you will be playing in front of a HUGE crowd. Channel all the energy and drive that you have left on that field since you were an elementary student and use it as a powerful force tomorrow.

Lastly, put all the questions to rest as to which Montrose Football team is the greatest in our rich football history. Was it the 1981 Team, the 1985 Team, the 1990 Team, or the 1992 Team? We can achieve a Regional Championship.

Make your last game in this town your greatest game ever. Everyone in this community respects your tremendous accomplishments. Now, after the fifty or sixty games you have played on this field, it is your chance to close the curtain on the greatest memories of a lifetime.

Good Luck,

The Coaching Staff

Eddie felt the anticipation of the game, but was too keyed up to sleep, tossing and turning before finally giving in. Once he was down, he slept like a baby before he joined his teammates early Saturday morning for a team breakfast. The fellas loved the attention that the cafeteria crew showed the coaches and players while feeding them a great breakfast. Eating together made them feel special; reinforcing that this was not an ordinary Saturday.

They all laughed when Coach Kitts appeared with a Bible in his hand. When he read the story about David and Goliath, the team understood the message that Orchard Lake may be bigger and better, *but they were not unconquerable.*

Nirvana blared from the boom box when Coach Annese entered the room, delivering the most powerful pre-game speech Maviglia had every heard.

Chills worked up his arms then overtook his entire body. He looked around to see if anyone noticed. It was then that Maviglia realized that every single guy in that room felt exactly the same. He could tell by their serious expressions and the determination their eyes held. Coach Annese had pushed them all to the edge; Maviglia knew they were ready to take the field.

Students and parents decorated the town placing 'Welcome to Ram Country' and similar signs along the main roads toward the school. Their mission was to dampen their opponents' spirits. But fans soon discovered that it took more than a few signs to bring down the tradition of Orchard Lake St. Marys.

Two Montrose J.V. players, allowed to dress for the game, warmed-up on the field. They felt cool while they caught punts during pre-game. One player threw a perfect spiral, with a slightly flat football, that thrashed though his friend's facemask, hitting him precisely in the eye. The friend needed medical attention when his pupil dilated, causing his eye to become so swollen that he couldn't see. The underclassmen felt foolish after they had the honor of dressing with the Varsity, and didn't want to tell Coach Annese what happened before the biggest game of the year.

The Rams knew that they were the underdog at the start of the contest, even though the coaching staff tried their best to motivate them for the challenge. Montrose planned to counter the stifling defense with their high-scoring offense, dubbing the contest as the 'Boys Bowl.'

Controlling the ball in the latter part of the game worked for Montrose the previous week, but then they didn't play against players like DiAllo Johnson, David Bowens, and Cameron Bineon. DiAllo was their quarterback who passed for 830 yards, ran for 250, and played free-safety. Bowens had 74 tackles, and Bineon was an awesome defensive end that Miami later recruited.

The Rams continually glanced over to check out the Eaglets as both teams warmed-up on the field. It was a bit intimidating to think that the Eaglets had four extremely talented players who were getting attention from Division I scouts like Miami and Michigan.

Ed tried to block out the stiffness in his neck, but it was difficult. He could hardly turn his head after jamming his neck. The team doctor said that his neck muscles were tight. Ed had done exactly what he was told, alternating 20 minutes of ice, with 20 minutes of heat. He couldn't practice, but nursed his neck the entire week. Ed wanted to play against Orchard Lake more than anything, even if he wasn't at his best.

The Eaglets seemed huge, averaging 215 pounds on a solid offensive line. They scored an average of 34 points per game, surrendering an average of only five points per game. Their seven shutouts in their grueling Detroit Catholic League held the defending Class CC State Champions, Detroit St. Martin dePorres, to only six points. Orchard Lake even defeated Class A Catholic League Champion Warren DeLaSalle by 21-0.

The Rams tried to control their racing hearts as they listened to Coach Annese in the huddle before the first play. 'They've got so many weapons it's going to be real important not to give them the quick-striking touchdowns.'

They listened to every word he said, but still had a hard time on their very first possession. The Rams hurt themselves by shanking a punt for a five yard net loss, giving Orchard Lake the ball at their 16. DiAllo capped the drive four plays later with a four yard TD, within four minutes of the start.

The Rams showed their character when they took their second possession 82 yards in 11 plays. Bobby tossed to his brother Jeff on fourth-and-goal from the six. Jeff was quick enough to beat the speedy Phillip Martin with an over-the-shoulder catch in the endzone five minutes later. Unangst's PAT was good, putting the Rams ahead 7-6.

Persails became the secret weapon for the Rams when he intercepted DiAllo's pass. But the Montrose offense came up short on fourth-and-two, then watched the Eaglets march 74 yards in ten plays. DiAllo hit David Bowens with a 27 yard TD. A good conversion gave Orchard Lake a 7-14 lead with 6:43 left in the first half.

Players on the field gained reassurance whenever they looked at Coach Annese on the sideline, finding him in total control. They gained confidence in knowing that he believed in them. The Rams were able to hang with the Eaglets. Persail's large, tall frame helped him pick-off another interception that he returned 20 yards. Persails was a sophomore and was amazed that he pulled off three interceptions against such an unbeatable team.

The newspapers had fun with Yuncker's next play, commenting, 'He looked like a locomotion when he ran through opponents and scored a one yard TD.' After that, his teammates dubbed him 'Choo-Choo Chuncker.' They were proud of how his powerful stride out-legged opponents. The PAT was good. The Rams tied the ball game at 14-14 with :39 seconds left in the half. Montrose played its best game ever, reaching their peak at the end of their season. *Teamwork was incredible.*

Orchard Lake made key adjustments during the intermission. They planned to shutdown the trap and the off-tackle play, that benefited the Rams during the first half. Bowens rocked one of the Montrose linebackers so hard that his head actually hit the ground before his limp body did creating a highlight film classic.

Montrose planned to ride its success as long as possible with the game tied 14-14, and 7:41 left in the fourth. The Rams continued to use Yuncker as a running machine to keep their ground game alive. Yuncker appeared unstoppable, using his leg strength to wear down defenders. It became tougher for opponents to come back and tackle him after he laid a few tough hits on them. Instead, they tried to trip him.

The Rams couldn't score on the series; things appeared to fall apart. Jeff had a high snap and the Rams only managed a seven yard kick. The Eaglets took over at the Montrose 21 yard line; five plays later DiAllo ran a 15 yard TD. Orchard Lake recovered a Jeff Klopf fumble on the next play from scrimmage at the Montrose 13. The Eaglets capitalized on the second of three Montrose turnovers by booting a 27 yard field goal with three minutes left.

Fans wondered, *Why were the Rams crumbling at the end after hanging so tough?*

It got uglier. Montrose lost the ball on its next possession then recovered a fumble on their own 30. They all knew in order for a team to win close football games, that they had to control the ball in the fourth quarter. With Bobby at the lead, they made a last ditch effort, moving to the 30 before time ran out. But the Rams never gave up until the clock forced them to.

The underdogs were not given much of a shot to beat Orchard Lake, the powerhouse of the Detroit Catholic League. The Rams pushed them to the limit before bowing out '14-24' on two fourth quarter scores. It made it even harder for the Rams to reveal their disappointment when the Eaglets received the Regional Championship Trophy.

The entire squad felt a brotherhood between them, but the finality of it ran deeper for three sets of brothers. Eddie and Jason embraced, unable to reject the fact that they had just played their final football game together.

Tim Leeseberg looked at his older brother Nate, and remembered how difficult it was in the beginning to play on the same team. He felt like everyone expected him to be as good as Nate, yet they were completely different on the field. Nate was shorter and stockier; Tim was taller and leaner. The program said Tim weighed 175; maybe if he was dripping wet with all his pads on, but the scales never tipped over 160 no matter how much he tried to put on weight. The Leeseberg brothers weren't real close in school, but football connected them in an extraordinary way, securing them.

Bobby had just played his last game with his brother, and couldn't imagine how Jeff felt. They had done so many things together that formed lifelong memories. It made them friends as well as brothers. It was a tremendous ride, but unlike jumping on the Magnum at Cedar Point, they couldn't just get in line and do it again. *This ride was over.*

B.J. felt terrible for the seniors, especially Jeff and Eddie, who played their hearts out. Eddie scored 16 TD's during the season and rushed for 800 yards. He played both sides of the ball, leading the Rams with five pass interceptions. When B.J. looked at Jeff he couldn't hold back his emotions and cried for their awesome quarterback who worked so hard. He knew that Jeff wanted to win a State Title more than anything.

Players realized that their coaches had done everything they could to prepare them. They went over drill after drill and play after play. It was up to the team to do the rest, and they fell short. Poor punting, turnovers, and penalties at critical moments had hurt them. The Rams had no idea that facing Orchard Lake would be so intense or how their speed was unstoppable. Bowens and Johnson proved they were Division 1 caliber. The Rams took pride knowing that they provided the Eaglets with their stiffest competition of the year.

Still. Their season was over.

The Rams gathered in midfield after the game for Coach Annese's final talk. 'You showed great heart and you have a lot to be proud of. You're a class act and I'm proud of you. You played your best game of the season today. We had it within our grasp. I can't say enough about how you performed today against an outstanding opponent. I am very proud of you.'

It made them realize how hard they played and how close they actually came, which forced the sobs to start. It seemed like the Varsity guys played against each other most of the season until that day. Playing a team with the caliber of Orchard Lake and holding them until the very end, brought the team closer as a unit. The Rams felt incredibly gloomy as they looked at each other, wishing they had reached that point earlier in the season.

Unangst looked around at the guys, feeling glad that he had a chance to experience Montrose Football. He felt a part of something great. The Rams almost beat a private school powerhouse like Orchard Lake St. Marys.

Maviglia sat next to Nate. They both released every ounce of emotion they had. Even in his moment of sadness, Maviglia felt a closeness and unity in his teammates. They learned to respect each other and looked out for each other. He was glad that he joined the team for his senior year. He cried with the best of them, forever drawn to the importance of that moment, realizing they had to accept that it was over.

Chadd looked around at his teammates, and felt that they all played aggressively. It was their defining moment of the season; they had played their best game. It suddenly felt like the closeness and the teamwork he remembered from the '92 Team, except now it was over. They waited too long to become a family. He wished the seniors could turn back the clock and start their season all over, with the closeness that they finally achieved.

It was a lesson that the 22 juniors vowed not to repeat. Playing against the best only instilled a greater desire, a bigger dream, of what they could accomplish in '94. They were already close, committed to each other, and made plans to make the most of their senior season.

Fans waited a long time for the Rams to walk off the field that day. Facing parents and friends at the last game was always uncomfortable, painful, and emphasized the finality of it all. Players tried to look tough and hide how much emotion they actually felt, telling each other, 'Keep your head up. Keep your head up.'

Jeff and Bobby hugged their parents, who couldn't hold back their tears. They realized it was a rarity to have two talented quarterback sons play Varsity football together. Their youngest son, Teddy, idolized his brothers, yet sometimes felt lost for attention during football season. Teddy's dream was to follow in their footsteps one day.

Jeff sat as still as a statue on the stiff locker room bench that day. He was locked in that position for over an hour, long after everyone else had left. The quarterback felt the soreness of his muscles. As if in a trance he sat motionless, thinking about the other sad times he experienced on that same bench. As a freshman, he watched the seniors bawl like babies after the '90 loss to Monroe. He tried to understand their pain as a sophomore when they couldn't get in the playoffs. He remembered the agonizing good-byes from a year ago after the close Marysville loss, and the painful farewell to D'ar.

Now, he felt the intensity of a senior's pain after playing his final high school football game. It hurt more than he anticipated. After so many wonderful memories in his three years on Varsity, his heart only focused on the painful ones. He couldn't find the desire to take off his uniform. Later, the team voted Jeff as their 'Most Valuable Player.' But that day, he didn't want to turn in #16 even though he knew Bobby would proudly wear it in '94.

Once November rolled around, Jeff tried to look forward to the Annual Football Banquet, realizing it was the ultimate send-off. Jeff read the personalized letter that Coach Annese wrote to members of the Varsity squad. It was his way of saying good-bye to the seniors and motivating the underclassmen.

Thirteen Rams received All-League awards. Despite being injured, Jeff received All-State Honorable Mention, while Eddie and Wingo received First Team All-State. Wingo had one more year as a Ram, returning with six other All-League candidates. They looked forward to a promising season with one more shot at a State Title.

A few weeks passed before Coach called a football meeting after school. He watched the massive group pile into the wrestling room, then wrapped up any final business from the '93 Season. Coach dismissed the seniors, waiting until the last one had left the room, then forcefully closed the door. The dramatic echo caught the attention of the seventy underclassmen who immediately felt the intense silence that engulfed the room. Annese returned the stare to the anxious eyes that faced him.

The team wondered what they had done to make him so upset. If they could read his mind, they'd understand that he had ample time to review the entire season, recapping the humiliation of their near losses to Chesaning and Bentley. Coach intentionally paused, then watched them squirm in their seats. He shocked them with his next move. Wide-eyed players watched Coach pick-up a plaque, lift both arms high above his head, then forcefully slammed the piece of wood onto the floor, shouting, 'THIS SEASON SUCKED!'

They were afraid to make eye contact with each other, and noticed that the air in the room instantly turned stuffy. Freshman Ryan Hodges felt his entire body react to the pitch in Coach Annese's voice. It was unlike any feeling he had ever experienced -- fear coupled by excitement. Hodge led the Freshman Team as their captain and quarterback. He already developed a love for Montrose Football, demonstrating that he was extremely dedicated. The more he listened to Coach Annese, the deeper the seed lodged in his heart. Hodge committed right then and there to do whatever it took. Hodge planned to work his butt off to bring his teammates together. He never wanted a coach to ever say that *his* season sucked.

B.J. knew that the '94 seniors already shared a brotherhood, as well as an incredible dream. They painted two special words above the weight room door in thick black letters. It became their crucible, bonding them together with an understanding that no one would ever quit. *Never. Commitment was incredible.* The new tradition was reinforced every single time a player finished his workout. Whenever he left the room, he instinctively raised an arm and jumped up to touch his favorite letter on those two sacred words:

'STATE CHAMPIONSHIP'

TRI-COUNTY CITIZEN PHOTO

#81 Tim Unangst, #33 Jason Clark, #21 Eddie Howell, #16 Jeff Klopf, #82 Mike Fisher, #12 Joe Heystek, #40 Chadd Patterson

7. DEDICATION - 1994

Heroes are made in the hour of defeat.
Success is, therefore, well described as a series of glorious defeats.

-Mohandas K. Gandhi

Tim looked to his left and saw the gleam on Nate's face after the second TD was scored. He watched Nate high-five his oldest brother Cheese before they slapped hands with their dad, and Cheeses' college buddy, who appeared equally thrilled. It was hard to believe that they were actually sitting in the Pontiac Silverdome, watching their favorite team in the state finals.

The entire Leeseberg family allowed football to be the nucleus of their lives for over a decade, becoming totally engrossed in the greatness of it all. Tim tried to ignore the selfish feeling in the pit of his stomach that gnawed at him. He questioned why 'his' team wasn't the one on the field, and he wondered if his older brothers felt the same way. All three went on with their lives: Cheese was married with kids of his own, Nate was a police officer, and Tim was a senior in college.

On the drive down, they talked about the chance of Montrose winning. They openly admitted their doubts at the beginning of the season. But now as they watched them play on the turf, Tim felt that this group of players rose above their potential, proving their worthiness. It was obvious that they loved playing for their school, performing like they rightfully deserved to be there.

They made the lengthy climb to the top. He recalled the many great players that went through the program. Then, this group came along and learned to play so well together that they earned their shot at a State Championship. Watching his school lifted to this level, left him with a feeling far greater than he ever imagined.

A genuine smile formed on Tim's face as deep pride warmed every blood vessel filtering through his entire body. His hand reached out to return the high five to his dad and his brothers, while soaking in the righteousness of the memory. He savored the moment, enjoying the proud look on all of their faces. It created a lasting impression, making him feel like they all paid a small part in making that magical moment happen.

'**S**ound Off' . . .'One, Two'. 'Sound Off' . . . 'Three, Four' . . . echoed through the makeshift campground across from the high school. Sleepy eyed campers, with crumpled morning hair, peeked from windows and slightly cracked doors, curious about the commotion. *Who were these loud teenagers making such a ruckus so early in the morning?*

Campers watched the group from a distance. Their voices grew louder as the gap cowered. The young men approached their campsites like a swarm of killer bees prepared to attack. About ninety boys devoured any available ground between campers. Some were coordinated, some were not. Some were tall, some were short. Some were fat, some were thin, but they all ran the course with attitude -- military style.

The savvy seniors tried to out clever the gangly freshmen with crafty sound-off verses before they reached the campers.

HEY BOBBA REBA (leader) - HEY BOBBA REBA (team)
Yo Bobba Reba (leader)- Yo Bobba Reba (team)

I WISH ALL THE LADIES - I WISH ALL THE LADIES
Were Holes in the Ground – Were Holes in the Ground

AND I WISH I WAS A WORM - AND I WISH I WAS A WORM
I'd Bob Up and Down – I'd Bob Up and Down

HEY BOBBA REBA - HEY BOBBA REBA
Yo Babba Reba - Yo Babba Reba

It was the one time that players didn't mind running. If they had to get up so early to cook pancakes, somebody better be there to eat them. Ninety teenagers jogged through the maze while they dodged picnic tables and tent stakes blaring, 'Wake up. C'mon, it's football season. It's time to eat blueberry pancakes.'

The Blueberry Festival Committee relied on the team's energy and muscles to set up tables and chairs in the entertainment tent every mid-August. They bestowed the team the honor of flipping pancakes during the annual festival, which started at 6 AM. It was a wholesome event that made growing up in small town America, a classic. Out-of-town campers spotted a preview of its character, giving the impression that something special was happening in Montrose.

The '94 Team faithfully worked out all summer, B.J. Dean made sure of that. He took his role as a second year Varsity captain very seriously. He only lived one block from the school, which made it convenient to monitor the weight room activity. The rule was black and white; if players didn't show they got a call from B.J. The senior captain tried to motivate the rest of them to work harder. Maybe it was because he had a taste of the great '92 Team. After playing with the best, he wanted to model the '94 guys after them. B.J. didn't make many calls though; this Varsity team thrived on being together. Those with outside jobs coordinated a time to lift together, often ending their workouts with a swim in Dean's built-in pool.

It gave players a chance to get to know Mauricinho (Mo) Targino. Mo was a lean, quiet-natured, dark haired boy with a gorgeous smile and noticeable white teeth. 'Mo' was the Dean's foreign exchange student from Brazil, who adopted the Deans for a year. Life was very different for the shrunken Dean family that now only consisted of B.J. and his mom. The older five Dean siblings were on their own. Mrs. Dean wanted B.J. to experience living with a brother.

The community cared about B.J. No one should have to experience the kind of pain that he did at age 13. *No one.* Death is hard enough at age 50 or 30, but 13 is too far from the natural order of things, especially when your dad is the superintendent of your school district. Fraser Dean was a good superintendent, a good citizen, a good man, and a good friend. People liked him, respected him, and still missed him. He was a part of the Montrose Community. His sense of humor made those around him laugh, especially his wife and six children. He was a tall, hefty man that believed in education, ethics, and fun family vacations that eventually got the best of him.

Gulf Shores, of all places. One minute they played catch with a football on the beach, the next B.J.'s dad saved a drowning cousin from the clutches of the ocean. Fraser Dean helplessly laid in the arms of his youngest son, until the end. *How does a 13-year-old boy ever get over that? How does an adolescent channel that anger?*

Competitiveness was deeply rooted in the Dean family and naturally became B.J.'s outlet. It was obvious that the youngest Dean had something to prove, *but to whom? His dad? His mom? His only sister? Or to show his four brothers that he had as much athletic talent and drive as they did?* Four years later the community still felt the loss of Fraser Dean, but protectively wanted B.J. not to. They wanted him to act like a typical senior, happy and carefree, without feeling abandoned.

Mo's arrival brought a refreshed energy to the Dean household. B.J. couldn't believe that Mo had never kicked a football in his life; everyone he knew played backyard football. But Mo had a few tricks of his own. He unashamedly gave B.J. a taste of what ruled in Brazil; then enjoyed the stunned look on B.J.'s face. Mo was an awesome soccer kicker. The wheels immediately cranked in B.J.'s head. *What would it take to make Mo a kicker? Could he compete with guys who played football for years?* B.J. couldn't count the number of times he held a football for Mo during the summer of '94, while they practiced every available hour. Mo listened while B.J. filled his brain with big plans to play Montrose Football together. B.J. wanted Mo to experience being one of the sweaty guys in the sweltering locker room whose chest pounded from emotion after listening to one of Coach Annese's motivating half-time talks. He tried to explain it to Mo, but didn't know if the message got lost in the translation. It was something that Mo needed to experience for himself.

When Mo arrived in January of '94, he barely spoke any English. It was a difficult adjustment. He quickly learned to put up with B.J.'s sarcasm and bullheadedness, which B.J. thought was a true testament of Mo's character.

Some players had Mo in class during his first semester. B.J. introduced him to the rest of the football gang at the beginning of conditioning. Mo shook their hands, 'El'lo, I am Mo. I want to be your keek'er.'

The guys were intrigued by his accent and teased his 'keek'er' pronunciation, which B.J. thought sounded like a line from Cheech and Chong. They quickly made friends, helping Mo develop his fluency in English. Slang gave him the biggest challenge, since he couldn't locate those words in his worn out translation dictionary that he constantly pulled from his back pocket. He was such a likable kid with good athletic ability and a tremendous leg. But they quickly learned that Mo didn't know squat about football. Some wondered if he would ever catch on, but his foot consistently put the ball through the uprights. B.J.'s friends soon became Mo's friends. The kicker quickly relaxed, becoming one of the guys, which helped Mo feel like he belonged. It became the best remedy for his homesickness.

B.J. made a few calls to his friends one summer day to meet at the football field and run some plays. He also called sophomore Ryan Hodges. 'Hodge' hung up the phone with a huge grin on his face. He didn't know too many of the guys on Varsity and figured that B.J. needed a fill in, since he was only a five-minute walk from the field. The truth was that Hodge made an impression during passing league over the summer. The captain wanted to unofficially check him out a little closer. Hodge took a spot at defense, battling hard against the offense, while Bobby Klopf ran scripts. Their energy seemed endless in the hot summer sun. They were restless for the start of football season.

Their dads were just as anxious, laboring away in the late summer heat, volunteering their skills to build a new press box for the complex. If they couldn't pound nails they grilled food, as they swapped stories about their sons. Steve Head's dad told a funny one about the Fourth of July when Annese called Steve, along with two other linemen, asking if they could meet at the school at 9 AM. Of course they would've canceled their plans in a moment if Coach asked them to; he had that kind of effect on them. When they arrived at the school Coach announced, 'Come outside, I want you to do something.'

Earlier, Steve asked his dad if he could use the car. Naturally, he presumed that Steve made up an excuse just to get the car. He wondered, *Who would ever practice on the Fourth of July?* Curiosity tempted the dad to drive around the school to the back parking lot to prove his point, then chuckled at what he saw. He watched the small frame of Coach Annese inspire his three biggest linemen to run sprints. They had straps fastened around their waists that were attached to old, dirty tires at the opposite end. The threesome looked like Belgium work horses plowing a field. It was motivation in its purest form -- no cameras, no spectators, no glory; just heat and guts. As a college coach himself he wondered, *How many high school coaches would take the time on a summer holiday to convince three big linemen to do that?* He appreciated their dedication, as he made a decision to keep his observation to himself. Mr. Head laughed while he drove away, feeling anxious for fall to arrive.

Annese didn't want his linemen getting lazy during the summer. Chris Wingo was quick for his size, which helped him receive First Team All-State in '93. He was a coach's dream at tackle. Wingo had speed and strength. His 6-4"-290 pound body became a legitimate Division I recruit. But Wingo was a complex guy. On the surface he was a fun loving person who laughed and joked with everyone. His success from playing Varsity as a sophomore helped him believe in himself and he worked even harder. His teammates looked up to him. They were undecided if it was because of his big smile, his raw athleticism, or his size coupled by his ability to kick the living shit out of them. Annese thought Wingo was the best offensive lineman Montrose ever had in terms of what colleges looked-for. He took it upon himself to have the entire package ready to go right out of high school, and made a commitment to help Wingo improve.

Summer was winding down. *In Montrose, that's when dreams began.* Conditioning officially started two weeks before the season opened. The `94 Team ran it like a serious business, a trait of the talented `92 Team. They knew what to expect, feeling proud to wear their black T-shirts that displayed, 'Montrose Football - Ram Pride.'

The seniors pooled their creativity to carry on the freshmen orientation. B.J. told Gary Strappazon, 'Run up to the school and get the cordless wind detector from the coach's office.'

Gary tried to defend himself when he cautiously looked at B.J., 'C'mon, I'm not gonna fall for that.'

B.J. replied with a straight face. 'No seriously. It's something Mo used in Brazil and he needs it for kicking.'

Gary thought he had better do what the seniors asked and mistakenly walked into the school with his cleats on. Freshman Coach Keith Williams was in the office. 'Hey Coach, do you know where they put the cordless wind detector?'

Coach Williams kept a straight face, playing along. 'It's not in here Strap. I think B.J. still has it.'

Gary didn't look too convinced when his coach started laughing. 'You're not really falling for that are you Strap?'

'Heck no.'

Gary felt relieved that his coach was straight with him. Like his teammates, he admired Coach Williams who was a young teacher that had it together. He was just old enough that freshmen looked up to him, yet young enough that he could still relate to them. He even called him Strap. Gary dreaded facing the boastful seniors. With every measured step he thought, *Why was I picked over the entire Freshmen Team?* He accepted his fate, sucked in his humility, and tried to be a good sport by the time he reached them – *empty handed.* Gary took a deep breathe, prepared himself for the snickers and hoots that greeted him from the seniors, who took advantage of their Varsity ranking. Coach Williams watched Gary become the brunt of their joke, then protectively stepped in. 'Hey Strap, time to get to practice.'

Gary was extremely grateful for the rescue and threw an appreciative glance his way.

Rob Edenburn didn't tease Gary as much as the others did. Marriage had toned him down a bit, even though he only tied the knot for two months. He didn't know how his teammates would react to having a *married guy* on the team. He felt a bit apprehensive about coming to conditioning, then discovered that they were still his buds. They treated him like one of the guys. His squad completely understood his love for the game. If they wore his shoes, they would want to finish their senior football season.

Most of them compared Ebenburn's situation to living with a girlfriend, *with benefits.* Being committed to a girl for 24 hours-a-day was something they didn't feel ready for. They teased him about *getting it* whenever he wanted. Edenburn laughed about that since his young wife was extremely pregnant. The thought of marriage didn't seem very appealing when they watched Edenburn leave practice to go to his job. He had to provide a home for his new wife and baby on the way. He was their brother. The squad supported him in any way they could. Seniors felt exhausted after practice and couldn't imagine trading places with all of his new responsibilities. Life was chaotic enough concentrating on football, school, and just being a teenager; they didn't want to worry about anything else.

Senior Jeff Lange found something new to worry about, his knee. He was anxious about conditioning and assertively took his turn at running through the chute. The moment he felt the excruciating pain shoot up his leg, he realized that his knee was seriously injured. He recalled, with unreserved disappointment, how he felt after breaking a bone in his hand during two-a-days in '93. And now this. Lange had a lot of heart, like his brother Charlie, the center on the '88 Team. He hoped that his injury wouldn't hold him down the entire season. Shannon Bowen took one look at his knee, then looked the other way. He nicknamed his friend 'Robo Knee.'

It grossed senior Mike Newell completely out after he caught a glance of Lange's injured knee. He wondered, *Do I really want to play football?* He didn't think he would miss football after focusing on basketball and baseball the past two years. But he did. It about killed him to sit in the stands during the '93 Season when Orchard Lake eliminated Montrose from the playoffs. He felt guilty that he wasn't on the field helping his friends, and made a decision to play football his senior year. True to himself, he brought his great hands and his 6'5", 200 pound lean frame to conditioning, giving the Rams another dimension at split end.

Thirty-nine Varsity players arrived on time, anxious to begin two-a-days. Mother Nature blessed them with temperatures that averaged in the low 60's, which seemed unusually low for Michigan's hazy days of summer. The coaching staff sensed a strong confidence that was absent during the '93 two-a-days. *Confidence was reassuring.*

Hodge worked out extremely well with the Varsity during conditioning. He was the lone sophomore on the team. His body was exhausted from the non-stop work out, but he was too proud to quit. After a few days, Coach Annese questioned Hodge, 'Do you want to hang with the Varsity this season or go back to J.V.?'

Hodge smiled at the opportunity in front of him and blurted, 'Heck no!'

He loved hanging out with the Varsity and endured their intense practices. Although he wished that Coach Annese had waited a few days before asking that question. After Hodge pushed his aching body to the max, he feared it might speak for itself, *Yes, move me back to J.V., this is too hard!* He knew that he wouldn't ever say that, no matter how much pain he felt. Hodge joined his new teammates at their first team meeting after conditioning. They talked about their team goals then Annese handed out a copy of the `94 annual motto. Hodge grabbed a paper from the top of the pile, allowing his fatigue to emerge. In spite of his high IQ, he oddly wondered, *How will I ever remember this?* It was a strange thought considering that he just aced chemistry as a freshman. Physical exhaustion must've set in, along with the realization that Varsity level was more intense compared to his freshmen experience. He concentrated on every word, as he slowly read the motto absorbing its full meaning. A sudden jolt of adrenaline flooded his veins, while goosebumps converged up his arms and he thought, *Wow, this is powerful.*

'1994 Montrose Football Annual Motto'

**'Each day of football becomes a personal priority to me.
I will use that day for my good and for the good of the team.
Then November 26th will be the greatest day of my life.'**

Without referencing a calendar, they all knew that November 26th was *States.* Coach explained that they were expected to memorize a weekly motto. 'Coaches will call you at random, asking you to recite the weekly motto. If you can't remember it, the entire team runs gassers.'

But it wasn't as hard as they expected. If someone asked them to recite a motto five years down the road, most could do so without hesitation, as easily as stating the Pledge of Allegiance. *Mottoes were sacred.*

The 25 seniors made a concentrated effort to make two-a-days a more pleasant experience. They ran in the gym all winter, and worked hard the entire off-season. Most of them had been in the weight room all four years of high school. Their attitudes and work ethic affected the underclassmen, creating a self-perpetuating machine. They learned the cycle at a young age by playing in a successful youth program. Annese hoped the juniors stepped up to fill the holes with confidence and maturity.

Coach Annese was in a good mood until roll call; then all hell broke loose. He gritted his teeth then lividly focused on the two juniors and one senior that didn't show. Never mind that he was preaching to the choir, he screamed and yelled at the players in attendance. They began a continuous physical exertion of ups-and-downs, push-ups, sit-ups, sprints, gassers and miles of running, until their missing teammates arrived. It was his way of teaching them accountability; he had the backbone to approach any wrongdoing. Players felt totally intimidated and pissed that a teammate had let him down.

'Oh Shit!' The words flew from Bobby's mouth. He remembered a horror story passed down from previous years about this very thing. A wise friend had shared it with him. 'If that ever happens, make sure you're the first to volunteer to find them.'

That's exactly what Bobby did, along with a few other seniors with cars. Shannon volunteered to drive his famous pickup truck, the 'Big Brown Cow.' Shannon was known to drive the family's racecar at the dragster track. He knew how to deck out a truck and was more than glad to help.

It was the one time that Lange didn't mind having an injured knee, his official excuse to avoid the punishing workout. He rode with Bobby to Jason Toney's house. Lange urgently pounded on the door, but no one answered. So they exceeded the speed limit, while they drove the few miles to the body shop where Jason's dad worked. He told them, 'Jason's home, he just sleeps like a bear. Go back over there and pound on the door again.'

They rushed back to Jason's house, hammering on the door in a panic, concerned about their buddies who experienced a world of hurt by now. In frenzy, they finally broke into Jason's house, finding him lifeless on the floor. He wasn't moving, but he was snoring, resembling a bear in deep hibernation. Bobby cautiously shook Jason's thick body, expecting him to awake and attack at any moment, discovering that Jason had a short fuse. Lange and Bobby looked at each other and wondered, *Is he worth all of this trouble?*

Lange flashed back to powerlifting when he spotted for Jason at nationals. Jason placed second in the 220 pound weight class, after lifting a combined weight of 1,080 pounds -- as a sophomore. Bobby was also aware of Jason's strength. He looked at Jason's large, thick body. Bobby surely wanted that strength on the line protecting him at quarterback. *Yeah, he was worth it.*

It took both of them to lug Jason into Bobby's `87 black, Dodge Daytona, that seemed to wail with 600 pounds of pubertal testosterone as cargo. Lange and Bobby felt like kidnappers, only their hostage outsized them. They tried to wake Jason up on the short drive to the school. The two seniors quickly convinced Jason that he really wanted to play Montrose Football, although he needed to improve his work ethic and accountability. No one doubted that Coach Annese would take care of that in a hurry. Their job was to get the junior to practice; for an experience of a lifetime.

The team was pissed after finishing a fourth round of 50 ups-and-downs on the hard, dewy ground. They wanted the no shows found soon. The lesson on accountability was received loud and clear, with an agitated sweat, 'Don't ever be late for practice without informing the coach ahead of time.' The physical punishment they experienced was pure hell, worse than any boot camp, but held the same underlying mission. Players discovered how much they could endure, yet realized that this wasn't what the coaches wanted to be doing either. They all wanted to prepare for the `94 Season, instead of wasting time fooling around over a few irresponsible punks.

The three missing players showed up for the second part of two-a-days. Before the second practice even started, B.J. told them, 'Get down and start doing ups-and-downs on the locker room floor.'

Coach Annese overheard one of the juniors justify his absence before dishing flack to B.J. The head coach confronted him as harsh words were exchanged. Coach didn't want any cancer on the team and abruptly ended the conversation when he scolded the junior, 'Go clean out your locker and don't come back!' *Dependability was mandated.*

The AWOL senior felt terrible that he had caused his teammates to endure such a horrible workout. He had no idea of the consequences and apologized to everyone, clueless of what awaited him. The clever excuse he concocted earlier was instantly forgotten. He was completely off base to think it would get him off the hook. B.J. tested his loyalty as he watched the senior willingly do everything that he asked: ups-and-downs, push-ups, sit-ups, running in place, followed by several rounds of pain and suffering on the hard, cold, locker room floor. B.J. made him pay, welcoming the other seniors to join in, while they declared themselves unofficial drill sergeants. They enjoyed the chance to challenge a peer, making him endure the same punishment that they did a few hours earlier. They all wanted to know, *Was he with them or not? Commitment was tested.*

The senior did everything that he was told, checking his own character in the process. He tried to suppress his own pain, while earnestly earning their respect. When it was finally over, he barely had the strength to lift his exhausted body onto the bench. But he did, then collapsed as he bent over to hide his shame, feeling the clamminess obsess his entire body. He felt like a dog that had just been whipped and stared at the floor in total exhaustion. The room fell silent as the senior watched a pair of dirty socks approach, then stop directly in front of him, and he wondered, *What next?*

Someone rustled his thick, sweaty hair while another squeezed his shoulder in support, then left him alone. In the moments that followed, he unsuspectingly stepped over the frightening frontier from boyhood to manhood. The incident was quickly forgotten; the score was even. *Compliance built integrity.*

B.J. gained the utmost respect from his co-hearts in the ritual. The experience and confidence that he gained as a junior captain during the '93 Season was valuable. B.J. possessed the charisma to stimulate players to work even harder. His presence was noticed when he walked into a room; his cocky attitude seemed to make him even more friends. He had his enemies, but most guys found him easy to follow, especially the underclassmen. They wanted to be just like B.J. Dean.

The afternoon practice went better than the morning one. Not one person was late; most reported surprisingly early. An invisible cloud of over anxiousness seemed to hang over the team and coaches wondered, *Was everyone trying too hard to do everything right?* Even experienced seniors were extra cautious about making mistakes. Their guarded moves caused them to botch drills by jumping offside and missing pitchouts. Coach Annese became so frustrated at one point that he personally took the handoff and ran the play, showing Steve Whorf what he expected.

Whorf was back in Montrose, trying to learn the veer after playing as a New Lothrop Hornet. His family moved from Montrose to the neighboring town before his freshman year. Whorf was a likable guy, a natural athlete who easily fit into either school system. He felt it was time to control his own destiny after being caught up in troubled family issues. Whorf moved in with Adam Stiverson's family. Adam's dad was a strong powerlifter. He was also the biggest parent advocate of the powerlifting program and helped Whorf. He agreed to become his guardian, if needed, which allowed Whorf to legally attend Montrose High School and graduate with his old buds.

Most of the Varsity knew Whorf from his early school years, after playing youth football with him. Overall, the Varsity was glad to have him back, although a few running backs were not very enthusiastic. It didn't take a rocket scientist to figure out that his presence created massive competition for a first string position. A few seniors felt shafted since they had already paid their dues. Competition drove them to practice even harder and became a reason why Coach Annese constantly preached, 'We do what's best for the team and avoid individualism.'

It was just the beginning of one of life's tough lessons. *Collaboration was expected.*

The Rams were in good condition overall, plunging headfirst into their playbook. From day one, the coaches wanted to work on all aspects, including audibles, which isn't the easiest thing for a high school team on their first day of practice. It explained some of their first day inaccuracies, but their goal was to be several weeks ahead of their competition by the beginning of the '94 Season. Annese worked on their audible system, so they could easily change things at the line of scrimmage, which proved to be their forte the past few years. Annese gathered his team at the end of their second practice. 'Not everything went perfect today. It's not supposed to, but it's best to iron it out now so that it becomes second nature once the games start.'

Two-a-days actually seemed fun after that first day. Annese and Reinhart constantly ripped on each other, trying to surpass each other's pranks. They never undermined each other, but easily resorted back to their college football days. Reinhart called Annese a spindle fiber because he was small in stature, and he made fun of his big nose. Reinhart worked year round in the weight room with the team to strengthen them. His desire to work harder made them work harder.

Bobby battled for the quarterback position with junior quarterback Shane Schlorf. Offensive coaches thrived on the competition between the two of them during the entire off-season. They liked what they saw in Bobby's arm, but also liked the quickness that Shane displayed. Many thought Shane's physique and quick movements emulated Jeff Klopf more than his own brother Bobby. Shane led an undefeated J.V. Team. He energetically moved in any direction while in a full sprint, making defenders slip up on their tackle. A part of Shane wanted the quarterback position, but the other half questioned his own confidence. He realized that his comfort zone wasn't quite ready to deal with the pressures that accompanied a Varsity quarterback.

Linemen thought Shane was skinny and cocky; two traits that didn't mesh in their book. They felt you shouldn't dish it out if you didn't have the muscle to back it up. Shane had his own strategy, he just out ran them.

Bobby felt *he* deserved the starting position since *he* had five Varsity games under this belt, including both playoff contests in `93. His dad kept close tabs on the situation, since he wanted Bobby to follow after his brother. Bobby earned the position in the end, which allowed the Rams to use Shane's speed as a back or a receiver. Bobby's style called a different cadence when he used 100 for one play, 138 for a veer, and 238 for a 38-veer pass. His colors indicated the count on two -- Blue 138. The team solidified early, perfecting a two-minute drill before two-a-days finished. The coaching staff had the team so well prepared and ready to go before the first game of the season. It gave them high expectations of what the `94 Rams could accomplish, if the cards dealt them a good hand.

Annese expanded his coaching staff, which increased their teaching. Veteran Coach Bob Hayes returned as a defensive line coach and Tony's brother, Steve Annese, worked with the secondary.

Hodge felt that he had so much to learn as a sophomore on Varsity. Steve Annese taught Hodge the little tricks, like how to come as close to that fine line as he could without cheating. The defensive backs had their drills finished by the time the assistant coach arrived at practice. The backs could've easily cheated or intentionally left out the 'W' drill, but they didn't. They backpedaled, broke forward, backpedaled and broke forward even though the drill played havoc on their quads. No one wanted to cheat, since they knew Steve Annese would ask if they had completed them. After all, he volunteered his time to help them and they appreciated the effort he gave. *It taught them honesty.*

Coach Destrampe wasn't afraid to tell them to work harder and he didn't put up with any crap. Players knew he was there on his own time to help them; he had so much knowledge to share. Coach D related well with the team, going the extra mile. And so did they. All of the coaches proved their unselfishness to their families and the team, contributing long, tireless, hours behind the scenes. *Dedication was extraordinary.*

Even before the season started, Annese labeled his `94 Team as 'the most intense and experienced' that he had ever coached. The team clicked early, enticing Annese to see just how many plays they could consume and digest. The coach invested the discipline and work ethic to make it all happen.

But they were not perfect; they were still teenagers full of curiosity and adventure. Two handfuls of them decided to go on a weekend camping trip before they settled into their senior year. Jimmy Woodward joined them. They went *upnorth* a Michigan term that referred to any town north, or west of Bay City. The seniors sat around a campfire telling jokes, while forming senior memories. It was the first time away from their parents, in an uncontrolled setting, if only for a weekend. Someone brought beer and Schnapps. They all ignored the pact they had signed during the pre-season, which stated that they wouldn't drink. Woodward felt a twinge of guilt and thought, *Who would ever know if they all swore to secrecy?* They didn't have enough booze for anyone to get plastered or barely get a buzz, just enough to get them in a world of trouble.

Somehow Coach Annese found out. He always found out. No one knew how, *but he did.* Coach made the guilty suspects form a row like criminals in a line-up at the county jail. He slowly approached them one-by-one, intentionally positioning his face just inches from theirs, like a Marine drill sergeant on the first day of basic training. He made their hearts thump all the way to their throats when he shouted, 'DID YOU DRINK? Don't lie to me!'

The consequences frightened them out of their skulls. No one had ever seen Coach so upset. His intimidation seemed much larger than his 5'8" stance. He scared the living truth right out of some. Others chose to deal with their own conscience, than take his reprimand. That was their business. Woodward stood at the end of the line, his edginess increasing with each passing second. Annese pressed even harder by the time he reached Woodward, determined to get a confession. Woodward was a young senior, not yet seventeen, and hadn't developed his poker face yet. He wanted to say 'No' like the rest, but feared Annese would see right through him. He couldn't lie with such intimidating eyes burning directly through his, from two inches away. Coach stood so close that Woodward could smell what he ate for lunch. The guilty senior realized there would be hell to pay either way, and finally hung his head. He whispered a painful 'Yes.'

The rest of the line didn't make any eye contact, but exhaled nervous air. They closed their eyes as the prickly needles rushed up their arms. *Oh Shit. Here it comes.*

Annese released vented breath, relieved that he finally broke one of them down. The others stood by, too frightened to change their story. *How could they alter it now?* Woodward became the scapegoat, realizing that he just lost his spot at defensive end that he had worked so hard for. But he refused to rat on anyone, in spite of being pressed for names. Woodward remained pissed at himself for screwing up and took his punishment -- *alone.*

Coach made the dreaded phone call to his parents. They instantly regretted the call, yet appreciated that Annese cared enough to make it. Mr. Woodward wasn't a violent person, but he was so angry with his oldest son that he fought to control his own emotions. He was still upset when Jim came home hours later and immediately noticed how nervous his son acted.

Jim dreaded the scene yet felt relieved that it was finally out in the open. 'Dad, I know you're mad and I apologize, but there's nothing you can do that will make me feel any worse than having Coach Annese in my face for ten minutes yelling everything he could think of at me. You can do anything: ground me, punish me, nothing could be more degrading then what I've already been through.'

His parents had never seen him so remorseful or apologetic, and realized the hard lesson he had learned. Forfeiting his chance to play the first three games was bad enough, but attending a series of AA classes was totally embarrassing, on top of getting grounded. His parents respected that he was man enough to tell the truth, knowing it had cost him dearly. At least he could live with his conscience but it made them wonder, *What lessons were really being taught? Practice the ability to lie with a straight face or be punished for telling the truth?*

Woodward never thought about quitting and attended practice every day. He continued to fight for a starting defensive end position when his three weeks ended. Woodward's reward came after football season when he applied to colleges. He attached an impressive reference letter from Coach Annese, outlining his determination and character. *Truthfulness was rewarded.*

Bobby woke up on Friday, September 2, 1994, ready to play football. He felt anxious when he joined his teammates at the school. Even the cafeteria ladies were excited about football season and cooked the team a hearty breakfast. They showered them with attention. Bobby felt weird. School hadn't even started yet because of Labor Day, and they were doing a ritual reserved for playoffs. It seemed everyone had football fever, including the cafeteria ladies.

Cheerleaders and parents processed custom vinyl designs on wooden football signs that read, 'We Support Montrose Football.' They were durable enough to last for years. Each Varsity player received a yard sign that displayed his number and name. Signs popped up in the windows of storeowners and front yards; even the Montrose branch of the U.S. Post Office proudly displayed one. It was obvious that summer was over; the town was ready for football season to begin.

The last day of summer vacation dragged by too slowly for Bobby. He wanted night to fall so they could start their season against **Hamady**. The coaching staff and team members arrived at the school earlier than expected. A few tossed footballs around while they rolled on the wrestling mats, but it wasn't dark enough to relax. Too much light poured in from the small windows at the very top of the two-story room. Danny Ruddy was light and made the hazardous climb on top of Wingo's shoulders, who stood on two rolled up wrestling mats. Ruddy reached the windows and securely taped the black team raincoats over them.

Players found their spot in the darkened wrestling room, knowing that was their spot for the rest of the season. That was gospel. Whatever superstitions they started for game one held throughout the season. The guys talked for awhile then closed their eyes, getting lost in the heavy beats of Nirvana and AC/DC.

Hodge carefully dressed in the locker room, anxious to play his first Varsity game. He noticed the room became suddenly still, so he walked down the quiet hall to check the gym, then the weight room.

No one. It was too early for the buses, which left him wondering, *Where did everyone go?* Nirvana's hit, *'Smells like Teen Spirit,'* greeted Hodge as he cracked the door of the pitch black wrestling room. He tiptoed over players before plopping down between two seniors. The lone sophomore felt relieved to find them, wondering why no one ever mentioned the pre-game ritual.

Bobby caught the football just as the soundtrack ended, while someone turned the lights on. He threw the ball to Shane, his back-up, and one of his favorite targets. They passed it around in an effort to unwind their ball of nerves. Electricity filled their veins the moment Coach Annese walked in. Coach came alive once he started his pre-game talk, motivating them in an unbelievable way. And then he left the room.

Jason resembled Newt from the '90 Team, and couldn't control his sensations or the grunts that escaped his body. Jason was a burly kid who was glad that he joined the team. He couldn't believe how Coach Annese made him feel like a fierce animal that wanted to hit somebody.

It was finally time to board the buses for the 30-minute drive to Hamady. Players felt the tension that hovered over them on the extremely quiet bus. Mo sat wide-eyed, unsure of what to expect from his first, live football game. The skinny teenager from Brazil sat with B.J., a tanned, muscle-rippling lineman, who took up more than his half of the seat. Mo earned the 'keek'er' position along with a new nickname, 'Mo the Toe.' He worried about some of the rules that simply got lost in the translation, wondering if the team assumed he understood it all. *He didn't.*

That became obvious when the official handed Mo the ball for the opening kickoff and said, 'Just wave when you're ready.'

Mo placed the football in the stand, stepped off his footage, then grinned at the ref and waved. He added a friendly 'El'lo' in his strong Brazilian accent. The official nodded and Mo continued to wave and said, 'El'lo', 'El'lo.'

The kickoff team wondered why Mo didn't kick the ball and turned to him, 'Mo, what's wrong?'

'Nothing. That man told me to wave.'

They realized that no one had explained the details and said, 'Mo, just kick it!'

He did, and the '94 Season was off. Whorf romped 28 yards on his first play back as a Montrose Ram. Yuncker scored on runs of nine, three, and 11 yards. Whorf was fast, strong, and had the speed in the backfield to accommodate Yuncker's power. They were great together; one had the strength of an ox, the other the speed of a cheetah.

Bobby scored on a quarterback keeper from two yards out in the first quarter, then connected with Newell on a 30 yard TD strike. Mo successfully kicked his fifth PAT to fire up his team when they broke for the intermission.

Tackle Steve Head stretched in an effort to bat the airborne ball, and missed. But Edenburn grabbed the interception then forced his 5'10"-200 pound body to run. Reinhart once dubbed him as 'Fatty' and Annese once said, 'You're too fat to ever get an interception.'

Edenburn felt invigorated when he proved both of them wrong. A huge smirk plastered his face as he ran past his coaches on the sideline.

The hard-nosed Jason Toney broke his foot after a tackle, but tried to disguise his pain. He wanted to scream like an old bloodhound, but refrained by belting out wild grunts instead. His grumbles released his throbbing pain, while fooling his teammates. They thought he was extremely pumped. Jason was a junior who earned a starting position and wasn't about to give it up, not even for a broken bone. As if his injury was a battle of honor, he sucked up the pain and continued to play. Jason was unaware of the permanent damage he instigated to his foot, which later looked deformed. At the moment, it felt worth it. He planned to keep it a secret, while blocking the pain from his mind. Jason figured that he could tape it tight for a few weeks and pop some Motrin during practice until it healed. He was harder-edged than most guys his age, and couldn't bare the thought of being called a 'Wuss'.

Starters were pulled after the first half. The game whizzed by with a running clock, once the Rams surpassed a 35-point lead. The offense relied on the one-two backfield punch of Yuncker and Whorf as their workhorses. Both of them were fearless and wouldn't back down from anyone. Yuncker's legs had strength of steel, while Whorf was one of the fastest guys on the team.

Bobbie felt real comfortable after connecting on two of three aerials to Newell, his favorite end, for 56 yards. The Montrose Rams racked up a '42-0' shutout over the Hamady Hawks before they headed home.

Annese chatted with the team after a tough week of practice for the **Chesaning** game. They talked about the latest episode of Seinfeld to unwind. Ruddy thought it was an opportune time to recite one of Jack Handey's 'deep thoughts' from the popular show, Saturday Night Live. Ruddy was one of the smartest players on the team. He planned to become a dentist. The future Dr. Ruddy used his wittiness to inject his own style of humor, while reading the daily school announcements over the PA. He customarily closed with a deep thought. The students got a kick out of them so he continued the tradition on the practice field. Ruddy grabbed his narrow chin and posed with a serious attitude while he recited:

> *'If you ever catch on fire, try to avoid looking in the mirror,*
> *because I bet that will really throw you into a panic.'*

The team enjoyed the camaraderie as they geared up for an unusual Saturday game against rival Chesaning. They gathered at a senior's house to watch *Judgment Night* that Friday night. The cafeteria ladies prepared a wholesome, pre-game team breakfast. It set the stage with a playoff atmosphere as two prep football teams prepared to battle for M-57 bragging rights.

Montrose anticipated that Chesaning would provide their stiffest competition. They were known as a hard-nosed team with several returning players. The Rams hosted the game, entertaining more than 3,600 fans who wondered, *Will Montrose extend its winning streak to 54 games, or will Chesaning put an end to the area's longest unbeaten winning streak?*

B.J. furiously ripped the paper as he broke through the hoop, facing the opposing crowd. He thrust his arms down and yelled, 'Yeah!'

It was an intimidating move that he copied from Corey Crockett of the '91 Team. He was anxious to mimic him.

Edenburn's special shoulder pads looked like the Hunchback of Notre Dame. He injured his shoulder early in '93, and it never healed properly. He avoided contact during pre-game warm-ups; partially because he didn't want to injure it directly before the game, and because that's what he had done the previous week. He felt compelled to do everything *exactly* the same. Whenever he made a tackle, he took his mind off of his injury by reciting his favorite motto, 'Pain is Temporary – Pride is Forever.'

The Chesaning Indians scored first on a 10 yard aerial then dominated the first half. The Rams fumbled four times, three were the direct result of the hard-hitting Indians. But Chesaning held onto their six point lead until late in the first half.

Tim Leeseberg pounced on the ball after a high snap occurred deep in Chesaning territory. He reacted like he did in practice, when Reinhart worked on their reaction time by randomly throwing balls. Leeseberg played end on the weak side, opposite B.J. He couldn't ask for a better guy to have on the other side.

The Chesaning defense held strong from the nine yard line. But the Rams scored three plays later when Yuncker plunged over from the one. Mo's PAT gave the Rams a 7-6 half-time lead, leaving the game wide open. Annese expected that the Chesaning coach, Bob Sager, was in the opposite locker room reminding his team of their heroic game from the year before. Chesaning delivered 27 second half points in that game, shutting Montrose down. Although Montrose hung on, it was difficult to forget that ugly 33-27 win. In '94, Montrose squeezed by with a one-point lead, but Annese felt confident that his Rams would settle down and take control. He pumped them up until they appeared like a pack of wolves on the prowl.

Joe Rizk ignited the fans when he burst into the clear, then made a 76 yard punt return early in the third quarter. Montrose fans were ecstatic four minutes later when Whorf bolted over from three yards out to finish a 52 yard scoring drive.

Hodge enjoyed the quick adrenaline rush when he grabbed his first interception. It turned into a mixed blessing when he fumbled it a few seconds later, then racked up a sack. The sophomore was determined to prove that he was capable of starting at defensive back.

Leeseberg showed great effort when he jumped and blocked a punt, the first of two for the night. Penter Holmes had challenged his starting position earlier that week, but Leeseberg wasn't about to roll over and give in. He only hoped that his coach noticed his efforts, along with the fumble recovery, proving his value as a starter.

The Rams enjoyed the conditioning advantage by routinely wearing teams down during the second half. Yuncker plunged over from the three, after the Rams pushed 37 yards in six plays making the score 30-6. Newell ran the two-point conversion in after Mo kicked the first three PAT's. The Rams gave the Indians a bitter taste of their own medicine when they scored one final TD. The Rams capped a 12 play victory to close the score '37-6.'

Other teams in the League that attended the Saturday night game wondered, *Will the perennial football powerhouse at Montrose High ever run dry?* The '94 Rams didn't lack a sense of history or pride; in fact they possessed intensity for both. Their influence in the conference naturally raised the bar. Other coaches realized they had to bring football to the level Montrose was at, or they wouldn't be competitive.

Bentley was one of those teams. The unsullied memory from their '93 contest was still fresh in the minds of both teams. How could they forget the night when the Bulldogs narrowly missed an upset over a questionable extra point that sailed wide at the end of regulation play? Bentley came to town determined to even the score in '94.

Annese countered the plan. He motivated his Rams to primarily control the line of scrimmage to physically dominate the Bulldogs. Bobby jumped out on a keeper, scoring late in the first quarter, and again half way through the second. The Rams were up 14-0. But it was payback time when Bentley took the ensuing kickoff and returned it 89 yards, before getting tripped at the Montrose one yard line. Bentley's kick returner was a stand out during their '93 contest and he obviously wanted revenge.

Reinhart challenged his studs, Wingo at 295 pounds, Stiverson at 250, and his other 200+ linemen to hold the Bulldogs at goal. It poured buckets when Jason screamed, while pumping his chest like Tarzan. He fizzed like a shaken pop can if he didn't release his vented adrenaline. The defense was determined to show Bentley just how strong they were. Montrose held Bentley on first down and again on second, as the downpour continued. Bentley fumbled on the third down and Ryan Persails pounced on it.

The momentum shifted on the next series when Yuncker broke two tackles. He used his famous 360° spin move then ran like a bull, determined to cross the goal line. He scored an 18 yard TD, proving to be their go-to-guy in crunch time. Instead of a close 14-7 score, the Rams were up 20-0 at the half, valuing their lead.

Yuncker's spin move was the play of the week when the 11 PM news aired. Rece Davis, the local ABC sports announcer, commentated his spin move, 'Yuncker's tougher than a $2.00 steak.'

Yuncker's TV clip became a highlight tape classic - with a bonus. Like a good stock tip that doubled in value, the clip gained even more credibility after Rece Davis accepted a position a year later at ESPN, the epitome of sports channels.

Annese planned on the extreme high humidity taking its toll during the second half, wearing down the many two-way players from Bentley. The Rams came out and reeled when Whorf ran 63 yards on the first play.

Bobbie plunged over from the one yard line early in the fourth. It was his third TD that he capped with a conversion pass to Rizk. The evening news dubbed the game 'Klopfomania' as Montrose shutout its third opponent by defeating Bentley '35-0.'

Annese stressed attitude and academics. Players were required to give an eligibility slip to each of their teachers, on Wednesdays, to report their academic grade as well as a comment on their attitude. The slips were turned in before practice and reviewed by the coaching staff. For every ineligible grade, or unsatisfactory attitude comment, they *all* ran gassers.

Coach ran a third-and-10 drill at the beginning of the season. The drill ran through a series of downs: third-and-nine, third-and-eight, third-and-seven, etc., requiring the offense to get a first down each time. They ran the third-and-four twice, and third-and-three twice, essentially running 12 plays. Annese wanted the offense to get seven first downs as the season progressed. It pitted the offense against the defense. The offense ran gassers if they didn't get it, the defense ran if they did. Annese continued to challenge them, raising the stakes to get eight, then nine, then ten first downs in the drill. No one wanted to run gassers; the daily drill allowed the offense to make the defense really good.

After a smooth pre-game practice, the team felt they were ready to face **Bendle**. They finished early, while the guys teased Edenburn, 'At least you won't be late for dinner tonight.'

Coach Annese jumped in as he looked at Edenburn. 'You know, I've never coached a player that was married before.'

Edenburn just smiled, proud of who he was. *Morals were valued.*

The mood was light. While they laughed, Ruddy seized the moment to recite another deep thought. He slowly shook his head while he looked at his teammates with a serious expression upon his face:

> *'If you ever drop your keys into a river of molten lava,*
> *forget 'em, cause man, they're gone.'*

The squad's boisterous laughter made Ruddy crack a smile. He felt satisfied, as if he'd just told them a good joke. His teammates wondered how Ruddy remembered so many deep thoughts. To their own surprise, they started to recite them along with their weekly mottoes.

A relaxed Coach Annese stood with his arms at his side. He watched his players rip on each other until their laughter drifted out of range. Then, he enjoyed a refreshing moment of solitude after a tough week of practice.

Newell and his closest friend, Gerrad Leitelt, decided to play a silly game of touch football, since they had a few hours to kill before the J.V. game started. Gerrad was a tall, quiet guy who worked extremely hard and didn't say much. The pair found a plastic miniature football, threw on some plastic helmets, and horsed around on the baseball field. Gerrad held the miniature football for Newell to kick, never giving his shoe size a second thought. Newell's huge foot kicked the ball so hard that he broke Gerrad's hand on impact. He felt pretty stupid. So did Gerrad, especially when he had to tell Coach. He couldn't say which was more difficult, his throbbing hand or trying to explain what they were doing. Needless to say, Annese was livid. The Rams faced the Bendle Tigers without one of their starting tight ends. Gerrad was disappointed that he couldn't play; he felt foolish coming to school with a cast on his hand.

Montrose and Bendle scrutinized each others' strengths during Powerlifting competitions. They competed against each other at Nationals in Des Moines, Iowa over the summer. Both the Montrose Varsity and J.V. Teams took first place while Bendle came in second – in the *nation*. That demonstrated the type of strength that the GEC League had developed; their rivalry naturally carried over to the football field.

B.J. was the lone two-way starter for the Rams. He made a great trap blocker at right guard because he was quick and powerful. No one wanted to beat Bendle more than B.J., or would need to match his focus, his work ethic, and his determination. The stakes were high; not only for their record, but the Dean family bragging rights were on the line. He didn't want to face his brother Noel, the opposing coach, with a loss. The motivation psyched B.J. up for the game.

B.J. was glad for the opportunity to play against his brother. He was thankful that Noel stepped in a few years ago, guiding him back to Montrose. B.J. needed a change after his dad died and attended a private, neighboring Catholic school during the eighth grade. Most of his new classmates planned to attend Flint Powers, a private Catholic high school. But B.J. found himself at a crossroads. He needed to decide whether to attend high school at Montrose with his old buds, or switch to Powers with his new ones. Noel convinced B.J. that Montrose was his best fit. Maybe it was his older brother intuition, but Noel knew that B.J. thrived in the Montrose environment. That was in '90, and B.J. was glad that Noel stepped in, especially since Montrose kicked Bendle's butt.

Montrose led 42-0 at the half after scoring on their first three possessions of the first quarter. The offense moved the ball extremely well, allowing Bobby to run in two TD's. Bobby hit Newell on two scoring passes over 60 yards. Newell's height was a great target for Bobby to hit on a pass across the field or down the field. Annese wanted to use a few more weapons than in past weeks, having four players sub for the starters. Yuncker and Rizk each scored a TD, allowing Mo to kick six first half PAT's.

Mo squib kicked the ball then watched as it hit one of the front line Bendle players before it bounced off. Montrose pounced on it to recover, then laughed at Mo's initial reaction. Mo sensed that he had done something very wrong. He hit himself on top of his helmet with both hands. 'I did bad, I did bad!'

His teammates realized that Mo still didn't entirely understand the game of football. Mo noticed his squad jump in celebration and changed his words to, 'I did good, I did good!'

Defense had been the Rams focus all season; they simply did not want opponents to move the football. They stonewalled Bendle's potent offense that came into the contest averaging 36 points a game. Annese commended Reinhart's defense during the locker room at the half, 'We're playing the best 'D' we've ever played!'

The Montrose starters played through the first drive of the third quarter then hated to come out of the game they loved. The Rams had great depth and the non-starters made excellent back-ups. Their scout team practiced against the best every single day, and would've easily started at other schools. Their hard-nosed ability kept their consecutive three-game shutout alive, matching a league record by finishing Bendle off '49-0.'

Reinhart's defense was serious about their shutout streak. They set a demanding goal to not give up one point in the GEC League, realizing **Byron** could be a challenge to shutout. Edenburn told Lange, 'Byron only lost three games in three years, all to us. We must really piss them off.'

It fueled his desire to stuff them again, forming yet another streak. It added to the pressure. The Rams took their bizarre superstitions seriously. Lange always wore the same T-shirt under his pads. Hodge made sure that he spent the night at Yuncker's house every Thursday, since that's what he did before their first game. Yuncker made sure he borrowed Bobby's black socks, but returned them after every game so his quarterback's mom could wash them; a tradition that started with their season opener.

Bobby made sure he wore the black socks with three white stripes at the top and rubbed Icy Hot on his back and legs before every game. *Every game.* The quarterback always arrived early and parked in the same spot in the school's lot. He popped his favorite cassette in, then leaned the driver's seat of his Dodge Daytona back as far as it would go, closing his eyes. *'We Will, We Will, Rock You'* blared from his car stereo, while Bobby's hands tapped the beat on the steering wheel. He let his mind forget about everything, as he got lost in the energized guitar rock of Queen.

Some players kept their erroneous fallacies to themselves, even though nobody considered anything weird at this point. Wacky superstitions worked for previous teams and became as natural to a Ram as brushing his teeth. No one wanted to claim responsibility or jinx their streak by changing a thing; no matter how disillusioned it sounded. Ruddy continued his deep thought at the end of every pre-game practice. He looked at his squad while his face held a solemn expression:

'It takes a big man to cry,
but it takes an even bigger man to laugh at that man.'

Byron's field greeted them with a steady downpour. The rain didn't prevent the diehard fans from cheering just four minutes into the game. Yuncker punched in from a yard out, bringing the physical aspect to their running game. But Byron answered early and blocked tough.

Persails had enough when Byron reached the red zone. He didn't want the Eagles to score and used it as motivation to sack their quarterback, then hovered over him, stressing his point. The sack ignited the Montrose defense that stopped their goal line drive, ending the threat. Persails did a great job at linebacker; he always knew what he was supposed to do and worked hard to get it done. Compared to some he was slower than a house settling, but he could throw a hard hit. He was only a sophomore and hadn't grown into his size 13 shoe yet. His coordination was still developing, and he had a bad case of asthma that often left him winded. It was common to see him sitting with his head between his legs controlling his breathing, but it never got him down.

But the Rams had breakdowns in their execution and looked sloppy after they lost three fumbles on the soggy turf. Teammates watched Coach Annese throw his hat, a sure sign that he was infuriated. Byron continued to show their toughness, but the score was too close for comfort. It helped when Bobby connected with Rizk on a 12 yard pass to score with :14 seconds left in the half, giving Montrose a 14-0 lead.

Newell used his tall lean body to grab a 25 yard reception, before romping to the Byron seven. He watched Yuncker put his shoulder down and plunge over from three yards out in the third. Later, on fourth and goal, Newell juggled a catch then recovered his bobble on the run to score a 27 yard TD. It was a huge play, revealing Newell's great ball handling skills. The theatrical stunt also generated jokes from his coaches about practicing for the girl's volleyball team. Annese greeted him at the sideline, 'Just catch the ball Newell, don't play with it.'

Newell returned one of his brilliant smiles, totally aware that his Coach was actually pleased. When it came to dishing out compliments during the season, Annese had a stinginess.

Bobby fumbled the ball late in the fourth, but managed to scoop it up in the backfield, running 47 yards for a final insurance TD. The Montrose offense was diversified enough to keep Byron honest. Bobby had his best passing game of the season when he completed nine out of eleven attempts for 142 yards. Byron refused to become the victim of a running clock. They became the first team to force Montrose to play the entire game. Montrose finished with 452 total offense yards, holding Byron to 123.

Annese felt happy about the '34-0' win, but disappointed in their sloppy performance. The Rams lost three fumbles, and had several crucial penalties that snuffed out scoring threats. The team intently listened to him when they gathered midfield after the game, 'We have to come out more assertive. Championship teams do that. You only get nine regular-season games and you should be ready to play every night!'

The team realized that they hadn't performed to their own personal expectations. They planned to focus on execution and fundamentals. Montrose didn't celebrate being the only squad in GEC history to post four shutouts in one season – *that wasn't their final goal.*

Montrose scored four times in the first quarter against **Atherton.** They punished the Wolverines after scoring 48 points in the first half alone. Annese was concerned that his starters were only playing the first half, which could hurt them in the post-season. He pushed them to play hard when they were in. The first string became angry on the sideline during the second half when Atherton drove into Montrose territory. The second string on the field breathed a huge sigh of relief when Atherton missed a 25 yard field goal. They would've felt like crap if their shutout streak ended with a three-point goal, by the League's only winless team. If a team scored on them, they expected it to be a TD. The Rams used the close call as motivation to play even harder the remainder of the game. Montrose held Atherton to only 42 offensive yards.

Yuncker and Whorf performed like a well-oiled machine. They helped the Rams roll up 344 yards to close the score at '62-0.' Mo kicked eight conversions, tying a league record. Montrose traditionally produced athletically tough defenses, but the `94 Rams had not surrendered *a single point* in their five league games. They proudly outscored their opponents 222-0. It was a record both the offense and defense were proud of. They vowed to keep their shutout alive. It seemed to be their short term driving force that outshined their 58 game winning streak.

When B.J. grasped the banner, he provided the same sense of hype for football that 'The Undertaker' and 'Kane' did for the WWF. He savagely ripped the banner when he reached midfield, then immediately faced the visiting **Lake Fenton** Blue Devils. He was probably the biggest muscle figure in the League and wasn't intimidated by anyone. Mo called him 'Rambo' when he flexed his fisted arms and yelled, 'YEAH' in his deep voice. B.J. looked like a caged animal anxious to be on the loose. Maybe he was a bit too cocky, but his actions only motivated his squad, firing up the crowd.

The media provided hype that Lake Fenton could present a scoring threat for Montrose. The threat increased their appetite to continue their five-game shutout. The offense came out hungry, helping Yuncker score a TD in the first :29 seconds of the game. Homecoming night generated exciting vibes when Gerrad, Whorf, and Bobby added TD's to end the first quarter at 27-0. It only proved that Bob Hayes Athletic Field was the greatest place to be on a Friday night in the town of Montrose. By the time the first half ended, Montrose dominated the scoreboard 58-0. The Rams developed an attitude when it came to their running game. They pounded on teams, forcing them to suck wind with nothing left in their tanks for the second half.

B.J., Mo, Wingo, and Bobby were king candidates that ran to the locker room with the team during half-time. Shawn Yuncker stayed on the field to fulfill his role as Homecoming King. He stood in front of the entire student body with his trademark, boyish smile, patiently waiting for the announcement of their Homecoming Queen.

The '94 Class did many things in an exceptional way, including electing their Homecoming Queen. The ballots resulted in a tie; a first in Montrose history. Yuncker made sure he congratulated both of them. He matched their height, as he stood sandwiched between their sparkling evening gowns, proudly wearing #22. They smelled so clean and fresh when they posed for pictures. Yuncker hoped that their perfume overpowered the dank stench from his clammy uniform. He didn't want to stink.

The starters found the second half boring from the sideline. But, they came alive once the Rams drove to the 45 yard line. Their kicking game had been strong all year, but was tested that night. The team wondered, *Would they attempt it? After all, it wasn't a close game, but it was Homecoming and Mo did nail one in practice the other day. Why not go for it?*

Mo's heart raced when the field goal team lined up. He paced three steps back, then two to the right before waving to the official. The hike was good. Mo's eyes intently followed the ball until he felt his left foot stretch under and through the ball as he booted the field goal. His eyes joined those of his teammates and the entire stadium. They patiently watched the airborne ball sail perfectly through the uprights on the crisp evening night. Mo thought it looked good, but his lack of confidence in completely understanding every aspect of the game caused a hesitation in his reaction. He stood motionless, waiting for his team's reaction. But the sideline didn't wait for the officials to motion their arms. They knew it was good and jumped up in celebration, thrilled to have some spice back into the game.

Mo's eyes followed the noise to the crowd. He allowed their excitement to rip though his entire lean body. He waved to the massive Homecoming crowd, who rose to their feet in a standing ovation. Mo was impressed with the warmth that the Dean Family showed, but he was overwhelmed when the entire community joined in. Mo not only broke the previous school record held since 1976, he surpassed it by 17 yards, setting a new GEC mark. Mo's huge smile beamed his pearly whites through his facemask and he thought. *I love it here. America is great. Montrose Football is great.*

Mo's kick only took a matter of seconds, but the celebration lasted for hours. In fact, it was good enough to stretch over many years. He realized that this one, special moment made his foreign exchange experience one of the most interesting in his life. He didn't realize at the time, that living a daily routine in another country with such a different culture so far away from his own family and friends, would impress him. That record setting field goal that transpired in a matter of seconds formed a wonderful experience. The vivid memory created the same emotion years down the road.

Mo never forgot the determination in his teammates, their unity, or their effort to win. He would forever remember the night he kicked a 45 yard field goal; the night the Rams defeated Lake Fenton '65-0.'

The Rams felt their practices proved to be tougher than most of their games. Even on offense day they were still going against the No.1 defense in the League and vice-versa. They battled tough since most of them only played two quarters before they were pulled. The Rams continued to reassert themselves as a formidable force.

A State Championship was what the Rams dreamed about every night, and what they worked for every day. They kept a close eye on the AP poll that continued to rank the Montrose Rams as number two in the state, second only to Orchard Lake St. Marys.

Ruddy's dry humor relaxed the team with a deep thought after an intense pre-game practice.

'Sometimes life seems like a dream,
especially when I look down and see that
I forgot to put on my pants.'

Montrose felt ready for the **New Lothrop** Hornets. The visiting Rams joined the standing room only crowd at New Lothrop's stadium. The Rams finished a 67 yard opening drive, when Bobby hit Newell at the four-minute mark with a nine yard TD pass. New Lothrop hit the Rams harder than any other team, upholding the rivalry between them.

The offense realized that Bobby wasn't as fast as his brother Jeff, but felt he could throw ten times better. They watched him develop, feeling he tapped into the peak of his talent. Bobby always seemed in control. Annese didn't give Bobby free will to audible off, but he executed his option on certain plays if the defense shifted.

He stepped back into the pocket while his eyes quickly searched for Newell, before letting one rip. They practiced so much that their timing was instinctive. Bobby knew it was slightly off as soon as he released it. Newell turned, stretched his lean 6'5" frame, then hauled in an awesome over-the-shoulder catch. The eight yard pass gave the Rams a 14-0 first quarter lead.

As if to add salt to the wound, Whorf was the back that scored the second quarter TD for the Rams. The last thing on the mind of a Hornet was to back down to the Rams, especially when their former teammate scored against them. The Hornets gained confidence when they recovered a Montrose fumble and seemed even more determined after halting their next drive at the one yard line. The strong-minded Hornets hit a receiver with a 43 yard pass, who eluded several Montrose defenders to score :25 seconds before the half-time break. New Lothrop fans rocked the stadium, making as much noise as they could. The Hornets responded as if they had just won the State Championship. Yet all they did, was *score* on the Rams. Like other league teams, their mission shifted from trying to *beat* the Rams, to being the first team to *score* against them. The Rams didn't realize how significant their opponent's task had become, or the amount of attention it had drawn to the surrounding Flint area. Instead, they were pissed, especially their captain. B.J. wanted their record to show goose eggs for the entire GEC League. He openly displayed his temper tantrum; his pissed-off state set the tone for the intermission. The mood in the locker room was anything but fun, in spite of a 21-7 lead. Wingo was so furious that he kicked the garbage can. Jason wanted to rip their heads off when he paced the locker room floor like a caged bull. The second string was just as furious. After all, they played the second half of every game, helping the Rams break their own league record of six shutouts. Some felt relieved that it didn't happen during *their* shift, while others were pissed that the first string allowed an opponent to score. The non-starters took pride amongst themselves. They stood a bit taller in the locker room knowing that *they* were the team that hadn't allowed any points. The second string honestly felt they had pushed the first string, making them better by having someone on their heels after their position.

Coach Annese felt their unrest the moment he entered the locker room and immediately responded. 'I don't know why they got so excited. It was only a moral victory, which is nothing but a loss in my book. I don't believe in moral victories. I'm glad this shutout deal is over with. Now we can focus on what we came here to do. It would've been nice, but the shutout wasn't a pre-season goal. It developed during the season and it was fun while it lasted, but let it go.'

The coaching staff concentrated on their second half adjustments. A look of renewed eagerness rested on players' faces. They were ready to play the second half. As if to claim ownership, Montrose fans yelled, 'WHORF, WHORF, WHORF,' after he scored two third quarter TD's. Yuncker added another.

Whorf wanted to play his best game ever, in spite of feeling like a trader. Going against his former teammates felt strange, especially since his younger brother still played for the Hornets. It seemed that both teams wanted to claim Whorf. The Hornets resented that Whorf bailed on them after three years. The Rams felt he attended Montrose Schools longer than New Lothrop, which made him more of a Ram than a Hornet.

The Rams continued to dominate with two fourth quarter TD's by junior backs Shane Schlorf and Jake Emmendorfer. Shane stretched to grab a high pass then raced 31 yards to score. The excited Montrose student body cheered in unison, 'WHORF, SCHLORF, WHORF, SCHLORF!'

Several Rams stood out. Division I recruiters had their eyes on Newell's great hands when he pulled in five passes for 93 yards, scoring two TD's. Mo made all eight PAT's, while B.J. and Persails led the defense. Edenburn and B.J. made a point to see Coach Destrampe directly after each game to tally their tackles. They strived to outperform each other. B.J. usually won, but that night Edenburn hauled in another interception and was on cloud nine.

New Lothrop felt good about their moral victory when they left the field, in spite of a '56-7' final score.

Edenburn's young wife delivered their baby girl after the New Lothrop game. The guys didn't expect to see him at practice on Monday, and were surprised when he showed up. He was late, but he was there. Curious minds had a thousand questions about the gory delivery process; all the stuff that wasn't covered in Sex Ed, but they didn't ask. Instead, they chewed on the bubble gum cigars he passed out claiming, 'Wow, Edenburn had a kid!'

The post-season was rapidly approaching, but Annese didn't want the team talking about the state finals. They agreed while they listened to him, although they all knew a State Championship was the driving force behind everything they did. He wanted their focus to win their first game, then the next. He told them, 'Teams are never successful when they look beyond what they have to do to achieve success. When we get to 9-0 and win the GEC League Championship, then we'll re-establish our goals to go four more.'

Hodge played defensive back facing all-state candidate, Newell, every single day. The exposure developed his quickness as a 150 pound sophomore, but he found himself getting burned day-in and day-out. If that wasn't enough, Wingo and B.J. came at him followed by Yuncker and Whorf, play-after-play. They all tested his skills, as well as his dedication. Hodge passed.

Edenburn felt brave after his two interceptions for the season, grabbing another during practice. It was a rare treat for linebackers to get the ball and Edenburn took off, juked left, then right. Annese looked annoyed while he watched from the practice field. He'd seen it happen too many times and yelled, 'We don't need to be doing that, someone will get hurt!'

The words barely rolled off his tongue when Edenburn hit a bad spot on the practice field. He twisted his ankle, feeling like an idiot. It hurt like a son of a gun, but Edenburn didn't dare mention it to his coach.

During the same practice, Coach Steve Annese had his defensive backs go against Tony Annese's offense. Tony Annese threw a pass to Newell, then watched as Shane laid him out, as hard as he could, to make an impression. Steve Annese praised Shane, 'Yeah, that's how you're supposed to hit!'

The post-season was near and Tony Annese was upset with Shane. 'You're not supposed to hit our guys like that! This is practice! You don't hit somebody that hard in practice!'

The two coaches went at it, yelling at each other. Players felt uncomfortable once they realized that neither coach planned to back off, just like when they were kids. The squad watched the unfamiliar quarrel, dubbing Shane as, 'Cheap Shot.' Shane didn't play dirty, but he did play hard. Anyone that came into his zone could expect a hit, even if the ball wasn't there. It became Shane's adage in practice, as well as in a game.

Ruddy lightened the mood after pre-game practice. After he recited his next deep thought, he watched the team shake their heads and grin:

'To me, it's a good idea to always carry two sacks of something
when you walk around. That way, if anybody says,
Hey, can you give me a hand?
You can say, Sorry, got these sacks.'

The media had fun with an article about the '400 Club.' If Montrose scored 20 points against **Goodrich**, they became the third team in the Flint area to score 400 points in regular-season play. Grand Blanc's 1979 Team currently held the record with 427 points, featuring former Michigan quarterback Steve Smith. The 1976 Southwestern squad was in second place with 400 points and was led by former Buffalo Bill running back Booker Moore. Flint Beecher's 1985 team held the third place spot with 395 points. The next three spots belonged to the Montrose 1992, 1990, and 1994 Teams ranging from 393 to 380 team points.

The Rams didn't react arrogantly to the article, although their fans loved that kind of attention. B.J. addressed the squad, 'Did you guys notice that both of the 400 point teams were both led by exceptional athletes? One pro and a quarterback for Michigan. C'mon, we're just a bunch of blue-collar guys who work hard.'

That they did. The Rams benefited from the results they obtained as a team. They were the direct result of what happens when dedication, hard work, and teamwork came together under the influence of a motivated coaching staff. He continued to dangle a huge dream at the end of the carrot.

Goodrich wanted to become the second league team to score against Montrose. But the Rams had other intentions. Bobby threw four TD passes, and finished the regular season without an interception. Coach Annese brought the seniors out of the game, one-by-one, allowing the fans to praise them. Some players waved, others nodded, while dealing with the bittersweet feeling of playing their final league game.

Montrose ran in four TD's, but Goodrich spoiled their bid for a seventh shutout in nine games, by scoring late in the game. This time it happened against Montrose's Second Team, forcing them to surrender their hard-earned bragging rights. Scoring on the Rams was a big deal to Goodrich, but Montrose shrugged it off since New Lothrop had already stopped the shutout.

The Rams kept the scoreboard operators busy, finishing the game with a '57-7' win over visiting Goodrich. They broke the top 400 Club record, stretched their regular season triumph to 61 games, and claimed their seventh GEC League Title.

The league win was cause for celebration, but the Rams remained cognizant of their loftier goals. They wanted to play for the ultimate prize. Montrose breezed through their regular season without much competition, realizing that the post-season was tougher. They expected to face quality football teams that were most likely undefeated.

Then it happened, and no one really knew quite how to react. Coach Tony Annese didn't intend to create a dilemma when he attended the GEC League voting meeting. He laid out his choices, then did something unheard of by nominating the *entire* Montrose Football Team for All-League status.

The entire team. Every single position!

Other league coaches thought Tony Annese had lost his mind. Monopolizing *every* vote was unheard of. That had never been done or even suggested. It either shocked or pissed off every single person in the room.

Annese defended himself. 'Look at what this team accomplished! We outscored our opponents 400-14. We had *two* 1,000+ yard rushers. We scored 437 regular season points and broke your Flint Area record held by a Class A school since 1979. We set nine school team records and four individual season records. This team displayed constant unselfishness. Our goals never focused on individual honors. It took an *entire team* to accomplish what we did. How am I supposed to pick 12 players that stand out? Plus, I have a place kicker that's broken league and school records. I really need 22!'

Wow!

Annese held his head high as he confidently walked out of the room, leaving his frustration on the table. He needed to speak to his A.D. before anyone else did, and called him the minute he walked in his back door.

The following morning, Varsity players were called out of class for a team meeting. 'Hey listen, the league enforced new rules. They're only allowing us half of what we wanted. We're allowed to nominate so many guys for first, second, and honorable mention based on where you finished in the league. We're only allowed to put up 12 total, and we wanted to put up 20. I look at it this way. If the Rams were split up and played on other teams in the GEC, you could all receive All-League. Even the second team kept the shutout going, while playing against our opponent's first string for six out of eight league games. There's only one person in the whole league that could start for us, the big sized center from Byron. I'm leaving it totally up to you guys to decide.'

Someone yelled, 'If all of us can't be All-League then none of us will!'

Annese was afraid of that and jumped in. 'No. You need to pick seven guys for first team, and five for second team.'

And just like that, he left the room. The team stared at each other for a good minute, trying to absorb what Coach just dished out. Some tried to pretend that the award didn't matter, *but to some it did.*

Tim Leeseberg thought about what it meant to forfeit his chance at the prestigious honor. He felt he was fast, maybe he didn't always get every assignment down correctly, but he worked hard and started every game. He had to or he could lose his spot at defensive end, because Woodward and Penter Holmes competed hard for his starting position all year. Leeseberg immediately felt the pressure of his two older brothers who made All-Conference. He knew how much it all meant and how proud it made his dad. Cheese's team started the streak, while Nate's team kept it alive. Somewhere in the middle of all that, his brother-in-law, Brody Mier, made All-League.

The youngest Leeseberg felt like he finally earned their respect, and now felt a bit shafted. He may not get the impressive award to prove his worthiness on the 'Leeseberg Football Wall of Fame.' But Leeseberg was a team player. It didn't seem appropriate at the time to say anything. After all, they were a football family and played for each other all year.

B.J. immediately stepped up, like he always did. 'Hey guys, I'm up for All-State so I'm withdrawing my name.'

Wingo was in the same boat and said, 'Same here – count me out.'

Each group of positions tried to decide who to elect. Some submitted names from the second team, instead of the starters, to unselfishly acknowledge the guys who worked so hard against them. Some positions drew names out of a hat; others took their fate with paper-rock-scissors. The running back spot came down to Shawn Yuncker and Steve Whorf. Yuncker knew that he was doomed before he even threw his hand out; he never was lucky at that game. The fate of two outstanding running backs, who had awesome seasons, now rested in the luck of the draw. Somehow that didn't seem right, since both supplied over 1,000 of their 4,774 yards.

When it was all said and done, rock cuts scissors. Whorf won. It wasn't Yuncker's lucky day so he shrugged his shoulders. 'Oh well, that's the breaks. Ya win some, ya lose some.'

Yuncker wore his trademark grin while he congratulated his partner in crime, telling himself that it didn't matter. He surrendered his kudos to an opposing school, whose season seemed mild in comparison to his.

Bobby Klopf, Jeff Lange, Mike Newell, Adam Stiverson, Rob Edenburn, Jason Johnson, and Mo Targino ended up with All-League First Team. The unselfish Second Team votes went to Shannon Bowen, Steve Whorf, Russ Vanderhill, Ryan Persails, and Shane Schlorf.

The team was glad when Yuncker later received Honorable Mention All-State along with Bobby Klopf and Adam Stiverson. B.J. Dean, Mike Newell and Chris Wingo made the All-State First Team.

Still.

The incident left a sour taste in the mouths of several. That taste curdled when the Rams decided to boycott their All-League photos in an effort to support their coach. A respected journalist had a field day with the issue. He published an article that unfavorably criticized Annese for placing his players in such an awkward position. He eluded that one day, when these players were older and wiser, they would look back on this situation with regret.

It was a debatable issue, and gave a few teachers the added fuel they needed. Although the majority of teachers enjoyed the excitement and hype that attached itself to a successful football program, a few academic only types resented it. Perhaps they felt their students would be farther ahead, if academic competitions received the same attention as football. To some teachers, football had become a huge distraction in their classroom. Some resented the disruption that the post-season hoopla created in the school year-after-year. While others disliked the attention that Tony Annese received, and the power that came with his success.

Only a few teachers actually had sons on the team who experienced the football program first-hand. They were aware of the long hours both coaches and kids put in, and realized the benefits their sons derived from participating in a successful program. They strongly supported Montrose Football. But the situation created awkward debates in the teacher's lounge, as if someone drew a line in the sand to separate them at a teaching unit.

Annese ignored it. He had playoffs to focus his energy on, and went to work preparing his staff and team to face **Shepherd**. Both teams had excellent quarterbacks, two quality running backs, and a big physical line.

Two extra playoff uniforms remained after the J.V. snatched theirs and players wondered, *What two lucky freshmen would have the honor?* Justin Woodward and Vicente Vigil happened to be in the right spot at the right time, but their fortuity came with a catch. They couldn't just dress for show; they had to actually practice with the Varsity and work harder than they had ever imagined. Coach Annese explained the tap drill, telling the two freshmen, 'Just stand there and take a hit.'

The two rookies looked at each other, wondering why everyone loved to pick on freshmen. Jimmy Woodward watched his little brother, Woody, get smeared. It made him feel proud that Woody was tough enough to hang with the big dogs, or atleast he thought he was.

B.J. soon humbled both of them with one of his forceful hits when he packed all 195 pounds of solid muscle into a blow. The rookies endured every hit knowing that their freshmen buddies anxiously waited to hear the gory details. Sharing their painful yet thrilling Varsity experience with other freshmen made each gratifyingly sore muscle worthwhile. They wouldn't think of complaining as the Montrose Football legacy invisibly transferred to a new batch of boys.

When the Freshmen Team learned about Hudson High School's '81' game winning streak set back in 1977, they calculated that the Rams needed 20 more games to break it. They were already hooked after realizing that *they* could be the ones to clinch the longest regular season winning streak in the state of Michigan. It would happen during the third game of their senior year, *if* the streak continued until 1997. Everyone expected that it would; they wanted the streak to go on forever

Aaron Emmendorfer and Woody anxiously checked out the size of the eighth graders who would be the juniors playing with them in '97. They were huge boys. It pleased them to see their future linemen already at work in the weight room. Even though it was three years away, they were eager for their turn at the helm.

Practice routines didn't change much during the post-season. Edenburn wore his smelly, dirty, unwashed socks like he had for every pre-game practice during the entire season. He refused to wash them, although he did wear clean socks under them. It didn't matter how rancid they smelled, he couldn't take a chance of washing the luck out of them this late in the season.

The coaches implemented a few new strategies after they scouted upcoming opponents, but basically continued what they had all season. Shepherd had a quick quarterback, an excellent fullback, and a pair of huge tackles that worried Montrose.

Ruddy waited until the team gathered after their pre-game practice. He applied a serious face, then delivered an off-the-wall deep thought for their first playoff game:

> 'When I was a kid my favorite relative was Uncle Caveman.
> After school we'd all go play in his cave,
> and every once in a while he would eat one of us.
> It wasn't until later I found out that Uncle Caveman was a bear.'

The guys mocked Ruddy with 'Ohhhh's,' yet appreciated his weird sense of humor. The Rams felt ready for the post-season.

B.J. changed the playoff tradition of watching an inspirational video and selected a comedy to relax his teammates. 'Wildcats' sounded good and Goldie Hawn was fun to watch. His teammates looked pretty comfortable when they walked into the wrestling room with bags of munchies, subs, or their favorite pillow. If they were nervous, they hid it well. Players let the movie take the edge off their pre-game jitters before they faced fourth ranked Shepherd. The squad left the school only to return hours later for a traditional team breakfast early Saturday morning.

Playoff time kept the level of interest at a fever pitch. Coach Annese prepared their minds, filling them with confidence and a solid mental attitude. They felt physically and mentally ready, while waiting under the goal post to take their home field. Lange's heart pounded heavily the moment the band started playing the Montrose Fight Song. The atmosphere injected a hefty dose of adrenaline. He felt great.

When the Montrose Rams took the field for the opening kickoff, the entire squad felt their hearts pound with anticipation. The Rams lined up a bit differently, wondering if Shepherd suspected anything. Mo rehearsed a walk-through in his head. He took a moment to glance at the stands, noticing the eyes of thousands upon him. The kicker sucked air through his nostrils, then slowly exhaled his nerves before waving to the official. It calmed him. Mo didn't want to botch his big moment, and positioned his foot at the perfect angle. He pouch kicked the ball high into the corner, exactly like he'd practiced. His boot gave the ball significant hang time. He watched the Shepherd receiver look up in total concentration. The last thing a receiver wanted to do was drop the opening kickoff in front of thousands. The receiver was caught up in playoff frenzy and hadn't settled into his game yet. In the midst of his excitement, he never signaled for a fair catch, as the scene orchestrated exactly as Annese anticipated. The rest was up to his Rams and he wondered, *Were they fast enough? Did they want it bad enough?*

Four Rams sprinted toward the receiver. Cheap Shot Shane reached him first, hitting his opponent hard, forcing the ball from his hands. The Rams jumped on the pigskin, recovering it before the Shepherd fans had a chance to take their seats. Montrose practiced that play over and over, which required them to do a full sprint to the corner. They were always left winded without reward, because Coach wouldn't let them lay anyone out in practice; it always ended with a fair catch. Shane felt awesome to actually hit someone, especially at the start of the game. The adrenaline pounded in his chest when he exited the field with the excited kickoff team. He watched the rowdy offense trade places on the field. He soaked in the noise from the delighted fans that went crazy with the opening crowd pleaser. Shane couldn't hide his smile when the Rams stole the opening momentum. *Nothing compared to playoffs.*

The Rams capitalized quickly when Yuncker bullied over from the three, then scored again on a four yard run. The strong back didn't know how many times he could score during the playoffs. Yuncker's dad was a jock in high school at Beal City, scoring 22 TD's during his senior season. His uncles still bragged about how awesome his dad was back in *his* day. Even though his dad was Yuncker's biggest fan, along with his mom, sisters, grandparents, aunts and uncles, he always wondered how he stacked up to his old man. He never told any of his teammates, but he secretly wanted to break his dad's record of 22 TD's in a season. Yuncker was at 20 and didn't want to end up two short if he could help it. *Family bragging rights were priceless.*

Shepherd battled back, blocking Mo's PAT for the first time all season. But the Rams were up 13-0. Stiverson and Steve held down tackle positions for the left side, facing two of the biggest offensive linemen Steve had ever confronted in his life. Shepherd's intimidating linemen stood 6'5"-290 pounds and 6'3"-280 pounds next to a 6'- 325 pound guard. Steve wasn't the quickest tackle in the world, but he had a lot of strength to go with his size. Steve entered the program with a background of baseball experience. But he caught onto football fast, developing into a good player. He was hooked on football, thankful that his family moved to Montrose a year ago.

Stiverson was a shy guy who worked hard in sports, particularly powerlifting. He proved that he had more strength than anyone did on the team, after lifting a combined total of 1,510 pounds at Nationals. Stiverson always seemed overheated when he walked around with a short sleeved T-shirt in the dead of winter. He always yelled 'DEETZ' before and during his squats and deadlifts, a phrase that became a private joke among the linemen. Stiverson used his strength on the line, but when he used the technique his coaches taught him, he was unstoppable. He helped the defense dominate Shepherd.

Shepherd hit harder than previous opponents making the Rams feel the force of their strength. Persails used his height to jump, then tipped the ball to

Dave Follet who made a circus interception at the Shepherd 25. Newell grabbed a key reception to get the Rams into scoring position, then Bobby scored from one yard out. The crowd roared in spite of a failed conversion, cheering as the Rams held onto their 19-0 half-time lead.

During the intermission, Coach Annese stated how he wanted them to set the tone early for the second half. The determined quarterback did just that. He broke free, then sprinted 55 yards, on the second play from scrimmage to score. Just sixty seconds into the opening half, Yuncker ran in the conversion in front of an ecstatic crowd. Montrose went ahead by 27-0. The Rams proved how physically strong they were, and continued to execute well. They swapped fresh players into the game until they finally wore the Shepherd Blue Jays down.

Rizk and Shane made a pact early in the season – to help each other return punts. They totally trusted each other, realizing when one caught the ball, the other threw the block. No matter what. On the next play, Rizk caught a deep Shepherd punt. Shane blocked one of the two approaching Blue Jays, while the other tackled Rizk. Rizk fought back, determined not to go down. But aggressive opponents dangerously piled on top of him. Shane was the first to reach his teammate buried at the bottom of the pile. As soon as he saw the look on Rizk's face, he knew his buddy was in trouble. Annese joined them moments later. It was hard to see his co-captain in such pain. Joe Rizk was one of those larger-than-life guys, so full of energy and extremely dedicated. When Coach saw Rizk blink tears away, he knew that his knee was seriously injured. Rizk was in immense pain. Annese quickly motioned for the rescue squad, then helplessly watched while they carried Rizk off the field. Shane watched in horror, wishing that he could rerun the play, blocking the defender that hurt Rizk instead.

It pissed off the Rams who took on an eye-for-eye mentality, marching 68 yards for their best drive of the game. Whorf capped the drive with a two yard TD, then scored the conversion with 7:04 left in the final frame. The Rams played with passion; they did it for Rizk.

The Rams substituted several players who were thrilled to get a taste of playoff action. Shepherd scored twice against the reserves, closing the score '35-12.' It was the most points that Reinhart's defense had allowed the entire season.

The Rams showed their excitement when they gathered in the center of the field for their post-game talk. Steve Head tried to join in the celebration, but felt sick to his stomach. He felt feverish when his teammates locked hands and walked two-by-two under the goal post. He didn't remember experiencing any symptoms during the game; playoff exhilaration totally blocked them out.

His parents thought it was odd that Steve slept the rest of the weekend, especially when they couldn't wake him for school the following Monday or Tuesday. They should've suspected it was more than the flu, because Steve wouldn't miss a chance to lose his starting position for round two of playoffs.

Montrose studied **Napoleon's** game film, focusing on their key opponents. The Rams didn't quite know how to react after reading a news article that claimed Napoleon as the underdog.

Annese didn't play along with their small fry theory; realizing that coaches played games through the media. He was guilty of that himself. He scouted Napoleon and discovered their exceptional linebackers. Napoleon's offense was also quick at getting off the ball. Annese stressed to the Rams, 'Don't get overconfident about what you read in the paper. Napoleon boasts one of the top running backs in the state. He rushed for 1,636 yards on 199 carries and their quarterback executes the wing-T offense well.'

The Montrose coaches worried about injuries. B.J.'s sprained ankle was questionable. He couldn't practice the entire week. Rizk's prognosis was much grimmer. The junior co-captain's right ACL required surgery; his season was as good as over. Rizk was the team's second leading receiver and left a big hole. A year ago he dealt with the scary parasite issue, and now his knee. Annese called Rizk's inspiring personality, 'the heart and soul of the team.' Shane agreed to fill in for Rizk at receiver, and still play running back for the I-formation. He would do anything to keep their dream alive.

Ruddy and Rizk were first cousins on their moms' side. Ruddy knew how disappointed Rizk felt. He decided to keep the deep thought on a lighter side for his sake:

> *'If you're robbing a bank and your pants fall down,*
> *I think it's okay to laugh and to let the hostages laugh too*
> *Because, come on . . . life is funny.'*

Rizk was the type of kid who didn't stay down for long. Ruddy noticed a smirk form on his cousin's face by the time he finished.

B.J.'s mood was cheerful when his doctor cleared his ankle to play on Saturday. When he joined his teammates on Friday night at the wrestling room, he brought an old Cheech and Chong video, *'Up in Smoke.'* The movie came out the year after most of them were born, but his teammates had never heard of them. B.J. often watched the duo by default of his four older brothers. He couldn't believe that his squad had never heard of the hippie-like comedian stoners.

Cheech and Chong were a big hit, allowing the squad to laugh through the entire movie. Players intentionally started every sentence with a slow, drawn out expression of, 'Hey man,' while their laughter released their nervous energy.

Steve tried to join in, but felt his heart race whenever he tried to laugh. Something was seriously wrong. He was frightened when he rolled over on the mat, then lay motionless. In the midst of the noisy commotion, Steve tried to force himself to feel normal again. But his body didn't cooperate. His teammates watched as his color turned pasty. Leeseberg thought Steve was having a heart attack and wondered, *Is that even possible at age 17?*

Whatever it was, it scared the hell out of the entire team, whose laughter immediately turned to concern. Steve was also scared. He shakily stood, then staggered out of the wrestling room, unsure of what to do next.

B.J. jumped up and followed him, 'Hey Steve, you all right?'

'No, I think I'm really sick! I'm goin' home.'

Steve wanted the comfort of his own bed. He stumbled out to his car in the parking lot. His younger brother Scott, who went by 'Flaco,' didn't have his driver's license yet. He willingly asked, 'Steve, want me to drive?'

'No, just get in.'

The Heads lived just around the block from the school. Flaco jumped into the car. He watched his older brother hunch over the steering wheel, while he drove the short distance home. Flaco opened the front door of their split-level house. Steve managed to make it up the flight of stairs before passing out and falling backward. Steve was a big boy. So was Flaco, who managed to drag his brother up the stairs to the bathroom where he splashed water on Steve's face. Steve woke up, took a few steps, then passed out again, this time knocking over the heavy grandfather clock in the hallway.

The noise startled his parents, who fearfully rushed their son to the hospital. They soon learned that Steve was bleeding internally, and assumed that he also had mono for the past two weeks. Steve never said anything; sacrificing it all for playoffs. Steve had pushed himself, denying his body of the rest it needed, until his immune system finally ran down. Once all of his test results were in, Steve was rushed to surgery at 3:00 AM to remove a ruptured spleen.

It was Saturday morning when Steve finally opened his weary eyes. The first thing he saw was his dad, then he noticed that Joe Rizk sat at the foot of his hospital bed, crutches at his side. Both were relieved that Steve was out of danger, but Steve felt cheated that he couldn't play. So did Rizk. They worked so hard all season for playoffs, and felt robbed of their chance to play in round two. Misery loves company. They shared their frustration after all of the effort they invested. Rizk still had one more year, but for Steve it was over. It made his incision throb even more.

Rizk joined his teammates a few hours later at their team breakfast. He updated everyone on Steve's prognosis. They were still upset after seeing Steve during the movie the night before. They thought his color looked strange. Some actually feared that Steve could die. Steve and Rizk's bad luck made the game even more important, while providing an extra incentive for Montrose to beat Napoleon.

The town of Montrose jumped on the bandwagon and supported their Rams in full color. It was a town whose fans were so dedicated that they made personal sacrifices. Senior Ryan VanGorder's grandfather, Rudy Poletti, was almost ninety years old. The man never missed a game. Rudy delayed eye surgery because he wanted to be able to see the Montrose Rams play in the Pontiac Silverdome for a State Championship.

Youth football kids also supported the Rams, by proudly wearing their jerseys to the Varsity games. Football was a positive symbol of their town for the young boys who hoped to play for the Rams one day. Youth football molded them while they progressed through the ranks, some as young as eight years old. The Rams success carried over to the younger players who were in awe of the Varsity. They already knew what was expected of *them* in the future.

Montrose took control on their opening possession, by marching 70 yards to help Yuncker score, only to have it called back on a penalty. The Rams tried not to get discouraged, but it was tough for a team to put a drive together and not finish it. But Yuncker never gave up, and scored on their next series. The Rams were up 7-0, and Yuncker was one TD from tying his dad's record.

Napoleon had an enormous heavy bell on their sideline. Montrose players found it hard to believe that they hauled it 105 miles. Napoleons' cheerleaders rang it whenever the Pirates did something good. It annoyed the hell out of the Rams, who became deafened by the bell whenever they stood near it on the field.

The Rams fumbled. The Pirates drove down to the 11, dangerously close to a TD. But B.J. and Hodge had enough and sacked Napoleon's quarterback, snuffing the drive. Bobby hit sure-handed Newell over the middle. The lanky receiver out ran two Pirate defenders for a 56 yard TD. It helped the momentum shift by the half, when the Rams took a 13-0 lead.

Montrose came out during the second half and struck quick, just like they did against Shepherd. The Rams wanted control of the game. Bobby raced 37 yards on the first play of their initial possession, changing the score to 20-0.

Hodge felt his heart race when he recovered a fumble at the Montrose 42. Then Shane took a quick pitch from Bobby, then ran behind Yuncker and Whorf who laid out good blocks for him. Shane made a highlight clip classic when he juked his opponent. He faked one way, but once he bit, Shane headed in the opposite direction. Shane extended his long stride and raced 46 yards, like a swift racehorse on the backstretch, then scored with six minutes left in the third period.

The defense was on fire when Leeseberg sacked Napoleon's quarterback, halting another drive. The Rams recorded seven quarterback sacks, lead by Persails with two. Shane hauled in a 43 yard pass from Bobby with 8:48 left in the game. Then Newell threw a great block. It gave him an adrenaline rush as he raced to find Shane in the endzone. 'You wouldn't have scored if not for my block!'

'I know man, thanks!'

Shane waited for Napoleon to come back. But the Montrose defense used an attack style, instead of a read and watch defense to wear them down. Napoleon's annoying bell didn't clang as much during the second half.

Montrose's second team saw field time in the final frame. The defense had so much pride and didn't want to get scored on. When the starters got pulled the Montrose defense threatened, 'You better keep the shutout going!'

Napoleon ran a little outside sweep, then scampered 36 yards down the sideline. The first string defense yelled from the sideline, 'Hey - stop him!'

Only five minutes remained in the game. The Montrose starting defense became pissed when the visitor's side of the scoreboard lit up. Coach Annese totally caught sophomore quarterback Brad Casciano off-guard, 'Warm-up, you're going in.'

By his sixth handoff, Casciano felt great to be the signal caller for the Rams. Jake took the handoff, then watched his #41 jersey outrace the Napoleon's defense. Jake scored on a 41 yard run to make the final score, Rams '41-Napoleon 7.' For some reason, #41 instantly became the favorite number of Jake's dad.

Montrose fans applauded when Coach Annese accepted the Regional Championship Trophy. He was a natural born leader that knew how to win, in a town that doesn't like to lose. Coach handed the trophy to co-captains B.J. Dean and Joe Rizk who hobbled onto the field without his crutches. The Rams noticed the long faces of the Napoleon team who stood opposite them. It was the Pirates first playoff berth since 1987. They had missed the cutoff with a fifth ranking, the previous three seasons. The Rams had walked in those shoes and knew how they felt. The memory was fresh enough to recall their disappointment from a year ago when the Regional Championship Trophy went across the field to Orchard Lake St. Marys.

The Rams had a rematch against the top ranked **Orchard Lake** in the next round. They faced the very team that threw a monkey wrench in their path to a State Championship in `93. Bentley, another GEC League partner in Class C, also advanced to the state semifinals.

Montrose kept the physical part of practice the same, but the team studied more film for Orchard Lake, than the entire season combined. Coach Annese ordered pizzas one night after practice, and invited the first team offense to his house to study game films. The following night, Coach Destrampe had the first string defense over to his house, continuing the custom.

Every Ram was primed. The guards reviewed their blocking assignments. Shannon was a tall, lean guy who played offensive guard. His extreme quickness was great for trap plays. Coach liked Shannon at guard, because he could pull out in front of the running backs.

The coaches wondered if players absorbed what they were trying to get across. The coaches made some of the positions take a written test. They wanted the defense to be able to immediately read their opponents' formations and instinctively react.

A few players felt shafted; Leeseberg fell into that category. *Why would Coach change what worked for them all season?* He realized it would take every clever strategy that Coach Annese could strum up to beat Orchard Lake St. Marys, but he simply didn't understand his next move. Perhaps it was testosterone kicking in, or just out right envy, but being replaced by Gerrad didn't make sense to Leeseberg. Coach wanted more strength on the weak side. Leeseberg knew that it would be hard to match the strength and speed of Orchard Lake. But having Gerrad play both ways, against that caliber of a team, didn't add up in his book. Leeseberg played that position the entire season, fighting hard to keep it when challenged. The disappointed Leeseberg tried to understand his coach's logic, *but he couldn't*. It all meant too much.

Lange didn't grasp his unfortunate luck either. He quickly dropped 20 pounds, from his already lean 200 pound frame, the week before the Orchard Lake game. Lange was diagnosed with mono and wondered, *How could this happen before the biggest game of my life?* Steve Head was naturally tagged as the culprit. But with spit flying around and everyone constantly drinking from the same water bottles, coaches were surprised that more players didn't get sick. The excessive swelling around Lange's neck prevented him from wearing his helmet, until the final pre-game practice. Self-talk was the only thing that made Lange feel healthier, *At least I'm better off than Steve is. He's still in the hospital.* Lange forced himself to drag his fatigued body to the practice field everyday, with barely enough strength to lie down on the sideline. But he wouldn't miss the semifinal game for anything. *Not this one.*

The Rams prepared hard the entire week. The offense pressed the defense to endure an intense stamina for an entire game. The first string had only played the first half of their two playoff rounds. That didn't groom them for the echelon of competition against Orchard Lake St. Marys.

Ruddy used a simple deep thought after their final practice before round three. This thought held a deeper meaning. Ruddy hoped that it wouldn't come back to bite the Rams:

'I hope life isn't a big joke, because I don't get it!'

The Rams wouldn't joke about their next opponent. Orchard Lake had good, solid athletes who pursued the ball well. They were exceptional on defense, and were led by 6'3" quarterback and receiver DiAllo Johnson. DiAllo was a tremendous athlete that was recruited by colleges like Notre Dame, Colorado, and Michigan.

David Bowens was another exceptional athlete who ran a forty in 4.6. His 6'4"-225 pound body played tight end and middle linebacker. Annese knew that the Rams had their hands full against such talented athletes, like they did in the '93 contest. The key to beating the Eaglets was keeping the ball out of their hands. Orchard Lake St. Marys was termed by many as the *best team in the state,* regardless of class. They proved that by beating Warren DeLaSalle, who was ranked No. 1 in Class AA at the time. They also beat Detroit Country Day, who was in the Class B semifinals, and Detroit Catholic Central, recognized as the most powerful football program in the state.

Steve wanted to attend the game. He begged his doctor to release him, so that he could watch from SVSU's sideline. He tried in desperation to explain

Montrose Football and everything that they had accomplished. Steve eagerly explained the team's goal to his doctor, begging him to change his mind. Mr. Head claimed full responsibility, promising to return Steve to the hospital immediately after the game. It was a special game for the Head family since it was held at the very college where Mr. Head coached baseball. And, it was the only time his two sons played on the same team together, since Steve was a senior and Flaco a sophomore. But their pleading went on deaf ears. It didn't matter how good they built their case, Steve's doctor wouldn't budge. He only cared about Steve's health, not his dream. *Destiny was denied.*

The squad surrendered their superstitions, continuing to do everything the same. On Friday night, B.J. brought the video, *'Cheech and Chong's Next Move,'* to the wrestling room. While the team stretched out on the mats at the school, their female classmates, and a few players' sisters, visited their homes and decorated their bedrooms. Streamers hung everywhere, hardly allowing room to walk through the jungle of crepe paper. It extended the inspiration way beyond the cheerleaders normal way of decorating football players' lockers on game day.

Shane anxiously woke up and looked out of the window; afraid it would snow on the third Saturday in November. The sky looked overcast and cold, but it wasn't snowing. He anxiously dressed, then drove to the school for the team breakfast. His heart pounded heavier in his chest when he saw red and black balloons tied on street signs. 'Good Luck Rams' signs were nailed to trees throughout the town.

When he turned down Feher Drive, a block away from the school, he felt the lump in his throat intensify. Nearly a hundred white signs, shaped like footballs, were impressively staked into the ground. The signs lined both sides of the street. Every player's name was on an individual sign, including the J.V. and freshmen players who dressed for playoffs. Shane felt special and excited as he drove slowly down Feher Drive. With one eye on the road, the other eagerly searched both sides of the street until he found his name. He hit the brakes and stared at the sign that displayed his birth name in large, red letters - 'S H A N E.' *Yeah, this was real. This was awesome. We're playing in the semis.*

The team enjoyed playoff breakfasts. It felt great knowing the entire town was behind them, as they prepared to play the toughest game of their lives. Even their jokes held a serious aura that day.

Yuncker approached Bobby in the locker room for his sock, the one that he'd borrowed the entire season. Bobby seemed nervous when he faced him, 'My mom lost it in the wash.'

Yuncker's natural smile quickly faded, forcing Bobby to look away. 'What do you mean. She lost it? Bobby I've got to have that sock.'

'I'm sorry man. We looked all over.'

'Why do moms always say that? How can you lose laundry?'

Bobby shrugged his shoulders. He did his best to avoid the jinx factor that slithered into his thoughts. Yuncker forced a smile on his face, trying to brush it off in his usual happy-go-lucky way. But it left him with an eerie feeling that continued to gnaw at him. *I just broke tradition. You don't do that on the biggest game of your life!*

Leeseberg couldn't believe the number of decorated cars that waited in the school parking lot as he boarded the first bus. The fire department's shiny red rig gleamed at the head of the caravan. Police cars managed traffic at intersections, assisting the caravan as it paraded through the town of Montrose. Local storeowners and residents along the route lined the main streets, giving the team a proper send off. The police escorted the caravan six miles east to I-75, then stopped traffic on the overpass to allow access to the expressway. Playoff spirit was contagious. Even strangers honked at the decorated cars, giving the thumbs up sign as they passed. Keeping the caravan together on the expressway became difficult and dangerous. When fans passed the buses and waved, players only stared back with serious faces.

The winner played at the Pontiac Silverdome the following week. The Rams were only one week away from their dream. The Rams wanted it. The coaches wanted it. The fans wanted it. Even their defeated opponents wanted it for them.

Steve wanted it. He felt totally helpless as he accepted the daunting fact that he was confined to a hospital bed instead of the sideline. Flaco was allowed to dress as part of the J.V. Team. He told his older brother, 'I'll be there for you Steve.' As much as Mr. Head wanted to watch Montrose play Orchard Lake St. Marys, he didn't have the heart to bail on his son. Instead, he brought a radio into Steve's hospital room. Together, they prepared to listen to the biggest game of the season.

The Rams received visiting team status, but were assigned to the home team bleachers due to the higher fan attendance. Fans could be heard in the bleachers, 'Well, if Orchard Lake didn't recruit players, and their families lived closer, maybe more people could attend.'

Obviously, that was a touchy subject for public schools. Perhaps having the underdog status added to the drama, encouraging other schools to attend the game. The host college made a wise move since fans set a new attendance record at SVSU that Saturday. More people attended the state semifinal high school playoff game than any Division II college home football game. *That was something.*

B.J. prepared himself to go against David Bowens, the big tuna from St. Marys who he faced both ways. Bowens walked into SVSU's tape room while B.J. had his ankle wrapped. B.J. felt his presence before he even threw him a glance. He swore that the bench moved when Bowens took a seat next to him. Bowens didn't speak a word to B.J. who wondered, *Is he playing mind games with me?*

Even though B.J.'s athletic frame was solid muscle, it was difficult to compare his 5'10"-195 pound frame to Bowen's 6'4"-240 pounds. B.J. gave himself credit for his physical strength, but in the back of his mind he thought, *Something doesn't quite measure up.* At the time, B.J. was clueless that the opponent, who sat inches away, later turned pro and played for the Miami Dolphins. B.J. just shook his head as he walked away thinking, *This ought to be interesting.*

The Orchard Lake Eaglets were already on the field when the Montrose Rams approached the goal post. Leeseberg stood near the front of the line. He couldn't help but jump up and down when he felt the energy of the standing crowd embrace their presence by shouting, 'LET'S GO RAMS. LET'S GO RAMS!'

The stadium was built in a grassy valley with a pond at the south end, beyond the goal post. The field was in great shape. It looked sharp with a variety of contrasting grasses that staggered every five yards. The players' eyes soaked in everything: the neatly outlined field, the huge built in bleachers, the professional press box, the overwhelming fans, and the fact that they were only one win away from their dream. Only one game away from playing in the Dome. *They could hardly stand it.*

A single drummer from the marching band started the prelude. Bum bum (pause), bum bum (pause), followed by a drumroll, as hearts pounded and fans sang, 'Let's give a rousing cheer for Montrose, the greatest school in all the land... '

The Rams energetically charged the field, heading toward the cheerleader's banner. B.J. approached the paper attached to the banner. He was about to burst through, when he heard the warning voice of Coach Annese pop into his conscience. 'Don't do it B.J. It's not appropriate this time.'

B.J.'s taunting ritual was something that he performed before every game the entire season, and it pumped him up. He figured it was bad luck to change his ritual now, and quickly resolved the debate underway in his head. By the time he reached the banner, he had a plan. When he slashed through the paper, he faced the Montrose crowd, instead of the opposing one, and deeply yelled, 'YEAH. YEAH!'

His arms formed a gesture, like something Stone Cold would do. It was a move that his teammates called, 'The Wild Man Thing.' The Rams were so pumped that several players soared airborne as they jumped on the jampile. Their adrenaline blasted through every vein, like water roaring from a broken dam. B.J. jumped on top. At that moment, he felt as pumped as any human being could possibly feel.

A small plane circled the field directly before opening kickoff. All eyes naturally looked at the brilliant blue sky as they read the trailing banner. 'Good Luck Rams, the Sky's the Limit – Go #64.' Fans quickly flipped the pages of their program to identify who #64 was.

B.J. Dean; they should've known. One of B.J.'s older brothers pre-arranged the gift for his little brother, the youngest of the Dean clan.

Yuncker tapped B.J. on the shoulder and pointed at the blue sky. B.J. read his name on the banner then turned around. He eagerly searched for his family in the stands. His mom rang her cowbell, which made her easy to spot.

He waved at them, then returned his gaze to the sky. In a symbolic way, it made him think about his dad. B.J. wished that his dad was sitting in the stands, sharing the experience of his most exciting game. A moment later, a strange feeling overwhelmed B.J. And he knew, that somehow he was.

Butterflies churned inside of the special teams, while they waited for Montrose to kickoff. The Eaglets had a good return, but the Rams stopped them. Orchard Lake ran a quarterback drawl. B.J. tackled an Eaglet, causing a one yard loss. Stiverson reached in, stripped the ball, and the Rams recovered. Montrose fans instantly jumped to their feet, screaming with delight when their Rams got the ball back so quickly.

Bobby threw a 25 yard pass to Newell, followed by a 25 yard run by Yuncker. Jason and Stiverson eyed their opponents with a mutual distrust, as they took their positions on the line. Jason was tough; probably the roughest guy on the team. He was known for eating things; a dead horse fly, a moth, a preying mantis, anything to win a dare. He was crazy and very entertaining, but turned into an animal on the field.

The Rams drove 53 yards in five plays when Whorf got stopped at the doorstop to the endzone. The fans thought they were in, but the Rams lacked a yard. Bobby ran a quarterback keeper on the next play, while his line blocked like their life depended on it. Bobby broke through. The Rams were on the board first, on their initial drive. Mo's PAT was good, making the score 7-0, within the first two minutes of the game.

B.J. thought, *Wow, this is cool. We're playing Orchard Lake; the No.1 ranked team, of all classes, in the state. We just stopped them, turned around and scored!*

Shane wondered, *Is it possible that this could be another game where we're going to keep running down, just like Shepherd and Napoleon?*

But the Montrose coaches knew better. They didn't think for a single moment that this battle was a blow away. The Rams held their own, while the ball went back and forth, using plays that struck with equal force.

The Rams had a powerful line with receivers that could read defenses. Shane carefully watched when DiAllo went off and another quarterback came in. The free safety had previously viewed hours of game film, while carefully studying his opponents' formations. Shane darted for the corner of the endzone and turned. He couldn't hide his enthusiasm when he grabbed an interception, feeling totally invigorated; his homework had paid off.

Bobby pitched to Shane. He ran outside then sprinted down an open field, cutting to the inside before he was tackled. Shane immediately wished that they could rerun the play. *This time I'd cut to the outside and run down the sideline for a TD.* Instead, the Rams drove 58 yards to the Orchard Lake 22 yard line. Bobby got sacked on third and fourth downs. The Rams began to see why Orchard Lake was ranked No.1. They came back faster than Shepherd and Napoleon did, and had the power to stop the Rams.

Orchard Lake took over at the Montrose 38. J.V. players watched Shane pick-up an opponent's leg, then whip him around when he made the tackle directly in front of them. The underclassmen were close enough to see the drive in his eyes, and knew how much Shane wanted to win.

The Eaglets drove down the field nine plays later when DiAllo scored a six yard TD to tie the game at 7-7, with 2:35 left in the half.

Bobby injured his ankle, so Shane switched to the quarterback position for a few plays. Shane was in a bit of a dilemma because he took a hard hit on this same play. He started to throw a block on DiAllo, who in turn laid Shane out. The guys teased him in the huddle. 'Yeah, Bobby saw how hard you got hit and faked an ankle injury.'

Shane was a little quicker than Bobby was, and the coaches hoped to throw off the Eaglets' timing. Shane was still dazed and didn't quite know where he was for a moment. He was supposed to run a 48-counter keep, where he faked a trap and ran outside. But he completely forgot the play and asked Yuncker, 'Which one should I dive at?'

Yuncker threw Shane a questionable glance, then tried to disguise his mistrust when he filled him in.

The Rams were not used to playing in close games, but they welcomed this one. Finding themselves in a tie at the half against Orchard Lake, was actually a bonus. B.J. realized that his teammates had not talked about this aspect. Up to this point, the Rams felt confident that they could beat everybody *except* Orchard Lake. Even though they boasted during practice, 'Oh yeah, we want to win this game. We're gonna go out there and kick their butts. They can't stop us!' In reality, the Rams were only trying to convince themselves. But facing such exceptionally talented athletes made them mutely wonder, *Do we even have a shot?*

The Rams played with attitude. Now, they actually believed that the unconquerable Orchard Lake St. Marys *could* be beaten. It required playing all 48 minutes of hard football, and a lucky break here or there, but it was possible. The Rams honestly believed in themselves, and couldn't help but feel the anticipation. At this point, B.J. thought, *We're at the half way mark and we're tied! We're hanging with these guys. We have a chance to win this ball game. We could be going to the Dome -- the Pontiac Silverdome -- next weekend. We're going to win this game! I just know it.*

The players focused on every motivating word that flowed from Coach Annese's mouth during his half-time talk. His words were packed with passion, inspiring every player and coach in the locker room. Annese was just as pumped as his team. No one wanted this to be his last speech, *including him.* Coach built up their confidence before sending them onto the field. Pure excitement flowed through their veins. Supportive fans welcomed the team, displaying more excitement than they ever had before. Fans were proud of how they battled against the best, and shouted in unison, 'LET'S GO RAMS! LET'S GO RAMS!'

Montrose threatened to break the deadlock on its opening possession of the second half. Newell ran a seven-route, attempting to catch Bobby's pass. But a short, defensive back knocked his hand away at the last second.

Damn. If it would've been one foot over, it could've been a TD. If only.
It was fourth-and-10 on Orchard Lake's 12. The Rams lined up for a 30 yard field goal attempt. A field goal should be a walk in the park, since Mo's record breaking 45 yard kick just four games ago. The Rams had a good snap and Mo booted it. But the amazing David Bowens blocked the field goal. That guy was unbelievable. He was all over the field the entire game. Bowens made some Rams think that he could beat them single-handed.

It wasn't over yet. As if an Angel of Mercy intervened, the football managed to land on the 12 yard line, directly in the hands of Montrose Ram #51 - Jeff Lange. *Was it Divine intervention?* After all, the Rams thought they had more Catholics on their team than their opposing, private, Catholic school. Since it was blocked behind the line of scrimmage, it became a 'live' ball. Coach Annese realized it. The officials realized it, but #51 didn't. While the Orchard Lake defense jumped up and down in celebration of their blocked kick, no one paid any attention to #51. He stood all alone with the crown jewel, the ticket to the Silverdome rested in the palm of his hands. The Montrose coaches screamed at the top of their lungs, 'RUN IT IN! RUN IT IN!'

If Coach Annese ever needed to get through to a player, this was the moment. He screamed until his lungs felt like they could collapse. Annese continued yelling at the top of his lungs from the sideline, like a panicked parent unable to reach a drowning child. All #51 had to do, was jog 12 yards into the endzone . . . *and score.* Twelve yards. Only two Orchard Lake backs stood between Lange and the goal, and one Ram stood between them. But no one realized the opportunity in front of him.

Was it a walk in the park? Not hardly. Lange probably shouldn't even be on the field. Maybe the mono clouded his judgment, although that situation had never happened before. The Rams practiced everything, *but they never practiced this.* They never even discussed it. And Lange wasn't a schmuck. He was strong and smart; one of the top in his class who led by example for those who slacked off in the classroom. He simply didn't realize his golden opportunity. Lange played with the ball in his hands; unable to hide his own disappointment that Mo's field goal was blocked. Then, as if Lange was on the practice field running through plays, he casually tossed the sacred pigskin to the official, as a helpless Coach Annese watched in horror.

Coach gave a final powerful yell from the sideline, unable to believe the lost opportunity that unfolded directly in front of his very own eyes. *This wasn't happening. This just wasn't happening.*

The official couldn't say anything. He almost appeared to hesitate before accepting the ball. He must've realized the ramifications that rested within that piece of leather, and the consequences Lange could suffer later. It caught the entire special teams off-guard, while they reacted to their hotshot kicker's blocked kick. Afterward, they all wondered, *What if?*

Annese forced himself to shake off the lost opportunity. The Rams were still in the game when the third quarter ended with a 7-7 deadlock. Orchard

Lake ran a 71 yard drive that took six minutes off the clock. Shane covered an opponent who ran a fade route, but DiAllo rolled out, cutting around what seemed like every person on the field. Like Bowens, DiAllo was everywhere. The Rams couldn't believe how gifted DiAllo was. Edenburn got blocked, then watched as Wingo missed him, then another Ram missed him. The Rams couldn't stop DiAllo when he scored a 21 yard TD, on the second play of the fourth quarter.

It was the reason DiAllo Johnson played wide receiver and special teams for the prestigious University of Michigan. The '94 Rams closely followed his career, realizing the caliber of play Division I required. They pointed him out while watching Saturday college games, 'Hey, I played against him.'

Sheer determination helped Hodge jump high enough to partially block the PAT, enough to make it fail. But the Eaglets were up 7-13. Orchard Lake had regrouped during the intermission. They got a handle on how to defend the trap, after Yuncker had such good success during the first half. The second half was slow for the Rams, who couldn't get anything generated offensively. They appeared afraid to pass after Bobby got sacked.

Then Bowens rocked Persails hard. *Really hard.* Persails held his bearing for a few seconds before falling to the ground, followed by the indomitable Bowens. Fans stood up, worried about the impact. Persails seemed to have won their personal battle, when he slowly stood first. He noticed that Bowens was still on the ground. They collided like two attacking bulls with a blow so robust that it stunned them both; enough to make them sit out the next play. Persails was a hero for a moment, while his teammates cheered him on. 'Yeah, you got up first and Bowens was still on the ground!'

A dazed and confused Ryan Persails was cognizant enough to tuck the scene into his memory bank. He later retrieved it when he watched Bowens *start* as a true freshman for the prominent University of Michigan the following year. His talent led the Michigan Wolverines in sacks the year before they won the National Championship. Persails remembered that he actually stunned the unstoppable Bowens, if even for a few moments. Then, the flashback continued and he recalled just how badly Bowens rocked him.

It was a golden opportunity for the Rams. They held Orchard Lake without a first down on their next possession. Then, the Eaglets had an illegal procedure called when they punted to the Montrose 14. They punted again. This time the ball only went seven yards and traveled out-of-bounds at the Orchard Lake 49 yard line with 7:11 left to play. It was a 37 yard bonus for the Rams and B.J. thought, *For sure we'll come back and score now.*

Not if Orchard Lake could help it. They had their own plan to go to the Dome the following weekend, and managed to shutdown Montrose. The Rams took a knee while an injured opponent was attended to. The Rams felt so frustrated that they couldn't score and told each other, 'We gotta go out there and do it. It's now or never!'

On fourth-and-three, Coach Annese called a play that the Rams had never used before. Yuncker looked at Shane when the huddle broke, 'Shane, just get the first down!'

'Yeah, I will, I will, I will.'

They only needed three yards. *Three yards.* Their hearts raced with anticipation while they listened for Bobby's cadence. He pitched to Shane at tailback, who tucked the ball and used every ounce of speed to run as fast as he could. Bowens sprinted from the opposite side, determined to stop Shane. One second Shane sprinted toward the goal, the next he was eating grass when Bowens stopped him. Shane fell *one yard short* of the first down.

Shane wanted it so badly and thought, *Oh my God. I can't believe I just got tripped. It's going to be my fault if we lose.*

The determined defense stopped Orchard Lake, giving their offense another chance to score. The defense was fired up, unable to contain their adrenaline rush. They passed every ounce of encouragement they had to the offense when they exchanged positions. But Orchard Lake held tough, forcing the Rams to give it up on downs, then stalled midfield with one-minute left in the game. Shane caught the punt and ran out-of-bounds with :55 seconds left. Like his teammates, he never gave up that the Rams could still win. It was possible. They were only down by one TD, but time was running out. Coach Annese called for a pass play. They realized this was their last shot. The Rams squeezed hands in the huddle, sensing a confidence as they faced each other. They were going to make this happen. They would live their dream. They just knew it.

John Hill snapped the ball, like they'd practiced a thousand times. Bobby gripped it, stepped back in the pocket, found his receiver, and released. Everything seemed to move in super slow motion. He followed the path. The entire stadium did . . . until the ball was caught. But it landed in the hands of an Eaglet, not a Ram. *Damn.* If there ever was a good time to have a turnover, that wasn't it. It didn't matter that it was the Rams only turnover of the entire game. The Rams felt confident they could pull off a victory in the final play and become heroes; an interception wasn't part of their plan.

Devastation instantly attacked them, like crash dummies hitting a brick wall. They felt a panic consume them and dropped to the ground like wounded soldiers. *No. It can't end like this!* They felt horrible and scared, like something very wrong just happened. They were such a disciplined team, and were coached to demonstrate good sportsmanship no matter what the outcome. Some didn't want to get up and congratulate the winners, including Jason and Wingo. They were two big guys who wanted to win so badly, and were not prepared to cope with a loss. Teammates pulled both of them up, then helped them gain enough composure to congratulate the state finalists.

Brad Casciano dressed as a sophomore and also wore #10, the same jersey as Shane, only he watched the heartbreaker from the sideline. Casciano never expected to get a chance to play, but joined in the post-game line up to shake hands. David Bowens noticed his #10 jersey and reached out to shake his hand, 'Good game man, you are so quick!'

Casciano instantly realized the comment was meant for Shane. But he looked Bowens dead in the eye and seriously replied, 'Thanks man.'

As if something snapped inside of Jason and Wingo, they once again surrendered to their emotions and fell to the ground, tuning out the entire world. It hurt like hell when they tried to deal with their inner pain. *How could they possibly begin to describe this grief to someone? How could anyone conceivably imagine what went into their program unless they actually lived it? They worked so hard and came so close and didn't prepare to have it end like this. Not like this.* It was difficult to accept that their dream was over. Their entire universe suddenly seemed misaligned. The Montrose Rams came so close. *So close.* So close to playing for a State Football Title. The Rams played at an exceptional level for a public school of its size, but it wasn't enough. They did everything they could for an entire year to prepare and wondered, *Why didn't it happen?* To the coaches and fans it felt like a repeat of the '92 Season. The familiar draining ache of watching someone fall short of his dream, painfully returned. Orchard Lake was every bit as good as their No. 1 ranking, and as compelling as their immaculate record. The Rams fought a good fight to the end, and went out as champions who battled on the field.

Shane took off his helmet as blood gushed from his nose. It was his first nose bleed and he couldn't stop it. He left a trail of dark red blood on the jersey of every teammate that he hugged. Someone snapped his picture while his face was covered with blood and he wondered, *Why did they do that?*

The locker room held the persona of a funeral parlor. The seniors stayed in one room, underclassmen in another. Shane laid on the bench, sobbing, while his nose continued to bleed. His teammates couldn't get it to stop and finally called for a coach to pack it. The underclassmen listened to their coaches. 'You guys did the best you could. You played one helluva game!'

Coach Destrampe took Shane aside, 'Don't worry Shane, you've got another year. We'll get 'em next year!' Shane was thankful that he had another shot, but those seniors were his buddies and he felt their pain. He couldn't imagine how guys like B.J., Bobby, Newell, and Yuncker felt. *They didn't have anymore seasons. For them, it was over.*

It was an excruciating way for it all to end. It was so hard to accept that it was really over. The coaches talked to the seniors for a long time in the opposite locker room. They wanted them to be proud of what they had accomplished; not dwell on what they didn't. But it was too fresh. The entire team gave all they had. The Rams honestly felt that they had a shot. The underclassmen walked into the room with an uneasy feeling, like going to see a dead person for the first time. They were immediately astonished.

If the bench in Saginaw Valley's locker room could speak, it would testify that the painful tears shed that day were real; as existent as the air they breathed. Emotions consumed everyone in the room. An action that normally made them feel stupid, didn't feel ridiculous or even slightly wrong. They didn't need to be discreet, or feel concerned about their appearance. The squad discovered the depth of their brotherhood as they released throbbing emotions. It was the only thing that actually seemed appropriate. *Openness was accepted.*

Coach Annese brought each senior in front of the team, hugging him with a sense of finality. His conviction portrayed that he suffered the loss as strong as the team did. It was difficult to pour his heart and soul into a program and come so close, so many times. He made the sacrifices and committed the necessary time to be a coach who made an impact. *Dedication was valued.*

A special kind of adoration swelled in SVSU's locker room when he offered his comfort and support. The team felt pure love and passion from their coach, while he composed himself. It was a moment that was difficult to erase. 'We just lost a semifinal game by six points to a team that dominated the top Class AA schools in the state. You're not going to totally control athletes like that. If SVSU had five of those kids, they'd be national champions. That's how good they are. We're not going to see those kinds of athletes on one field in Class CC, or any other situation other than the conditions that Orchard Lake has. That's just the way things are. We battled a team of that caliber with heart and determination right to the very end. I'm very proud of the way you played.'

Assistant coaches conquered lumps in their own throats, forcing out the soothing words that seniors so desperately needed to hear. No one rushed the painful, final good-bye to a record-breaking high school football season. The underclassmen found it tough to saunter through the gloomy senior line. The heart-to-heart brotherly hugs, and the sound of cracked voices, saturated the room, prying open their own tears.

B.J. looked at Jake, repeating the very words that seniors told him just one year ago. 'You guys do it next year. Make the most of it. You can't go back. It will be over before you know it!'

Persails told Edenburn, 'You guys have nothing to be ashamed of.'

Edenburn racked up the best stats over any other game that he ever played, but it didn't lesson the ache in the pit of his stomach. He was done.

Jake, Shane, and Persails felt a desire that burned deep in their souls to finish the quest. They experienced firsthand how much it all meant, which molded them as underclassmen. Witnessing such a devastating loss only contributed to the mystery that kept the Montrose Football tradition alive and strong. The juniors had just stepped up for their '95 Season; determined to be the team that made it to the Dome.

That Saturday afternoon, it seemed that Shane stayed in that locker room forever. He tuned out everything while he wrestled with his emotions, feeling alone and numb. Shane relived the play over-and-over in his head, trying to gain one more yard before Bowens tripped him. Dang, they desperately needed that down. He continued to beat himself up. He couldn't believe that it was over. Two seasons later, Shane became a regular fixture in that same locker room as an SVSU Cardinal. He sat on that very bench, remembering the `94 game with a new perspective. It was then that he realized just how strong the `94 offensive line really was. He compared SVSU players to B.J. Dean, Chris Wingo, and Adam Stiverson. He recognized that the Rams had the perfect combination of energy, size, strength, and speed. He felt that every player on the `94 Team could've played college football.

B.J. stared out of the window on the bus ride home, which seemed easier than looking at his friends. They all appeared so distraught. Maybe it was the saddest event some of them had ever faced. But B.J. had experienced a much deeper demise – *death*. It gave him a base from which all other pain compared to. At that moment, it helped keep things in perspective. He didn't feel like a loser, although some of his teammates did. B.J. had prepared himself for the end of his football career before it ever began. At the start of his freshman season, he consciously made a decision that he would never miss a practice, nor would he ever give less than 100%, for anything surrounding football. As he looked back, he felt that he had done everything in his power and gave 100%. B.J. decided right then, that he wouldn't have any regrets. Somehow, it made the semifinal loss easier to grasp.

For some, the loss left them feeling empty and horrible. It contained such a sense of finality. They wondered, *How could a football game leave us feeling so desolated?* The players felt it the strongest, but the feeling was shared by those closest to them. Watching a team concede their dream was extremely tough. After school on Monday, the guys naturally gathered in the locker room, as if to seek comfort from its sheltered haven. It unofficially held the status of a private sanctuary of sorts; not just anyone could enter it or would want to. For that, they were glad. About ten seniors showed up and didn't quite know what else to do. They just looked at each other, realizing that it was over, yet hoped it was a bad dream and it really was time to put their pads back on.

Thanksgiving arrived a few days later and the guys wished they were in better spirits for the holiday. They wanted to be, but their hearts wouldn't cooperate. Most of the players attended the State Championship on the day after Thanksgiving. They watched Constantine vs. Orchard Lake St. Marys. Emotion overwhelmed the Rams when they saw the pride and support from the Constantine fans. They knew that the town of Montrose would've provided that same strong support. Players appeared like lost souls while they quietly stood in the endzone, proudly adorned in Montrose Football jackets. Orchard Lake ate up Constantine from the start. The Rams watched their formations and called out, 'Here comes a pass to the corner.'

Sure enough, their prediction held true while others nodded with assurance, as if they just aced the test. Montrose watched Orchard Lake carry the game away, defeating Constantine 35-7. The Rams felt the knife pierce their chests, wrenching another notch in their hearts. The score for the State Championship game was never even close, which made *their* semifinal loss even more difficult. They didn't say it, but in their hearts they knew the real

Championship game was played the week before. The two best teams in the state just met *a week too early.*

Many coaches felt that the MHSAA had a monopoly on a team's success by playing with the regions every year. It was tough for public schools to compete with the exclusive private schools, yet Montrose represented the public school system well.

All that remained was to send the Rams out in style. The Freshmen and J.V. Teams each posted a 9-0 record and the Varsity ended 11-1; that was worthy of ample recognition. Their families bought tickets to a classy football banquet, instead of bringing a dish to pass. Chris Annese made sure the cafeteria was beautifully decorated in red, black, and silver. The cafeteria crew catered a fancy meal that made players question, 'Why doesn't our school lunch look this good?'

B.J. addressed the crowd as their team captain, speaking into the microphone with confidence. The death of their fathers connected him with Coach Annese in a unique way over the past four years. B.J thought that Coach Annese was the most stimulating football person he had ever met; his record spoke for itself. B.J. ended his talk with, ' . . . and I just want to thank Coach Annese for making me a better person.'

The team gave their coach a standing ovation. Not only did he have a true mindset to set up the technical aspect of the game, but he also possessed the exceptional drive and adamant desire to win and succeed. The seniors wondered, *Does Coach have any idea how their experience affected them in a way that changed who they were? Does he realize the impact he had on their young lives or the influence he still has on their futures?*

Annese defined motivation. Yeah, at times he made them so mad, yet he inspired them, and taught them what hard work really was. He swore at them, praised them, and trained them on how to become champions. Yet he humbled them when they were cocky. Coach shamed them into never quitting at whatever they did in life. He made believers out of young men, while shaping them into manhood. They learned how to be accountable to each other, while deriving the benefits of being on a successful team. He led them to great success. Coach suffered their bitter defeats right alongside them, instilling a burning desire -- a quest to become State Champions.

The seniors listened to his *last talk* as their coach, realizing that he altered the way they now looked at the world. Players who entered the program discovered that they were not the same when they left. As young men, they learned who they were through football. They would be forever changed; some in ways noticeable to others, some only to themselves.

The Football Club presented each Varsity player with a wood plaque that stated, 'Montrose Rams Best Team Ever.' Coach Annese wrote individual letters to each senior, citing their strong points. They each stood modestly taller after reading his comment, then choked at the end of his letter.

At the end of the banquet, the lights were shut off and the 1994 highlight film rolled. The players laughed when they relived their smashing season, while AC/DC and Nirvana jammed in the background, calming them like they had before every game. The joyful mood changed to somber, once they realized it was now *a memory*. Kenny Roger's voice sang *'Through the Years'* and the film changed to super slow motion. Annese traditionally included this song on every highlight tape, hoping one day that the guys appreciated its hidden message. Their grave mood turned even more somber when the Orchard Lake game hit the screen and VanHalen sang, *'Dream Another Dream – This Dream is Over.'* The song had a soothing undertone that lingered in their heads, long after the banquet ended. Unfortunately, so did its message. There wasn't a dry eye in the room when Mariah Carey's clear, angelic voice sang her popular hit, *'Hero.'* Players must've heard that song a hundred times on the radio, but never focused on her words. Each line in the song was intended to ease their heartache and make them feel stronger; as if she wrote *'Hero'* especially for them.

Like the rest of the players, Leeseberg was thankful for the darkness. Tear-filled eyes absorbed every inch of the huge screen, while the team soaked in every last memory. He recognized the beat to Bob Seger's *'Famous Final Scene'* and felt his heart drop. It carried the same solemn message as Taps being played at a military funeral, signifying that they were seconds away from the grand finale. The team watched a recap of trauma and dignity, wondering why their season ended like it had. The `94 Rams wrote an amazing saga that they could be proud of, which only made their finale harder. The silence in the room echoed throughout the cafeteria, forcing them to swallow hard. They watched themselves on the large screen one final time.

B.J. felt their energy and their power as the team sprinted from the goal post, then exploded through the sign. The video mesmerized the entire team, as the large squad piled on their pre-game cluster. They were so full of life, that it was impossible to suppress the electrifying thrill of how much it all meant. Only Bob Seger's soothing voice could appropriately recap the emotion of their season, like he had on every highlight film. They absorbed every soulful phrase, as if hearing the lyrics for the very first time. The solemn steel guitar engulfed their thin-skinned hearts, whining as it echoed through the still room. It touched a sensitive chord in everyone present. Seger's crisp voice was husky and smooth as he gently forced them to cope that it was really over. His soulful words sang true:

> *"Think in terms of bridges burned. Think of seasons that must end.*
> *See the rivers rise and fall. They will rise and fall again.*
>
> *Everything must have an end. Like an ocean to a shore.*
> *Like a river to a stream. **It's the famous final scene.**"*

TRI-COUNTY CITIZEN PHOTO

Orchard Lake Playoff Game: #84 Gerrad Leitelt, #10 Shane Schlorf and #77 Chris Wingo

TRI-COUNTY CITIZEN PHOTO

Orchard Lake Playoff Game: #22 Shawn Yuncker, #51 Jeff Lange, #16 Bobby Klopf, and #64, B.J. Dean

TRI-COUNTY CITIZEN PHOTO

Coach Annese addresses the 1994 REGIONAL CHAMPIONS

8. PERSEVERANCE - 1995

Great works are performed not by strength but perseverance.

-Samuel Jackson

It hit them the moment they walked into the Dome and took a seat in the Main Event Restaurant; a familiar scene to the Annese brothers. They recognized the team on the turf by their uniforms, but immediately noticed something different about them. They watched the team run through plays, but the pang of envy was a new addition. Not being on the field with them felt undeniably strange.

After watching championship game-after-game, year-after-year, the brothers could tell the teams that were absolutely thrilled to play in the Dome from the ones that were just excited. Maybe it was because some schools played in the Dome so many times that it was more of an expectation than a dream, and they lacked the wonderment. Or maybe they were a lucky team that tiptoed through their region without paying any dues, and didn't fully appreciate what an honor it was to play here. They couldn't help but notice that this game was different for the team on the field. It held a glowing ambiance that something very special was happening, not just for the team but for their entire community.

The Annese brothers watched in silence. The atmosphere seemed to cast a spell over the players donned in red and black, and their fans fully clad in corresponding colors. It felt strange, like the game was being played in a dream and they weren't part of the cast -- or were they? They wanted to be the coaches who stood on the sideline, not the ones who watched from the windows above the upper deck. Yeah, the restaurant had great seats and the food wasn't bad, but for once they wanted to be the team on the field below. They wanted to feel the cushion of the turf and speak into the headsets and take advantage of the TV breaks. They wanted to see the glow on players' faces when the echo from the roar of the crowd sent chills through their bodies. They wanted to win a State Championship just as much, if not more, than any coach that ever stepped foot on that magical turf.

They finished their dinner and left the restaurant, wondering, 'Will we ever get here? What are we doing wrong? We have the passion, the program, the work ethic, and the talent. What else does it take? What more could we possibly do?'

Shane Schlorf was surprised when Coach Annese approached him before school started early one April morning, then handed him a box. 'Here Shane, this is for you.'

As he lifted the burgundy colored box, his heart began to race. Shane carefully read the gold words engraved in the rich cherry wood and felt his heart pound rapidly. He read the phrase again, wondering, *Why did Coach Annese give me this plaque?*

Success
**'The difference between a successful person and others is not a lack of
strength, not a lack of knowledge, but rather in a lack of will'**

-Vince Lombardi

He looked up with a confused expression to thank his coach, but he was
gone. A strange feeling instantly engulfed Shane as he quickly shook his
shoulders, warding off a cold chill. *What was going on? Coach didn't hand
out plaques until the end-of-season banquet.* He tried to discard any possible
reason that lurked in his mind and planned to haunt him throughout the day.
He listened when Dan Ruddy read the sixth hour announcements. Shane's
head perked up when Ruddy said, 'All Varsity football members are expected
to meet in Mr. Kitts' classroom directly after school.'

Shane felt his heart sink, and was afraid to confront what he feared the
most. Joe Rizk ran into Shane shortly after school. 'Hey, any idea what the
football meeting's about?'

'I have no idea but something's up. Coach Annese gave me a cool
Lombardi plaque this morning.'

Rizk raised his eyebrows. 'Oh yeah? He gave me one too. Something's
going on. You think he's leaving?'

Shane let out a heavy sigh. 'I sure hope not.'

About that time Coach Annese walked into the room, cutting to the chase
as soon as he faced the kids. 'You're probably wondering why you're here.
What I have to say is not easy for me, but I wanted to tell you myself. I've
accepted another head coaching position at Ann Arbor Pioneer.'

An astonished hush fell over the room, while they tried to absorb the
news. Players felt completely helpless that their legendary coach was
leaving. The soon-to-be seniors immediately felt abandoned, as if they'd just
been told that their parents were getting a divorce and their family was
splitting up. Shane couldn't stand it any longer and selfishly blurted out.
'But you can't leave yet; I have one more year!'

The exact thought flashed through the minds of the rest of the upcoming
Varsity. Annese expected that very reaction as the guilt yanked at his
conscience. 'This has been one of the most difficult decisions of my life.
I've been blessed with great coaches to work with and outstanding players. I
honestly couldn't have asked for a better situation. The attitude of you
players is tremendous. Throughout our lives, we're always looking for new
challenges. In my heart, I need to see if I can build another program. You
have a strong tradition here. I know you'll have a great season if you
continue to work hard.'

Heavy sighs and irritable voices saturated the room, making it difficult for
Coach to face them. 'I know you don't understand now, but this is a great

opportunity for me. You've got a solid foundation built here and you'll be just fine. I want to see if I can build a program at a Class AA school.'

It disturbed Tony Annese that his '94 Squad felt like failures after they played a very close game to a team that went on to win the State Championship a week later. Memories of a frustrated player beating his head on the sidewalk after that semifinal game created an anticlimax. He wondered if he did any justice to the program he implemented, even though they barely lost to a team ranked 17th in the *nation. Did I stress dedication and goal commitment to the extreme that they felt like failures when a State Championship wasn't accomplished? Had I built a program that became so competitive for players to outperform their predecessors?*

That wasn't his intent, and it bothered him to the point that it became a factor in his career decision. Everyone in the room felt sad; they simply were not ready to see him leave. It was difficult to care about *his* future; they were only interested in *their own.* Rizk selfishly wondered, *Why couldn't he wait until my senior year was over? It's only one more year. Was that too much to ask?*

Shane, Rizk, and Jake Emmendorfer were caught up in their own selfishness, unable to hold back their emotions. Annese instilled a strong pride and work ethic, making players believe in themselves in a positive way. Now, players felt like he had abandoned them before they started their senior year. It was a painful breakup. The threesome stood with the others and told Coach Annese how he made a difference in their lives. But it felt like their family was being pulled apart – *and in a way it was.*

Coach Annese had built a dynasty at Montrose after eight years at the helm. He won 61 consecutive regular-season games, claiming the past seven GEC Championships. Montrose had a strong football program before he arrived, but he definitely elevated the level of performance. He left Montrose 71-11, setting a Flint area record for best winning percentage amongst coaches with 50 wins or more. Annese would always cherish the relationships with players and the friendships they made. He knew they would stay in touch. Annese honestly regretted that he didn't give the supportive town of Montrose a State Championship before he left.

Coach Reinhart served as the acting head coach while Administration posted the position. He did his best to erase any fears and told players, 'We still have a good season to look forward to.'

Then, the coaching staff left the room, giving the squad a chance to talk. Before the meeting, the team felt good about their powerlifting success and the upcoming '95 Football Season. But that all changed in an instant. They suddenly felt betrayed, and took their frustration out on each other. It didn't take long for a fistfight to break out, as emotions bounced off the walls of Room 157. Too many people had jumped ship on them. Not only Coach Annese, but his two brothers that assisted were leaving. Coach Joe Morse agreed to be a part of Pioneer's new staff, and Coach Mike Sullivan accepted an assistant coaching position at SVSU. The Rams experienced the common reality of what happens when coaches move on, taking their staff with them. Only that time, it happened to *them*.

The Rams' center recently announced that he planned to transfer to Orchard Lake St. Marys to play football with the reigning champions for his senior year. He wanted to play for the team that stopped Montrose in the playoffs the previous two years. Maybe he wanted to take advantage of their educational benefits, but the team only focused on his sharp words about 'wanting to play for a State Championship Team.'

Normally Jake was on the quiet side, but he couldn't resist calling the center -- Benedict Arnold. He asked, 'How could you betray us? You've played with us for three years! Orchard Lake barely beat us in the semis!'

Jake was a committed player. After that day, he didn't want to talk to the ex-center, which was a common reaction from the entire Varsity squad. They were a group of high school kids that combined rejection with adolescence, labeling their ex-friend as a traitor. Another team member received a similar letter from Orchard Lake – Shane.

Shane decided not to tell anyone about *his* letter after observing the team's response to their center bailing on them. He obviously caught the eye of Orchard Lake coaches after playing such a good game in '94. The letter stated that it was *not* a recruitment letter, and portrayed how their school offered a quality education in a beautiful setting, and visibility from college football coaches.

But Shane loved playing for the Montrose Rams and refused to transfer his senior year. He just couldn't do it. He wouldn't be a traitor; he remained a Ram. Shane planned to do everything in his power to win a State Championship for Montrose, in spite of everyone bailing on them. It only made him even more determined . . . until paranoia set in. Shane feared that a teammate would find the letter, so he ripped the opportunity into tiny shreds before throwing it away. He didn't want to chance anyone accidentally finding his letter, and made an assumption that he even considered transferring to Orchard Lake. *Loyalty was admirable.*

Shane's heart sank after reading the April 30, 1995 edition of the Tri-County Citizen, which featured a letter to the Editor from Coach Tony Annese:

'ANNESE SAYS FAREWELL - THANKS TO RAM FOOTBALL FAMILY'

To the Terrific Ram Football Supporters:

It is with a deep sense of emotion that I write this letter to you. I have resigned my position as head football coach at Montrose and accepted the head football position at Ann Arbor Pioneer High School. I do so with a heavy heart knowing that Montrose has meant so much to me over the last eight years. It is very difficult to relinquish something that has been such a large part of me, but the opportunity at Pioneer High School is one that I cannot turn away from. I leave Montrose with tremendous pride and admiration for the community, school administration, teachers, and most importantly, the students and players that have enriched my life beyond description. I am indebted to so many people who have made my stay in this community magnificent. I could not have been happier with my experience in this wonderful town.

I would like to thank the school for their willingness to create a positive climate to run a successful football program. You made a tremendous difference in our success and I hope it continues to foster for my successor. Thank you to the Board of Education, Administration, Faculty, Support Staff, Maintenance and everyone else around the school who made my job easy.

I have been blessed to have many organizations and individuals demonstrate a willingness to the program in a number of ways. The Ram Football Club and the Montrose Athletic Boosters have been instrumental in making Montrose Football a 'first class' operation. The Montrose Youth Football Program should get a lot of the credit for the success of our football program. Thank you to all the coaches that were more than willing to support us. People have volunteered countless hours for the good of the program. You have meant a lot to me, not only in your help to the program, but also in your friendship.

A head coach is nothing if he does not have a good staff. In my situation, I had the best coaching staff in the state. Often, I got much of the praise for the success of the program when my staff deserved the accolades. We have been together for a long time now and it is difficult to leave such loyal people, but I know the football program will continue to be successful with the outstanding coaches that remain. I will miss you guys and every Friday night I will be thinking of our 'Ram Pride.'

I sincerely feel that the community of Montrose makes coaching football at Montrose a tremendously exciting experience. Friday night football will never be the same for me, because of the tremendous fan support we received. Our fans embody the true emotion, excitement, and love for the game of football. I know in my heart that I will never be in a situation again where the fan support is so great. Thank you.

Dan (the Editor) I would like to thank you for your coverage of Montrose Football. You are a valuable member of this area, and you make high school athletics very meaningful. Your greatest strength, however, is that in the eight years I had the pleasure of knowing you, I cannot remember one time that you printed something that would hurt one of my players. That, in and of itself, is quite remarkable. Thanks for your tremendous coverage and friendship.

Lastly, I would like to thank all the players that I had the pleasure of coaching. As I think back over the last eight years, I am astounded at the quality of football players I have had the opportunity to coach. But, what is more astounding, is the number of players that I have coached that are quality human beings. I truly feel blessed to have had the opportunity to be associated with so many great people. The greatest gift that I will take with me, and forever have in my heart, is the love that we developed as a 'Montrose Football Family.' I am going to miss you guys. You have had a dramatic influence on my life and I will never forget you. I love you!!!

Sincerely,

Coach Annese

The letter was clipped and tucked away in former players' scrapbooks, signifying the end of the Tony Annese era. It was their final letter from Coach Annese, their mentor. Annese wanted each one of them to walk away with an impression that they were a part of something very special. Former players felt he molded them and helped make decisions about college and their futures. They missed him after they graduated, and looked him up at college games, appreciating that he was still interested in them. They cherished their football highlight films and personalized letters that he wrote them. They appreciated everything he taught them and used those traits to be successful in college and in life. Former players often called him from college when they needed advice or to share life's special moments like when they became engaged, got married or had their first child. Coach also received calls when they were undecided about career choices, or when they were in trouble.

Some depended on him during their darkest hours, when they experienced the pain of death. And just like in football, he stood by them through the good times and the bad. They were family. Many followed in his footsteps, becoming teachers and coaches. They called him when they won big games as well as when they lost close ones. Their paths still crossed at football clinics and golf outings. Some felt comfortable calling him 'Tony' but most still preferred 'Coach Annese.' They appreciated who they became and what they accomplished, because of him. He provided them with an experience they would treasure for a lifetime.

Word spread quickly that Annese moved on, causing critics to thrust their '95 Season aside before it ever began. Several assumed that the only place left for the Rams to go was down, after experiencing such incredible success. A few players tried to lead others in the wrong direction, distracting the powerlifting team. People naturally assumed that the Rams would start to lose a few games and become a mediocre team. Some questioned if that would start in '95. What outsiders didn't realize was that the team fed off the Rams' tradition. Not only was it in their blood, it was embedded deep into their souls. Instead of tearing them apart, their situation bonded them together, making them even more determined to show what they could accomplish in '95.

The Montrose A.D. quickly posted the position for the head football coach. He realized the benefits that the school derived from having a well disciplined football program, and wanted to avoid any uncertainty. A six-member selection committee interviewed eight applicants, and unanimously selected Denny Reinhart for the head coach position. Reinhart was the physical education teacher at the Montrose Middle School and was raised in Montrose, graduating in 1979.

Reinhart earned the right to be the head coach for the Rams after serving as the defensive coordinator for the past eight seasons. He joined the staff when Annese took over in 1987, and was a big part of building the winning tradition that Montrose was accustomed to. His defense dominated the GEC League in 1994 when they shattered the GEC record for the fewest points allowed in a season. His defense impressively allowed only 14 points in eight league games. Montrose had an established program and he planned to keep in place what was already working. Reinhart felt that it would be a smooth transition when he stepped in, since he knew the kids and the program so well. He was anxious to put his own coaching philosophies into practice, wanting the program to go on without missing a beat. He carefully selected his assistants.

Craig Destrampe demonstrated his commitment when he joined the Rams in 1989. Destrampe gladly accepted Reinhart's offer to replace him as the defensive coordinator, taking on the responsibility of the linebackers and defensive ends. Coach D was a favorite assistant coach, even though he had a quick temper when his guys screwed up. His eyes held a trust that his players were special to him. He was barely in his forties, still had a lean athletic build, and always wore a baseball cap. The team teased him about his hair resembling Michael Bolton, while others called it Billy Ray Cyrus hair. Coach D was D'ar's dad, which gave him extra status points since D'ar was still admired as a Montrose football legend.

Goose had just graduated after pursuing a baseball career at the University of Miami of Ohio. After blowing out his shoulder in baseball, he often wondered if he should've played college football instead. He played his last football game in '89 when Montrose didn't qualify for the post-season, in spite of an undefeated season. Goose was left with a sense of unfinished business, realizing that Montrose Football was still in his blood. Reinhart's timing was perfect, uniting the magnetic force that reeled Goose back to the football program that he loved. He gladly accepted Reinhart's offer to work with the defensive and offensive backs; a position vacated by Coach Steve Annese. Goose was young enough to relate to the kids, yet old enough to gain their respect for his football knowledge. Goose became 'Coach Clolinger.'

Reinhart asked Rob Edenburn to join his staff and work with the Freshmen Team. Edenburn was a recent graduate, who already missed the camaraderie of his '94 Team and everything that accompanied it. Edenburn remembered how depressed he felt after the loss to Orchard Lake. His situation was different than his teammates; his last game ended with a heavier definiteness. Not only did he say good-bye to football; it was an official ending to his teenage years. After Orchard Lake, he went to work full-time to support his wife and new baby daughter. He graduated with his teammates, but realized that he would never wear a football uniform again. Coaching gave him a chance to be a part of a game that he loved. Edenburn gladly accepted his new responsibility with an energized heart.

Monty Stiles finalized Reinhart's new crew, teaming up with Edenburn to coach the Freshmen Team. Coach Stiles wasn't new to the coaching world.

He had coached football at Bendle High School with Noel Dean since 1991, and teased him about being Noel's eighth grade baseball coach. Stiles always assumed that he would coach his favorite sport -- baseball, but became quite passionate about football after four years with Dean. Stiles gave up coaching at Bendle since he was going through a divorce. Bendle was too far of a drive and his kids needed him at home. Stiles had an eyefull of tears when he told Dean and Setzke that he wouldn't be back. They both knew that he was hooked and told Stiles that he would go crazy if he didn't fill all of his time. They both suggested that he coach at Montrose. The timing was perfect; Reinhart brought Stiles on board. Now he could coach in the school district where he lived and taught at since 1985. Coach Stiles was anxious to get started.

The Varsity did their best to avoid rumors that their program would decline. They tried to shun the desolate feeling after five of their coaches dumped them. The players were convinced that Reinhart, and his new staff, would lead them to a successful season. The new seniors had a burning desire to achieve more, after their hard loss to Orchard Lake. They were committed to making a different outcome for *their* senior year. But they lived in the shadows of the awesome, record breaking `94 Team. Graduation had cost the Rams 25 seniors, including the entire offensive line and six athletes who earned All-State honors. The Rams had a lot of talent that remained from the `94 Squad, but many of them didn't see excessive playing time.

Reinhart admitted, 'One day there will come a time when the cupboard is bare,' but he wasn't ready for that to happen any time soon. The coaching staff and the players were compelled to prove a point, that they could still flourish in spite of their inexperience. For the most part, Montrose was a working class town, a blue-collar community where people were used to working hard. If a team lacked athletic ability, they made up for it with attitude, and worked even harder.

Shane and Rizk returned as seasoned standouts. Shane started at free safety, flanker, and back-up quarterback as a junior, but Reinhart planned to use him at wide receiver. Shane was the fastest back the Rams ever had; he proved his speed when he qualified in two events during the state track meet.

Junior Ryan Hodges started at quarterback. His quick reflexes and strong running game helped him lead the Varsity with six pass interceptions as a sophomore defensive back. His actions revealed his love of the game, allowing the seniors to quickly gain confidence in him as their leader in `95. Hodge studied the playbook until he knew it inside out. He practiced throwing passes to Rizk, Shane, and Jake throughout the summer until they became comfortable with each other.

Most of the players met at the school over the summer to strip grass from the middle of the football field, replacing it with sod. The field was crowned in an effort to never play another 'Mud Bowl' again. Recycling the cut out sod from the main field to their practice field in the sweltering sun became a physical workout, but they couldn't complain. After all, it was *their* field. The team conditioned together during the entire off-season to keep in shape. They actually looked forward to two-a-day practices, until they met *him*. No one recognized the big guy with the short, dark hair who wore wild, baggy, zebra print pants. The stranger chased senior Ryan Ross down the practice field yelling, 'You gonna touch that line boy, you gonna touch that line?'

The man insisted that Ross didn't touch the line when the team ran gassers bellowing, 'You owe me another one!'

His large frame had the size of a college lineman. He wore his hair quite short on the sides with a slight spike on top. His trim mustache and serious attitude, compiled with his size, bestowed him with an aura of badness. The stranger strutted authority, acting like he belonged there. Ross had the good looks, which gave him added confidence to be a bit cockier. He looked at Ryan Persails with baited breath, 'Who *is* this guy?'

The easy mannered, tall and lanky Persails never overreacted. He slowly shrugged his broad shoulders in an exaggerated fashion, before replying in his own laid back way, 'I have no idea.'

Reinhart introduced the new arrival as assistant Coach Jody Coon. The blistering heat didn't even phase Coon, but some of the linemen couldn't seem to ignore their sweltering faces. The big guys felt overwhelmed by the heat during the second practice. When they ran over to the sled for the next drill, they overheard senior Dave Follett utter between gasps of air, 'Hey, we need to rest for a minute!'

Coon stopped dead in his tracks and sharply turned around. His deep voice and degrading eyes were humiliating when he belted out, 'WHAT?'

'It's really hot, can we just have a quick rest?'

'What's your name boy?'

'Follett.'

Coon looked totally annoyed. 'Everybody get down. FOLLET needs a rest. Everybody get down . . . except FOLLETT and start doing front, lean and rests until I tell you to stop.'

Follett felt like an idiot as he shook his head, regretting that he ever opened his mouth. If he could've found a hole to crawl in, he gladly would have. Not only did he manage to piss off his new coach on the very first day; he ticked off his teammates in the process. Their only consolation was to witness how foolish Follett felt, grateful that *he* said it and not *them*.

Coon was new to the coaching world and quickly developed his own style. He drew from techniques that his high school and college football coaches used on him, combining the old-school strategy of confront and demand. The nature of the game was to be tough. He yelled a lot, often without praise, drawing from his authority and tactics that he learned from the police academy. Most of the linemen felt apprehensive about his techniques, but it provided the positive results that Coon wanted.

There was a reason for Coach Coon to be a part of Montrose. *Was it coincidence?* Sheriff Jody Coon was assigned to the Montrose City contract in July, 1995, the same summer that Reinhart recruited his new coaching staff. Coon was amazed when he started his patrol in the small town of Montrose and saw kids running around the track, playing catch and working out on their own. As a sheriff, he often saw the worst side of troubled teenagers and the smut that often attached itself to that lifestyle. Montrose Football gave him a refreshing perspective. It inspired Coon to be in contact with teenagers who were not always in trouble. It did him a world of good to deal with kids that did wholesome things with genuine goals and important dreams. He introduced himself to Reinhart as the local sheriff and couldn't believe the opportunity offered to him, 'Would he be interested in coaching the line?'

Would he? Coon jumped at the chance. He attended high school in Genesee County and naturally followed Montrose Football since the streak's infancy. So did his dad. Montrose fans didn't realize that the streak went beyond their small community. His dad compared it to Joe Dimagio's baseball streak. It was something that a lot of people state-wide tracked, not just those around Genesee County.

High School football in Michigan rivaled Texas football. Many men followed good athletes and teams, traveling around the state to watch the game-of-the-week. Those same guys followed Montrose Football and their seven-year streak. Even when Coon played football at Northern Michigan University, he continued to follow Montrose Football. It became a habit when he read Saturday's sports section; he naturally checked, *Did Montrose win again? Was their streak still intact?* He even followed D'ar stats back in 1990 when he started working for the County. Even though he didn't personally know anyone associated with Montrose, he checked on the Rams. *How many yards did D'ar rush for? How many TD's did he get this week?*

After Coon was exposed to Montrose Football, he honestly felt that the program rivaled any high school program in the nation. He was thrilled for an opportunity to be a part of that strong tradition; a privilege that he took seriously. He was ready to give something back to that cycle of football. Shaping kids was a huge responsibility and he was amazed that parents trusted the coaches with their kids, their prized possessions. Coon wanted their experience to be a positive one, although some players questioned that. He knew firsthand, the influence a football coach can have on a teenager's life. He wanted to make a difference; even if he was portrayed as hard core. He wanted them to emulate the good things and learn from the bad, not become one of the troubled teenagers that he dealt with as a sheriff.

During his interview, Coon was told that the offensive and defensive backfields would be strong, but the line was inexperienced at the Varsity level. The key to their entire season rested on the how fast the line developed their skills. Coon stepped up to that challenge, striving for perfection. He had a short window to get the guys ready and wanted to continue that excellence. *Failure wasn't an option.* Call it pigheadedness, inflexibility, stubbornness, or just plain determination, Coon believed hard, realistic, stair-stepped training made good linemen. Whenever the line messed up, Coon's deep, forceful voice belted out, 'This is what we have to do boys!'

How could they complain? Whatever punishment Coach Coon dished out, he did along side of them, with a huge grin on his face. Linemen respected that, in a weird way and developed a love-hate relationship with him. The hard workers loved him; the not-so-diehards despised him. Even the mere sound of Coon's voice made their stomachs churn.

Coon had a few years on them and realized how he applied the traits he learned from his football experience to his daily life. Maybe they were too young to appreciate it, but he wanted his players to do things the right way and strive for perfection. He wanted them to grade themselves on their own performance, because one day they would weave their attitude and work ethic into college and careers. Coon felt that America had lost some of its structure, and that kids would act better if they had more of it. Football players quickly learned about consequences when they didn't abide by the rules; coaches didn't tolerate it. *Life was simple.*

Young people needed discipline and structure; most strived for it -- football provided it. When Coon watched players respond to his discipline and tactics; he wanted to step back and say, *Wow! This really works!* But Coon disguised that side of his personality. He wanted his line to develop a stubborn will to never give up. His workouts became a boot camp for the non-military bound. Coon shamed his line into not quitting when several wanted to. His mission was to instill a drive in them to do more right than wrong, so he pushed them extremely hard. The new coach considered his position as an awesome responsibility. He influenced his guys to be successful, beyond just winning on Friday night.

Jason Harris didn't make it through both sessions on the first day of two-a-days. The morning practice was enough. Everything seemed different, with so many new coaches and the constant yelling. It all had a new vibe. So much had happened since the last time he wore a football uniform, that he simply couldn't see the point. He felt so uncomfortable that he didn't return for the afternoon session, and didn't mention the *real* reason why. He figured that someone would ask if they really wanted to know.

Coon didn't realize what was going on in the young lad's life. He barely met Harris after becoming totally caught up in the adrenaline of first day practice. Coon would've made a great drill sergeant, and singled out junior Chris Leitelt. He pushed his shoulder pads then viciously drove the junior a good 20 yards until he fell. Leitelt thought, *This had to be tougher than a military boot camp. It had to be.* His resolve grew more resilient during each practice. Reinhart nicknamed him 'Bulldog;' a name that had sat on the shelf since Mike Sullivan's days on the '91 Team.

Coach Bob Hayes helped Bulldog with his technique, making practices somewhat fun. He always had something positive to say. Maybe it was because he saw how hard Bulldog worked, and felt the need to offset Coon's tone. Hayes was a part of Montrose Football and a teacher since the late sixties, although he now walked with a limp. The very field they played on was named in his honor. His hair was gray and he wore Elton John glasses when he drove around the practice field in a golf cart, easing the pain from a bad hip. Hayes wore a huge championship ring on his right hand. When players glanced at the size of his hands, they were reminiscent of how tall he once stood as an All-American.

Reinhart's new staff came together, gelling as a coaching unit. Players squeezed an element of fun into practice whenever they could, ripping on the coaching staff if they broke the no swearing rule. The squad shamed their coaches into running a gasser, then watched their competitive egos race each other during the final leg. The coaches even laughed when Corey Rush (Crusher), Schlorf, and Persails were the masterminds behind the freshman initiation to retrieve the 'left handed smoke shifter.' The threesome called after the rookie, who nervously ran with apprehension. 'Get your butt in there and get it. Run!'

Joern was a German exchange student and didn't quite understand what freshmen orientation was all about. Like Mo, some things simply got lost in the translation. Joern wanted to experience the game of football, even though he had never played it. It was the thing for guys to do if you attended Montrose High. Joern (pronounced Your'n) quickly realized that he had a lot to learn in a short amount of time, if he wanted to make the most of his year in the States. Both parties learned from the experience, and the team became extremely patient with him. They ended each practice after Joern caught a pass and scored. He was a good sport when the team gathered around him to yell their breakdown at the end of practice. Joern celebrated with his teammates who intentionally added a slight American slang to his name, 'Way to go Urine!'

One part of practice wasn't quite as fun and players dubbed it *Coonaerobics*. Sweaty and exhausted linemen needed a distraction and thrived when Dan Ruddy yelled out, 'We're the hogs. C'mon Baby!'

The phrase originated back in Dan Dierdorf's days with the Washington Redskins and made its way into Miss Piggy's dialogue on the Muppet Show. Smart, funny and well liked -- that summed up Ruddy. It was the reason his senior class voted him as their 'Most Likely to Succeed.' Even though he was injured, he came to practice everyday and did what he could. His attitude was in the right place, and his comic relief sidetracked his teammates.

Sophomore Adam Powell was brought up to fill the vacant position at center. Adam's willingness to do whatever Coon asked caught his eye. Adam was green, but coachable. His freshman experience basically included: inside veer, outside veer, and a few pass plays. Varsity level ball was much faster and Adam soon discovered that he needed to quickly step up. Coon was demanding on the rookie, but constantly told him, 'You can do this Adam.'

Adam never gave up and relentlessly worked on his technique. He wanted to get it down perfectly and frequently asked, 'Is that what you want Coach?'

Adam respected Coach Coon who was hard on him, but also patient. He told the center what he wanted and then showed him, until Adam had it down. Coon was impressed at how quickly the young center progressed. Adam got in his stance and fired out; then struck with perfect body posture. Adam wanted to learn and Coon wanted to teach; together they became a good team.

Jake was in for a surprise the night before his first scrimmage. His girlfriend, Chrissy, was full of spirit and persuaded a few of her friends to help tee-pee his house. She dumped borrowed real estate signs and cones in his front yard. Since his parents were good sports, she thought they would laugh about it, but they didn't. Even though they were strong football supporters, they had a lot of pride in the beautiful home that they recently built in a new development, and didn't want the mess. Jake thought it was funny until his parents made him clean it up before he left for the scrimmage. The delay made him late; it also made him mad. He vigorously threw each item into the back of his old Ford truck. Jake picked-up Ross then decided to drive over to Chrissy's house and dumped every single item on her front lawn. 'There, let's see how she likes picking this crap up!'

It made him feel better and eased his anxiety about being late, until he pulled into the school parking lot. A teammate ran out, 'Hey, Reinhart's pissed at you guys.'

Jake felt the apprehension the moment they entered the locker room. Coach wasn't just mad, he was furious and screamed at them before they had a chance to explain. He wanted players to maintain the same accountability and responsibilities that the program always had. He informed the entire team that they would all run a gasser because of Jake and Ross. *Promptness was expected.*

Reinhart huddled the team together on the practice field the night before their first league game against **Atherton,** and spoke from his heart. They talked about their season and how the GEC League seemed more evenly matched in `95 than in the past, when the Rams stood on top. They talked about taking their season one game at a time. He persuasively told them, 'When you're on top you can only do one of two things -- stay on top or fall off. We've worked hard to prepare for this season and we're ready. The way you perform tomorrow will determine the tone you set for the season. You guys have been a part of the Montrose tradition for several years, waiting for the torch to be passed to you. Now it's your turn to carry the ball. Everyone's watching to see what happens to the Montrose Rams this year.

We need to go out tomorrow, work hard, and show everyone what this team is capable of and get that first W.'

They set team goals, and tried to ignore the fact that Montrose shifted from Class CC to Class B in '95, which seemed to cause battles with the playoff point system. The seniors couldn't help but think beyond the regular season. Of course they wanted to keep their 61-game winning streak alive, which fit hand-in-hand with their ultimate goal. They dreamed about the Dome, and could almost taste it, after coming so close less then a year ago. It only strengthened their mission to prove the doubters wrong. They faced Atherton the following night for the '95 Season opener, and memorized their motto for their first game.

'Our Time Has Finally Come'

Persails put on his '91 Detroit Lions Barry Sanders Super Season T-shirt under his game jersey when he dressed for Atherton. He wore that T-shirt to every football game that he played during the last three years, and planned to continue his tradition. The shirt now stretched tighter across his broad shoulders, allowing his 235 pound frame to display the paper-thin fabric that was practically worn to shreds. But Persails was determined to wear it during every game in '95. There was a reason his senior classmates voted him as 'Their Biggest Eater.' Persails could eat before, after, or during a game. He didn't let nerves get in his way. Persails got more than his share from the all-you-can-eat buffet when the guys went out to eat their Thursday pre-game dinner.

Persails finished eating just when his cousin 'Crusher' pulled in the driveway to pick him up for the game. They hooked up with senior Nick Powell, then walked to the drinking fountain located behind the football field in their stocking feet. They each picked one sour grape that represented week one, then ate it. They grew up with He-Man, the power of Castle Gray Skull, and Molly Ringwald was their heartthrob. The wild grapes gave them power, and their new tradition brought them luck. The threesome joined the squad in the wrestling room with their wet, dirty socks shortly before Coach Reinhart came in. 'Okay special teams, let's go.'

The Rams took the field together and yelled '95' as they walked under the goal post. The squad felt the energy rush as the band started the school fight song, before smashing through the cheerleaders' hoop. They excitedly jumped on the jampile near their sideline. Everything appeared the same to the team and the fans, who sprung to their feet in a hearty welcome.

Hodge was appointed as one of three team captains. He opted to take a back seat and allowed seniors Rizk and Persails to take the field for the coin toss. His turn for that came the following year; he chose to lead in the huddle instead. Hodge was cast from the perfect quarterback mold; a talented leader, quick thinker, great attitude, and a good student. The guys respected him.

The Rams made their presence felt on the very first play from scrimmage. Hodge took his first handoff for the `95 Season and successfully passed to Jake. The Rams scored on the next play that followed a thrilling catch when Rizk dove on the one yard line. Rizk felt great to run like the wind after his knee surgery to repair a torn ACL during the `94 playoffs. Rizk only stood 5'7"-170 pounds, but was extremely quick when he shot across the goal line to score the first TD for the Rams.

Reinhart didn't know what kind of shape Rizk would be in, after watching him limp on his knee during the middle of summer. But Rizk combined his love of the game with his hunger to work hard to strengthen his knee. The third year Varsity player was a threat at running back and wideout in the split veer, proving that he was a dangerous weapon. Reinhart worked with his new quarterback, while each provided his ideas, testing their new roles. Reinhart realized that Hodge saw the field differently from the quarterback position. He knew what the Rams were capable of and often asked, 'What do you think we should run?'

Hodge welcomed the chance to make suggestions then carry the play through. It seemed that every time the Rams touched the ball -- they scored, generating confidence and a chance to snuff their pre-game jitters. The determined Rams didn't waste any time by scoring six first period TD's with lightning quickness. Bulldog added a safety, while Hodge added an interception. The Rams were able to seal a '67-0' victory with their new cast of characters; Rizk, Shane, Crusher, Jake, and Visser helped score ten TD's.

While many high school teams lacked an accurate kicker, the Rams were blessed with two: Steve Visser and Tommy Unangst. The offense kept both of them busy all night. Tommy was the youngest brother of Sean and Tim, both former PAT kickers. Tommy wanted to be as successful as his older brothers, yet understood he had to share the spotlight with Visser.

Jason Harris sat in the bleachers with two other juniors, Tony Thornburg, and Dave Lyman. All three had played freshmen and J.V. football; each had their own reasons for not coming out in `95. But watching their classmates play their first Varsity game *without them* helped them realize how much they missed it, especially Harris. He was a big kid with wire-framed glasses and a great smile. The junior couldn't stand to sit in the stands; he wanted to be on the field in uniform. Harris couldn't escape the peculiar feeling and was ready to explode. He didn't know if he could begin to explain the strong intensity that exploded inside. Only one thought rested on his mind, *I have to get back on the football team!* Harris suddenly felt like a giant weight was lifted from his shoulders when he announced to Thornburg and Lyman, 'Hey, I miss this too much. I'm gonna see if they'll let me back on the team.'

As Lyman and Thornburg listened to Harris rant and rave, they realized how much they missed football too. The threesome decided to approach Reinhart directly after the game, which couldn't arrive fast enough. All three were both nervous and anxious as they approached the post-game huddle.

Butterflies danced in their guts while they patiently waited until Coach finished with the press, then anxiously popped their question. He didn't seem opposed to the idea but said, 'It's not up to me to decide. It's really up to the team.'

The team discussed the idea at films on Sunday. Some didn't think it was fair to let them come back, since they didn't participate in the grueling two-a-days; as if surviving them qualified membership. Captain Joe Rizk felt differently. He knew a little bit about what Harris experienced over the past year and thought he was brave to make the move. That took guts and he voiced his opinion. 'Hey, if letting them back on the team only makes us better, then why shouldn't we?'

Harris endured a restless sleep. He couldn't wait to get to school the following morning, to ask Coach what the result was. Harris thought positive and packed his practice clothes and cleats into his backpack, just in case.

Reinhart informed Harris, 'The team's letting all three of you back on.'

Harris breathed a sigh of relief, impressed that his teammates never treated him badly after he originally left. They never held it against him and he respected that. Thornburg, Lyman, and Harris were all well liked and eager to get started.

Coach could tell by the anxious look on Harris' face that he would work hard, making up for lost time. Coon would make sure of that. Harris was a lineman, therefore, he spent his first day back with Coach Coon. At first Harris wanted to hate Coon. He didn't realize how intense the man was until he made them do so many push-ups. It became even stranger when Coon got down on the ground and joined in. Harris didn't know quite what to think of Coon and thought, *That man is nuts! He's all over the place.* Other linemen had previously warned him, 'If you just do what Coon says, everything will be okay.'

The coaching staff realized they were under the watchful eye of the entire League. Reinhart was pleased with their opening performance after amassing 354 offensive yards, while holding Atherton to a minus 12 yards.

Everyone knew **Chesaning** would be tougher competition as they prepared for week two with a new motto:

'Lets Teach The Copy Cats A Lesson,
It's Time To Take The Indians To School'

Players arrived at the school in time to get taped, then listened to AC/DC and Metallica while relaxing on the wrestling room mats. Fred Knuess worked the music before games. Knuess was a tall, fairly quiet teenager who tended to keep to himself, and enjoyed football more than many realized. Since he controlled the music during the first week, he had the job before every game. He chose several heavy songs, some with an angry message from Nirvana and Ministry. He made sure that he played *'Mother'* by Danzig to get the team rockin' before the game. Hodge and Rizk threw a football back and forth until Coach D popped his head inside the door. 'It's time guys.'

They gathered their stuff and loaded the bus for Chesaning. The short bus ride was quiet while players stared out of the windows; some lost in the music from their headphones. No one talked while they focused on their upcoming game. One of their favorite teachers that lived in Chesaning, had ragged on players all that week during class. They didn't know if Mr. Tithof gave them a true warning or just meant to have fun when he remarked, 'Chesaning's really good this year, you better watch out.'

As Persails warmed-up on Chesaning's field, he stopped to glance as Coach Clolinger approached. Clolinger was the creative coach, always trying to pull funny pranks. He walked onto the field during pre-game practice, clad in an Indian jersey and a feathered headband. Persails wondered, *What's he up to now?* Clolinger looked at him, 'Hey, I overheard the Chesaning quarterback say, 'You guys couldn't hit water if you fell out of a boat.'

'Yeah right!' Persails never appeared to be rattled by anyone, but the comment still bugged him. Clolinger knew that Persails performed better when he was mad, that's why he was a rare third-year Varsity player.

Clolinger had a way of connecting with players, making it obvious that he loved to coach. Coon got a kick out of watching Clolinger interact with players; his coaching style was completely different than Coon's. Clolinger used word power to improve his vocabulary by picking a new word card every day. It became a game that the other coaches teased him about, especially when his goal was to use the word-of-the-day at least 20 times. Players and coaches became the perfect targets. That pre-game day, the word happened to be *quagmire*. Clolinger asked Shane, 'What's going on with the line, they're in a *quagmire* out there.

Shane asked, 'They're in a what?'

Clolinger replied, 'a *quagmire*.'

'What exactly is that?'

'Go ask Coach Coon.'

Shane had never heard of the word, and threw his coach a puzzled look. The truth was, neither had Clolinger before he memorized it earlier that day. Shane approached Coon in the middle of a drill, 'Hey, Coach Clolinger wants to know what's wrong with your line?'

'Nothing's wrong, why?'

'He said that your line's in a *quagmire*.'

Coon threw his head back and laughed, shaking his head as if it was a private joke. He had just learned the word earlier that day but confidently responded, 'You don't know what a quagmire is? It's a dilemma or a sticky situation.'

When Coon started laughing, Shane threw him the same strange look that he gave Clolinger earlier. Shane realized that Clolinger appeared subtle compared to Coon, but also had a unique way of getting at players.

Coon hooked up with Harris after practice, 'Hey, you want to tell me why you came out so late?'

Harris faced his new coach, 'You really want to know?'

Coon nodded, 'Yeah, I do.'

Harris had not exposed his story to many, but once he did the floodgates unlocked. 'The last time I wore a football uniform was when they let me dress for the Orchard Lake semifinal game last November. I was only a sophomore and knew I wouldn't get to play, but I wanted to be on the sideline. That was the best team Montrose ever had and I wanted to be a part of it. When the coaches asked if I wanted to dress for the *game* I told them no, I wanted to dress for the *Dome*. I had no doubt that the Rams would win it all.'

'My parents were divorced, so I was surprised to get a call from my dad two days before that game. He invited me to go hunting at my grandfather's cabin with him and my uncles. I didn't want to miss my chance to be on the sideline with the Rams. I was totally caught up in Montrose Football, and I told my dad that I couldn't go. He said he understood and wished the team luck. I never saw or spoke to my dad again. He was killed in a car accident a week later, and died on Thanksgiving at 1:30 in the morning.'

Harris' voice choked while Coon quietly listened and nodded to continue.

'I was kind of numb when it first happened. It was strange, but it didn't really get to me until Christmas. My sister and I went to visit my father's side of the family. That's when it hit me. I started to realize everything that my dad and I would miss. He would never see me play a game of football, graduate, get married, or see his grandchildren. He wouldn't see any of it. I had an opportunity to spend some time with him, and I chose football over him. I realized that I didn't know it would happen but after it did, football suddenly didn't seem as important. I spent the next eight months in a haze. When school got out, I just went home. When spring came around, I spent every waking minute of my free-time sitting on my grandma's deck missing my dad. I had no motivation at all. As the season got closer my mom kept telling me that I needed to play football, but I didn't know if I should. Coach Annese left and everything seemed like it didn't matter.'

'What's really strange is that my father and I didn't have the greatest relationship. My parents separated when I was in the fifth grade, so I decided that I would live with him so he wouldn't be alone. We lived together for about three years and moved to a couple of towns in Michigan, then to Maryland, and back to Michigan. My father was an alcoholic, which ultimately was his downfall. It ruined his marriage and my family as I knew it. It finally led me to move in with my mom who lived in Montrose. I told him I was coming out for the weekend to visit her. When Sunday night rolled around, I called him up and told him I wasn't coming home. It was then that we had a fall out. He basically, in so many words, disowned me. So I became a resident of Montrose and the only possessions I had were the clothes on my back.'

Harris threw a cautious look at his new coach who still seemed deeply interested, so he continued. 'We didn't speak again until the spring of '94. He called me and said he would like to see me. So we met at a restaurant and talked. Things went well, but our relationship really wasn't what it once was. I finished playing my freshman year of football by then and worked hard during the off-season to get ready for my sophomore year. He seemed interested and we talked a lot about the football program.'

'A couple of months passed and my dad called again. This time he invited me to my grandfather's cabin for the weekend. It was late July and I knew two-a-days would be starting soon, so I used it as a last minute get-a-way before the grind of the season began. It was a great time. Looking back, I felt like someone from above made sure that weekend happened. It was the last meaningful time I ever spent with my dad. Our differences disappeared during that weekend. He didn't have one drink and he was great to be with. Then my sophomore season started and we talked once a week. He worked second shift for G.M. so he never got to see me play, but he always seemed interested in how we were doing, and he encouraged me. We didn't lose a football game all season. Then I dressed for that Orchard Lake St. Marys game. My dad got in an accident and died a week later.'

Coon felt the story tear at his heart, and put his arm around Harris' shoulders. They talked for a while and Coon told Harris, 'You can only control so much. There's no use in agonizing over things you can't control.'

Harris felt better after they talked. So did Coon. It was the first of many talks between the two of them. Coon took a personal interest in Harris, filling a void in the young lineman's life. Harris looked at his coach in a different light after that first chat.

Harris felt ready to face Chesaning; the entire team did. The Rams entered the game focused, but faced the same demeanor from the Chesaning Indians. Montrose jumped out first, marching 69 yards on seven plays. Rizk plowed over to score within five minutes, then Hodge scored on their next possession on a 30 yard run. Hodge found his way at quarterback, hitting Ross with a 23 yard TD pass at the start of the second period for a 21-0 lead. Chesaning put together an impressive drive, scoring right before the end of the first half. But just when it appeared that the momentum would shift to Chesaning, Rizk broke free from a defender, romping 65 yards to pay dirt.

The Indians marched down the field, making it to the five yard line. Hodge focused on their quarterback, then instinctively stepped in front of a Chesaning pass at the two yard line. He caught the pass in stride, then jolted 98 yards in the opposite direction. Hodge grunted every step of the way, scoring his second TD in front of an overflow crowd.

Hodge's interception changed the complexion of the game, and served as motivation during half-time. The Rams were on fire at the start of the third when they scored on their first possession. Hodge flashed 65 yards to pay dirt just :13 seconds into the second half. The junior quarterback made his debut, having the game of his life. The Rams had plenty of players to field an offense and defense, since only Persails and Shane played both ways and special teams. Shane also played as a shooter on the kick team; he never left the field and loved every minute of it.

The Montrose defense forced four Chesaning turnovers, a pair of interceptions, and two fumble recoveries. Hodge hit Shane on a 48 yard pass for their final TD, while Visser kicked his seventh PAT to close '49-7.'

New Lothrop was next. The Hornets showed improvement and planned to give Montrose a run for their money. Clolinger assigned the next motto:

'Great Teams Do The Common Things, Uncommonly Well'

Crusher and Persails tagged along with Powell in their stocking feet to pick and swallow three sour grapes from the vines near the drinking fountain. They remained committed to their weekly tradition, which gave them power and luck in return. That night, they played with wet feet.

Superstitions continued to overrule logic regardless of how well the team prepared. Players touched their special brick whenever they passed the equipment shed. They habitually jumped up to touch the 'State Championship' sign stenciled above the weight room door whenever they left the room.

Rizk and Shane were pysched when they entered the field and faced a packed crowd of over 2,000 Montrose and New Lothrop fans in the stands. Rizk scored on a one yard run, breaking a scoreless tie late in the first quarter. He appreciated the Rams' good trapping guards that never gave up, and opened big holes for him to burst through. Players respected each others' skills, enjoying the results they achieved by working together. Jimmy Beardsley ran up to Rizk after he scored, towering his 6'2"-200 pound body over him. 'That was for you Rizk!'

Rizk just grinned. 'Thanks Jimmy.' He appreciated the big lineman, confirming why his senior class voted Jimmy as having 'The Biggest Mouth.' Jimmy definitely wasn't shy.

Hodge and Rizk connected on a 13 yard pass for his second score. The duo was so tuned into each other that they connected on almost every pass. The fans loved it. The twosome made it look simple and unrehearsed, but their perfect timing came from hours of passing to each other.

The Hornets fumbled a punt at their own 15, and the Rams recovered. Hodge then slanted in from the one for a 19-0 lead. Hodge was in the midst of orchestrating an 80 yard drive, but was constantly distracted by Rizk's talking. 'Rizk, quit talking to me when I'm under center. I've got enough to think about.'

Rizk replied, 'Sorry man, I just see things opening up.'

Crusher caught a 44 yard pass, and made it to the five yard line to set up another Rizk TD just before the half. The Hornets gave it up on downs and punted to Shane who ran it back 70 yards just before the half. The rival schools battled on the field just as hard as they did on the wrestling mat. It was a typical Montrose-New Lothrop hard-hitting game; the second half wasn't any different. Ram coaches overheard players comment during the half, 'This was the hardest we've been hit all season.'

Shane hauled in three of Hodge's passes then plowed 29 yards to score. Later, Rizk burst across the goal line on a five yard run to close at '48-13.'

Reinhart saw improvement in his Rams who seemed to gain experience each week. A pleased coach told them, 'We did a lot of things right, but we were inconsistent at times. We still need to work on some things.'

Some Montrose fans sacrificed the New Lothrop game. Instead, they traveled to Adrian College for a Friday night college game to watch Eric Hyde, Brent Baksa, and Barry Gross, former members of the '92 Squad.

On Saturdays, many Montrose fans attended the SVSU Cardinal games to watch former players. Mike Sullivan now coached the offensive line, while pursuing his teaching degree at SVSU. He missed coaching from the Montrose sideline, but he loved the college level of competition. Sullivan felt right at home with six Montrose athletes: Led from the '91 Team, D'ar, Barnett, and Tony Beardsley from the '92 Team, and Eddie and Jeff from the '93 Team. Fans dubbed SVSU as 'Montrose North.' Most of the former Rams played different positions than they did in high school. While many high school quarterbacks made great defensive backs, Jeff became a wide receiver. Led was in his senior year and played strong safety. Eddie played defensive back, Beardsley played linebacker, Barnett played free safety, while Dar still hung on to his running back position.

Montrose Football felt honored after Jason Liddell received the prestigious $25,000 Burger King Scholar-Athlete of the Week Award. The national award went to SVSU's special scholarship fund, allowing Liddell to give something back after graduation. While Liddell led the Cardinals in tackles, he majored in Accounting and carried a 3.89 G.P.A.

The only two teams without a league loss, Montrose and **Goodrich,** faced off next. Goodrich averaged 228 yards per game with the I-formation, while the Rams averaged 400 yards per game with the veer. The Rams took this game seriously as they studied their Goodrich motto:

**'The Big Game This Week, This Month, This Year
Is Being Won Or Lost Right Now'**

Reinhart pumped up his defense during pre-game. 'Defense will decide the game tonight. Whoever stops the other team will come out the winner!'

The Rams caught the Martians sleeping when they recovered a pooch kick after Shane scored on the opening drive. Their strategy was to hit Goodrich hard at the start, while trying to catch them off-guard. It worked again when Ruddy recovered an on-side kick, helping Montrose shoot ahead 24-0 by the half.

The Martians listened as Coach Tom Alward told them that they couldn't give up any more big plays. It seemed they were so keyed up to stop the big play, that they made mistakes that led to the big play.

Trash-talk livened the playing field. It could've been a different ball game if Goodrich had played the first half like they did the second. The Martians scored after the half, followed by a Hodge TD pass to Shane. Goodrich took the ensuing kickoff 80 yards to score with 1:55 left in the third, closing the gap to 31-12. Both teams scored again, but the Rams closed the win at '38-18.' It was the closest regular season game since '93, and the most points the Rams had allowed since. Reinhart addressed his young squad during their post-game talk. He was pleased with the 453 total offensive yards and the way the defense played. 'We need to work on special teams. We can't just expect teams to fold up. We've got to keep coming after people. I'm pleased with the 'W' but we need to get that killer instinct in us!'

The Rams prepared for the **Hamady** game, living by their weekly motto:

'Basics, Basics, Basics
It's The Little Things That Will Make You A Champion'

Shane reached over to shut off his blaring alarm clock the morning of the Hamady game. He instinctively held the back of his hand to his forehead, which felt terribly hot to his own touch. Shane frowned after reading the thermometer mark at 103°. He popped four aspirins then forced himself to go to school. Nothing could prevent him from playing football on Friday night. *Nothing.* The aspirins he took throughout the day didn't reduce his elevated fever. The trainers placed ice packs under his arms and helmet then sat him on the bench, while the Rams warmed-up on Hamady's field. Even Doug Noble, the video man, said, 'Here Shane, take some more aspirin.'

Shane's dad came out of the bleachers to check on him before the game. He noticed his son's flushed cheeks and felt his scorching forehead. 'Shane, I don't know if you should play.'

'I'll be OK dad.'

Special teams took the field to warm-up. Fancy convertible sports cars surrounded them, while waiting to parade the Homecoming court that lined Hamady's football field. Jake positioned himself to catch Tommy's practice field goals, but worried that the sports cars were parked too close. He walked over to the drivers. 'Hey, we're kicking balls over here. You might want to move your cars!'

They ignored Jake so he mentioned it to Coach Reinhart. 'Hey, kick them anyway. If they won't move the cars, don't worry about it!'

A few of Visser's balls bounced off the hoods of the bright, shiny sports cars. The drivers were getting pissed, yet still refused to move them. Jake did his best to prevent contact. He thought, *If I owned one of these convertibles, instead of my rusty old Ford, I wouldn't want it dented.* Hamady was the first team that held Montrose scoreless during the first quarter. The Rams hurt themselves by fumbling twice, causing curious minds to wonder if the winning streak would be broken that night.

Shane continued the tradition that he and Rizk started before their first game of wearing black spandex leggings underneath their football pants. Rizk approached Shane midway through the first quarter, 'You need to take them off or you'll overheat.'

'I can't Joe, it's tradition!'

A few minutes later, his boiling fever felt like it spiked even higher so Shane broke tradition and took them off.

Persails reached for a Hamady player and broke his long, middle finger in the process. He didn't notice how red and swollen it was until he came off the field. Persails tried to ignore the immense throbbing during the rest of the game, but he thumped it whenever he set his position on the line. He feared being placed on the injured list, and decided to use his left hand. It became a move that he used the rest of the season, since he refused to get proper treatment.

The Hamady and Ram players on the field played a clean, hard-hitting football game, unaware of the antagonism underway on the sideline. The visitor bleachers were undersized to house even a portion of the Montrose fans, forcing the overflow to stand along the sideline. Antsy parents kept closer tabs on their kids that night and found it difficult to concentrate on the game, with so many distractions.

A Hamady student had contacted Montrose High earlier that week and made a threat about Friday's game. School Administration notified parents to take extra caution during the game. Unmarked policemen patrolled the sideline while heavily monitored gangs strolled by, clad in silver facemasks. A motorcycle raced along the fence line on the visitor's side, which bordered a dark, thickly wooded area. It seemed strange to the fans, and made them feel a bit anxious. Authorities wanted to avoid racial fights, since the crowd contained a predominately black Hamady student body facing a predominately white Montrose crowd. A Hamady cheerleader was injured on the home side of the field when Jason Pollard, playing linebacker, accidentally tackled her after finishing a play out-of-bounds. It instigated a Hamady gang to patrol the visitor side stating, 'We want revenge.'

Former superstar, Shawn Yuncker, was home from college. He became concerned when his girlfriend, a Ram cheerleader, saw a masked gang member flash a gun at her when he walked by. The cheerleaders were upset and felt like open targets. They decided that they didn't want to cheer anymore and sat in the bleachers. It pissed Yuncker off and he got into a shouting match with one of the gangs and yelled, 'C'mon. Bring It!'

Yuncker felt ready to take the gang down and wrestle. He used his strength as a rookie on the wrestling team at Olivet College, and was in great shape after intense practices. When the gang stopped near the Montrose bleachers, a player's dad, backed by several others, told the Hamady gang, 'You guys just keep on walking.'

The dad caught up to Yuncker. 'Hey, these guys don't want to wrestle Shawn, they'd just as soon shoot you. Don't provoke them. Just let it go.'

Even the players seemed distracted until Rizk livened up the sluggish bench. He hauled in Hodge's pass, then jolted 80 yards to burn the first lights on the scoreboard midway through the second quarter. Hodge passed to Ross for a 20 yard strike on their next possession, but the undaunted Hamady Hawks came back and scored. The score at the half was 12-6, as the Hawks handed the struggling Rams their first wake-up call. A locker room wasn't available, so the displeased coaches tucked the Rams away in a corner of the fenced in field. Players hung their heads when Reinhart's biting words ripped into them during his public half-time speech.

Whatever he said seemed to work. The Rams became focused and played the kind of football they were capable of during the second half. Jake lit the fuse when he scored a TD then tacked on the conversion. It was the play that started to turn things around and loosened up the Rams. Hamady had a hard time shutting it off once the Rams turned it on. Shane completely forgot about how sick he felt when he hauled in a 58 yard TD and grabbed two interceptions. Rizk scored three more TD's, claiming the area high record of 14 for the season. Rizk and Hodge put on a show, helping the Rams amass 444 total offensive yards. Persails managed to lead the defense with 14 tackles in spite of his broken finger to close '41-6.'

The coaching staff continued a motto that focused on the basics:

'Great Teams Are Constantly Good At the Little Things'

Homecoming festivities refueled the school's spirit the entire week as the Rams prepared to host **Lake Fenton**. Mike Fejes, Follett, Shane, Rizk, and Ruddy were elected as king candidates during the pep assembly.

The Rams' offense took command, erupting for 57 first half points. Rizk stayed on the field during the half, fulfilling his role as Homecoming King, then waited with the oversized crowd for the announcement of the Queen. He wore the same green T-shirt under his football jersey that Eddie wore when he was elected King in '93. The shirt was a parting gift from the back who wanted to keep the luck around. After Rizk posed for pictures, he joined his teammates in the locker room. The atmosphere seemed pretty relaxed with their huge lead. Players asked, 'Who got Queen?'

'Chrissy did.'

Jake was pleased to learn it was *his* girlfriend that won, and played an inspiring second half. Rizk, Shane, Hodge, Jake, Casciano, and Fejes all put points on the scoreboard to walk away with a '64-6' victory. Rizk and Shane each rushed for over 100 yards, while Jake piled up another 77. The Rams were thrilled that the victory moved them a step closer to another undefeated regular season.

Players studied the weekly motto in case they were asked to recite it off the cuff during practice for Bentley:

'When It's All Said And Done, There's A Lot More Said Than Done'

Hodge resembled Crockett when he slapped Flaco's helmet after he missed another block during the Bentley game. He scolded, 'They keep drilling me in the back and it's getting old!'

Flaco got the message and vowed to be quicker. The Rams only led by 19-0 at the half, with Rizk accounting for all three TD's. Maybe it was a combination of Montrose having an off night and Bentley wanting revenge. Whatever it was, Flaco became the scapegoat. Every coach managed to say something to him during the half, including the video crew. Flaco already felt like crap, and their comments only infuriated him. He didn't realize what he was doing wrong, but would try to fix it. The entire team got the message when Coach laid into him in the locker room. 'You can just start walking down I-69 all the way back to Montrose if you don't start playing better!'

The Rams averaged 51 points a game through the first five games of the season. It was expected to continue no matter how tough their competitors were. Jake, Hodge, and Casciano pitched in to score second half TD's, ending the game '38-7.' The defense held strong by preventing Bentley from scoring when the reserves went in and upheld their shutout. But the bus ride home lacked any sounds of celebration. Even though the Rams played a respectable second half, they couldn't blame everything on Flaco. The team had room for improvement.

After the coaches analyzed game film, Reinhart felt that **Bendle's** contest could be their toughest opponent yet. After watching the Bendle kids at camps and powerlifting competitions, he realized their program elevated to a higher level. The coaches wanted their Rams to reach deep when they wrote Bendle's motto:

'You Can Imitate Everything A Champion Does:
But You Cannot Imitate What He Has Inside Himself'

Persails announced -- 'Hey, Rocky videos at my house after school.'

He wasn't surprised when ten guys showed up, all trying to relax before the Bendle game. They knew it would be a tough game. The media pumped up the contest that Bendle could be the toughest 5-2 team if they beat Montrose.

Reinhart teased his team after pre-game practice, 'Wow, that makes me want to go 5 and 2, don't you?'

The Rams knew that a 5-2 record wasn't acceptable in Montrose, and would tarnish their eight-year winning streak. The GEC Title was still on the line. But the Rams faced two of their toughest opponents during the final games of the season -- Bendle then Byron.

Every team in the League seemed to be gunning for the Rams; even more than previous years. Reinhart needed an extra incentive. He walked into the dark wrestling room before the game and turned on the lights. He spoke to their hearts, while mentally preparing them to face Bendle. He placed a different cassette in the tape player, then told the team to pay special attention to the words, before shutting off the lights and making his exit.

Players instantly recognized the beat of Quiet Riot's popular song. They closed their eyes, and completely focused on the words to 'Winners Take All.' The song absorbed their deepest emotions, motivating them in a new way. Shane and Ross already felt psyched for the game, yet allowed the song to grab an emotional piece of their heart. Every single player in the room wondered how preparing for a crazy game of football could stir their emotions to such a high level. The moment united them as a team. They were ready to take a stand and conquer all, determined not to take a fall on their home turf.

A biting, cold wind greeted diehard fans bundled in heavy coats as they entered the Bob Hayes Athletic Field in Montrose. Regardless of the rigid temperature, fans were excited to watch the battle unfold that Friday night.

The frozen Ram fans were stunned when Bendle blocked a punt with a safety, drawing first blood midway through the first period. The Montrose defense stopped Bendle's next possession, but the offense couldn't get a first down. The Tigers seemed to shut down their running game. It only pissed off the Rams whenever they looked at the scoreboard, 0-2. With :15 seconds left in the first quarter, Hodge dropped back in the pocket, then delivered a perfect 39 yard TD on-the-spot to Rizk. Visser's PAT jumped the Rams ahead 7-2. The Bendle Tigers knocked twice inside the Montrose 25, but were stopped by a motivated defense. The game could've turned around if Bendle's second quarter field goal would not have misfired, or if Shane had not picked-off a pass, which he returned to Bendle's 45. The passing game clicked for the Rams. Hodge connected with Rizk on a 27 yard catch, then hit Ross on a 10 yard TD pass. It was the toughest league game the Rams had played, but Reinhart continued to pump them up for the second half battle. The stubborn Tigers were just as tough as Reinhart expected. The Rams felt lucky to have a 13-2 half-time lead.

Shane ran a sweep, bursting 45 yards down the sideline on their opening drive of the second half. From the corner of his eye he saw Bendle's safety, who was labeled as the top running back in the League. Shane pumped his legs faster, telling himself, *He's not going to catch me!* Shane outraced him, and felt the defender gave up at the very end. He thought, *You never give up on a play. Never!* Shane scored within three minutes to open the half, followed by Visser's second PAT.

Persails didn't want Bendle to catch on to the calls that the offensive line used, so he spiced things up by creating phrases on the fly. Their guard, Brian Miller, laughed at Persail's originality, so did Bendle's line. The trash-talking, hard-hitting battle continued until Montrose closed the score at '20-2.' The Rams showed they could bend, but didn't break. Montrose limited Bendle to 15 total offensive yards during the second half, and a minus 25 yards in the fourth quarter. Sophomore Nick Loafman led the defense with 14 tackles closely followed by Pollard and Persails. Bendle's program revealed results and seemed to be tougher to beat each year. Hodge felt lucky that the Rams scored the 'W,' but felt Bendle shut them down with the exception of a few big plays. Hodge shook hands with the opponent that he faced all night. They respectfully told each other, 'Good Game!'

The exhausted Ram quarterback and safety paused for a moment. He respectfully looked his opponent in the eye, wondering if he could read his mind. *We easily could've lost this game.* The two opponents later became football roommates in '97 at Ferris State.

The Bendle Tigers came to town to do some damage. It appeared their mission was accomplished, after leaving a physically exhausted team on the Montrose field. The Rams were severely banged up after the Bendle game, but realized they couldn't let up for **Byron,** who held a close third place in the GEC League. A loss would force Montrose to share the League Title with second place Goodrich. 'Second' simply wasn't good enough. It became the driving force during Byron week. Reinhart realized playing two tough teams late in the season banged them up, but also prepared them for playoffs, *if* they qualified. He closely watched what was happening in the region, but kept their main focus on Byron.

'One Week To Determine Your Destination - Outright Or Share - Are You Going To Be Ready For More?'

It didn't matter that the Rams were ranked second in the state, they were still fifth in the hunt for a Class B playoff berth coming into the last game of the season. One of the top four contenders ahead of them had to lose in order for the Rams to earn a spot. Reinhart sent scouts to all of the playoff contender games and told his Rams, 'We can't control the playoffs. We can only control how hard we play tonight. All we can do is win and hope for the best. If we take care of business tonight, there's a chance we'll be in the playoffs with some outside help.'

The seniors could almost taste the unfairness that the '89 and '91 Teams experienced, after having undefeated seasons without a playoff invitation. Rizk and Shane shared their dream of going to the playoffs. That desire burned in their souls since their freshmen year; they wanted a shot at the State Title. Shane wanted it so much that he could taste it and looked at Rizk. 'We just gotta get in!'

Annese called Reinhart from Pioneer, discussing their chances. MHSAA did their best to make a system fair and equitable, but the injustice hits home when *you're* the undefeated team who's ranked fifth in a region with a group of stacked teams. They both believed it would be much fairer to take the top 16 teams in each class and split them into regions. Montrose attempted to avoid the same situation a year ago by petitioning the Metro League, which consisted predominantly of Class B schools, for membership to play football. Despite Montrose's willingness to remain a B team, Metro school principals rejected the idea due to scheduling concerns, among other things.

Persails made his own motivation when he wrote 'Mason' on his right wrist, and 'Port Huron Northern' on his left. They were two of the teams that needed to beat out top ranked teams. Like his teammates, Persails felt slighted that other teams wrote the Rams off because Coach Annese had left. It irritated him when people underestimated their ability -- and their dreams. It would be so unfair if Montrose beat Byron, then still lacked enough points to get in. He slammed his own fist on his locker, and pitied Byron who would be on the receiving end of his frustration. Persails wasn't the only hungry Ram. The defense was so livid when they took the field, that they caused Byron to fumble the opening kickoff. Byron didn't let up though, as nervous fans watched both teams fumble the ball six times within the first few minutes of the game. Extreme nerves battled through a sloppy, scoreless first quarter.

Byron used their exceptional 220-pound quarterback to their advantage. The guy ran a 40 in 4.6 and was tough for the Rams to bring down. A year later, Shane became his teammate at SVSU, but that night they were opponents. The Rams finally settled down after Hodge hit Shane on a 35 yard TD, breaking a scoreless first half. Follett intercepted Byron's quarterback pass near midfield, then watched Rizk catch a pass from Hodge and score with six seconds left on the clock. It gave the Rams a 14-0 half-time edge. The hard-fought score was close, but the Rams didn't want it to be their *last* game. The teams battled for a scoreless third quarter, until Rizk burst through for his 23rd touchdown. It gave him the area high, racking up 1,600 all-purpose yards; an effort that later earned him All-State First Team honors.

Persails wiped the mud from his wrists. The words 'Mason' and 'Port Huron Northern' stared back at him. He only hoped that they wanted to win

their games as much as he wanted to beat Byron. Persails racked up 11
tackles that night. Loafman was only a sophomore, but proved to be as
determined as Persails, matching his numbers to lock in a Montrose victory.

Shane intercepted a Byron pass and ran 65 yards to score with :11 seconds
left. The game was actually closer than the final score of '27-0' revealed.
Byron moved the ball well, but their seven turnovers did them in, especially
the four that the Rams recovered. Montrose also fumbled four times, but
managed to settle down once they scored.

The win generated a tremendous amount of hope for their playoff chance.
The Rams shook hands with Byron, and were impressed that they were good
sports who handed out congratulations instead of trash-talk. Montrose
huddled in the middle of the field, but hardly celebrated. Reinhart told them,
'I'm proud of your consistency, not just in winning the League Championship
outright, but how you carried out your commitment and tradition.'

The Montrose squad quietly sat in the middle of the field, with the same
anxiousness of a concerned family member waiting for the results of
emergency surgery. They appeared to hold vigilance, while waiting for the
outcome of their post-season future to be revealed. Friends and families
patiently waited from a distance, hoping their undefeated Rams got their fair
shot. The seniors felt an added sense of urgency; they didn't want to
suddenly be told that football was all over for them. *Not yet.*

The Montrose coaching staff gathered around their A.D. They listened
while he made calls from a cell phone, verifying which playoff contenders
won. The air was tense; the team felt like they were sweating bullets. Ruddy
stepped up and offered a distraction. There was a reason he was on the
student council and president of his senior class; he simply knew how to deal
with people and they responded to him. The guitar playing Ruddy had the
patience to time his jokes to provide a greater effect. He broke the tension
with a famous deep thought, carrying on a tradition from the '94 Season.
Ruddy slowly wrapped his thumb and index finger around his chin, then
solemnly looked at his teammates and recited:

> *'Whenever anyone asks me about love, I think for a minute*
> *and then I spin around and pin their arm behind their back and say,*
> *Now who's asking the questions?'*

Their laughter soon halted. A hush fell over the team as Coach Reinhart
approached. His short, choppy steps seemed to take forever to reach them
camped in midfield. Persails noticed the serious look on his Coach's face,
which made him antsy.

'Well guys, I've got some news to tell you.'

The team examined their coach's face for a clue; their future rested on the
edge of his mouth. They huddled in closer, silently praying that the playoff
gods wouldn't play a cruel joke on them in '95. Shane felt his heart hammer
in his chest, *Please have good news. We gotta get in.*

An instant smile broke loose from Reinhart's poker face when he yelled, 'We're in the playoffs!'

The Rams valiantly jumped up and celebrated their playoff opportunity for the fourth straight year. Their enthusiasm overshadowed the fact they had just won their eighth consecutive League Title, matching an area record held by Fenton High School from 1960-1967.

Persails kissed the smeared, but legible names on each of his wrists after learning that Marysville lost to Class A Port Huron Northern, and Dewitt lost to Mason. He specifically picked those two teams because of past football wars, and blissfully grinned from ear to ear. Montrose made the Class B playoffs. The '95 Rams had a chance to keep their tradition alive, as well as their 70 game winning streak.

The GEC League demonstrated its strong football ability when three of its nine teams made the state playoffs: Goodrich qualified for Class CC, Bendle for Class C, and Montrose had an away game at **Fowlerville** in the Class B post-season. Players memorized their first playoff motto:

'Prove You Belong – Find The Pot At The End Of The Rainbow'

Containing Fowlerville's speed and their passing attack would be the trick to beating them. Montrose wanted to use the same tempo during practice to avoid additional playoff pressure, but added a new twist to their regime.

The media played up the fact that Fowlerville had several good wrestlers that were small and quick, and used their wrestling techniques on the football field. The Rams countered by pulling up their own quick wrestlers, Aaron Emmendorfer, Winston Ruffin, and Justin Woodward from the J.V. Football Team. Jorod Bush and Brian Owens were two other sophomores that didn't wrestle, but were smaller, quick, and tough. The sophomores felt honored to contribute to the Varsity Scout Team, even if it meant getting their butts kicked every night during Fowlerville week. Reinhart called the J.V. group 'Desert Swarm,' and placed them on the defensive line against the first string offense.

The 'All Guts No Glory' role was a tough one. The sophomores knew it was their job to help prepare the line for what to expect, and they loved to hit. Their J.V. Season was over, and the stimulating exhilaration of playoff preparation helped relieve their soreness from the strapping linemen who pounded on them every night. They had dues to pay; their turn on Varsity came the following year.

Coon was pumped about the post-season; he wanted his offensive line to be well prepared. Coon worked his squad extra hard, and could tell they were exhausted after a grueling week of practice. It was time to share *his* story. He gathered them in, then told them about his terrible motorcycle accident shortly before the start of his junior football season in college.

'I was on my way to an early football camp at Northern Michigan University. On my way to practice, a lady ran a red light and broadsided my bike. The accident laid my right foot wide open and severed so many tendons, they practically had to reattach my foot. It was a mess. I didn't want it to be the end of my college football career and underwent therapy. I took rehab for an entire year, but it didn't seem to work. So I went to this sports specialist down state in Lansing. He took a ligament out of my upper leg and reattached it. I underwent more therapy -- determined to wear my football uniform again. After two years of rehab and two surgeries, I was able to dress for our last game. It was my senior year and I knew I couldn't play, but it meant so much to be able to put my uniform back on and walk on that field with my teammates. I went through two years of therapy just to live one down. That's how important it was.'

Coon had the line's undivided attention. Harris listened with the rest of them in awe. He couldn't imagine going through all of that. After that day, he never thought twice about what Coon asked them to do. Throughout the season, his respect for Coach Coon grew. Harris had a better understanding of why Coon worked them as hard as he did.

Persails brought a funny video for their pre-game movie ritual, 'We're Gonna Get You Sucker.' Before they boarded the bus for the first round, Crusher, Persails, and Powell met at the back entrance to the locker room before Saturday's game. They took off their shoes, then walked 400 yards to the grapevines for their pre-game grape ritual. It was week ten of the season, which required them to each eat ten sour grapes before the game. The grapes had brought them luck and power all season; they didn't dare stop their ritual now. The sour fruit slid down their throats, while bitter expressesions plastered their faces.

The community of Montrose joined in its traditional playoff caravan on a brisk, but sunny Saturday afternoon. They paraded through town before the hike to Fowlerville. It was the Gladiators first playoff berth, although they had won five League Championships in the past ten years. They faced one team during the regular season that played the same type of veer offense as the Rams. Montrose listened to Fowlerville's trash-talk during warm-ups, 'You guys are just a big play team and we're gonna shut you down!'

It only increased their incentive to beat Fowlerville, yet pissed them off at the same time. The captains exchanged a strange expression when Fowlerville wouldn't shake their hands before the coin toss. As they walked back to the sideline Rizk said, 'That's a first.'

Persails replied, 'Don't worry about it, they're just messing with us.'

The battle was on. Reinhart addressed his Rams before the game. 'We're a good ball club. We know what it takes to be successful in the playoffs and we're coming into this game with that attitude. Turnovers will be a key that we need to control.'

Reinhart worried about turnovers, since the Rams turned the ball over ten times in the past three games. He knew they could play better, since they hadn't turned it over all season up to that point. He reiterated Fowlerville's quickness and their small, 150 pound defensive linemen who liked to shoot gaps, penetrate hard, and mess up blocking schemes.

Rizk couldn't hide his stress and puked before the game. To the fans, Rizk appeared quick and confident on the field, but his squad often heard him hurling before the games. *Nerves.* Both teams possessed good defenses, but Fowlerville was the first team they faced who matched their speed. The staff wondered, *Would this be a high scoring battle or a flat-out war?*

Hodge called a 39 veer. Jake took the handoff and gained 25 yards on the opening run of the game. Hodge took a second to absorb the wonderful feeling, as the echo from the fans deafened the field. Fans in the post-season developed a personality of their own by openly showing their support every inch of the way.

The Rams marched 65 yards on their opening possession, facing a stiff wind. The extremely cold temperature caused the players' breath to form smokestacks in the huddle. Reinhart called a veer pass from Fowlerville's four yard line. Shane ran a drag and Ross was supposed to run a corner. Shane wasn't sure if Hodge's pass was intended for him, but he jumped three feet into the air and thought, *I'm catching this.* He reached high, grabbing an awesome nine yard catch as if his life depended on it, then twisted his body before he landed face up. He glanced at the gray overcast sky for a moment, then swiftly searched for the precious white chalk line. Once he saw that the upper half of his body was over the line he yelled, 'Yeah, I'm in!'

A burst of adrenaline shot through his body. Shane quickly jolted up, only to be greeted by all 235 pounds of Persails who smacked into him with such force that it compelled Shane back on the hard ground. The collision from his own teammate stunned him and he thought, *If that's how Persails congratulated a teammate when he did something 'good', I'd hate to screw up.*

On their next possession, the Gladiators pushed from their own 35 to the Montrose two yard line. Fowlerville's quarterback had a golden opportunity on fourth-and-inches to tie the score, but the sneak failed when the defense formed a brick wall, causing a fumble. The determined Rams got the ball back, as well as the momentum. Reinhart repeatedly told the defense the past few weeks that *they* would decide the football game. Now, they honestly believed him.

Fowlerville's defense held the Rams, who called for the punt team after a short drive. Sophomore center Adam Powell snapped the ball high, causing Visser to go down at the 25 yard line for a minus 16 yard loss. Fowlerville had a chance to even the score, by trying a surprise attack with an end-around-trick play. Hodge played safety. He came across to Casciano's side of the field before diving in front of a halfback-option pass for an

interception. It was the exact move that Casciano planned to make and
Hodge knew it. Hodge sheepishly approached his good friend. 'Sorry man.
I just had to go with it.'

Casciano felt a bit shafted, but was glad they got the ball back. 'That's
okay. As long as we got it.'

The two teams continued to battle. An official yelled at Persails when he
pushed an opponent. His 6'3" frame made him an open book on the field.
He couldn't get away with anything, and was pissed that the Gladiators were.
Persails reached his breaking point after a Gladiator grabbed his private parts
one too many times. The referee acted like he didn't want to hear it, giving
Persails the impression that he would kick him out if he mentioned it again.
It went on deaf ears when he told Reinhart, who chewed on Persails for
talking to the official. Coach simply didn't want any penalties. Persails
decided to rise above his frustration, and took a few cheap shots of his own
whenever he could get away with it.

Later, Hodge was pissed when he grabbed Jake's facemask in the huddle.
'Is that guy faster then you? Is he stronger then you?'

'No' blurted Jake.

It would be hard to find a more dedicated player on the entire field then
Jake. He worked hard and played with effort; but faced a tough, talented
opponent. Hodge's reaction startled Jake. It was the first time during the
entire season that Hodge laid into anyone. The Rams' quarterback felt that
Jake's opponent tackled him too easy after he ran a 42 trap. Up to that point,
Hodge felt uncomfortable yelling at the seniors since he was a first year
quarterback. But this was playoffs. He needed top effort on every play to
lead them to victory, in spite of the near freezing temperature or how talented
their opponents were.

Hodge was an overachiever; his tone lit a fire that spread through their
veins like a wild virus. The Rams grabbed hands in the huddle, intently
listening when Hodge called the next play. When he looked each player
directly in the eyes, something magical happened in that moment. His
attitude communicated the message; *The Rams came here to win.* Hodge got
the ball out quickly and made high-speed reads. He expected himself to make
the play, or hit his target if someone was open. His adrenaline shifted to
overdrive when he scored on a five yard TD with 4:19 left in the half.

The Montrose Rams were excited with their 14-0 lead, but knew they had
a tough second half. Players felt frozen by the time they reached the locker
room during intermission. Heat never felt so good. Getting warm seemed to
be the only thing on anyone's mind. Shane was unbelievably cold, the
coldest he ever remembered playing. It was sunny earlier in the day, so he
only wore a sleeveless T-shirt under his uniform, the one he'd worn all
season.

The Ram fans were dressed for the weather, yet still felt cold. Once the
team left for the locker room, the fans took over the salamanders set up on the

sideline to warm their frozen feet. It started to snow during the second half, as temperatures teetered at freezing point.

Jake cut his knuckles on a play when he slid on the slippery snow. His hand became trapped between his pads and the frozen ground. Jake wiped them on his black pants as he ran to the huddle, then held his hands up. 'Joe, I can't feel my hands!'

Rizk feared they would get a penalty when he looked at Jake's bloody hand and yelled, 'Jake get out of here!'

Montrose opened the second half with a squib kick to avoid a big return by the Glads. They ended up punted to the Rams, then stripped the ball from Hodge at their own 19, but couldn't pick up a first down. Shane fumbled the punt, then Fowlerville fell on the football at the Montrose 38. But the back-to-back turnovers by Montrose allowed Fowlerville to get back in the game.

The Gladiators attempted to score on a pass to the endzone, but Hodge had other plans. He fully extended his body and dove, then heroically made a one-handed interception in the endzone. It became a highlight film classic that showed how Hodge played with his heart and soul, inspiring his squad.

Montrose got the ball back. Hodge handed off to Rizk who broke loose on a 50 yard run, then an opponent stripped the ball from his grasp. Powell was surrounded by five opponents but decided to dive through them, and miraculously ended up with the ball. The crowd watched for the official's signal, then cheered as the defense ignited the team.

The Rams played their best game ever as a team. Jake ran outside, while Shane stalk-blocked the corner. The Rams continued an 80 yard march. When an opponent came through, Shane turned and blind-sided him, continuing his reputation for cheap shots. Jake took his game to another level after earning 122 yards on 13 carries. He proved to Hodge that he wanted to win the game just as much as the quarterback did.

Hodge displayed the poise of a veteran quarterback by running the veer perfectly. He had a great game after rushing for 176 yards on three TD's, threw for a fourth, and grabbed two interceptions. It appeared that he couldn't do anything wrong and the coaches took advantage of his powerful drive to succeed. Hodge plowed the final nine yards to score with eight unplayed minutes in the final quarter. He followed that score with a six yard insurance TD with 2:37 left in the game.

Hodge raised the bar after Jake's first run of the game then continued to lead by example, gaining respect from his teammates. The quarterback always gave credit to his team. He realized how their exceptional level of play gave him opportunities that contributed to the '27-0' final score.

Pollard, Loafman, and Casciano led the defense that game. They excitedly approached Coach D to remind him of his earlier comment. 'You said if we shutout a team during playoffs that you would buy steak dinners!'

Coach D stood speechless; he knew how much they could eat.

'Continue What We Started-A Sample Of The Pot Is Within Our Grasp'

Montrose faced **Frankenmuth** for the Regional Championship Game. The two teams confronted each other in a pre-season scrimmage and were familiar with the split veer offensive attack. Coach John Blankenship brought his Eagles to the Rams' veer camp during the past four summers. Both teams used a split-back veer that was new, and a lot of defenses hadn't been exposed to it. Each team had top quality quarterbacks who could make decisions on reads. The Eagles and the Rams possessed stiff defenses that led to undefeated seasons, helping each of them win their conferences. Core running plays were the same for both teams. Frankenmuth used more drop-back passing, while the Rams used a play-action attack with three backs. Both teams were able to simulate their defenders during practice, but their similarities gave each other the advantage to stop it.

Reinhart was concerned that Frankenmuth's large offensive line would be the biggest the Rams faced all season. Containing the quickness of the Rams' running backs worried Coach Blankenship. Winning came down to who executed the best, who made the fewest mistakes, and who made the big plays. Little did either team know what awaited them.

Coach Coon needed to prepare them to face 'Muth's huge line and drilled his linemen. 'It all starts here fellas. We're gonna work harder than anyone else. Those skilled positions don't need to work as hard as you. We're gonna run from station-to-station. We're gonna hit the trap, and the chute, and the sled, over-and-over until you feel like you can't hit it any more. But you CAN and you WILL. You create the play, you're gonna work harder than anyone!'

He tried to to push them beyond what they could stand. When they looked like they would drop he yelled. 'Life's not fair – learn that lesson now. You're not gonna get a fair shake every day, so let's not gripe about it. Let's go to work!'

Coon saw the drive that Brian Miller possessed. He wasn't a big guy for a guard who stood 5'7"-175 pounds, but he was tough and strong. Miller never complained. *Not once.* He was driven, worked hard, and did everything that Coon asked. Miller felt ready. The entire offense did.

Montrose High held awesome pep assemblies throughout the season, but the students took it to another level by going crazy during playoffs. The coaches fired up everyone in the gym. When the band played the school fight song, the students rose to their feet. Playoff frenzy created an excitement that invigorated the whole gymnasium. Everyone clapped and cheered. The entire student body felt they were a part of something very special before sending their Rams off to face the Frankenmuth Eagles.

The Rams gathered in the wrestling room on Friday night to watch *'Hoosiers.'* Watching the movie together was one of Shane's favorite playoff rituals. He observed how his teammates pretended to take their minds off Saturday's game, but he knew inside they were all in overdrive. Like the Hoosiers, the Rams felt like the underdogs after scrutinizing the size of Frankenmuth's line. The Rams feared that their running game could be at a disadvantage, and were thankful they were a big play team with tremendous speed.

The moment Shane woke up that Saturday morning, he quickly looked out of his bedroom window. *Oh great, it's raining!* He partially dressed, then left for the team breakfast at the school. The rain ceased and the weather turned cold. Fans adorned in winter coats had already decorated the town and gathered at the school to caravan. Fans formed a human tunnel from the school to the bus, and were shocked to see that players were not dressed very warm.

Shane nodded off on the 40-minute ride to Frankenmuth, but noticed that it was lightly snowing as the bus pulled into town. By the time they stepped off the bus, the wet snow fell harder but it wasn't blowing -- *yet.* The team arrived early and used a locker room inside the school. A bitter cold wind greeted the special teams when they entered the field a while later. The snow continued while they warmed-up, creating a powder cover over a slushy surface from an all night rain. Everyone wished they had dressed warmer when the wind suddenly picked-up. The conditions had changed dramatically while they warmed-up. When special teams returned to the school they announced, 'You guys won't believe how much snow's on the ground.'

Shane spoke, 'It's a blizzard out there! The field's covered with snow!'

'Yeah right,' was the general reaction. The squad assumed Shane was exaggerating, until they stepped out of the school. Players were amazed at how much snow had accumulated in such a short time. Miller tried to ignore the biting wind that slapped his face. He couldn't recognize a hole as he stepped on the snow-covered field, dipping both feet into ice cold water. Miller's feet felt frozen before the game even started. It was difficult for anyone to keep their balance when they spread out to stretch on the field. Players wondered, *How in the world will we control our balance during the game?*

More then 2,000 fans braved the below zero wind chill, to watch the No.2 and No.3 ranked teams in the state battle under arctic conditions. The Montrose fans invaded half of the home bleachers in an effort to avoid the violent winds that bit their faces on the visitor's side of the field.

Frankenmuth won the coin toss. The Eagles used weather strategy to work with the 30-mph gusting winds that blew directly up-and-down the field, in the midst of the driving snowstorm. Bundled fans stood for the kickoff, their eyes barely peeking from covered faces. They cheered when Fred Knuess caused the Eagles to fumble on the first possession. The Rams felt crazed with excitement when they recovered at their 28.

Montrose wanted to take advantage of having the wind at their backs during the first quarter. Hodge moved out to the left, then tried to stop when he saw a defensive lineman approach. After sliding two yards in the snow, he regained his footing before he passed, displaying the ability of a confident quarterback. It was a classic move to start the game, definitely highlight film material. Shane ran a reverse on their second possession, managed to get outside, then raced down the sideline on the slippery, snowy field. The howling wind blew so violently that Shane couldn't see the bright orange pylon. He had no idea where the endzone was. The back kept running as fast as he could in the slick snow, yet felt he was moving in slow motion because the referee kept pace with him. The official ran 70 yards alongside Shane, who kept his eyes glued on the black and white stripes the entire way. Shane didn't stop until those stripes went vertical. The back was thankful that the official ran parallel, but admitted it was the strangest TD he ever scored. It broke a scoreless tie at the 5:13 mark of the first quarter. Miller was the long snapper for the extra point. He tried his best to make the snow-covered ball go where he intended, but it never made it. The high snap forced Rizk to pick-up the slippery pigskin and go for the back-up conversion. But the snow obstructed his speed, halting his efforts.

Persail's finger got smashed between a defender and his helmet, yanking his entire nail off. The throbbing was instant and the sub-zero wind only increased his pain. He tried to block it out, along with the fact that the game was just beginning.

The Eagles fumbled on their next possession, but the Rams were unable to capitalize on a golden opportunity. They simply couldn't move as fast in the snow. Frankenmuth pushed down the field to the Montrose 36, then called a precious timeout with :18 seconds remaining. They preserved valuable seconds while the gushing wind was still at their backs. The Eagles ran a play up the middle, then caught the Rams asleep on a no-huddle offense. Frankenmuth quickly lined up using a twin set. The coaches yelled from the sideline, but the nasty, horrible wind inundated their voices. The Rams tried to quickly get set. Casciano was the only defender facing the twins, and quickly looked-for Shane who lined up on the opposite side. He should've called a timeout, but it happened so fast. Instead, Casciano covered one receiver, but got burned when 'Muth's quarterback hit the other wide receiver for a 36 yard TD strike on the final play of the first period. Casciano immediately felt guilty, hoping it wouldn't come back to haunt the Rams. Frankenmuth cleverly used the clock and the wind factor to score, but the fierce weather forced their PAT to sail wide right, creating a 6-6 tie.

Each team turned it over on downs, unable to get any traction on the ice-caked field. It was hard to do anything on the slick, frozen ground. Every time they moved their feet, they slipped. Frankenmuth almost bobbled their next possession when the quarterback fumbled the snap midfield on fourth-and-one. The ball amazingly bounced to a teammate who grabbed it and pounced forward for five yards. The Eagles had help with a controversial Montrose penalty, finishing off a 55 yard drive. Frankenmuth's quarterback scrambled down the left sideline for a 15 yard TD with 1:47 left in the half. The PAT was again knocked flat by the wind, giving Frankenmuth a 6-12 lead.

The undaunted Rams drove 67 yards on 11 plays when the Eagles were called for roughing the passer on fourth-and-15. While the seconds ticked away, Hodge ran a bootleg then passed to Rizk in the endzone. Rizk fell down when he turned around, but his quick reflexes instantly shot up. Rizk desperately tried to grab the pass when a defender bobbled it off his fingertips. Rizk stood only 5'7", which allowed the height of the Eagle to easily waver a head taller. But Rizk used his determination to tip the ball his way. He hung onto it for dear life, making the TD that heroically tied the game just as the buzzer sounded. The PAT sailed wide due to the fierce wind, tying the Regional Championship Game 12-12 at the half.

Shane suddenly forgot about his icy toes and frozen arms, when he ran to the endzone to celebrate with Rizk. He didn't think anyone would even be able to score in the horrendous conditions and the Montrose Rams scored twice, but so did the Frankenmuth Eagles. When they broke for the intermission, Shane felt positive that the Rams would come back and win.

Coach Stiles had brought his six-year-old son, Mickey, to the game. He was all decked out like the kid from Christmas Story, only he felt frozen. Mickey was blown clear back to the bench on the opening kickoff when a tackle ended out-of-bounds. By the half, Coach Stiles found Mickey laying against the heater and feared he would catch on fire. Thankfully, a friend took Mickey to McDonalds where Stiles planned to pick him up after the game. When they left, Mickey looked at his dad and said, 'I'm never coming to another football game as long as I live.'

Micky wasn't the only one who felt that way. The players' chilled, frozen bodies escaped into the Frankenmuth High School to thaw during the half. It was the first time they remembered being thrilled for a half-time break just to warm-up. The school became their haven; heat never felt so good. Reinhart had only worn a sweater and like his team, felt chilled to the core of his bones when the wind chill fell below zero! He didn't want to be all bundled up and warm, then tell his kids to not allow the weather to affect their play. That wouldn't sit right with him; he would tough it out just like they had to. Most of the running backs, along with Hodge, only wore T-shirts under their uniforms. They felt long sleeves interfered with their ball handling.

Shane looked down at his fingers, 'I feel like I'm being poked with nails.'

Rizk moaned, 'I can't feel my hands.'

Hodge rubbed his sleeveless arm, 'My arms feel like rubber.'

Senior tackle Jason Toney couldn't resist presenting a lineman's perspective, and held up his frosty hands. They had turned purple and his gruff voice said, 'How would you like to set your frozen hands down in the snow every single play and hold them without moving?'

The backs were stunned. His comments provided a crucial reminder of what the line did for them. It left them with a strange comfort, knowing that someone else actually felt colder.

Coach Reinhart came in; 'We've got two minutes before we go out.'

Players barely thawed during the half when it was time to return to the field. 'Coach, is there any way we can stay in a little longer? I'm just now starting to feel my fingers.'

The ghastly look on Miller's face etched in Reinhart's memory. Miller never complained about anything. He was one of his toughest players on the team; a quality that earned him First Team All-League. His comment seemed totally out of character, giving testimony to the horrible conditions. Miller's hands felt frozen like the others, but his left hand got stepped on just before the second period ended. The coldness only intensified the ache, along with his frozen feet. The cold temperatures from the Fowlerville game now seemed mild in comparison of playing in a horrendous snowstorm.

The exciting game held the fans hostage during the half; they were too frozen to move. A few ventured the biting wind to buy hot chocolate or wait for a turn in the warm restroom to thaw their frozen feet. Most fans never left their seats, choosing to take cover under wool blankets. Hoods were pulled down to cover their faces, while curious eyes peeked through the smallest openings, afraid they might miss something.

No one had ever attended a game under such horrid, frigid conditions. Fans couldn't believe that the officials didn't postpone the game. Montrose would have easily returned on Sunday to finish. The blizzard seemed to hover over the Frankenmuth field. Portable radios provided updates of college games, and other playoff games throughout the state that experienced cold weather and some snow, but no other game announced blizzard-like conditions. Fans questioned why they even stayed. The truth was, they didn't have the heart to leave. Even Mr. Polletti, who was near ninety-years-old, attended the game, but wasn't dressed warm enough. His frail body had to be miserably cold, but he persevered. If the Rams could play in this storm, he would stay and watch them, which was the general consensus of the crowd.

It would be the last football game for one team; a memory played in unbelievable conditions that they would love to forget. The blowing snow intensified during the third quarter, making its bite even colder. The Rams had the wind and started drives on the Eagles 45, 33, and midfield. They kept the Eagles pinned deep in its own endzone for the entire twelve, cold minutes.

The Eagles planned to survive the third quarter; their defense helped them accomplish that. Coach Blankenship could erase his fears about being unable to contain the Rams or stop them from getting out in the open. The Rams couldn't take advantage of their speed or use any of their trick plays, while the bitter snowstorm persisted. Hodge wondered how they could attempt to pass when they could barely see their own hands at the end of their arms.

What was usually an advantage for the Rams, became a hindrance under the arctic conditions. Montrose didn't have the size to beat the Eagles with their running game, and the weather continued to prevent their big plays.

The Rams became frustrated when nothing seemed to work. Hodge pitched to Shane, whose hands were so numb that he couldn't feel the ball. He actually looked down to see if he caught it before he tucked and ran; only to slip and fall seconds later. Hodge's pitch to Rizk started out at the right angle, until the wind grabbed it, taking it all the way back to the line of scrimmage. It was absolutely the nastiest conditions that either team had ever played in.

The secondary and underclassmen that dressed for the game wore the Montrose calf-length raincoats, while they watched from the sideline. They donned an extra layer of clothes since they manned the sideline, but still were not dressed for a blizzard. Players took turns gathering around the two heaters, then barely detected the smell of melting rubber in the whiteout. On the other side of the field, an Eagle opponent held his cleat too close to the heater, then jammed his foot in the snow when it caught on fire.

Frankenmuth adjusted during the half and changed to running an I-formation. Since the Eagles were a veer team, the Rams had not practiced defending it -- and it showed. The Eagles continued to fool the Rams by driving the ball three to five yards a pop. Like the rest of the seniors, Shane felt a sense of urgency to get it done and thought, *No this can't be happening!* He ran up to Coach Destrampe and pleaded, 'Just put me on the field Coach. Let me blitz somebody.'

'I can't do that Shane, we don't know if they're going to pass or not.'

The Eagles kept their drive alive and caught a 14 yard pass on third-and-eight. The Rams desperately tried to hold the Eagles at goal, but couldn't get enough traction to confine their size. Frankenmuth plunged over the endzone from one yard out after they drove 65 yards in 15 plays to take the lead. The Eagles had their backs to the wind, which didn't interfere with their PAT and changed the score to 'Rams 12 – Frankenmuth 19.'

It was do or die for Montrose. Nothing seemed to go in their favor either offensively or defensively. Hodge was unable to look his teammates directly in the eyes when they huddled. He didn't want them to see his lack of confidence. The quarterback continued to work with his coaches who were unsure of what to run next. The backs couldn't drive opponents when their feet continued to slip from under them. It was extremely frustrating to have the speed, and not be able to use it. The Rams punted on fourth-and-out, and swore that it hit a Frankenmuth receiver's leg. Miller pounced on it, shouting, 'That's our ball! That's our ball!'

The official shook his head, 'No, it didn't touch him!'

The Rams nearby pleaded, 'How can you say that? It bounced off him, didn't you see it?'

It would have been a big play for the Rams. Instead, it proved to be the turning point of the game. Both teams had a tough time playing under the worst conditions either team had ever faced, but Frankenmuth adapted to the conditions better because of their size and ability to move chunks at a time.

Brian Miller almost felt relieved when the clock ran out except it had the wrong ending. Like everyone else, he wanted to get out of the freezing blizzard, yet he didn't want his last game to end like it did. *Not like that.* He never would've imagined such a bizarre ending. In spite of his frozen feet and aching hands, he dropped to the snowy field on the very spot that he stood. He didn't want to move. The rest of the team gathered with the coaches while he sat by himself, as if it a trance. He couldn't believe that it was over.

Coon, the tough line coach, kept a watchful eye on Miller, and came over to help. He looked after his boys. He picked Miller up, patted him on the back, then walked him back to the team. Coon knew how much the game meant; that scene tore at his heart. He was so proud to be a part of the Montrose Rams, and he felt their pain. Coon had to suck it up after the game when he attended his nephew's birthday party in Frankenmuth. He was a good sport when his in-laws showed no mercy by planning a menu of Ram stew, leg of lamb, and Ramburgers.

Seven points. One touchdown and one extra point allowed Frankenmuth to move to the semifinals. The conditions were so horrible by the time the clock ran out, that both teams lined up for a quick handshake. Fans raced to their cars for shelter from the biting wind. It was the strangest ending to a playoff game that any of them had ever experienced.

The bus ride back to Montrose was painfully quiet. Initially, the loss didn't appear as dramatic as other playoff losses. Their heartache was somewhat sidetracked, as their bodies reacted to the pain of thawing. After the guys settled in and were protected from the wintry storm, the realization of what just happened hit them hard. Miller felt a deep sadness, *I'll never wear a football uniform again.*

Shane's shoulders drooped as he stared from the bus window, shaking his head in disbelief. He couldn't stop the tears that flowed down his frosty cheeks as the realization sunk in. *I just played my last high school football game.* He wanted a State Championship more than he ever wanted anything, and wasn't prepared for that wacky ending. He felt destroyed.

Hodge watched Shane's reaction. He felt terrible that he didn't lead the seniors to the Dome. He tried so hard, but Mother Nature played a dirty trick on them that day. The loss was also tough for Reinhart, his first as a head coach.

The team was barely thawed by the time the bus pulled into the Montrose High parking lot. The coaches came into the locker room to address the team. They tried to ease their pain, reiterating that there wasn't much they could do under the conditions. Coach told them, 'We couldn't do so many things that we are capable of doing because of the slippery, snowy field, and horrible wind. It was a major disadvantage for us because we rely on our quickness and explosiveness on offense. Not necessarily the best team won today.'

Reinhart honestly felt that Montrose had the better team, but the conditions hindered their team speed. It was the first and only time that he felt a game should've been postponed because of the horrendous conditions. He was surprised that somebody didn't get frostbitten in the blizzard.

The locker room slowly thinned out until only Shane remained. He didn't even feel the cold chill from his damp uniform, as he sat motionless on the hard bench. The loss clutched at his heart. He never experienced anything as bottomless; he simply didn't know how to react to the throbbing ache in his chest. Coach D felt bad for Shane and made an effort to lighten his heavy heart. 'Don't take it so hard Shane. You're going to play more at the next level. At least you're not through. You still have more football to play.'

Shane appreciated Coach D's words but he couldn't find much comfort in them that day. He wanted so badly to win a State Championship. He felt that the team didn't live up to the expectations placed on them, and that he let everyone down. Dealing with the loss was the toughest pain life had dealt him. By the time he threw his bag across the seat of his S-10 truck, he felt emotionally and physically exhausted. Shane appreciated that someone started his truck and had scraped the thick ice from his windshield. He smiled to himself thinking, *Dad was here.* Mr. Schlorf was extremely proud of his son and felt grateful that he moved his family from Minnesota to Montrose four years ago. He felt helpless that Shane didn't accomplish his dream, and felt powerless that he couldn't ease his son's pain. But he was glad that his oldest son got to experience Montrose Football; one day Shane would feel good about his experience.

Montrose had one of the best programs in the state as far as Shane was concerned. The State Champion Ring would've been the crown jewel. Shane took a deep breath before he started his truck. He found a touch of comfort knowing that he would wear a football uniform again. Maybe he would have a chance to play for a collegiate national championship team and still have a shot to earn that championship ring. He held on to that very thought, which seemed to lesson the sting of their loss. Before he drove off, he remembered the Lombardi plaque that Coach Annese gave him before the season ever started.

'The difference between a successful person and others is not a lack of strength, not a lack of knowledge, but rather in a lack of will'

Shane felt a sense of pride in knowing that he never quit on any play, or ever left any doubt that he lacked the will to win.

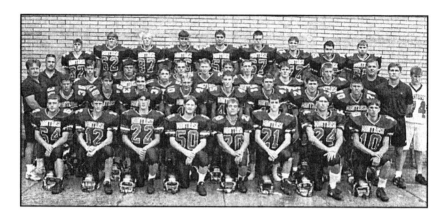

1995 TEAM PHOTO

Playoff Blizzard: #16 Ryan Hodges, #86 Fred Knuess and #55 Ryan Persails

9. INTEGRITY – 1996

Sometimes it is important to discover what one cannot do than what one can do.

-Lin Yutang

He came hours early and stood in line, as if he was going to a rock concert, then raced for a seat near the front. He grabbed the row directly behind the team, getting as close as he could without actually being on the turf. Hodge didn't care how silly he looked with a 12" red and black letter 'R' painted on his chest.

Damn it. They were in the Dome; in the Pontiac Silverdome. He had paid his dues for that moment. No one would take it away, nor prevent him from celebrating. Not even the attendant who insisted they put their shirts on could dampen his spirit, or that of his eleven teammates whose chests spelled out their school mascot. They tried to abide, but their shirts came off every time the cheering started. Most were now college students who didn't intend on being obnoxious; they simply couldn't disguise the excitable vigor of being in the Dome. Hodge felt a strong sense of relief knowing that it wasn't impossible for the Rams to play here. He often wondered if they had been jinxed, or barred by some unwritten statute that denied them for so long.

Bulldog, his teammate, stood nearby but didn't act crazy like the guys with the painted chests surrounding Hodge. Bulldog was voted as their 'Most Dedicated Player' his senior year, an honor well deserved after he worked so hard. Being in the Dome meant so much to Bulldog. He felt an honest happiness for the team, but couldn't deny the selfish envy lounging deep in his own heart. He wanted to be in their shoes and do this for his town, for his own dream. The team on the turf didn't have to play in a blizzard, or face a private Catholic school. Yet they overcame their own obstacles, earning integrity along the way. They were destined to play here. They made it. They actually made it. Finally.

Hodge knocked on the back door then casually let himself in, 'Hey Aaron, you ready to go?'

Aaron yelled from downstairs, 'I'm getting CD's. I'll be right up.'

Ryan Hodges noticed an open box of plaques on the floor, then picked one up out of curiosity. He was caught off-guard by the unexpected lump that instantly formed in the base of his throat as he read:

'HEART AND DETERMINATION CREATED THE CHAMPION'

'If You Want Something You Never Had
You Must Do Some Things You Have Never Done'

Aaron rapidly clomped up the stairs before Hodge could return the plaque to the box. He immediately noticed the sheepish look on his friend's face and asked, 'What's wrong with you?'

Hodge felt guilty for peeking and handed over the plaque, 'These are cool. Have you seen them?'

'No, my dad wanted me to wait 'till the banquet.'

Aaron's dad, 'Sparky,' had ordered the plaques from the Football Club. Hodge watched Aaron respond with the same heartfelt reaction, minus the stabbing ache. Aaron had one more year to play, but Hodge was done.

Hodge grabbed the CD collection while Aaron grabbed a bag of groceries, before headed to the school in Hodge's '83 red Ford Ranger. Being at the school on a Saturday morning seemed strange; the halls were vacant and visibly quiet. A handful of guys were on a mission to create their football highlight film. It was the first year that Coach Reinhart gave players total control over production of their own film. They planned to make it the best one ever produced, in spite of being pressed for time. But they were used to working under pressure and had the energy to pull an all nighter, if needed. Reinhart appreciated their enthusiasm yet smirked under his breath, realizing they didn't have a clue of how much work awaited them.

Seniors Josh Haney and Steve Visser were anxious to get started, and met Hodge and Aaron at the school promptly at 9 AM. The group felt ready to jump in, after spending four hours on Friday night getting familiar with the Tech Lab equipment. Keeping everything organized, with teammates coming and going throughout the day, started to get a bit chaotic. Everyone wanted a piece of the screen, and provided their input as a guarantee. Their enthusiasm transferred to Aaron, while he watched them relive their senior season. He vowed to stay with them until they finished, making fast food runs when they whined about being famished. They had already gulped down every ounce of groceries that he'd brought from home, but food seemed to refuel them into the early hours of Sunday morning.

Hodge recapped memories from their pre-season quarterback camps that he attended with Brad Casciano and Aaron. Casciano was the back-up quarterback, while Aaron was a likely candidate for the job in '97. The threesome became best friends, challenging each other at every camp. They set a goal to outrun every team to the next station each time the air horn blasted, no matter how tired they were. Their enthusiasm got the attention of other coaches, especially former players now coaching at other schools. It reminded them of the determination they had while playing Montrose Football. They wanted that drive to exist in the hearts of their new teams.

Hodge thought the Rams practiced long and hard, until they ran into Shane at the SVSU camp. The former Ram compared his freshmen college football experience with high school two-a-days. The physical practice wasn't that much harder than Montrose Football, but the extensive review of film and instruction made the days horrendously long and tortuous. At college, they started to watch films at 5 AM, often ending at 11 PM and worked like hell in between. They took small breaks and ate light meals for three straight weeks. Casciano look at Hodge, 'I guess six hours of two-a-days doesn't seem quite so long.'

Shane realized that Hodge was college material, and updated him about the recruiting process. SVSU evaluated players to determine if they fit into the philosophy of the coaching style, assuming they could teach any lacking mechanics. It was a total different concept compared to high school; gassers were not issued as punishment when someone screwed up. If a college player fumbled the ball four times during practice, he would probably lose his position. It was that simple; they either performed or they were done.

It literally took the crew hours to carefully select the perfect music for each game, then timed the lyrics to particular plays for the precise effect. They knew the end result would be worth the extra effort. The last game clip was inserted early Sunday morning at 3 AM, after a sleepless 18 hours of reviewing film, pausing scenes, and adding titles. New technologies captured their creativity, making the '96 highlight film extra special because it recapped *their* senior year when *they* were the stars. Barely any footage was cut from actual game films in an effort to preserve the details of their entire senior season. It resulted in the longest highlight film in the history of Montrose Football. Eddie Richardson hit the lights, as the crew anxiously sat back to watch the final product in its entirety. Their hearts raced as the first title scrolled across the screen:

'Seniors Your Place in History Is Now Etched Upon the Rock'

Hodge felt his throat tighten when his best friends appeared on the screen. It made him realize that he played the best game with the greatest friends that he could've ever played with. Once it was all over, he realized how priceless the friendships he developed through football really were. Teammates pushed each other to the limit, drawing out their best. Poison's appeasing voice echoed *'Something to Believe In,'* providing new meaning to the lyrics, while serenading hard-nosed Ram drills. 'Fear the Ram' scrolled across the screen as the familiar deep, radio voice from the WWF announced, 'Welcome to the main event. Let's get ready to RUMBLE!'

Fears were cast away, replaced by hungry egos that hung it all on the line to earn a starting position. They all realized the stupidity of it, yet thrived on the no-holds-barred, free-for-all battle when linemen and linebackers faced anyone that challenged their position. The video crew moaned when Nick Loafman and Jason Pollard collided to prove who was the toughest. Once they reached the heat of the battle, the adrenaline rush intensified because every coach and player studied them. Neither Loafman nor Pollard wanted to be the one on the ground when the final whistle blew. Loafman had been unable to lift weights until he recovered from a recent shoulder surgery. Even though his strength wasn't at its peak, 'Loaf' felt great to be back in the driver's seat, striking on all cylinders.

The intensity showed on all of their faces when Guns and Roses blared, *'Welcome to the Jungle'* through the rest of Ram drills. They thrived on the physical contact that forced them to face their own fears. The fitting lyrics from the distinctive voice of Axl Rose whined, begging them to make each other bleed.

Winston and Jorod caused another moan from the crew as they crashed into each other, fighting for a running back position. Each stood only 5'5"-160 pounds, and were the only black brothers on the team. Winston was quick and ran the fastest 100-meter dash in the League. Jorod had the heart of a lion and loved the contact no matter how big of an opponent he faced.

The crew laughed at themselves completing a bear crawl gasser, instead of running it. The two largest tackles on the team, Harris and Flaco who each weighed 240 pounds, fell an entire length behind the team. Both stopped to puke and catch their breath, while their flushed faces displayed exhaustion in the sizzling, August heat. On top of that, Harris had a stomach virus that made him hurl every five minutes. When Harris lost 50 pounds in less then a month due to a virus, his teammates realized that he wasn't faking. Harris amused the team with his various leg cramps during veer camp. His hamstrings began to cramp by the end of camp. Harris seized his legs while trying to stretch, causing his quads to cramp. His entire body felt like one severe cramp. Richardson piped in, 'Remember when we had to carry his fat butt to his car because he couldn't straighten his legs enough to walk?'

'Yeah, he looked like an arthritis patient when he tried to unfold his cramped legs in the back seat. It was weird. They just wouldn't move.'

Somehow Harris survived an endless night of brutal, painful cramps, which in comparison made two-a-days seem easy.

Casciano laughed, 'Remember when we told that freshman that the water was *too wet* and we sent him after the dehydrated water mix?'

Richardson replied, 'Yeah. Just before we ran our laps, Hodge yelled at him to hurry up. We need the mix before we're done!'

They all laughed at their own originality, cherishing every fun memory. Aaron shook his head, a grin pasted on his face. 'Remember when the J.V.'s left for practice and Josh put all of the open locks on backwards?'

'Yeah, then he acted like he was the hero with the bolt cutters and they actually thanked him for helping.'

They constantly played tricks on Reinhart, like hiding his keys then watching him search everywhere, getting pissed in the process. Coach Clolinger or Brian Tripp were usually the guilty perpetrators, but Harris walked into the coach's office one day, and wish he hadn't. He tried to hold back his laughter after seeing the small couch turned upside down with a slit in it, as Reinhart's hand intently probed for his keys. In spite of all their jokes, they couldn't wait for their season to start.

One summer evening, Hodge, Harris, Loafman, and Aaron slept behind the scoreboard on the football field. They gazed at the clear starlit sky, while the August night enveloped their dreams for the '96 Season. They all had visions of playing in the Pontiac Silverdome; Hodge wanted to lead them there more than anything.

Each senior adopted a junior and continued the ritual to eat a pre-game meal at the same restaurant *every* Thursday night. The linemen chose an all you can eat buffet, while another group went to Ponderosa. They challenged who could pile the ice cream on the highest. Every Thursday night, Bulldog, Tripp, Harris, and kicker Tommy Unangst headed to their favorite Italian restaurant for stromboli with ham, cheese, onions and breadsticks. Hodge adopted Aaron, while Casciano undertook Woody, as part of their Fudruckers group. They ordered the same food, sat in the same chairs with the same guys every Thursday during the entire season. Aaron took a plastic, red Fudruckers Coke cup home then placed a sticker with the score of each victory. That innocent Coke cup held as much status as a tribal scalp. It became his badge of honor that he kept on the nightstand next to his bed.

Whatever rituals happened before the first game had to be continued throughout the season. That was gospel. Nothing could change on pre-game night. Paranoia had seeped its way into the '96 Football Team, leaving them fearful that any change could break their phenomenal 70 game winning streak. Players loved their streak and wanted to ride its success for as long as they could. The Rams were closing in on Michigan's all-time record for consecutive victories at 81 games.

Coach Coon told his new offensive line, 'It's our chance to run with the baton boys. We don't wanna break it.'

Reinhart didn't want them to think about the streak or live on the laurels of the great teams of the past. He told the Rams at the first game, 'We're a brand new team and we'll take one game at a time to maintain our focus.'

Coach felt that his Rams were experienced and had unlimited potential, but also realized that they were a young team. He hoped they improved each week because of their depth, and the fact that players continued to push each other for positions. Montrose Football was a tough program that encouraged players to come together; or else they could fall apart. The incoming junior class had never lost a football game since they started playing youth football at age eight. Juniors didn't want to just be on Varsity, they wanted a starting position and stepped up to battle the seniors. It pushed them all, while the competition helped the team gel. The coaches always looked to fill the gaps early in the season. Coon focused on what his offensive line looked like. Who was injured? What positions were lost to graduation? Who appeared ready to step up? Who wasn't playing up to their potential?

The video caught the crew's attention when the music stopped and the pre-season TV interviews aired. Nick Powell and Hodge were two seniors selected to talk to the press, as they tried to hide their nervousness. *They failed.* The sportscaster opened with a comment stating the seniors were only nine years old when the streak started then asked, 'Are the Rams overconfident?'

Nick Powell replied, 'No. We just want to do what we can.'

The newscaster quickly pointed the microphone in Hodge's face; 'You don't want to be the team that breaks the streak!'

They couldn't help but laugh at Hodge, their self-assured quarterback and fearless leader. Hodge always exhibited confidence, but suddenly turned shy the moment a reporter poked a camera in his face. 'True. We don't want to be the ones that lose and we won't worry about that right now. We'll just go out there and play our game. If we win, we win.'

Richardson blurted, 'Yeah - right Hodge. It's all you ever thought about.'

The truth was, the squad constantly worried about winning. When Hodge injured his right shoulder during their first pre-season scrimmage, it forced the offense to change their entire passing game plan. The flankers were disappointed that Hodge's arm wouldn't be ready by their season opener. The key quarterback went to therapy the morning of their first game and asked his doctor for a release note. He would go absolutely crazy if he had to watch from the sideline and was desperate enough to forge a note, *if he had to.* Hodge never went anywhere without a football in his hand, which made it convenient when his doctor asked him to step outside and throw a few passes. Hodge never relayed to anyone just how painful his lat felt after releasing a few passes. But he sucked it up, telling himself, *Act like it doesn't hurt. Don't flinch. It will all be worth it if you just hide the pain from doc for a few more passes.*

The elated quarterback took a deep breath when he left the sports clinic a few minutes later. He gripped the precious release note in one hand, his football in the other. The plan worked.

They crew watched **Atherton's** motto scroll across the screen:

'The Difference Between Mediocrity And Greatness Is Usually A Small Amount Of Effort'

It was a muggy, Friday Michigan evening when the Rams lined up for the opening kickoff. Fans even wore shorts, which was quite the contrast to the last game played in the Frankenmuth Blizzard. Their favorite Pearl Jam song, *'Even Flow,'* opened their season as guitars and drums provided a slow, catchy beat. They remembered how their hearts pounded on the field. They felt flushed with excitement as the raspy voice sang out, 'Feel it.' The fans on the sideline felt it too. It was football season; everybody was excited. The film crew painstakingly removed the confusing scene when the Rams foolishly lined up, facing the wrong endzone on Atherton's field. The coaches were embarrassed and upset before the game even started and rightfully yelled; 'You're not focused! GET IN THE GAME!'

Hodge stood on the sideline and watched Casciano take his spot at quarterback. Coach Reinhart asked Casciano, 'What do you want to run?'

Casciano replied, 'Let's run a sprint.'

Reinhart nodded in agreement. Just ten seconds into the game, Casciano's pass was abruptly intercepted leaving the quarterback helplessly pinned to the ground. That ten seconds seemed like an eternity. He was so embarrassed when the weakest team in the League picked off his first pass of the season, before running 29 yards for a touchdown. It was the last thing anyone expected, as unrepeatable words gushed from coaches. Doubt seeped into the minds of even the most dedicated fans who wondered, *Was that just a fluke or are we in trouble this year?*

Crusher towered over Casciano then reached out his hand to help him up. Casciano slowly shook his head, 'I can't believe that just happened!'

Crusher confidently replied, 'Don't worry, we'll get it back.'

Casciano remorsefully jogged to the sideline to face the displeased offensive coaches. He soon redeemed himself when he ran for a 12 yard TD to tie the game. The punt team used a squib kick then watched an Atherton receiver catch it, while only partially raising his arm. Two junior backs, Vicente Vigil and Woody, attacked the receiver full throttle from ten yards away. Vigil and Woody loved to hit and were conditioned to go until the whistle blew. *It never did.* The highlight film accented the two defenders that appeared to run right through the receiver. The official later blew his whistle and called, 'Late hit.'

Woody and Vigil defended themselves; 'You never blew the whistle!'

The official couldn't argue and they all recognized it was time to take a deep breath, calm down, and get their first game jitters under control. The squad anticipated trouble when Reinhart called a timeout. They nervously watched his short, choppy steps make his way toward their huddle. Reinhart had a special way of cocking his head to one side when he was mad, then stared into space for a minute before he lit into them. The Rams found themselves in a tied ball game early in the second half, against a team whose best record during the past six years was 2-7. Reinhart told Hodge before the game, 'Be prepared to go in if we need you to execute a ground attack.'

Hodge stood helplessly on the sideline, edgily waiting to go in. Casciano had played both ways, as well as special teams, and felt the humidity wear on him. He wasn't very vocal with the team, and the guys didn't respond to him like they did to Hodge in '95. Reinhart didn't want things to get out of control and approached his injured quarterback. 'It's time Hodge.'

Hodge eagerly accepted the offer to take the helm, immediately getting the team into the flow. His natural leadership sparked the offense the moment he stepped on the field, bringing a confidence that raised the level of play.

The heavy metal lyrics of *'Bang Your Head'* blared when the Rams jumped ahead 34-12 at the half, restoring the faith of their fans in the process. The video crew felt Jorod's tough block then laughed when Pollard grabbed an interception. He took out five opponents when his 225 pound body performed a spin move, then used a stiff arm to juke his foes. Pollard, a future navy man, usually had a shadow of a mustache. He always led with his forearm to an opponent's head whenever he tackled someone. Pollard was one of the bigger guys on the team with a huge neck and golden blonde hair that he parted on the side.

Hodge stayed in the game until the middle of the third quarter when Casciano replaced him. Casciano boosted his own confidence after scoring another TD to close with a '54-12' victory.

The Chesaning motto appeared:

'Attitude Is More Important Than Aptitude'

The coaches worked on a lot of things to gear up for **Chesaning**, especially the offensive line. Coach Coon was a very demanding coach. He disciplined his line with Coonerobics every time someone screwed up. Push-ups were dubbed, front lean and rests. Players did more front lean and rests, ups-and-downs, and sit-ups then anyone cared to remember. He constantly drilled, 'Consistency takes the small stuff out of the way.' He wanted them to do it right until it became second nature, almost mechanical.

Coon looked forward to practice everyday. He found Montrose Football phenomenal, and felt it had the atmosphere of a college football program. Except for the extra hours of reviewing film, their physical practices were more grueling than a lot of college programs. It was a blast to work with the kids, and he developed an emotional bond. Once they adapted to his style, players got into his program, doing whatever he asked.

Junior center Adam Powell respected Coon. Any coach that jumped in, and completed each punishment with his squad while sporting a huge smile, deserved it. They started their second year together. Adam felt that Coach Coon had already taught him so much. On the other hand, rookie Jared Smith didn't quite know what to think of Coon, but definitely felt intimidated by him. The only sophomore on Varsity quickly figured out that if he worked hard, they would get along fine. Coon resented slackers. Jared went by 'Dauber,' compliments of his freshman coach. Monty Stiles dubbed him with the name a year ago because he was a big, blonde-haired kid that looked and sounded like Bill Fagerbakke who played Dauber on *Coach;* a popular TV sitcom that football coaches loved. Only the Rams' Dauber was smart.

Harris played guard and tackle as he started his second year with Coon. They developed a trust between each other after Harris shared the loss of his father a year ago. He knew that Coon was a true lineman at heart and respected the man, but his workouts were grueling. Harris thought to himself, *That man definitely has atypical tendencies.*

Coach Coon preached his formula for success to his players: Effort – Courage – Discipline – Enthusiasm. He noticed that Montrose players already used those qualities, but didn't recognize them as a blueprint. His goal was to drill the formula into them so they would use it throughout their lives, not just during football practice and games.

Coon worked second shift for the Sheriff's Department, but flexed his hours during football season, splitting his shift on Fridays. His wife soon learned to share him with football, mid-summer through Thanksgiving. Coon put the extra hours in, which seemed pale in comparison to the time that Reinhart and Destrampe dedicated. Reinhart gave Coon Sundays and Mondays off for a break. Mondays became 'Defense Day.'

Kids were coachable and willing to do what Coon asked . . . and more. He loved it when they stepped up to his challenge. He saw them work out in the off-season to improve their own performance. He walked into the school during the winter and found Loafman, Aaron, and Woody working out with strength shoes and pulleys, making a game out of it. The threesome wanted to increase their strength, jumping agility, and speed. Players took football seriously, and did the little things during the off-season. He could tell they enjoyed being a part of it.

Chesaning's first year head coach, Jim Szappan, brought his Indians to the Bob Hayes Field in Montrose on Friday the 13th. The Rams waited for the Indians to take the field first. They made their first home game, grand entrance through a new smoke tunnel, a contraption built by the Football Club. Sparky masterminded the tunnel. He stretched pipes for braces then covered them with a thick, black tarp that formed a dark tunnel, 10' wide X 30' long. The dark tube angled from the new team room to the football field. Sparky realized how precious high school memories become. He wanted to contribute all that he could to make his youngest son's football experience something special.

Smoke came from the tunnel, which added an eerie backdrop when the Montrose Rams made their entrance on the field. It sparked some drama to their season home opener, and the fans loved the effect. Hodge watched himself on the tape as he led the Rams out of the smoke to the goal post, walking two-by-two. Watching it gave him the same rush that he felt on opening night. He jumped up-and-down before racing through the human tunnel on the field. He was the only one who noticed that he didn't trip when he crashed through the cheerleader's hoop that read, 'LETS GET READY TO RUMBLE.'

Casciano asked Hodge, 'Remember how we practiced running through the hoop that day?'

'Yeah, I didn't want to go down as the first captain to fall flat on his face.'

Hodge had spotted the undecorated hoop against the wall by the locker room after school. 'Hey Dude, I have an idea.'

They made sure that no one was around before they moved the heavy hoop to the middle of the hall, trying to avoid scraping the shiny floor. The metal hoop was welded to a brace at the bottom. Hodge feared that he would be the first Ram to embarrass himself on his opening stanza. Maybe he was a victim of watching too many bloopers on television, but it made him want to practice. So Hodge and Casciano jumped through the undecorated hoop several times. Breaking through the hoop was a special moment that kicked off their home football games; neither wanted to botch it.

AC/DC blared *'Back in Black,'* while the film showed them dressed in their black home jerseys and pants. The Rams looked tougher in black, symbolizing them as hard-hitting bad guys. Montrose ran ten straight plays that covered 80 yards, eating up half of the first quarter clock. Reinhart told Hodge, 'They're creeping up on the run, let's sneak a pass in.'

Hodge's shoulder felt good when he connected with Nick Powell for an awesome one-handed, 26 yard TD reception in traffic. It was Powell's claim to fame. They accented his awesome right arm as he grabbed the pass in super slow motion. When a teammate gave that kind of effort, it enhanced the squad's motivation quicker than any inspiring speech ever could. It was the catch that youth football players talked about all season and tried to emulate. The photo earned the privilege of being the cover of the `96 Highlight Book, as well as a special effect that was repeated three times on the tape. The crew commented after each replay, as if watching it for the very first time. Casciano got excited and yelled, 'God, I loved this game!'

Richardson hauled in a long punt then followed great blocks by Pollard and Flaco, running 85 yards down the left sideline to score. The big play gave the Rams a shot of adrenaline; they scored 22 second quarter points. Coach Bob Hayes greeted Flaco on the sideline. Flaco loved Coach Hayes who had a wealth of knowledge and taught them how to get away with *stuff.*

Senior Dave Lyman took his position on the kickoff team. He was small and quick. Lyman pounced on a fumble recovery before getting buried at the bottom of the pile. He didn't care that his face was smashed so far into the ground that he actually saw bugs crawling inches from his face. He was pinned under several opponents, but hung onto the ball with every ounce of strength he could muster. Lyman's heart raced knowing that he had the ball; he couldn't wait for everyone to pile off. The moment he became free, he popped up, threw the ball high into the air, then instantly panicked. *Did the ref even know that I had the ball?*

Thankfully, the official was on top of things and signaled for the Rams to take possession. Lyman went crazy, having the best game of this life. He made the tackle on five kicks, an effort that later earned him, 'The Animal of the Year' award. Coach Destrampe liked the aggressiveness that he saw in Lyman. He noticed his potential as early as two-a-days, and wanted him on the kickoff team. Lyman was one of those players who only saw a few minutes of playing time on special teams, but gave his all when he was on the field. He attacked with fresh aggression.

Four minutes later Hodge audibled off a fade, which Richardson caught with an awesome over-the-shoulder, 23 yard reception in the endzone. Richardson was a good-looking guy that always had a smile, and a girl. He was a happy, adjusted teenager who loved football and enjoyed being with the guys. Richardson considered Hodge a good friend. Hodge was a mobile quarterback who delivered the ball on time, allowing his offense to look good. Visser kicked the PAT to make the half-time score 21-0.

The Rams and the Indians headed to the new team rooms that the Football Club built at the north end of the field. While players conditioned in the August head, their dads constructed a building that contained a 24' x 30' visitor team room and a 28' x 30' home team room connected by a 16' overhead. Youth football claimed the entire upstairs to store their equipment. The Football Club paid $26,000 for materials, while donating their labor. The fruits of their labor provided the school with a building valued at $150,000. Dads that couldn't pound nails volunteered to cook for the crew, who were all anxious for the '96 football season. The black roof on the fire engine red, block building was a sharp addition to the stadium, providing teams close access to locker rooms.

The Rams were motivated when they reentered the field. Jorod hit his opponent with such force that the Indians fumbled the second half kickoff. Hodge broke free then raced 25 yards to pay dirt, then Tommy kicked the PAT. Aaron jumped up for an interception that Hodge planned to grab when Pollard accidentally hit Aaron, knocking him into an opponent. Hodge was located behind Aaron in pitching position, unaware that Aaron's foot was trapped. Aaron hopped on one foot, while trying to get loose as Hodge took off down the field, assuming he was in position. In that split second when he went to pitch, Hodge turned around and yelled, 'Aaron don't pitch it!'

It was a fun game and the Rams beat Chesaning '35-7' that night.

The crew moaned in unison when the motto for game three scrolled across the screen. Casciano piped in, 'I remember looking at Coach Clolinger as if he was crazy when he made us memorize that one.'

Most doubted their own ability to commit the absurd, long motto to memory, then laughed as they recited it in unison months later. It ended up being a phrase they would never forget.

'A Winning Tradition Is Like A Cable,
Each Day A New Thread Is Woven
Until The Finished Product Becomes Unbreakable'

Casciano asked, 'Do you think Clolinger spent the entire day in the ISR Room strumming up difficult mottoes for us to memorize?'

'Probably', was the general consensus.

The squad called Clolinger 'Pretty Boy' behind his back. He had the striking good looks that caused more then a few female students to intentionally get into trouble for a chance to sit in his ISR class. But Clolinger had football on his mind.

New Lothrop fans packed the visitor bleachers, as they prepared to watch their Hornets tackle the Rams. Walking out of the smoke tunnel for the second time stirred the same adrenaline rush in the Rams. In an effort to create thicker smoke, the Football Club supplied a 55-gallon drum of dry ice at the entrance of the tunnel. Hodge watched as the team made their exit from the smoke tunnel, but his pain overshadowed the moment. After injuring his shoulder during practice, he wasn't able to start that week, nor play the entire first half. He watched from the sideline as the Hornets drove down the field to the Montrose four yard line. The Montrose defense stopped them, while the heavy metal sounds of Metallica blared the lyrics to 'One'.

Visser broke loose, sprinted 96 yards for a TD, then tacked on the PAT late in the first quarter. A forceful New Lothrop hit caused Visser to fumble on their next possession at their own 16. The Hornets capitalized by scoring with 4:21 left in the half, but their failed extra point left the score 7-6. It seemed that the Rams were a completely different team when Hodge wasn't on the field, resembling the '91 Team when Crockett was injured. Hodge became extremely frustrated from the sideline when he watched the Rams only make one first down on nine offensive plays.

The Rams stopped the Hornets again when Aaron tackled his distant cousin after he caught a pass. But Aaron hit his opponent with such force that his facemask drilled deep into Aaron's stomach. His neck felt the excruciating pain, leaving him shivering on the ground. Sparky worked the chain gang and joined the medical crew on the field, while his mom held her breath in the stands. She prayed that it wasn't a neck injury. Watching your son lay injured on the field had to be one of the worst parental fears in the world.

Aaron was able to walk off the field, then watched the Rams get the ball back only to fumble again. New Lothrop recovered, then threw a scoring pass to lead 7-14 at intermission. The New Lothrop fans went wild with excitement, in anticipation of breaking their opponent's precious streak. It marked only the second time, in the 72-game winning streak, when the Rams trailed at the half. By the time they reached the team room, the Rams had fumbled the ball, missed passes, missed blocks, and placed blamed on each other.

Lyman silently stood in the back of the room, until he reached his breaking point. He couldn't keep quiet any longer and forced his way to the front to address his teammates. 'Starting for the Rams is like an opportunity of a lifetime. I played hard against you guys all week on scout team defense. You guys are the best team in the state. You're so much better than what you're playing. I know I won't have a chance to play the second half but if I did, I'd play my heart out.'

His delivery was packed with emotion, forcing the starters to do an honest gut check. Guilt consumed them for not playing up to their full potential. Reinhart came in and laid it on the line. 'If you don't come out ready to play a good football game, you're going to be in for a war.'

A different, focused team took the field with Hodge at the helm. Montrose drove 65 yards on their first possession. Hodge sternly grabbed a junior's facemask in the huddle, looking him square in the eye. 'You missed your block!'

He immediately set the intensity in the huddle, and the tone on the field. It became blatantly obvious how much of a leader Hodge really was. Winston took the hand-off then pranced 27 yards to score. Visser's PAT tied the game; the war was on. The Rams intercepted New Lothrop's first possession. Hodge broke two tackles en route on a 24 yard run to score :22 seconds into the quarter. Then Tommy kicked the PAT, putting the Rams up 21-14.

Tommy's quiet and shy demeanor absorbed the great sensation as the crowd stood, cheering for his kick. It was one of the greatest feelings in the world. He loved playing Montrose Football, and carrying on the kicking tradition of his two older brothers. His parents were extremely proud of him, not only because he was the baby of the family, but they never expected him to play football with his heart condition. Tommy had openheart surgery when he was only 16 months old. His doctors never really wanted him to play any physical sports, but he did so well playing soccer and running that his parents had him evaluated again. Tommy did better then anyone expected, was given a chest protector, and joined the football team. His mom constantly worried about Tommy being used as a tackling dummy during practice, fearing that his chest bone could get broken. The fact that he was able to follow in his brothers' footsteps and have similar memories, made every game special. The Unangst Family quickly discovered that the Montrose Community was a sport minded town, whose support figured heavily in the team's success.

New Lothrop was still in the game until Visser scored again on a 29 yard run with 6:15 to play. The Hornets drove deep. Senior linebacker Jason Pollard made a big interception at the Montrose 17, with five minutes unplayed. Junior back Joe Fedechenko got his second interception followed by another Hodge TD with :22 seconds left in the game, closing the score '34-14.'

Both teams were banged up; especially Loafman who had a game high of 12 tackles for two straight weeks. Loafman was a good student who could be a lot of fun, but had a serious side when it came to football and wrestling. His strong athletic build resembled B.J. Dean, and he hit his opponents with as much force. Loafman's girlfriend, along with his two sisters, kept his hair in style with a fashionable spiked cut that required hair gel.

New Lothrop came to town extremely well prepared, honestly believing they had the skills to beat the Rams. The Hornets played a hard fought battle; the toughest the Rams had faced in '96. Reinhart couldn't imagine **Goodrich** hitting any harder the following week, and had the Rams memorize the next motto:

'TEAM – Together Everyone Achieves More'

The Goodrich game tape rolled to the mollifying voice of Lenny Kravitz who sang, *'Believe.'* The crew intentionally picked that song because of its lyrics. The Rams believed in themselves the entire time; so did the coaching staff. But it felt awkward to be the first Montrose team that was expected to lose. Reinhart told them, 'I intentionally played up your injuries to the media and credited Goodrich's talent during my interview.'

Reinhart sounded pretty convincing in the paper when the media planted doubt in the minds of some Montrose fans. They couldn't help but wonder, *Could Goodrich really beat Montrose?* Both teams were undefeated in the GEC League as they prepared for the showdown. Goodrich had the home team advantage and was stacked. Montrose was the only loss that Goodrich experienced in '95, and realized that they wanted revenge. Goodrich made the state playoffs for the first time in school history in '95. And like Montrose, their town was just as excited and extremely supportive. The media hailed Goodrich as the 'Streakbusters,' by featuring articles about their confidence to end the Rams' eight-year dynasty. It created a huge game hype that became intensified with the GEC League Title on the line. The contest also impacted the Class CC State Playoffs, since Montrose was ranked fourth in the state, while Goodrich was ranked sixth.

Goodrich Coach Tom Alward publicly stated, 'This is why you play these kind of games. We want to be part of a big game like this. The kids are ready to go. As with anything, the streak has to come to an end sometime and we'd like to be the ones to stop it. They're not going to beat us with their past laurels. Their mystique was worth points, but that's not the case Friday. My kids firmly believe they're going to win.' Alward also stated that he would have mixed feelings if the Montrose streak ended Friday. 'Montrose has been a big source of pride for a lot of GEC teams. We hate to see the streak come to an end, but it has to one day and we would like it to be a GEC school. And, if it's a GEC school, we would like it to be Goodrich.'

The media referred to Montrose as *the underdogs.* The Rams were sick of hearing how Goodrich would destroy them and break their streak. Not one Ram thought he was better than anyone else on the team. They were a group of guys that planned to work together to keep their tradition alive. Reinhart didn't want them to dwell on the streak, but to focus on practice, improving every day. He addressed the streak pressure during practice. 'It's okay to be proud of the streak, but we need to realize that so far we've only won three football games.'

The first day of practice during Goodrich week was dubbed 'Sleeveless Monday.' Teammates traditionally ripped the sleeves off of any player's shirt worn to practice on a Monday, and kept them in a drawer in the weight room. When cold practice days came around, players pulled them over their heads like a stocking cap under their helmets. Coach Clolinger soaked footballs in a bucket of ice cold water until they became waterlogged. The quarterbacks and the center dunked their hands into the freezing water without wiping them, to prepare for the cold, rainy weather predicted for the Goodrich game. Clolinger took the edge off Thursday's pre-game practice by dressing in a mocked up Goodrich football jersey with the opposing quarterback's number. He took several sleeves from the weight room drawer and pulled them over his head and arms, giving the team a laugh, 'Oh yeah - Custer.'

The Rams prepared hard all week, except for Hodge. He watched from the sideline with limited activity, after knocking off a torn muscle capsule under his shoulder blade. He chuckled while asking Casciano, 'Remember how panic stricken you were when you arrived at the school before the game? You ran up to me, 'Hodge, I can't find my Nike socks!'

Hodges' wide eyes gave Casciano a frightened look. 'What do you mean you can't find your socks?'

The two quarterbacks looked at each other with skepticism. 'Casciano, this is the Goodrich game. Nobody is supposed to change anything!'

'I know Hodge, but I looked everywhere. My step-mom must've thrown them away when she did the laundry.'

Not that he could blame her. The bottoms were paper-thin and full of holes. He wondered if he ever actually mentioned that they were his *lucky* socks. Casciano didn't want to jinx the team but he was worried. He'd worn those lucky socks to every game since his freshman year. He tried to be optimistic, since he still had the eight of clubs. He carried that card with him whenever he played, and hoped it satisfied his superstition.

Coach Destrampe found a boiler room inside the Goodrich High School, and gathered the entire team alone for a few minutes before the game. Reinhart held up a letter as he seriously addressed the team, 'This letter is from someone who was very special to this program, and has a place in my heart and probably yours. It's from Coach Tony Annese:'

> *'I wish I could be with you for tonight's game. No matter where I coach, my heart is always in Montrose. I want you to think about all of the times that Goodrich was supposed to beat Montrose and we beat them every game. Compare the scores each year during the streak:*

1988	34 – 8	1992	41 - 19
1989	43 – 0	1993	35 - 0
1990	40 – 6	1994	57 - 7
1991	23 – 8	1995	38 - 18

> *Goodrich may talk themselves into thinking they are as good as you. They have to say that the 'mystique is over.' They're not sure, they have to try and talk themselves into it. But we know! We are the Rams and the mystique is not gone. With Hodge leading you, and ends like Crusher and Powell, and a line that will make things happen, you can't go wrong. Make your defense dominate and make us proud.*

> *You guys have the talent to make it to the Dome. I hope you have a spot for me in the press box.*

> *Coach Annese*

It sure lit Crusher up who thought, *How could we let Goodrich beat us? How could we go out there and lose to a team that hasn't done anything special? They've never won a State Championship or even a League Championship. No! He wouldn't let it happen!*

Casciano yelled, 'If that doesn't pump you up, nothing will.'

Hodge remembered how that letter choked him up. It forced him to speak through a firm lump in his throat when he yelled, 'I am so pumped up right now I just want to go after them.'

Each teammate felt the emotional impact of that letter. No one felt ashamed to show his feelings; even Crusher who normally wasn't the emotional type. It was exactly what the Montrose Rams needed to hear before the game, that *someone else* believed in them.

Harris was sick of listening to all of the comments during the past year, about Goodrich beating them. Motivation seeped through every pore of his skin as the Rams walked out of that room. Harris felt confident that Goodrich couldn't stop them. His coaches taught him that they could accomplish anything they set out to do with hard work and true dedication. He believed in them. It was the reason why he worked so hard in the weight room. As a sophomore, he placed first in Nationals, bypassing his competitors by 300 pounds. His best lift included a 475 pound squat, a 325 pound bench, and a 475 pound deadlift.

The coaches did their best to prepare them, now it was up to the Rams. Their confidence appeared restored when they grunted and yelled; their hearts raced when they left the school. Each step they took between the Goodrich High School and the football field filled them with even more determination. By the time they stepped on Goodrich's field, the Rams were ready to play the kind of football they all knew they were capable of.

An overflow crowd packed the Goodrich stadium, while fans made their way through the muddy parking lot. The planks that were set up to guide the fans became slippery from the mud. The intensity of the media hype drew many former Montrose players to the game. Mike Sullivan was incognito as an SVSU college recruiter, enjoying his press box view where he stood between the Goodrich and Montrose staff.

Hodge kept everyone in suspense on the status of his injury, because his doctor didn't give him clearance to play until after school that Friday. Reinhart's game plan was to be more physical and dominate the line of scrimmage. Hodge opened the game with a 38-veer pass to Crusher at tight end. It was the first time Montrose used that play so it wasn't on any previous game film for Goodrich to scout. Crusher's 6'3"-220 pound body appeared huge on film as he loomed over opponents.

The Rams drove the ball within field goal range. Tommy kicked a 30 yarder, putting the Rams on the board with five minutes left in the first quarter. He felt thrilled to score first, especially since he didn't play that much in '95, after an injury held him back. He got stronger by working out in the weight room during the off-season. Tommy realized the privilege to kick for the Rams would be shared with Visser's accurate foot.

The momentum shifted to the Rams when Aaron intercepted Custer, the Goodrich quarterback, with a 21 yard return. It was a sloppy, messy game that was dubbed as the 'Mud Bowl.' The Montrose Rams wore their white away jerseys, which soon turned black and barely revealed their numbers. The Goodrich Martians wore bright gold pants that turned a dark, muddy brown as both teams played smash mouth football. Hodge's hands were full of mud after he got tackled. His white hand towel was drenched, so Harris pulled up his jersey. 'Here, wipe them on my shirt!'

Goodrich's free safety triggered, trying to take the pitch away. The Rams gave up their possession on a fumble three plays later, but not for long. Flaco recovered a Goodrich fumble two plays later, and the Rams regained possession. Hodge called the play in the huddle. They broke and lined up. He got set in his quarterback position, then felt his mind go completely blank. The signal caller tried not to panic, but he had a total brain skip, forgetting the play that he called seconds earlier in the huddle. *Shit. That's never happened before. I always remember the play. What's going on? I can't just run it because I'll look dumb.* Hodge realized that he needed to get his groove back after sitting out for a week. He stalled while seconds ticked dangerously close to a penalty, creating even more apprehension on the offensive line. He decided to audible off, 'One-39...One-39!'

The line exchanged peculiar glances, trying to understand why Hodge decided to audible off the play that he just called in the huddle. They laughed about it later, but at the time Loafman thought, *I'm glad he audibled off because I thought we were running a One-39.*

Crusher easily caught Hodge's 13 yard pass while he towered over opponents, then ran it in for their first TD. The Rams didn't waste any time and scored again on their next possession, after Hodge plowed over from the one with just over six minutes to play in the first.

Goodrich hopped back into the game by jolting 62 yards a minute later. Aaron tried his hardest to catch his speedy opponent, but the Martian was too fast and made the score 17-6. The video crew laughed out loud while they watched a Goodrich opponent attempt to tackle Crusher. *He didn't budge.* The opponent walked away, then turned around and stared at Crusher, as if in disbelief. Crusher just stood tall, *with attitude.*

The Rams played their best pass defense ever. Instead of using a free safety, they played two guys seven yards off the line of scrimmage. As soon as they read a pass, depending on which side had the power, the third back rotated to free safety. Goodrich tried to run off power. Both teams were evenly matched, but the Rams extra back was free to tackle him. It worked well, giving the defensive backs a variety of different responsibilities. Aaron thrived when they turned him in where he anxiously stood, ready to take his opponent down and thought, *this feels cool as hell.*

Bulldog felt pumped to be back in the game after being sidelined with a knee injury. He twisted his knee on one of the last plays of a pre-season scrimmage when he was double-teamed. Bulldog may be short but he tackled Custer hard, causing a fumble at their 28. Watching their quarterback being helped off the field with a hip-pointer became Goodrich's last demise. Bulldog laid the foundation for the Rams who dubbed the game, 'Custer's Last Stand.'

Coach Coon continued to use Bulldog as an example during practice. Coon often grabbed Bulldog and threw him around whenever anyone screwed up. As weeks passed, it made Bulldog mad. He grew tired of being the example, by a coach whose height and weight looked gigantic next to his. Bulldog wouldn't tell the other coaches for fear of being labeled as a crybaby. By the end of the season, he considered it a compliment. Especially since it came from hardheaded Coach Coon, who knew that Bulldog could handle whatever he dished out. It was one of the reasons his teammates voted Bulldog as their 'Most Dedicated player,' an honor he shared with Harris.

Hodge scored earlier in the second half, helping the Rams pass their biggest test of the season by sealing a '23-6' victory. Hodge was an all around likable guy; his classmates even elected him as their Homecoming King. He led them during the off-season in the weight room, and was one of the strongest players for the Rams. Reinhart called him a 500 pound squatter who benched 300 pounds. Not too many quarterbacks were national powerlifters, which gave Hodge an edge, making it difficult for defenders to tackle him.

Coach Clolinger didn't want any of them to become overconfident after their big victory. He selected an appropriate motto for the **Hamady** game that sounded like a Chinese proverb:

'He Who Is Satisfied Has Nothing More To Achieve'

Clolinger didn't need to worry about the team being overconfident; but they were over-excited because of Homecoming. The Football Club improved the smoke tunnel fog for a better effect. Walking through the thick, white fog before facing the huge Homecoming crowd, gave the Rams an even bigger rush. The offense was on fire when they rolled to an insurmountable 26-6 lead. Visser rushed for three first quarter TD's, then Crusher scored after Hodge hit him with a four yard pass in the second.

Hodge watched the film and remembered when Aaron started at running back during the second half. 'Aaron, I hated when you went in motion and smacked me hard on the ass. I always continued the cadence and acted like it didn't hurt, when I really wanted to grunt out a few choice words at you.'

Aaron just laughed, 'That's why I did it. I knew you couldn't do anything about it.'

Montrose Football was synonymous with running the ball. Winston, Hodge, and Jorod led the attack while the Rams amassed 370 rushing yards in front of a delighted Homecoming crowd. Winston, Powell, and Aaron scored the second half, while Tommy kicked five PAT's. The student body screamed, 'Tommy GUN, Tommy GUN' before each attempt. Tommy was glad to carry on the Unangst kicking tradition, and was thrilled that Visser got more action as a running back.

Hamady tacked on their second score early in the third to lure the Hawks within 26-12. Casciano and Aaron watched the screen while they each grabbed an interception. Aaron commented, 'It's the coolest feeling after you dive for the ball, then listen for your crowd to cheer.'

The Rams had the game locked in with only four seconds left when Lyman gave his all, like he always did when he had a chance to play. He dropped his head when he speared a Hamady opponent, then went down hard. The squad forlornly watched as the ambulance took Lyman away, which suddenly put a damper on the '47-18' victory.

The lyrics to '18 and Over' by Skid Row followed by Ozzy Osbourne's 'No More Tears,' rocked the crew as the motto for **Lake Fenton** appeared:

'If You Stay The Same You Will Go Backwards'

Lake Fenton practiced hard under their new head coach, who returned to the scene after his previous term between 1981-1986. The Blue Devils jumped on the board first with a field goal to cap their opening drive. The Blue Devils scored first, but their lead was short-lived when the visiting Rams put 35 points on the board, before allowing Lake Fenton to score again.

The Rams surprised their opponents by striking with an air attack. Hodge appeared to be fully recovered from this shoulder injury, when he passed for 207 yards for four TD's. He hit ends Powell and Crusher for two each. Since Hodge was healthier, Reinhart worked on their passing game to resolve kinks before the post-season. The break gave running backs, Visser and Winston, time to nurse their knee injuries. The video crew laughed at the scene when Crusher scored in the endzone, with two defenders latched to him like a bloodsucker stuck on your big toe. Crusher just stood there with a tall badness about him. He always walked with his arms out wide, appearing like a leaner version of Andre the Giant. Crusher didn't budge, and the camera angle made his frame appear larger than his 6'3"-220 pounds.

Aaron found his niche at running back and helped the Rams get off to a quick start. After the intermission, he dodged opponents then energetically burst 60 yards to score on their third play from scrimmage. The students chanted, 'Tommy Gun' after he kicked each of his six PAT's. The Montrose defense shutdown Lake Fenton's running game, forcing them to pass, then grabbed two interceptions.

Reinhart was pleased with his team's '42-17' victory, but disappointed with the fumble and 11 penalties. Montrose felt ready to take on Bentley, growing anxious for a home game with their smoke tunnel. Pantera's vulgar display of heavy metal power screamed, *'RESPECT . . . WALK . . . ARE YOU TALKING TO ME'* as the **Bentley** motto scrolled across the screen:

'A Goal Is Nothing Unless You Put Forth The Effort To Achieve it'

The Football Club perfected the art of making smoke, which pumped up the Rams when they ran through the tunnel. Darkness now fell earlier on Friday nights in Michigan, giving the smoke tunnel an eerier ambiance. Casciano looked up at the crowd after the players went through all of their hype and wondered, *Where are all of our fans?*

They considered the large crowd that sat in the Montrose bleachers as their diehard fans. But the stands didn't appear packed, and the human tunnel didn't seem as large as it usually was. The team did their job and felt prepared for Friday night. They expected the fans to be at the game. *Did fans just expect them to win and wait until the post-season to jump on the bandwagon?*

Casciano mentioned it to Stacie, one of their cheerleaders, when the team gathered at her house to watch Monday Night Football. She looked at him with a serious expression, 'Maybe if you lose a game more people will come.'

The team glared at her as if she had just lost her mind. It was taboo to even mention the word losing; a subject the Rams refused to joke about.

The game got underway when Hodge connected with Powell on a 14 yard strike to get on the board. Bentley actually took the lead when they connected for a 63 yard bomb, made the conversion, and went ahead 7-8. Moments later, Hodge connected with Richardson on a 10 yard strike to take the lead and keep it. The Montrose Rams concentrated on little things and shutdown the Bentley Bulldogs. The video crew watched a Bentley running back jolt down the Montrose sideline. Richardson stopped him in his tracks, then Pollard smashed him into the sideline. The crew moaned out loud as they felt the impact, then anxiously rewound the video to watch the strike again. Pollard intimidated his opponent by lingering over him after the impact, as if gloating because he was taller.

Montrose capitalized on a chance to work on their passing game and pass protection. Hodge passed for 212 yards and used Crusher, Aaron, and Powell as his favorite targets. It was time for a trick play, so Hodge threw a lateral pass to Aaron, who threw a long pass to Powell at tight end. The Rams managed to score six TD's in the air during past two weeks. But they also worked on their ground attack when Jorod scored back-to-back TD's, while Hodge and Visser each ran for two.

Fedechenko returned an interception 55 yards to pay dirt while Casciano and Woody each grabbed an interception. Hodge played safety and was next to Woody when he grabbed one and yelled, 'Ball, Ball, Ball!' Woody pitched then cut back to be in pitch position and yelled, 'Ball, Ball, Ball,' while they worked the ball down the field. The game was a blast and everyone got in on the action, posting a season high victory, '62-14.'

Tripp was a senior and went in at free safety toward the end of the game. It was Tripp's first year to play football; his family formed his fan club whenever he went in. His only sister traveled two hours every Friday to watch the Rams, while his dad entertained the crowd from the press box as the announcer. Bentley threw a long pass toward Tripp who stood alone at the goal line. It was his big moment as all eyes focused on the endzone. Tripp felt his heart race as the scene unfolded. In his dismay, he felt everyone watch the ball hit his chest before it bounced off. The film crew made sure that Tripp's moment-in-time was accentuated as a highlight film classic. To make matters worse, Bentley scored on the very next play. If Tripp had a chance to go back to that one moment in his life and change something – that one play would be it. He appreciated that Clolinger was one of the few people that sympathized with him. Clolinger was down to earth, and made Tripp feel that he could always count on him whenever he had a problem. Tripp tried to rise above his embarrassment, while enduring the teasing. But he drew the line when the high school principal couldn't resist the urge to bounce his keys off his chest during the dance following the game. *Embarrassment was mortifying.*

Casciano played quarterback and was a bit intimidated by Bentley's linebacker who appeared to weigh 350 pounds. The Rams quickly nicknamed him 'Tiny.' Casciano laughed when he recalled how he didn't want to play back-up quarterback and face Tiny. He teased Aaron, 'Know what I suggested to Coach Reinhart? You might want to put Aaron out there and let him get some snaps in since he's gonna be your quarterback next year.'

Aaron threw a punch at Casciano, 'Thanks. Some kind of friend you are.'

The crew shifted their eyes back to the screen. Tiny tried his best to time every play, but continued to get blocked when the Rams ran the veer right past him. The Montrose offense wasn't quite set up on the very last play of the game. Aaron was still in his upright position as he looked around, before calling the play. The fresh quarterback heard Tiny's loud breathing before he even started his cadence. Aaron thought, *Oh Tiny is trying to fake me out, and he's doing a pretty good job!*

Suddenly, all 350 pounds of Tiny jumped through the line and caught the center off-guard before tackling Aaron, who only weighed 150 pounds. Aaron never had a chance to even call the play. The officials immediately blew the whistle and threw the flag to take control of the situation. They wanted to free Aaron from the weight of the bulldozer who laid on top of him.

Aaron's dad worked the chain gang, and was positioned near the Bentley bench. The chain gang generally heard comments from the opponent's bench throughout the game, but did their best to keep their mouths shut. Sparky, named for his quick temper, came unglued in the face of Bentley's Coach Duncan, feeling the attack was intended to injure his son.

The penalty appeared obvious, causing warranted remarks from the Montrose coaches, players and fans. It wasn't a funny play at all, and Aaron could've been easily injured. Since he wasn't, the crew heightened the attack in super slow motion, and laughed. Special effects were used to duplicate all 350 pounds of Tiny as he crossed the line. The crew moaned each time they replayed it, anticipating the impact. They each personally felt the weight of big, bad Tiny as he jumped on Aaron, making the rookie quarterback look like a midget. The crew turned the clip into a highlight film classic.

The Rams faced **Bendle** next, gaining confidence in their abilities as a team. Clolinger built on that when he selected the next motto:

'Let's Not Limit Ourselves In What We Can Do'

Noel Dean left Bendle to take the head coaching position at Lowell High School, leaving Jeff Setzke as Bendle's new head coach. Setzke's loyalties resided with the Bendle Tigers, even though he still lived in the town of Montrose.

Hodge passed to Crusher with 2:32 left in the first quarter to break a scoreless tie, then passed to Visser who plowed across with :46 seconds left in the half. Bendle's defense was tough, holding the Rams to just 50 rushing yards at the intermission. Reinhart was livid at the half, and gave the offense a wake-up call. They all realized that two touchdowns meant it was still anyone's game. But the Rams came out charged to open the third quarter. Jorod raced 65 yards to score less then two minutes after the intermission. He made a three yard plunge for his second TD with five minutes left in the third. Hodge closed the score with a 10 yard run in the fourth.

Tommy Gun kept his right shoe tied as tight as he could, but it still didn't feel tight enough. He retied it until his circulation felt like it was practically cut off. He paced off his steps, three back and two over, then swayed his arms back and forth until he found his zone. His eyes never left the tee, while he used his peripheral vision to watch the play unfold. As soon as the ball hit Casciano's hands, he knew he had to go. He was four-for-four when he kicked his fourth PAT, to close the game '35-0.'

The defense played a great game. Loafman led with 11 tackles, followed by Pollard and Woody with nine and seven hits. The Rams disallowed Bendle to get past the 50 yard line, holding them to 67 total yards. The victory over Bendle guaranteed a share of the GEC League Championship. The Rams were one game ahead of Goodrich in the league race with one game left. But instead of celebrating, the team knelt down midfield after the game. No one spoke a word for well over a minute, forcing everyone to feel the silence. They didn't smile or appear happy while they listened to Coach Reinhart, who was so upset with his team's performance that he bit his lip.

The Rams didn't execute well and racked up 12 penalties. Reinhart screamed, 'We can't execute that way if we want to do anything down the road! We took a step back tonight, but that may be good for us. It put us back in our place! We'll correct our mistakes and go back to work in practice come Monday. We're a good football team and we'll keep working at it.'

Montrose didn't feel good about their win when they walked off the field, focusing on the fact that they had more work to do. Families and friends patiently waited for the team to complete their traditional march from the field to the bus. They felt awkward saying 'good game' when their serious faces held undeserving expressions in spite of the five-touchdown shutout.

The media interviewed the Rams during Byron week after they secured another League Championship with one game left. Reinhart admitted, 'The longer the streak continues, the harder it will be to maintain it.'

Teams like Bendle and Goodrich followed the same program that Montrose had used for years, and were closing the gap. The Rams used to be able to outwork teams for a win, but that wasn't the case anymore. Other teams copied what made Montrose successful, becoming more competitive. Most players embraced the challenge of keeping their streak alive, but the pressure of the streak kept some athletes from participating in Montrose Football. Those kids outright admitted to coaches, 'They didn't want to be the ones to lose.'

The players wanted to keep the streak alive through '97, giving the Rams a chance to break the Hudson's state record of 81 regular season wins. Each team felt responsible to keep the tradition up. Nobody wanted to be the first team to lose, and felt the obligation to keep up the success. Loaf didn't want to look ahead that far. Like his teammates, he wanted to remain focused on the goals they had set for the post-season in '96, but the press constantly asked about the streak.

The video started the **Byron** game as a sadness engulfed the Tech Lab. It was the last home game for the Rams. They appropriately selected one of Motley Crew's greatest hits, 'Home Sweet Home,' which serenaded them as the weekly motto rolled across the screen:

'If It's Worth Doing - It's Worth Doing Well'

It was a cold October, Friday night when the teams took the field. Hodge watched himself lead the offense and commented, 'That was the only game I ever used a hand warmer.' The crew watched their heads bob on the screen as they walked from the smoke tunnel to the goal posts.

Visser scored twice in the first quarter, then made a third touchdown with :34 seconds left. The Rams closed the half with a score of 20-0. Montrose opened the third period with a 68 yard drive that Hodge capped with a 16 yard TD. Then Reinhart pulled the senior starters out one at a time, as fans acknowledged their due in honor of their final league game.

Hodge, Crusher, Brad, Harris, Flaco, Bulldog, Visser, and the other seniors felt bittersweet as they walked off the field; happy for the recognition, yet sad that it represented closure.

The Eagles avoided a shutout when they scored a pair of late game TD's against the Montrose reserves on long runs of 77 and 75 yards. Other then that, the Eagles managed just five first downs. The action was spread between ten Rams that carried the ball. Winston served as their workhorse while Loafman, Pollard, and Flaco spearheaded the defense. Tommy Gun made a 31 yard field goal to end the score '33-14.'

It marked the ninth straight GEC League Title for the Rams, breaking an area record. Their win also marked their 79th consecutive win, leaving the Rams just two wins shy of the state record. The seniors contributed all they could to the regular season winning streak; it was up to the juniors to make their mark in '97. The football streak generated plenty of excitement for the school, and marked a positive image for Montrose. Opponents couldn't help but notice the support the Montrose fans provided. A happy head coach smiled when he gathered his Rams midfield one final time during the regular season, 'Now you can enjoy this.'

It was the last time they played on their home field, since the post-season took them on the road. Crusher yelled, 'Now it's time for the real season to begin.' The team held their helmets and modestly celebrated their outright League Championship, and their undefeated season.

Hodge and Visser lingered in the center of the field after everyone had left. Viss looked up at the empty stands, while soaking in the new team room and the smoke tunnel one final time. Hodge stared at the north goal post, then hesitated in order to control his emotions before he spoke. He could see his breath when he said, 'I feel so weird right now. It doesn't seem like we just played our last game in Montrose.'

Viss understood completely and shook his head. They talked for awhile, realizing how long that they had been friends. Football was an integral part of who they were. Even though they had playoffs to look forward to, they sensed a conclusion to a very special part of their lives.

The Rams drew Frankenmuth for the first round. Painful memories of their 12-19 loss under blizzard conditions from the '95 playoffs resurfaced; no one could ever forget that game. Reinhart felt confident that his Rams improved immensely since the Eagles dominated Montrose in a pre-season scrimmage. Frankenmuth and Montrose ran similar veer offenses. Reinhart's offense may not appear as flashy, but the Rams were diversified in their passing and running game. They felt their offensive line was physically stronger and looked good. The Montrose defense was designed for the linebackers to make the tackles anchored by Loafman and Pollard. The Montrose secondary was tested throughout the season and controlled their opponent's ground game.

The Rams gathered in the wrestling room Friday night and watched *'Happy Gilmore,'* relaxing before their first playoff game. Dads prepared a team breakfast for the coaches and players at the school on Saturday morning, appearing as anxious for the game to start as their sons were.

Coach Reinhart came up to Brian Tripp and spoke without warning. 'You get to say the prayer Tripp.'

Tripp came from a Catholic family and had listened to many a prayer in his day. He was a fast thinker with a good wit when he added a different twist, 'Dear God, thank you for this food, and let us kick Frankenmuth to hell. Amen.'

The team laughed and cheered, 'Amen. Yeah. Let's kick their butts!'

Hopefully, God understood just how important this game was to the Rams. Then the motto for **Frankenmuth** appeared on the screen:

'If You Want To Accomplish Your Dream, You Must Live Your Dream'

Top Gun's 'Danger Zone' blasted the room, energizing the video crew as visions of Tom Cruise and fighter planes popped into their heads. The crew specifically picked that song since they lost on Frankenmuth's turf in `95, and had to drive back into their town and reenter the danger zone again. Montrose wanted revenge and Kenny Loggins set the intensity.

Montrose fans came out in strong numbers, joining the customary caravan. They left their small-decorated town and headed the short 25 miles to Frankenmuth. A police escort led them eight miles east on M-57 to the neighboring town of Clio. The Clio Police cooperated by setting up a roadblock at the main light in town, to keep the caravan together. The special teams' bus led the way, but the driver confused everyone when she carefully maneuvered completely around the police roadblock in the center of town, instead of making a left turn. The second bus that carried the team and coaches, made the northbound turn. Police motioned for the huge caravan to also turn north, while fans wondered, *Where did the first bus go?*

The superstitious team naturally became paranoid, since the buses had never been split up on the way to a game before. They didn't want anything to jinx them. It was a playoff game; they didn't dare change anything. Players on the second bus questioned Aaron, 'Hey, where's your mom going?'

Aaron didn't have a clue until he heard his mom's shaky voice come across the two-way radio. 'Tell Coach Reinhart that I'm so sorry. This is the way I always go to Frankenmuth.'

She wasn't aware of the shortcut and wondered why the police had set the roadblock up a mile early. When nobody followed her, she became worried. Reinhart sensed the anxiety in her voice and replied, 'We'll pull over and wait for you on Dixie Highway.'

The team knew Aaron's mom well and enjoyed teasing her about dodging the police escort, which was not a simple task with a bus. The northbound bus pulled off the busy road; the confused caravan started to follow. It became dangerous when puzzled motorists farther back in the caravan, wondered what to do. Reinhart came off the bus and motioned the caravan to keep moving. The special teams bus finally caught up and pulled off the road, then neither bus could get back on because of the long caravan. Fans honked and waved as they passed the buses, wondering why they had stopped. *Did they have bus trouble? Was a player sick? Did they forget some equipment?* The players didn't talk on the bus, but anxiously watched the caravan, recognizing their own families and friends. They wanted to shout, *Hey we're the team. Let us out so we can play!*

The caravan tailgated while they waited in the parking lot, cheering when the Montrose buses finally arrived. Fans welcomed the partially sunny, but cold November afternoon as they packed into Frankenmuth's stadium. It felt tropically warm compared to their last visit in '95.

Hodge saw so many former Montrose players from the '95 Team at the game and told the squad, 'We need to play this game for them.'

The Rams fought hard trying to set the tone, but Frankenmuth's defense only allowed four yards on their first five plays. Hodge stayed on the field and moved to defensive back. He ran a slant and went down with his opponent, catching his arm under a 'Muth player. Crusher played end and watched the 'Muth player grab Hodge's arm and pull it back. Crusher was gutsy. He thought the opponent might break Hodge's arm and smacked the 'Muth player on the helmet as he towered over him. If Crusher was heavier, black, and stacked with gold chains he would resemble Mr. T. He sent a message, 'Don't mess with my teammates fool, especially my quarterback!'

The official watched the process and didn't give Crusher nor the 'Muth player a roughing penalty. But somehow in that mess, Hodge ended up with a pass interference flag. The 'Muth player, Crusher, and Hodge actually became football teammates at Ferris State in '97, and later laughed about that play. On their second possession, Hodge rolled out to the left on a sprint. He didn't have anyone to pass to, but knew that Visser would open up, so he waited then threw to him near the sideline. After the play, Reinhart screamed at his quarterback, 'NEXT TIME, RUN THE FREAKING BALL HODGE!'

On the very next play, Hodge burst around left end and exploded for 60 yards. The quarterback had his own style when he held the ball. Hodge used quick, short jerks with his arms, back and forth, while exercising the veer option until he broke free to score. He laughed as he watched his reaction on the screen, remembering how excited he felt at that moment. Hodge tried to think of something clever to do in the endzone before the guys came up to celebrate his playoff score. The crew watched as Hodge held his arm straight then pointed three times, before he gave the ball to the official.

Casciano asked, 'Why did you do that?'

Hodge laughed at himself, 'I don't know. It was the only think I could think of at the time.'

The crowd roared after the Rams scored. Tommy Gun felt his leg start to shake. He knew it was an important kick; they always were during playoffs. He convinced himself, *You gotta kick it now. You can do it. You've got your lucky black T-shirt on, (the same 1989 Detroit Pistons Bad Boys Champs T-shirt that his brother Tim wore when he kicked). You've got your lucky socks on, the ones you wore all year. You can make this.* He did, and the Rams were ahead 7-0.

'Muth scored on their next possession during the second quarter to tie the game. The Rams answered when they drove down to the two, then Hodge took it in, putting the Rams up 13-7.

Adam Powell, the Montrose center, jumped on a Frankenmuth fumble at their 40 yard line. Five minutes later, the Rams quickly took advantage of the gift by bolting over from the one yard line. The two-point conversion pass failed, but the Rams were up 19-7 with just over two minutes to play in the half.

The Rams kicked off, then caused a fumble after the Eagles returned it 13 yards. The Rams recovered, and heard their fans go crazy. It was a big turning point for the Rams who marched nine plays into field goal range. With :22 left, Tommy Gun delighted the crowd with a 24 yard field goal.

The momentum shifted as the teams departed for the intermission with the Rams up 22-7. Instead of a tied ball game, the Rams found themselves up by nine points as a result of two critical Eagle fumbles directly before the half.

The crew became emotionally charged, while they soaked in the lyrics of their favorite Quiet Riot hit, *'Winners Take All.'* It held a special connotation, since the team listened to it during every pre-game ritual. The song reinforced their bond to stand together and not fall.

The Eagles found themselves in more trouble after botching two plays after the half. The Rams covered 72 yards and eight plays on their second drive. Hodge ran a 38-veer pass, Richardson ran the drag, then Hodge hit Powell in the seam for a 20 yard scoring pass. Hodge was a mobile quarterback who made accurate throws and limited possible mistakes. He served as a fuse, making his offense look extremely good. Tommy Gun's PAT was good, and the students cheered, 'Tommy GUN'... 'Tommy GUN.'

But Hodge became upset on their next series when his fourth quarter pass was intercepted. On the very next play, Casciano came right back on defense, grabbed an interception, and returned it to the Frankenmuth 39. Casciano's arm took a hard hit from a 'Muth player's knee on the play, and he thought it was broke. Later, he learned that it was a bad sprain, but it hurt like hell during the rest of the game.

The Rams made things happen. Hodge ran down the sideline, then pitched to Richardson who scored on a 44 yard run. Hodge's athletic ability was exceptional, but what gave him merit was his levelheaded demeanor. He could admirably stay calm in a crisis.

The Rams recovered the on-side kick, then Jorod exploded on the Rams first down for a 51 yard TD. Tommy Gun kicked his fourth successful PAT, along with a field goal. It was the best game that he ever played. He felt that he could've made his fifth attempt, but the snap was high. The Eagles scored one final TD at the end of their rematch, making the score '43-21'.

That time, Montrose advanced to the regional playoff round in '96, instead of Frankenmuth. The Rams savored the taste of sweet revenge. Landing on the flip side of the coin provided a pleasing redemption for the seniors, as they shook hands with the Eagles. Hodge made direct eye contact with his opponents as he worked his way through the line. He easily distinguished the seniors. Their faces held a deeper sadness, a realization that for them it was over. It made Hodge feel relieved, yet thankful that he wouldn't be the one sitting in the stands the following Saturday afternoon.

The room became extremely quiet when the soothing voice of Quiet Riot sang, *'Life's Been Good, Life's Been Bad.'* The Rams couldn't catch a post-season break and faced **Detroit St. Martin dePorres**. For the third time in five years, Montrose found itself pitted against what was considered 'the best team in the state' in their class, maybe any class, before reaching the Pontiac Silverdome.

The pairing was included in Son of Swami's predictions from the Detroit Free Press that forecasted 'dePorres 22 – Montrocity 20.' Detroit St. Martin dePorres was the top ranked team, the returning State Champions. It marked their 16th playoff trip, which set a new state record. Detroit dePorres previously won a record nine State Championships, winning *each time* they reached the semifinals. With that history, Montrose knew dePorres would be tough to beat.

Hodge mulled over an article that referred to dePorres as being wary of the Montrose explosive offense because the Rams could throw, run, and use power football. dePorres surrendered an average of only 6.3 points per game, and wanted to keep control of the option game the Rams used. The article stated two of the state's best quarterbacks would go head-to-head. It provided Hodge with an extra ounce of confidence, while reaffirming his belief in the Rams even though they were the definite underdog. Hodge cut out the article and kept it in his main folder, so that he could read it over-and-over during every class. Even though the quarterback was a good student, Hodge couldn't even think about academics during dePorres week. *Football ruled.*

The coaching staff critiqued Detroit dePorres game films for hours before showing them to the team. Hodge tried to block out the overall size of the dePorres linemen and the fact that quarterback, Kevin Glenn, was being wooed in football by the University of Michigan, among other top colleges. Goodrich lost to dePorres in round one by a similar score of their loss to Montrose during the regular season. It gave Hodge a positive angle, so he intentionally overlooked the many other factors that contribute to how teams match up. Reinhart tried to compress their fears and told his defense. 'We're definitely the underdog but we're not afraid of them. We can play with them.'

Joshua was interrupted as he sat in class writing a paper on Friday before the dePorres game. The secretary called him to the office. 'You need to get to the hospital Josh, your girlfriend's there.'

She must've noticed the shocked look on the senior's face and added, 'Dont worry Josh. It's probably just false labor.'

Josh stopped by his locker then popped his head into class. He told Hodge, 'I gotta get to the hospital. Tell Aaron to come.'

Aaron was Josh's cousin and had promised to be there for support. Hodge and Aaron left school during last hour. Both walked into the maternity ward fully clad in Montrose Football uniforms, except for their cleats. They couldn't help but stand out with Aaron wearing #18, and Hodge at his side donned in #16. They actually looked out of place while they gazed at the newborn baby. Both felt thankful that little Josh had already been born and didn't turn it into an all day ordeal. While they were eating lunch at school, he found his way into the world and was born at 12:17 PM. How considerate, he wouldn't make his new uncles late for pre-game practice.

No one would miss a playoff practice. When Josh didn't show up, Reinhart asked, 'Where the hell is Haney?'

Aaron replied, 'He's at the hospital.'

At first Coach didn't believe them and thought Aaron was just covering for him, then realized he had a case of his own pre-game nerves. *Everyone did.* After a good practice, the Rams gathered Friday night to watch the video, *'The Last Boy Scout.'* By the time they left the school, the team felt pumped and ready to face dePorres, the defending State Champs.

Hodge went home and flipped through his '95 football highlight book until he found the Vince Lombardi page, *'What It Takes To Be No.1.'* He found a deeper meaning each time he read one of Lombardi's quotes. Hodge focused on his favorite one, while he mentally prepared himself to face dePorres.

> *'Every time a football player goes out to ply his trade he's got to play from the ground up, from the soles of his feet right up to his head. Every inch of him has to play. Some guys play with their heads. That's okay. You've got to be smart to be No.1 in any business. But more important, you've got to play with your heart- with every fiber of your body. If you're lucky enough to find a guy with a lot of head and a lot of heart, he's never going to come off the field second.'*
>
> Vince Lombardi

Many fans paid the $10 fee to ride chartered buses and avoid the drive through inner city Detroit. Montrose players and fans felt uncomfortable, while gazing at the abandoned graffiti-covered brick buildings from the bus windows. The small town of Montrose suddenly seemed like a safe haven, protected from the hard street life of inner city Detroit.

The November temperature required fans to don winter coats. The Michigan sky already held a gray hue, a dismal overcast that lasted for months. The Rams' mascot thought she heard thunder while she warmed-up with the cheerleaders. But when she turned around, she noticed it was the dePorres team bus pulling into the stadium. The Eagles made their appearance known by pounding on the bus ceiling to the rhythmic beat of loud rap music when they arrived at McCabe Field.

As soon as the motto appeared on the screen, the Tech Lab fell completely silent, as the familiar gut wrenching feeling returned.

'Proper Mental Focus Will Make Your Dreams A Reality'

VanHalen's hit, *'Dream Another Dream This Dream is Over,'* crooned while the tape showed the Rams warming up on McCabe Field. The Rams found themselves checking out the players as they stepped off the bus. Visser thought, *They're trying to intimidate us by having their biggest guys get off first!* The same sentiment crossed Hodge's mind, *My God these guys are huge!*

The Rams heard that a fax had been posted in the Eagles locker room, listing their scores. Its intent was to serve as an incentive to prevent Montrose from scoring that many points against dePorres.

The game was on. The Rams gained a glimmer of momentum and surprised dePorres when their defense stopped the Eagles on three-and-out, turned around and scored. Within the first five minutes, Visser took a pitch from Hodge then burst 55 yards to the endzone. The Rams gained a morsel of confidence after drawing first blood and naturally thought, *Maybe we have a chance after all!*

Crusher experienced the same feeling when they played Frankenmuth and told Hodge, 'We can actually do this, we can hang with them!'

Hodge was just as pumped, 'I know. We can fight these guys!'

The Rams had dePorres stopped on fourth down. Glenn seemed to be able to scramble forever, before throwing a 13 yard scoring pass three minutes later. Detroit dePorres went up 7-8. The Eagles moved the ball down the field, using their 6'8" player as an easy target. He towered over the Montrose defense who became frustrated after watching him run midfield, then put his hands up for an easy catch like Shaq on the basketball court.

The defense shared its frustration in the huddle and asked Coach D, 'How do we defend that?'

They appeared even bigger in person than on film. The Eagles had five exceptionally super athletes that worked behind a line averaging 270 pounds. Two-hundred and seventy pounds! Detroit dePorres plunged over from the two, just :16 seconds into the second quarter to move ahead 7-14.

Reading keys became a challenge for the defense. The Rams could barely see where the ball carrier was, once dePorres' huge line stood up. Dauber played defensive line for the first time on Varsity. He went up against a 280 pound dePorres opponent, and couldn't do anything. Dauber tried to spin, then tried to run around him only to get knocked down. Dauber's opponent laid all 280 pounds on him, then helplessly watched Glenn get by.

Casciano joined the punt return team on the field, yelling 'GEDO.' He caught the ball and faced right, but kicked all the way left. He was supposed to run slightly to the right, but ran straight instead. Casciano felt the force of a dePorres opponent grab his facemask, then drill him in the stomach, causing him to lose control. Casciano's scratchy voice tried to yell 'facemask,' but it sounded more like a whisper as he fell to the ground. He was instantly rewarded, if you could call it that, when the official pitched his yellow penalty flag.

The Rams had never faced such an undisciplined team as dePorres, who received 11 penalty flags in the first half. Hodge thought the Rams could capitalize on that, but dePorres had energy, muscles, and size. They were so talented that they simply played over their mistakes. The score held at 7-14 until late in the first half, while the Rams experienced the toughest game any of them had ever played. But hanging with the powerful top ranked Detroit St. Martin dePorres, seemed to generate stamina for the Rams. Montrose honestly felt they had a chance to win -- with a little luck, and everyone on the field giving extraordinary effort.

The Montrose defense exerted everything they had, and managed to push dePorres back to fourth-and-20. But they only became disheartened after dePorres broke loose on a long run and scored with just over two minutes left in the half. The Rams needed to calm down and play their game. A desperate hush fell over the Montrose crowd on their next possession, when Aaron fumbled the ball on the exchange from Hodge. The talented Glenn, who now played defensive back, picked it up and showed off his tremendous speed. He raced 50 yards to score with :33 seconds before the intermission.

Hodge thought, *Damn. Glenn is unstoppable.* Under other circumstances Hodge would've enjoyed playing defensive safety, but that game was too intense. He missed that side of the ball most of the season after battling a pesky shoulder injury. It kept him from the two-way duty he had as an outstanding back in '94 and '95. The Rams needed Hodge to run the offense, set the tone on defense, and spread his indomitable will to special teams. That day he played dePorres with his heart, which felt big enough to carry the entire team.

Montrose learned how quickly momentum can shift when they broke for the intermission. Two touchdowns transpired in :121 seconds, leaving the field 7-30, instead of the desired 7-14.

Montrose players gathered in a white tent that the Football Club hauled down as a makeshift locker room. The coaching staff realized what a great team dePorres was, possessing all of the required tools. Their size and speed made either a passing or ground game difficult for the Rams. The game plan shifted to special plays. Reinhart motivated them the best that he could. He finished his half-time talk by saying, 'We're still in this ball game. Nothing less then 100% is expected from everyone!'

Reinhart had his Rams pumped to come out and score, make the two-point conversion, and surprise dePorres with an on-side kick. The Rams piled hands in their huddle. They committed to each other that no matter what the score was -- no one would give up.

Hodge took the snap and ran a screen. Aaron thought, *They've probably watched film and realize that the only time I go in as a running back is when I get the ball.* That time Aaron ran through the line for the screen as a decoy, then slid when he hit the mud. He quickly looked up, saw Hodge, and thought, 'Forget the decoy, I gotta get up. Hodge has no one to throw to!'

Hodge saw the gigantic #55 head straight at him and quickly thought, 'Aaron get up, Aaron get up.'

Aaron popped up and felt the chunks of mud in his palms. He tried to break apart and crumble the chunks of much while he ran. Aaron turned just as his quarterback threw the pass. Hodge thought, *Here you go buddy. Please catch it.* Aaron grabbed the pass on the run, thankful that his muddy palms acted like glue and actually helped the ball stick to his palms. He jolted down the sideline, like a deer being chased by a cheetah, before being atrociously tackled.

Next, Hodge hit Richardson with a 50 yard pass, then watched as he got tackled just short of the goal line. With eight minutes left in the third, Hodge gave his squad hope when he bolted over on a one yard plunge, closing the gap to 13-30. The Rams' conversion failed, but not their determination. They went for the on-side kick, just as they had discussed during the half.

The Rams refused to quit. The Montrose kickoff team lined up with a renewed spirit as they broke from the huddle. Tommy Gun kicked a perfect on-side kick. The Rams honestly believed it traveled the required 10 yards, then used their quickness to pounce on the pigskin. Several Rams surrounded the ball and jumped up to celebrate, then became instantly discouraged when the officials ruled otherwise and penalized the Rams.

Harris thought, *Damn. It was the break we needed but wouldn't get.*

The Eagles scored on their next two possessions. A huge dePorres defender laid a mean, questionable block on Woody, enough to knock him out cold with a concussion. Reinhart walked across the field to check on Woody, but never made it that far. He was so frustrated by the lack of a call and stopped to tell the closest official. Reinhart's frustration continued when he unloaded on the next two officials. By the time he reached midfield, Woody was being transferred to the sideline.

Richardson also had a concussion, but managed to make a dive on fourth down. His effort kept the drive alive for the determined Rams who bravely battled back. Hodge got a pass off to Visser, then immediately felt a sharp pain when the helmet of the enormous #55 smeared directly into his rib cage. Hodge went down while fans held their breath, as they watched the injured quarterback lay on McCabe Field.

Aaron watched intensely from the sideline and selfishly thought, *Please don't get hurt Hodge, then I'll have to take the helm and face these monsters!*

Hodge slowly emerged from the ground, trying to get his breath back as he slowly made his way to the huddle. He had time to get the next play off, then Coach called a timeout to check on his quarterback. Watching his squad continue to take such a physical beating, frustrated Reinhart, but he did his best to encourage them. The second year head coach wanted to advance as much as his players did, but there was only so much they could do under the circumstances.

Parents privately surrendered their hopes for a State Championship in exchange for healthy kids. Near the end of the game, parents just wanted it to be over. They simply didn't want anymore concussions or serious injuries.

Hodge called another trick play, then handed off to Casciano who pitched to Aaron. But Casciano's sprained arm wasn't fully recovered from the Frankenmuth game, and he couldn't straighten it out completely. He watched in horror as the pitch traveled over Aaron's head and thought, *Damn. We practiced that pitch a hundred times and we never dropped it. Why now?*

In desperation, the Rams tried their 'brother-in-laws left' play. Hodge and Aaron cut up field, but the quick dePorres defenders were on them like crows pecking road kill. Hodge quickly ran back to stay in pitch position, but Aaron couldn't pitch to him and they both ended up backpedaling. Even the best laid plans went to hell fast. Nothing worked. There seemed to be no getting around the mighty dePorres Eagles.

Bulldog tackled his opponent and showed remarkable heart when his 5'6" body refused to let go. His teammates watched Bulldog hang on to his opponent, who almost doubled his size and strength. *But Bulldog never gave up.*

It was late in the fourth when Hodge called a 12 pass weak. Powell bounced off his opponent and fumbled the ball, before dePorres picked it off. Hodge played safety and ran after the Eagles back-up quarterback. He tackled his opponent, then started to swear.

Coach D and Hodge knew each other so well after being together for three years. Players knew they were in trouble whenever Coach D called them pal or buddy, but neither word was heard that day. *Not that day. Not during that game.* Coach D recognized that Hodge was out of character and pulled him out for a few plays before he got into trouble.   Coach D adamantly announced, 'All right juniors, let's get ready for next year. You're goin' in!'

The Rams played with integrity and never quit, even against seemingly insurmountable odds. They used the best of their abilities, giving everything they had when the deck was stacked high against them. *Integrity was earned.*

Hodge looked at the scoreboard late in the fourth. The score was '13-46' and they were out of time. The Rams were so busy playing the game, they didn't realize they couldn't catch up. Hodge finally comprehended the inevitable; the Rams could *not* win this ball game. The quarterback prepared to call the play in the huddle, then felt his body shake uncontrollably. He battled to prevent fear from monopolizing his intuition. The quarterback used every ounce of control that he could muster, in order to hold back the gut wrenching feeling that brewed inside. Hodge tried to gain control before facing his teammates.

Harris felt his stomach churn and took deep breaths, trying to generate some positive energy.   He couldn't give up or give in under any circumstances.

Admitting defeat with five minutes to go was pure torture. Casciano sat on the bench with his injured arm during the final quarter. He felt helpless when he couldn't help his teammates. Jorod felt powerless while he stood next to Casciano on the sideline, until he couldn't control his emotions any longer.

Hodge felt the weight of the world on his shoulders, as he prepared to call their final play. He placed all of the blame on himself, and could barely relay the play in the huddle. His voice cracked as he looked at his best friends; choking on his own words. 'This is the last play we'll ever run together.'

His teammates felt unsure of how to respond after watching Hodge perform as their tremendously strong leader the entire season. He was their friend, as well as their quarterback. They respected how much he cared and how hard that he played. No one blamed Hodge; only himself. Hodge's unconquerable spirit made the squad want to give everything for their final play. They wouldn't quit or go down without a fight to the bitter end. *Determination was visible.*

The Rams left their huddle, thankful that their facemasks provided somewhat of a barrier from the outside world. Linemen took positions, giving each other a concluding glance before Hodge called their closing play, like war buddies about to jump out of the foxhole. They were prepared to give everything left in them, one last time, knowing there was no way in hell they could pull out a victory. Hodge swallowed hard, hearing an unfamiliar sever in his own voice as he called the cadence. The play unfolded and seemed to move in slow motion, while the Rams acted out their final scene.

No one quit until they felt the stab of the final buzzer. All too quickly, the clock ran out and the unpleasant monotone echoed in Hodge's ears. He rolled over in the mud, and stared at the grayish-blue Michigan sky. Hodge felt an unfamiliar ache in the pit of his stomach. 'It's over. It's really over.'

Crusher helped him up, 'C'mon Hodge.'

The Montrose Rams shook hands with the dePorres Eagles and wished them luck. The Detroit St. Martin dePorres Eagles were crowned State Champions two weeks later. No one could stop them.

Reinhart gathered his Rams one final time in the center of the field, commending them for their ceaseless effort. He knew it would've taken a perfect game, as well as some luck, to beat dePorres. It just didn't happen. Visser rushed for 113 yards on 19 carries, while dePorres held the rest of the Rams to 37 yards on 16 tries.

Montrose should appreciate that they forced Detroit dePorres to go to their second set offense. But the Eagles played their best game of the season. In spite of 300 penalty yards, they ended the game with 507 total offensive yards.

When Coach D walked off McCabe Field, he blamed himself for not defending them better. Witnessing the same painful final scene, year-after-year, wore him down. The only thing that changed each year was a new cast of characters. They came in different shapes and sizes, but their common denominator was that they all had huge hearts and an invincible determination. Self-doubt consumed the defensive coach and he wondered, *Should I hang up coaching the game I love so much? Will we ever break away from these private schools and the benefits they possess?* It was tough to avoid feeling their deep pain. He knew how much it all meant, but facing their anguished expressions became harder each year.

Coach D felt his chest tighten when Lyman hugged him. 'I learned so much from you. I want to thank your for moving me to special teams and giving me a chance.'

Other defensive players tugged at his heart when they piped in, telling Coach D how much that he meant to them. It was all he needed to refuel his desire. Coach D knew he'd be back again in '97.

The familiar tranquil guitar refocused the crew's attention back to the screen. Even though Bob Seger wasn't in the Rock and Roll Hall of Fame yet, he was a favorite on every highlight film. Seger's rasping voice and healing lyrics reached the essence of their souls, as he sang the comforting words of *'The Famous Final Scene:'*

> *'. . . Like a guest who stayed too long,*
> *Now it's finally time to leave.*
> *Take it calmly and serene.*
> *It's the famous final scene'*

The film crew watched their own tormented expressions through their helmets as the camera closely zoomed in. They watched their fans reach out and touch them, in an effort to ease their ache. Reliving the heartbreaking scene just a week later, forced the knots to revisit their throats. Watching it on the screen, felt just as agonizing as it did that Saturday they walked off McCabe Field.

The Rams escaped to their makeshift tent, where they could say their distraught senior good-byes in private. The white canvas walls couldn't hide their heartfelt sobs, as parents and girlfriends reluctantly waited nearby. Hodges' rigid jawbone exposed how miserable he felt for not leading the Rams to accomplish their dream and blamed himself. *Maybe if I had done some things differently, we could've won instead of feeling like we just got the snot beat out of us.* Hodge hugged each one of his teammates and commended them all; 'You never gave up!'

He watched them get knocked down and get right back up and go. Everyone tried so hard . . . maybe too hard. Detroit dePorres taught them a few lessons that their sore muscles wouldn't forget. They fell short of victory and tried to stand tall on pride, but it was tough. Many tears were shed under the white tent that day. The Montrose Rams once again faced the difficulty of closure, without accomplishing their dream.

All of the coaches tearfully embraced the seniors, while they shifted down the senior line, followed by the underclassmen. Like physicians who tried to harden themselves to death, coaches tried to protect their own feelings and not surrender their emotions. Coaches had faced the familiar scene so many times, yet it still seemed like an impossible task after seeing their tormenting expressions. They shared a season together and would miss this group of seniors. The only bright side to such a dreary ending, was that no one was seriously injured.

Brian Tripp felt crushed; it was difficult for him to realize that it was over. The coaches taught him to be responsible and to accept things for what they are and never give up. Even though he only played football for one year, the guys all felt like his brothers. They knew each other so well and were closer than most real brothers were. Tripp knew that he would remember his football experience for a lifetime.

Harris tearfully looked around at his best friends, feeling strange. Seeing everyone so distraught made him feel like the best time of his life had just ended. The guys had all accepted him back, and helped him work through the death of his father. They were like one big family that grew up together. Suddenly, everyone had to move out and go his separate way. He wasn't ready for that send off. As much as the loss hurt, Harris was glad that he decided to play football; he couldn't imagine where he would be without it. He knew he wouldn't play football in college and later told the staff that he wanted to coach with them; a commitment that he carried out for the next five years. It made Coach Coon extremely proud.

Bulldog knew that he would attend college and have a bright future, yet at that moment he felt that his life had no other purpose. Even though he had three brothers at home, he knew that he would miss the brotherhood he shared with his squad. Sunday afternoons without films and food would never be the same.

Flaco looked around at the commotion and felt an empty sadness seize his gut. It left him feeling numb.

Richardson felt football had been his life for so long. He knew that he would be lost without it. The guys would still be friends and play basketball and baseball, but it wouldn't be the same. Nothing compared to football.

Hodge felt odd to be on the receiving end of the hugs. He had been the one who comforted the seniors on the `94 and `95 Teams. Now, it was difficult to grasp that *his* senior season had just ended. He embraced one of his best friends, senior Tony Thornburg. He respected that Thornburg worked as hard as anyone did all season even though he didn't play much. It made Hodge wonder, *Could I do that?*

Loafman clutched him, 'I'm so sorry Hodge. I want you to know that I tried as hard as I could.'

Hodge knew that Loaf put forth his best effort; he always did. What he didn't know at the time was that Loafman fought dePorres with a sprained ankle. Hodge pulled his head up, while his anguished face looked the junior directly in the eyes. He forced words through painful sobs, 'I know Loaf. Just do it next year!'

Loafman made All-State Honorable Mention for the second consecutive year, and would be back with the Rams in `97. Hodge and Crusher made the All-State First Team, honors they took to Ferris State University where they had football careers with the Bulldogs.

It was difficult for Hodge to face Aaron, whose face held the same distraught look of Loaf and Woody. It was as if the juniors knew how badly Hodge wanted to go to the Dome, and understood his pain. Once again, Hodge recoiled to being the comforter, finding himself reassuring Aaron. Aaron searched for the right words to say to his best friend. He finally spoke above the knot in his chest, 'I just wish we could play forever so it wouldn't have to end.'

Hodge couldn't talk, but nodded his head in agreement until sobs consumed both of them. The emotional aftermath left Hodge with a throbbing headache on the silent bus ride home, that seemed endless. He briefly spoke with Coach Reinhart. They compared Detroit dePorres to Orchard Lake St. Marys. Then he stretched out his legs in the aisle of the bus to prevent them from cramping.

Richardson felt drained, while he dealt with his own sense of loss. He was usually an upbeat person, and wondered if life would ever seem fun again. A while later, he caught a glimpse of Crusher's head as it banged hard against the window on a bumpy road. Crusher was embarrassed and quickly glanced around to see if anyone had noticed. Richardson couldn't help but smile to himself. His grin shattered his own sad mood; a welcoming sign that time would heal. He wouldn't stay down for long.

It was different for Josh; everything changed for him that Friday. He wondered why some people felt he shouldn't play in the dePorres game, which ended up being one of his best. He didn't know if it related to the extra excitement of becoming a dad, or if he was just pumped to be in the playoffs. Having his baby born the day before, helped Josh deal with the loss a bit easier than the others. He didn't have time to dwell on the game for long. Josh needed to get to the hospital and bring little Joshua home after the game.

The theme from '*Top Gun*' played again while the crew watched a recap of their season. The high school band formed a tunnel at a home game. The Rams ran in slow motion and watched Hodge charge through the paper that was tightly wrapped around the hoop. The thrill of Friday night football returned as he watched himself throw the paper aside, then formed the jampile. They all looked so happy, young, and full of life.

The great plays of the season recapped Nick Powell's one arm catch, Visser's long run when he was almost taken down, and the night Tiny squished Aaron. Then the dePorres game reappeared. Hodge felt his eyes swell with tears as he watched the Rams walk two-by-two. The tape changed to super slow motion as players jumped on the jampile, oblivious that they were about to play their last game together. The lyrics that Kenny Rogers sang, captured the integrity of that game. His words reminded them of how hard it was to stop the dream that they all shared. The crew felt exhausted after spending the entire weekend producing their highlight film. But they finished it, feeling good about the end product. Being together with the guys and laughing again was refreshingly therapeutic. Reliving the sadness of their final game offered a form of closure to the sport they all loved.

Hodge went home and plopped on his bed and thought, *If only their season had a different ending.* He was voted as their 'Most Valuable Player' and led them to a 10-1 record, pushing their regular season winning streak to '79' games. Hodge simply didn't want it to be over, and felt depressed as he stared at his bedroom ceiling. He would never forget working out with his boys, going to camps with them, and all of the stuff they did for football because it was fun, and they did it as best friends. If he had to do it all over again, he wouldn't change a thing. Maybe they fell short in their bid for a State Title. But high school football was about the never ending bond that guys develop with the friends they grew up with, played football with, and lifted with at 6 AM. Football taught Hodge about teamwork, helping him discover the honesty of having integrity. He knew that winning and losing shouldn't be the main focus of his high school football memories. They would all go on and win and lose while experiencing the ups-and-downs of life. But the times they had in-between and the friends they made during the process, would always stand for what was genuine and important to him.

Friendships were priceless.

TRI-COUNTY CITIZEN PHOTO
#16 Ryan Hodges, #9 Steve Visser, #87 Corey 'Crusher' Rush

TRI-COUNTY CITIZEN PHOTO
#87 Corey 'Crusher' Rush, #66 Jason Pollard, #71 Scott 'Flaco' Head,
#81 Justin 'Woody' Woodward

10. COURAGE – 1997

Hold your head high, stick your chest out. You can make it.
It gets dark sometimes but morning comes.

-Reverend Jesse Jackson

He couldn't come out of the motorhome. He tried.

The tailgaters shared football stories and were colorfully loud, while they partied directly outside of his door. He watched his teammates whip off their shirts and paint letters on their chests. They asked Bo what letter he wanted, but he just shook his head and walked away, unable to speak.

Bo Moore couldn't join them. He just couldn't.

The pain was too fresh. He stared at the outside of the building, while the ache in his chest grew deeper by the minute. Physically being at the Dome reopened his wounds, making him realize just how close he actually came to playing here. Only one word haunted him -- Why?

His teammates felt the same intensity, but covered it up in other ways. Bo couldn't. He stood tall, strong, and tough on the field, but once he stepped off, he thought about it all too much. His mom worried that her son wouldn't compose himself in time to watch the game. His family couldn't understand his reaction. Hell, Bo didn't understand his own reaction; how did he expect anyone else to?

It hit him like a brick wall the moment they entered the parking lot. The leftover emotional baggage from his season suddenly resurfaced. Bo thought that portion of his life was buried when he went to Ferris State. He told himself, 'C'mon Bo, you play football at a successful Division II college. You've got four more years before you turn in your uniform, and you get to play on turf every week.' For the life of him, he didn't understand why he couldn't haul his big butt out of the motorhome and join in the celebration. After all, he was Bo Moore, their class clown; the guy who made everyone laugh. Now, he took shelter in an obscured motorhome to hide his unstoppable tears.

It was finally time for the game, but Bo refused to come out. He sat frozen in the motorhome, lost in his own world. No one wanted to leave him alone in his depressed state. The principal was able to pull a few strings for an extra press pass, the final ticket that lured him.

Bo found the courage to cast his own demons aside when he entered the Dome; his high school principal, Doug Kinter, was at his side. They stood on the turf next to the team, marveling at the sensation firsthand.

He was actually here. Bo physically stood on the spongy turf of the Pontiac Silverdome, soaking in every radiant detail with a quivering mouth and wet eyes, but he was here.

Brian Owens didn't play Varsity football in '96, and he missed it. Everyone told him that he would. More than a few players had made that decision over the years when it was their turn to step up to Varsity, and it drove the coaches and players crazy. The usual reasons ranged from, 'I gotta get money for a car,' to 'I don't know, I just lost interest.'

Some coaches privately said that they would rather the players be honest and say, 'I ain't playing cause you're a prick. I don't like working that hard.' *Honesty was respected.*

But Montrose Football required a strong commitment year round. It is not for the faint hearted, and had been joked that some rules governing athletes at Montrose High might be at odds with certain parts of the U.S. Constitution. It was simple with Owens; he decided to hang out with the party crowd last season, withdrawing from all athletics.

Owens wanted to jump back in for his senior season, but felt awkward after ditching his teammates and going, as they say, *the other way.* He gathered enough courage in the spring of his junior year to ask to be taken back. He would start with Aaron Emmendorfer. The two had been inseparable during their summer years as kids. Owens privately hoped that Aaron would understand how badly he wanted to get things back on track, which of course meant playing football again.

The slight junior walked leisurely toward the weight room on the north end of the building. The sound of the music and weights being racked increased with each measured step. The combined sounds had the flavor of a type of industrial music – guitars resonating with the semi-rhythmic, heavy steel clanging, but Owens didn't run toward the familiar sound.

In his own way, he reasoned that when one walks toward the likelihood of rejection one walks slowly. But this was more important than shoring up his ego before asking the best looking girl in school to the prom. He could live with a 'no' from a girl. Owens was asking for something much more important than a date; he wanted back on the team. Crossing the threshold of the weight room was his first statement of purpose, because one didn't go to the weight room to watch.

When the young Owens stepped into the room he felt nervous, but strangely at home. He pulled a deep breath. His senses seemed alive again. More than ever he wanted to be a part of it, to breathe the dank, musty perfume of old sweat, to practice with his friends again, to battle on Friday night.

Owens parked beside the red plyometric boxes that were stacked just inside the door. He spotted Aaron and Woody. The three met and walked into the hall, stopping at the drinking fountain. It was there that the usually quiet Brian Owens opened up. His friends stood quietly, while he told them how much that he missed the camaraderie and the discipline that football provided. Owens exhaled a deep sigh, then stated how badly he wanted to be back on the team.

Aaron and Woody walked the short distance to Coach Reinhart's office and made their appeal. Reinhart made it clear that he preferred to let the team decide Owen's fate at their pre-season meeting. Captain Nick Loafman stated firmly that, while he didn't have anything personal against Owens, he didn't want to take a chance on *anyone* or *anything* bringing down his senior year. That made sense to every player in the room, Aaron and Woody included.

The coaches, as far back as Annese, consistently stressed sacrifice. That the team would reap the rewards when each individual gave up the parties, the job, the car, and spent long afternoons and weekends powerlifting. *That was the promise.* Owens broke that chain of sacrifice a year ago, and it surprised no one to hear their captain remind them of that fact. Loafman always lead by example. Always. He defined commitment, so his word carried weight.

Aaron and Woody went to bat for Owens, passionately addressing the 27 other players seated in Room 157. Aaron spoke first. 'Hey, I just want to say one thing. We all played sports with Owens since we were eight years old. I know that Owens' isn't a real big guy, but he has no fear and is one of the hardest hitting guys I've ever faced. He's at a crossroads and needs our help. Whatever we decide today could make a big difference in his life. I think we should let him back on the team.'

Woody watched his teammates shift their weight, while they uncomfortably stared out of the classroom windows. He needed to speak up. 'Hey guys, think about our youth football days. Remember when my dad coached us and everyone came over to watch game films? We spent more time rewinding Owens' famous hits, than we did learning what we did wrong.'

They'd forgotten about those days, then laughed when they recalled how they moaned after watching Owens nail someone. The thickness in the air finally lifted, while some still straddled the fence. They respected how Loaf felt, yet shared the opinions of both Aaron and Woody. Aaron, Loafman, and Woody all gained valuable Varsity experience in '96. Like everyone else in the room, they had high expectations for their upcoming season. Maybe this would be the year. No one dared to say it, but they all thought it – *State Championship.* Previous teams worked their way to the Dome's doorstep only to suffer crushing defeats and they wondered, *Could Owens make the difference?*

When they were finished, Aaron and Woody faced a sea of uncomfortable expressions. Their teammates wore looks that would revisit their adult faces when truly weighty issues were at stake – mortgages, marriage, children, *the big things!* For now, the question before them was, do we make an exception? In the end, the Varsity Rams empathized with Owens. No one could imagine not playing Montrose Football, especially in '97. They too would want another chance if they wore his shoes. The only stipulation was that Owens worked as hard as the others did and stuck it out. They didn't want any quitters on their team, not in '97.

Aaron found Owens and shared the results. The young Ownes couldn't hide the sparkle in his eyes as the sides of his lips formed a shy smile. He promised not to let anyone down, vowing to work twice as hard to make-up for lost time. Aaron knew that he would. *Acceptance held conviction.*

During the summer, Loafman was impressed with the work ethic that Brian Owens displayed in the weight room. Being one of the guys again considerably boosted his morale; and his dad, a long-time fan, was thrilled. To have a son play Montrose Varsity Football – well, it's an indescribable feeling. 'Yeah, my son's playing football for the Rams this year,' was information dropped into any conversation. It didn't matter what was being discussed: truck axles, oysters, the sharpest kitchen knives. Anything. Dads gave each other knowing looks at games, subtle nods of the head that meant, 'We Bad.'

Summer workouts didn't seem like much work to Owens because he had been reborn into the program. Others complained about the soreness and how the coaches cracked the whip from a distance, but he knew they appreciated the discipline as much as he did. They all knew that championships aren't won during the season; they're won in the off-season.

At Veer Camp, the Rams saw Coach Annese with his team from Jenison. Eric Hyde was there with the staff from Carman-Ainsworth High School. Eric watched all of the teams throughout the day, feeling proud that Montrose was still the classiest team in his book. Even though several other schools had caught on and were building strong football programs, many were still trying to get their program to the level that Montrose had developed over the past ten years. Eric told his kids, 'Here's a school that's half the size of ours and look at how they do things. Montrose is so much sharper than other teams here. Watch how they run from the huddle to the line of scrimmage. Other schools with good football teams just nonchalantly walk up to the line. Montrose coaches don't even tell their players to run, they just do it.'

The Montrose program gave other schools a model to compete with. Eric realized it was just a small thing, yet it represented the tradition of Montrose Football. He was proud that the Montrose coaching staff continued the traditions since he played in `91. Eric wanted to interject so many of the Montrose attributes that were instilled in him many years ago.

That pride encouraged the squad to apply a new coat of paint to the weight room walls. It gave the room a crisp, fresh look that was worthy of painting a new phrase over the entrance -- *Those Who Stay Will Become Champions.* Each player jumped up and touched the word *Champion* whenever they left the room. The phrase instigated after a potential junior quarterback switched schools over the summer. What stung was that it wasn't just any quarterback, it was a *Klopf* quarterback. Teddy, the youngest of the Klopf brothers, wouldn't be a Ram in `97. The rumor was to relocate closer to his dad's job. But that didn't make sense to the players and they wondered, *How could they move after his two older brothers shined as quarterbacks for the Rams?*

Losing Hodge to graduation opened the quarterback position with Aaron and Teddy in top contention. Aaron was a senior and shifty, but was also injury prone. Teddy was a junior and showed the skills that both of his brothers possessed. When Teddy left at the last minute, it threw a monkey wrench in their offensive scheme. Aaron gladly stepped in the driver's seat, but it left the Rams without a qualified reserve. They hoped it didn't come back to bite them.

Two-a-days were grueling. Coach Coon felt the huge responsibility of getting his offensive line ready. The eyes of the community and the entire state were upon them, watching this little school to see what they would do with their winning streak. It was his third year with the Rams. He noticed the pressure increasing each year, but the '97 squad seemed to be up for the challenge. Coon wanted to live up to the expectations placed on them, while trying to keep the pressure off of his guys. He realized the powerful emotions attached to the streak and found it humbling to be a part of it; a side he rarely showed to his squad. Friday night was a big joy ride. People that Coon knew outside of Montrose, didn't understand the internal pressures related to the streak and told him, 'You're making it bigger than it is.'

Coon wondered, *am I?* It was easy to get caught up in the hoopla that surrounded Friday Night Football, and not just because of the streak. He addressed his line on the very first day of practice. 'Don't let the mystique override what we have to do.'

Bo Moore injured his ankle, yet he tried to keep up with the rest of the line during 'Coonasthetics.' He did his best to run and do all of the push-ups and sit-ups. In the midst of the workout he heard Coach Coon say, 'You're gonna feel like you can't take another step. But you CAN! And you WILL!'

What made it worse was that Coon yelled his commands with a grin on his face, like he really enjoyed what he was doing. He tried to instill some enthusiasm as inspiration, while he worked their butts off trying to motivate them. Coon couldn't stress discipline enough, hoping his players realized this very work ethic would carry into their lives long after football. Coon yelled, 'You want to be the stronger link in the chain.'

Bo feared failure. Coon thought he saw his tackle have wet eyes and asked, 'What's wrong with you Bo?' Bo feared that he wasn't pulling his weight with his injured ankle. 'Coach I don't want to be the weakest link!'

Coon just shook his head. Bo was his most dedicated and hardest working lineman. 'You don't have to worry about being the weakest link Bo. Just do some sit-ups and get off your ankle.'

Coon could tell by Bo's reaction that he was getting through to them. He eyed his new sophomore, Greg Yeaster -- the big guy they called 'Pooh Bear.' Coon knew he was Division I recruit material after the very first practice. The rookie stood 6'1"-235 pounds and was a coach's dream. He had good hands to go with his huge, large frame and had good speed. Pooh Bear was smart, young, and coachable. Coon realized what a good thing he had in '97. Offensive line coaches don't often get the opportunity of having a huge line; and the Rams were blessed with good teams year after year. Other teams may get one guy with the size, but not a team full of big, strong linemen. His line was huge and he couldn't wait for the '97 Season to begin.

Adam Powell found two-a-days physically exhausting and did nothing but eat, sleep, and practice for two weeks. He was an experienced center with two Varsity seasons under his belt, and was anxious for *his* senior season. Adam was a dark-haired teenager with a quiet nature. He was a strong wrestler with an athletic build and a smart pair of eyes. Adam's reflexes were quick; he snapped more balls to Aaron than he cared to count. Adam worked his butt off for two solid weeks, rehearsing the handoff so many times that it became instinctive. He felt ready. Coach Coon had trained him well.

After two-a-days, Reinhart felt that the '97 Rams were physically the strongest team as a whole unit, that he'd seen since coaching at Montrose. Five of them squatted 500 pounds in powerlifting, and he planned to run their multiple veer offense behind that powerful offensive line. That was his style; everything started with the line. Five starters were back on the offensive line and senior backs Winston and Jorod ran behind them.

Winston felt right at home on the team. He had been friends with most of the squad since elementary school. He was short, but strong; a member of the State Championship Wrestling Team. 'Winny' had recently lost both an older brother and his mom. He found himself struggling to deal with the pressures of death; something most of his teammates had not experienced. He figured they wouldn't understand and was glad when Coach Coon developed a soft spot for him. Coon took Winny under his wing, by letting him ride around in his patrol car. It gave them a chance to talk outside of football. Winny wasn't even one of Coon's linemen, but the coach saw a chance to have a positive impact on a young man. Coon's reactions revealed that the hard drilling coach had a soft spot after all.

The seniors were not very receptive that a freshman girl had joined their macho football program. She naturally became an easy target for their annual prank. Gary Strappazon had the prank pulled on him when he was a freshman and welcomed the payback. 'Hey, the Ram Stand's in the way. We need you to run to the school and get the lug nut key to unlock it so we can move it.'

The Ram Stand was a new addition that the Football Club purchased. It looked like scaffolding and allowed coaches to stand high above the practice field for a better view. Gary's story didn't sound too far-fetched, so the female freshman tried to be a good sport and abide. A rampant Coach Kitts stormed out to the practice field a few minutes later, with the girl closely behind. Kitts demanded, 'Why are you guys playing these stupid tricks?'

The masterminded seniors defended themselves. Gary quickly spoke up, 'Hey Coach, just yesterday you talked about the importance of keeping traditions alive.'

His mood became lenient. 'Yeah, your right, but why did you pick on the girl? As soon as her mom finds out she'll chew on me because you're picking on the *only girl* that came out for football!'

Kitts heard several comments, 'Well, if that's all she's got to complain about, she better toughen up.'

Their conversation was distracted after they heard the deep, strong, voice of Coach Jody Coon echo across the field. 'You gotta keep your butt down and your head up and DRIVE.'

Nothing pleased Coach Coon more than a hard, executed hit; his linemen responded to him. His expressions favored a southern drawl especially when he accented the last word and yelled. 'Plant your feet and DRIVE! I want your back into it BOY!'

The skilled positions mocked him from a good fifty yards away. Aaron tried his best to run the veer with his butt down and his head up, while handing off to Jorod. The running back mimicked Aaron while Bo's deep voice repeated Coach Coon's famous phrase. Then he looked at Aaron, 'Can you imagine doing this in a game?'

Aaron broke loose, running in a stance that modeled an Indian rain dance, with knees bent, butt down and short, choppy steps. I can just hear the fans, especially our dads, 'What the hell are those boys doing?'

It gave the squad a good laugh before a hard practice.

Players all had homes to go to after practice, except Jorod. He found himself between a rock and a hard spot and needed to find a place to live before school started. His parents died when he was young and the strict foster home that he lived in made him leave because he broke a house rule. The team wanted Jorod to stay, the coaches wanted him to stay, and Jorod wanted to graduate with his friends. He needed to finish his football career at Montrose. Jorod was one of two black players on the team, but race wasn't an issue; they all felt like family. Jorod didn't want to be shuffled to another foster home or attend an inner city Flint school. His younger brother still lived at the foster home, and he wanted to attend the same school.

Bo's family not only took Jorod in; they adopted him and made a home for him. It may have been awkward for their extended family to accept, but the Moores felt it was the right thing to do. Jorod was a good kid that needed a stable family environment -- a base he could always call home. *He needed a chance.* The entire team felt the goodness that developed after the Moore family adopted Jorod. Humanity overruled race, bonding the team stronger as a unit. Bo and Jorod received strange reactions whenever they introduced themselves *as brothers.* They merged their personalities to provide comic relief to their family, as well as the entire team. It wouldn't be hard to confuse the two of them; Bo was as white as Jorod was black. Bo stood 6'3"-210 pounds, and towered over Jorod at 5'6". Jorod laughed at everyone's reaction when he told the story, 'I'm a reverse albino and both of my parents were white.'

The Rams were ready for the season to start. Their pre-season T-shirts firmly stated, 'A Decade of Perfection.' The staff and team sensed history in the making with a chance to tie, then break the state record for regular season wins. Reinhart addressed his team on the very first day of practice. 'We're a marked team. Everyone will be gunning for us this year and we have to take them one game at a time. We need to keep focused on our ultimate goals.'

The '97 group of seniors always faced the pressure of lofty expectations. They had remained undefeated since youth football and through three season of high school. People pointed at them for quite some time and said, 'Wait until they are seniors.'

They lived with that awareness for some time and couldn't wait for their season to start so they could do something about it. Their annual motto for '97 became 'Unfinished Business.' The seniors were second graders at the Montrose Carter Elementary school when the streak first started. They idolized the nine Varsity teams since, while anxiously waiting for their turn. When they were freshmen, they calculated that *they* would be the team that made Michigan high school football history. And like their fans, they assumed the streak would be in tact and waiting for them. Uniting the size and strength of the class behind them, with their speed and love of hard-nose football, created a great combination. It was their time.

Montrose wanted to surpass Hudson's High School mark of 81 straight regular season wins, a record that stood since 1977. Montrose had played Atherton for the season opener that past two years; a team that historically finished near the bottom of their League. Montrose changed their schedule for '97 and played Atherton as their *last* league game. They could've arranged to play their least competitive games as their first three of the season, as insurance to lock in the state record . . . *but elected not to.* A decision could that could haunt them later. But they wouldn't attest the opportunity for people to say that Montrose took the easy way out. They wanted to face their fierce hard-hitting rivals from **New Lothrop** for their opener and kept their non-league game against Chesaning as their second. Chesaning was the last team that defeated Montrose during the regular season in 1988, by a seven point lead. But no one expected the unimaginable stress that loomed over the squad once the season started. It seemed the entire town had bought into the hype by ordering trademark Montrose Football jackets. Orders for red and black coats, shirts, and hats were rushed. A local retailer from a neighboring town enjoyed the sales and told Montrose fans. 'You people are crazy. I get more orders for Montrose coats then I do for all three area schools combined.'

Varsity parents got into the action by making large, wooden signs shaped like football helmets. Each player had a custom-made sign in his yard before the New Lothrop game. Players felt something was definitely special about the upcoming season when they memorized their first game motto:

'Our Work Ethic During The Week
Will Determine the Outcome - Friday night'

Players removed their helmets and took a knee, when Coach Reinhart addressed them in the weight room before boarding the bus. He accented their tremendous strength, good size, and hard work ethic that gave them the potential to be dangerous. No one mentioned the ten year streak, but it was on everyone's mind. They all realized what was at stake. Reinhart sternly told them. 'This team hasn't done anything yet. You've got to prove yourself when we step on that field.'

When the team walked outside to board the bus for their season opener, they were greeted by a caravan of fans; a tradition normally reserved for the post-season. Car flags displayed their mascot, while white shoe polish decorated car windows -- 'We love our Rams.' It seemed everyone in town felt the extra anticipation of history in the making.

Joe Persails stared from the bus window as they drove through the small town of Montrose. His given name was Joseph Robert, but his two brothers called him 'Joe Bob' as a child . . . and it stuck. He was tall and lean like his older brother Ryan, and his large feet never appeared to be in a hurry. Joe Bob watched as residents waved or gave the bus a thumbs-up sign to show their support. The season opener had the flavor of playoffs, but the extra attention added surmountable pressure. By default, the Rams had become a part of something that was bigger than they were. They didn't discuss it but everyone thought, *We can't lose a game. We just can't.*

The extra attention forced the butterflies in Joe Bob's stomach to flutter a bit faster; he wondered if the others felt the same. He often sported a bright white smile, but that day his face looked nervous. A far cry from being elected as the 'Class Clown.' He looked across the aisle and watched Aaron throw a football as close to the bus ceiling as he could without touching it. That ball had to feel natural in his hands, he never saw Aaron without it. Joe Bob noticed the serious expressions on the faces of his friends, and he knew they sensed it too. The atmosphere on the bus contained more apprehension than a regular season opener, while they mentally prepared themselves to ignore the distractions that came with chasing history.

Aaron's distant cousin was quite athletic and played for the Hornets, and shared the same last name. A pre-season article referred to New Lothrop's Emmendorfer as the 'Real Deal.' The squad jumped on that one by teasing Aaron the entire week about not being the 'Real Deal.'

The bleachers filled quickly, forcing fans to hug the fence for a decent spot. Jorod took the handoff then exploded on the very first play of the game. The Rams drove deep into New Lothrop territory early in the first quarter, then fumbled. Aaron wiped his hands on the shabby, white towel that he tucked in his pants. It wasn't just any white towel; it was a torch disguised as a Christmas gift from Hodge. The small, worn towel didn't appear very valuable, but if it could talk it would share a few stories of its own. In a way, it kept a part of Hodge on the field. Aaron crossed over with a quarterback keeper from a yard out to score late in the first. Steve Visser's younger brother, Scott, prepared to kick his first Varsity PAT. The junior kicker tried to settle his heart rate down as he marked off his steps, concentrating on his form. He booted the ball, while his eyes followed its path until it soared between the uprights. He felt a huge smile shape his face, an expression that mirrored his brother's reaction on the sideline.

The second period was packed with action. Woody fell on a New Lothrop fumble at their 30 yard marker early in the second period. The Rams marched to the three when the Hornets stalled their drive to the delight of the their fans. Scott booted a 20 yard field goal seven seconds into the second quarter for a 10-0 lead. Woody scored the second TD on a 10 yard reverse play for the Rams, then watched Scott accurately kick his second extra point. The Real Deal got the Hornets back in the game when he picked-off Aaron's pass, and ran 34 yards to score.

The Rams found themselves in a third-and-long situation and thought they would need to punt, until Winny pulled them out. The Rams formed a wall as Winny squirted through an opening, then bolted 55 yards to score a minute before the intermission. The 24-6 half-time lead took the edge off the nervous energy that surrounded the visitor's side of the field.

Even D'ar from the '92 Team was there. The former Ram was a shining senior at the college level, yet still enjoyed Montrose Football and watching his dad coach. He closely watched Aaron and Owens perform on the field. D'ar flashed back to '91 when the twosome ran the kicking tee to him when he was the place kicker and they were the young water boys. Now he watched Aaron hold the ball for Scott; prepared to use his quick quarterback skills if the snap went bad. Aaron and Owens had grown into their oversized Varsity jerseys that once hugged their ankles. The two of them always made sure they offered D'ar a drink before they ran off the field, unable to hide the awe of standing next to him. Being the water boys exposed Aaron and Owens to intense huddle talks and intimidating pre-game speeches at a very young age. They subconsciously absorbed it all: *the good, the bad . . . and the ugly.*

Both teams took the field prepared for another round of smash mouth football. Aaron eluded a tackle, tucked the ball, then ran seven yards to pay dirt. Scott kicked another extra point with 3:01 left in the third. Loafman acted like the quarterback for the line, calling audibles along the line of scrimmage. After a full year in the weight room, he was even bigger and stronger than his junior year.

Darren 'Corky' Corcoran was on the hard-hitting kickoff team. He always attacked with such force that he managed to break an opponent's bone every season – including '97. Corky was the second guy from the end on the right side of the field, and laid a good hit on a New Lothrop receiver when he sped down the sideline, unintentionally taking out his opponent's wrist. Corky was one of the few guys on the team who had a real mustache, giving him a tough guy look on the field. But off the field, he wasn't mean at all. Corky had a quick laugh that his senior class voted as their 'Most Funniest.'

Gary loved to play defensive end. It sucked his junior year when he had mono. He started four games at guard before he got sick and sidelined for the `96 Season. The best he could do was function as the snapper for PAT's, but he never quit. Gary knew that he would be back for his senior year. He wanted to play defensive end ever since watching old highlight films of Jason Katt from the `90 Team. Now he had his shot, and wanted to perform just like Katt did. Gary was thrilled to earn a spot at defensive end his senior year, but was still learning his new position. He had a great play followed by a bad one, so Coach D nicknamed him 'Space.'

Reinhart seemed relaxed after his Rams used a mix of power and finesse to lock in their 80th consecutive victory. The Rams made some mental mistakes typical of a season opener, while some kids made their first Varsity debut. Overall, Coach Reinhart was pleased with their performance. Loafman led the defense with a great showing of 14 hits, followed by Dauber and Owens. The strong offensive line enabled the Rams to form offensive weapons in Jorod, Winny, Aaron, Owens, and Woody. Aaron displayed his talents by scoring three TD's and rushing for 85 yards to lead his team to a '38-12' victory. His cousin had a great game for the Hornets, but the Rams voted *their* Emmendorfer as the 'Real Deal.'

Scott made his older brother proud when he followed in his footsteps by kicking five PAT's and a field goal. Steve Visser watched from the sideline, struggling with the emptiness of not being able to don a uniform again. He accepted the reality that he had to relive the game through his younger brothers.

The Rams felt larger than life as they boarded the bus. They transferred that energy to week two, and learned the weekly motto to prepare for the most important game of their young lives against **Chesaning:**

**'When Your Peers Drive You,
It's Far Greater Than When A Coach Does.
When You're Sitting In The Locker Room
And You Look Over At That Guy. . .
You Have To Be Responsible And Accountable To Him.
You Can't Fool Your Teammates!'**

The coaches realized how easy it was to get bitten if they looked too far ahead. They didn't discuss being on the verge of tying Michigan's longest winning streak. Ishpeming High School halted Hudson's streak in the state finals in 1975, the first year of the playoff system. Hudson must've been disappointed when they failed to make the 1976 state playoffs with a 9-0 record. Their regular-season-winning streak stopped at 81 with a 3-0 setback after holding it since 1968. The Rams wanted to claim it.

But ignoring the state record was easier said than done. Unbelievable media hype encompassed Montrose High; it seemed everyone wanted a story. The team found it hard to block out the publicity as the spotlight shined on their small town football team. The streak had become a fascination of the town, and was something previous players took tremendous pride in. The dynamics of the streak made the situation extremely difficult for the '97 Rams. They were the ones who carried the weight of ten years on their shoulders. Most players managed to wave off the media after pre-game practice that Thursday, and again after school on Friday, hours before the big game. The coaches wanted practice to be the same as any other game, although the distractions were obvious. No one wanted the dynasty to end. The Rams needed to focus on a second win against Chesaning who just came off a big 20-14 season opener, shocking Millington.

The team tried to avoid talking to the press, who instead focused an article on 25-year old assistant Coach Chris Clolinger ('Goose' from the '89 Team). He was a 16 year-old junior quarterback when Montrose lost to Chesaning by 7-14 on September 9, 1988. Ten seasons later, it was still the Rams only regular-season setback. Clolinger wanted to keep it alive as much as anyone. That game seemed like forever ago. He never imagined what the '88 Team started would've ever gone that far.

Gary managed to dodge the media by safely reaching the locker room without an interview. He asked Bo, 'What do they expect us to say? Of course we want to win. Of course we're nervous.'

Bo shook his head, 'I don't know. I ran from them too.'

The squad was so nervous that they could barely concentrate on school, or sleeping, or eating, including the linemen. Linemen never had trouble eating, but the media's presence added to the overwhelming pressure they already felt. The Rams were just high school kids playing a game they loved, but everyone was caught up in the hype. The team looked intensely serious as they dressed for the game. The short bus drive to Chesaning was extremely quiet, while players tried to block out records and streaks and focus on the game of football. They were about to face an experience that would affect their goals, their dreams, and their destiny.

Loafman joined the other captains and officials midfield for the coin toss. An official told Loaf that he was being disrespectful and to take his helmet off. Loaf responded, 'We always wear our helmets. It's Montrose tradition.'

The official insisted that he remove it, or not play in the game. Loaf tossed Bo a strange look and abided, yet felt the confrontation was odd as he tried to brush off the strange feeling.

Nobody's expectations were greater than their own when the Rams lined up on Chesaning's field in front of an overflow crowd of 3,500. The official placed the ball in the middle of the field, while Woody and Kris Brown lined up as deep receivers. They tried to tune out the noise, the band, and the extremely exciting hype, which made their heartbeats thump powerfully in their chests. The Rams marched down the field, eating up eight minutes on their opening drive. Woody took the handoff from Aaron and worked his way down the far sideline. He cut for the corner of the endzone, knocking down the bright orange pylon as he crossed. His teammates celebrated the score in the endzone. They assumed they were on the board, then watched in disbelief when a female official gave the no score signal.

Woody asked her, 'Why didn't my touchdown count?''

She penalized the Rams on third down claiming he stepped on the line. Spectators standing in the area thought it counted from their angle, and threw questionable glances at each other. Reinhart argued the play to no avail. The officials huddled for an unusual long time, as if in the midst of a big debate. But the end result didn't change her call. It was a lost opportunity for the Rams, who made the best of the situation by sending Scott in to kick a 36 yard field goal instead. His accurate foot lit up the Montrose side of the scoreboard 3-0, instead of what could've been 7-0.

Reinhart told his Rams, 'The game's early, we'll get it back.'

The Indians jumped offside on a well-rehearsed fourth-and-two punt near midfield, keeping another Montrose drive alive. Winny's 20 yard TD capped a 64 yard drive for the Rams, while Scott's PAT provided a 10-0 lead at the half.

The score was dangerously close against a quick team like Chesaning, coupled by the high number of penalty calls against both teams. The Rams lost a fumble on their own 43 yard line, just four minutes into the third.

Gary rushed in to block a punt. He wanted to stop it so badly that he dove, but he wasn't as close as he thought. Gary felt his stomach smash against the hard ground, like doing a belly smacker in the pool without the buoyancy to cut the force. His adrenaline was in overdrive when his reflexes immediately shot his body back up, oblivious to the sting in his stomach.

The Indians utilized a pass interference call against Montrose and a 17 yard run to reach the five yard line early in the third, but Loafman recovered a Chesaning fumble and ended the threat.

Woody ran a pass route and couldn't believe that a personal foul was called against him. Again, he asked the ref, 'What did I do wrong?'

He was told that he was trying to pick a fight and could get kicked out of this game. Woody returned a look of mistrust as he relived the play in his mind. *This is offense, and I'm the one going out for a pass. I'm sure I am going to stop en route and pick a fight with an opponent.*

It seemed the officiating had become dishonorable. He felt violated for the second time during the game, a feeling shared by several teammates.

Aaron stiff-armed his opponent, while pushing the side of the helmet as he tried to outrace him. He heard a loud Chesaning coach yell 'FACEMASK!'

Aaron thought to himself while he ran, *Yeah right. Nice try coach!* But his expression shifted to concern after seeing the official whip out the yellow flag, calling an offensive facemask penalty against him. Aaron thought, *I don't believe this.* The only justice came later when Aaron watched the play in super slow motion on the game film, claiming his innocence.

Reinhart had passed his frustration point. The head coach was outright pissed from so many penalties when he faced the crowd, theatrically throwing his hands in the air, 'Can you believe this crap?'

Aaron was also frustrated but tried to grab the attention of his Coach as he chased after him. 'What play do you want?'

Time was almost out, and he desperately needed a play. The Rams already had two delay of game penalties and couldn't afford another. Aaron got sacked for a safety two plays later with 4:46 remaining in the third, when he fumbled in his own endzone. It was a big play for Chesaning, pulling them within 10-2, forcing the Rams to kick from their own 20.

A 15 yard return of the free kick set the Indians at their own 45. Chesaning drove 55 yards in seven plays, then scored on a four yard TD. The defense battled hard, trying to block out the importance of the game when they stopped Chesaning's attempt for a conversion. Montrose kept a 10-8 lead with less than two minutes left in the third quarter. The Rams could not believe the penalties; it was difficult not to retaliate. Dallas Parks lined up behind Dauber when the female official called him offside. They couldn't remember ever having a female official, and looked at each other in disbelief. *This is such an important game. Where in the world did they find her?*

The Rams felt the officials continued to stop their game whenever they got their momentum going. Montrose had depth and traditionally wore teams down in the second half. Chesaning had many players going both ways. But the Rams lost their advantage when the elongated timeouts gave their opponents plenty of time to catch their breath.

Dauber received Varsity experience as a sophomore in '96, and knew what to expect on the line and thought, *This is getting ridiculous.* He spoke to the officials, asking them to watch the illegal games that were being played on the line. An official only stared back at him, giving the impression that his request fell on deaf ears. Later, an Indian player appeared to intentionally kick Dauber in the head while his teammates witnessed. Dauber was pissed because he felt the female official witnessed it too. He wondered, *What the hell, I just got kicked in the head!* He thought for sure that a penalty would be called against Chesaning. Instead, Dauber received the warning -- *he couldn't believe it.*

The added stress and visibility of the important game affected Montrose fans in ways they never imagined. It infuriated coaches and players on the sideline when officials ignored the incident. Trent Perior witnessed his own confrontation when an opponent continued to kick him as he tried to get up. He played defensive tackle, and felt pumped after the Rams stopped the

Indians. At first it caught him off-guard and he thought that it was accidental, but then the guy kicked Trent again. Trent was an easygoing kid who usually sported a Hollywood smile. His senior classmates even vote him as their 'Most Gullible,' but he wasn't falling for any pranks. *Not that night.* Not with everything that the Rams had at stake.

Coon saw the official reach into his back pocket. He anticipated that another flag would be thrown, which was something the Rams couldn't afford. Trent faced off on the field after the play. Coon yelled, 'TRENT, GET OFF THE FIELD!' He didn't want Trent to get the penalty, and the way things were going he felt the Rams would be the guilty culprits. Trent inched his way toward the sideline, but didn't move fast enough for Coon who met him on the field. He didn't intend to grab Trent as hard as he did, but his emotions were flying high. *Everyone's were.*

Stress levels impacted the entire audience. Coon grabbed Trent's jersey, fearing that he would take revenge. 'WE'RE NOT PLAYING THAT GAME. THE ONE WHO RETALIATES ALWAYS GETS THE PENALTY!'

Coon was an expressive coach, but the officials' actions had his adrenaline at full throttle. Coon embraced Trent by his shoulders, wanting to get him off the field. But their feet became entangled in the mass of cords on the sideline, and they tumbled to the ground. A parent unfortunately caught the moment on video, while taping the game from the sideline. Without focusing on the cords at ground level, the tape appeared that Coach Coon forcefully threw Trent down. The parent later turned the tape into a fiasco, which led to a reprimand that threatened the coaching position Coon loved. *Retaliation was unsupported.*

In spite of that, Aaron was determined to lead the Rams to victory. Early in the fourth, Aaron fought with everything he had until he crossed the endzone for a 34 yard TD. When he turned around to celebrate, he couldn't believe what he saw. The bright yellow flag lay on the ground, the result of a clipping penalty called against Bo, negating his score.

It was Bo's worst nightmare; he couldn't believe the call. He swore on his soul that he didn't clip anyone. Again, Reinhart went to bat for his team, while Bo nervously paced his large body in a circle on the field. He nervously stated, 'THERE'S NO WAY THAT I CLIPPED HIM. NO WAY!' He tried to control his actions and thought, *I would bet my life on it. I would know if I hit someone from behind. If only they could replay the video, they would see. But this was high school, not the pros.*

Reinhart argued the call, while the officials held another prolonged huddle. Woody's dad stood with the silenced crowd, waiting for the outcome. A sick feeling consumed him after he sensed what was happening. He realized how difficult it was to make up two lost TD's in a game of this magnitude. But nothing changed -- Aaron's TD remained unscored. The crowd uttered their disappointment, while Bo stood in disbelief. His heart sank to his knees, like a jury who just sentenced an innocent man. He knew the game film would support his story, but that didn't mean squat at the moment. It was such an important TD in a game that was much closer than it ever should've been.

The unjustified call set off an unconquerable determination, allowing the pissed off linemen to make a huge hole for Aaron, who plowed through for a 20 yard run. The Rams were poised to score with a first-and-goal from the Chesaning five. Trash talk came alive. The determined linemen tried to crack the Chesaning defense, but they dished the trash right back.

Jorod was stopped for no gain on two consecutive carries over right tackle, after picking up four yards on a first down. Players suggested running it on the other side, but Reinhart had confidence in his strong side. Coach would run behind that side all night long; and he called the play again. It was eerily similar to Chesaning's win over the Rams in '88 when Montrose was stopped on three consecutive running plays behind the same blocker from the Chesaning five.

Aaron looked at his squad. 'We need this one guys. Let's make it count.'

The line was determined to cross on four-and-inches. Jorod saw the chalk line as he crossed over and thought, *Good I'm in.*

In most books crossing the plane constitutes a touchdown. *Not that night.* The whistle was never blown so the play never stopped, giving Chesaning a chance to push Jorod back. Players wondered, *Didn't it matter that he crossed the plane?* To no one's surprise, another extended official timeout was called.

Montrose coaches fought their case desperately to avoid losing yet another critical TD. Fans stood in silence, waiting for the results that seemed so visibly obvious from the bleachers. Once again, the officials reconvened for an elongated period, while the crowd of 3,500 waited for the outcome. Each prolonged discussion further questioned their officiating ability, giving the impression that the officials were in constant disagreement. Their actions unnecessarily created a tremendous amount of stress for everyone in attendance. The Montrose coaching staff publicly displayed their frustration when the head official once again signaled, 'No Touchdown.'

Unbelievable.

The Rams had never been in such an unusual position. Having three potential touchdowns unscored in one game added to their disgust. The important record setting game had turned into a mind-boggling nightmare, in front of their very own eyes. They couldn't help but wonder, *What the hell was going on?* It appeared to some that the outcome was determined before the game ever started.

The goal line stand naturally pumped up Chesaning's defense, and contagiously sparked their offense. The Indians felt the momentum shift, while the Montrose Rams felt their frustration increase. But they never gave up. Gary recorded a tackle in the endzone on the next play, while Jorod grabbed the ball as he hit the ground, landing on his back. The ball brushed against his chest for a brief second then bounced off. But he never had control of it, and the Rams pounced on it in the endzone. One official signaled a TD, the other a safety. The officials had another drawn out, private huddle, while a confused crowd anxiously wondered, *What would the conclusion be this time?*

The Montrose coaches shook their heads in disbelief when the official, who called the TD, let the other official sway him. Two points were awarded to the Rams instead of six, as well as surrendering the chance for a PAT. It barely stretched their lead to 12-8 instead of 17-8. The Rams only hoped it wouldn't come back to haunt them. Both sides felt the unnecessary frustration from the abundant penalties. The Montrose offense dominated the field, but their unfortunate penalties fell on scoring plays. The intensity of the game was evidenced when the whistle blew 12 times for 120 penalty yards for the Rams, while the Indians were set back 64 yards on six infractions.

Some hard popping occurred on the field; a lot of things happened on that field as evidenced by nine Montrose fumbles. The Rams desperately struggled to hang on, and only gave up one. Players usually took care of business themselves, but the Rams had too much at stake that night. Frustration showed on their faces while coaches preached, 'Maintain your focus. Don't retaliate!' The staff tried to calm them down in the midst of the dogfight. Reinhart had to handle his own focus and intensity, in light of how distorted the officiating had become. They tried to treat it like any other game, but Montrose had everything to lose and Chesaning had everything to gain. Each penalty brought confusion, and neither side could guess what the outcome would be. It was the most frustrating game that players ever played, coaches ever coached, and fans ever observed.

Montrose couldn't sustain their next two drives and exchanged the ball twice. In spite of everything that happened, the Rams held on to their small lead throughout the entire game. Aaron glanced at the scoreboard and told the offense, 'Just under three minutes – we can do this!'

The Indians partially blocked Loafman's punt which set up Chesaning at the Montrose 45, only 18 yards from where the Rams punted. The Indians trailed by 12-8, then reached the 10 yard line after driving 45 yards on three passes. With seconds left on the clock, the air became so thick that the Rams could barely breathe. They fought for control. The clock seemed to move in super slow motion, as if it didn't want to proclaim a winner. The question on everyone's mind was, *Could Montrose hold Chesaning on four plays from the ten yard line?*

The Chesaning quarterback threw a pass in the endzone on first-and-goal. Aaron intently followed the ball then desperately grabbed it, determined to end the threat. But his own teammate, Joe Fedechenko, collided with him. Fedechenko was so focused on stopping the play, that he prevented his own teammate from gaining possession.

The determined Rams defended their turf on second-and-goal, as their hearts pounded rapidly. They fought hard during the entire game for such a small lead, while frantically trying to keep their winning streak intact. The Rams had to block the pass. Their eyes intently followed as the quarterback released. Woody stretched his lean torso and batted it down. Montrose had stopped two of their plays at goal line, with seconds left on the clock. The defense felt pumped and anxiously yelled, 'C'mon guys, we can do this!'

If the crowd wasn't emotionally drained, they were not paying attention. High school football is all about heart; there was enough heart on that field for a room full of transplant patients. It was third-and-goal from the Montrose eight, when the Chesaning coaches attempted to get their quarterback's attention. But he didn't notice in the hectic atmosphere, and called the play on his own.

If the Rams ever needed some God-given luck, that was the moment. But luck went to the home team when the Chesaning quarterback hit a diving receiver on third down. Two Montrose defenders hit him hard, but the Indian managed to hang on. He decisively grabbed the touchdown pass and became an instant hero. While Chesaning missed the PAT, the scoreboard attendants got caught up in the excitement and ran the clock out. Hundreds of Chesaning fans rushed the field to celebrate their history-breaking two-point victory, but were quickly ushered off. The clock was reset for the final ten seconds.

Ten seconds. Ten years of winning came down to ten seconds.

The stress on the sideline, as well as in the stands, became overwhelming. Montrose fans surely supported their team, but felt too panicky to even cheer. Their abnormal stillness seemed frightening. The Rams tried to regain control, while ignoring the terror that prematurely crept in.

Chesaning's squib kick was muffed then downed at the Montrose 42. The Rams had never experienced such intense pressure as they trailed by 12-14 with ten seconds left. It was hard to believe that things could've gone to hell in such a short time. The Rams felt pitted against an unfortunate force that overpowered them. The town of Montrose held its breath, as if they were frozen in time. The bleachers grew painfully quiet as fans watched Aaron throw a 10 yard pass to Woody. He caught it, giving the one last play from scrimmage -- *one final hope.*

Scott's mom nervously cupped her face in her trembling hands. She felt the pressure that rested on her son to kick a field goal. Scott made a 35 yard field goal in the first quarter; she felt confident he could do it again. But when she looked-up, she was surprised that special teams never took the field. It left her wondering, *Why wouldn't they kick it? Didn't they have enough faith in Scott?*

Hope dimmed in the final few seconds of the fourth quarter as the offense anxiously grabbed hands in their huddle. If the Rams didn't answer now, *it was over!* The entire last quarter seemed like a cloudy haze, but they tried not to panic. Aaron looked in the faces of his squad, and saw a collection of expressions – confidence, concern, worry, and fear, but was determined to lead them to victory. His voice was calm when he called the final play. 'We can still pull this off guys.'

Woody grabbed the quarterback's facemask before the huddle broke, 'Aaron – I'll be there for you!'

Aaron nodded, trying to control his racing heart and the pressure that he was under. The team tried to tune everything out, but their hearts knocked so loud that it echoed in their ears. Adam's heart raced as he fingered the laces on the ball. If he ever needed a perfect snap, that was the time. He carefully listened while Aaron called the play. Adam felt him grab the ball, while the center forcefully blocked his opponent, protecting his quarterback. Adam couldn't see what happened behind him, and hoped that Aaron faked his handoff, backpedaled, and found his open receivers.

Woody and Kris ran out for the final Hail Mary pass, confident they could pull it off. They desperately needed to keep their precious streak in tact. It was the play Woody and Aaron had practiced all summer. The last play of the game when the quarterback called out, 'The Rams are down by two.' He dropped back in the pocket, then scrambled to get free while searching for Woody. Aaron found him alone in the corner, then launched the perfect spiral. Woody outmaneuvered his defenders, positioning himself at the final second for the perfect game winning catch in the endzone, while fans screamed with delight.

Except that time it wasn't their fans cheering. The Montrose Rams never imagined that they would be in such a position. It was their last hope for the game winning touchdown; a chance to get the Rams out of the serious mess they were in. Aaron suddenly felt the force of an opponent tackle him, and felt his entire world instantly crash. *No. Not sacked. Not now. Oh God, please not now!*

Woody ran his pass route but when he turned, he saw the commotion. His eyes quickly searched for Aaron. *C'mon buddy, where are ya?* He didn't see him scrambling; he didn't see his quarterback anywhere. He only saw opponents jumping up-and-down. Woody immediately felt his breathing become rapid, while a cold chill shot through his entire body. *He couldn't breathe. He couldn't move.* The receiver couldn't believe that Aaron went down; that wasn't part of the plan. Woody never felt the ground as his limp body dropped, laying exactly where he landed, while a horrific feeling consumed him. Panic set in. *No. Oh no. It's over. The streak is over. It's all over!* His arms buried his helmet under his jersey, as the weight of ten years forced out his sobs. Once they started, he couldn't control them. He didn't care who watched. He couldn't think about anything; his world just ended.

Kris had the same reaction 20 yards away from Woody. Both receivers fell like wounded soldiers, wishing the earth could swallow them and remove them from that gloomy night. Instead, they fell prey to the magnetic force that seemed to pull them over to the dark side.

Aaron heard the flat sound of the buzzer echo in his helmet. He couldn't believe that he got sacked. *It had to be a horrible nightmare. I just need one more chance to get up and run it again.* He glanced at the clock, wishing he had a few more seconds. That's all he needed, time to get one more play off. Instead, that awful buzzer droned in his ears, leaving a concluding echo that locked in the scoreboard '12-14.'

It was over. The sacked quarterback saw hundreds of Chesaning fans pack the field, while their band played their school song. Aaron felt nothing but nauseating fear. The hairs on the back of his neck stood on end when he yelled, 'NO!' He buried his helmet deeper under his arms, unable to control his emotions. *It couldn't be over. Not like this.* His stomach churned, giving him a sick feeling. He had never felt so terrible in his entire 17 years. Aaron didn't want to be the quarterback that lost the streak. He had worked so hard and gave so much. *Why did it happen?* The streak was so important. He begged through sobs, 'Oh God, please don't let it end like this! Please.'

Lost in his own world, he didn't see his squad drop like flies around him. It was a pitiful site, which made their dads feel terrible. They wanted to reach their sons, but were stuck in the long bleacher lines. Parents realized how much stress they were under, and couldn't imagine how the players felt. They were a savvy football crowd, who felt disgusted by the officials' calls. Heads shook in disgust after witnessing policemen escorting the four referees away -- *that was pitiful.* Spectators at the game would never forget the frustration those four indecisive referees created. They felt officials should never create an environment filled with such confusion that a police escort was necessary. Referees were expected to have integrity, and be fair and knowledgeable in the game they officiate. All three traits were questioned that night; it was just easier for one team to swallow. Parents hoped that all four officials had a conscience, and that game would haunt them for a very long time.

The game lasted :12 seconds too long -- *if you were a Ram.* Montrose lost their chance to make history and tie the 81 game state record. It became a lost opportunity that may never occur in a Michigan High School again, or possibly the entire country since football teams implemented stronger, competitive programs.

The field turned into pandemonium when everyone went wild in one way or another. The noisy Chesaning fans crashed their side of the field with crazed excitement. The Chesaning Indians were just starting to see the results of the changes that second year Coach Jim Szappan brought when he styled his program after SVSU. The win helped the Indians turn the corner and gain the confidence that launched exciting things for the Chesaning program.

The opposite end of the field looked like the Battle of Gettysburg, with the injured lying precisely where they dropped. Some huddled, some squatted, while others fell to the ground. They didn't know how to react to the empty, hollow feeling that devoured them, leaving them chilled, numb, and scared. They felt so low; some even wished they were dead. Dying had to be easier than facing the gloomy, burdensome pain that overtook their entire body. The Rams felt so ashamed, like they had disappointed the entire town of Montrose. *How could we ever face former players? How could we face anyone?*

The moment the dreaded buzzer blew, Scott felt like their entire season was a loss. He hung his head and thought, *In an instant we went from being a legacy to being a normal Friday night team.* Dauber had been Scott's neighbor for a long time and scolded, 'Pick your head up. We're not done yet!'

The young Cross brothers were the water boys who stood inches away from their heroes. They idolized the Varsity and didn't know how to react. Josh, the older Cross brother, wanted to help. He guardedly tapped Loafman on the shoulder. When the captain looked at the young lad, his face held so much anguish that it frightened the eleven-year-old. He didn't know what else to do and immediately started to cry.

The Rams appeared inconsolable. No one wanted to get up, which only made the scene more grueling with each passing moment. Staying on the field wouldn't change the outcome of the game. Coach Reinhart finally told his assistants, 'Let's gather them up.'

Adam sat on the ground, feeling like a big part of his life had just ended. His arms surrounded his helmet, as if he tuned out the world. Adam glanced at his line coach after hearing his name and noticed Coach Coon's sad expression. It broke Coon's heart to see his rough, tough, line so broken -- especially Adam. They'd been together for three years and made a good team. Coon respected Adam's work ethic. He was a phenomenal player who was fun to coach, but this scene crushed him. Coon extended a strong hand to his center, 'C'mon Adam.'

Even with coaxing from assistant coaches, some players still couldn't respond, and seemed lost in their own sad world. Facing anyone exposed the deepest part of his soul. Woody and Kris were the farthest away from the team. Their parents were trapped in the bleachers and watched from afar, wishing someone would help their sons through this awful experience. Neither Kris nor Woody would get up after several assistant coaches attempted to help. Coach Persails (their old J.V. Coach) finally spoke some comforting words, coaxing them to stand as he walked them back to the rest of the team.

The '97 Rams carried a heavier burden than any team before them. Montrose regrouped and appeared to handle defeat as graciously as they could under the circumstances. The dazed Rams strolled through the line to shake hands in a state of walking unconsciousness. They were surprised that Coach Reinhart didn't yell at them when they gathered for their post-game talk. *Not that night.* Reinhart was worried as he looked at their anguished faces, realizing they were totally beside themselves. The loss was extremely difficult to accept and players wondered, *What would become of us now?* He needed to find a way to rescue them. Afraid they could go over the edge, he had to pull them through the tough situation they were suddenly forced to deal with. Even though ending the streak was inevitable, no one wanted it to end on *his* shift, especially under such bizarre conditions.

Reinhart had witnessed disappointed players before, but nothing compared to the horror displayed in the faces of his `97 squad. He realized that night would have a dramatic impact on their lives. Instead of showing anger or making excuses, Reinhart kept things in perspective. He became amazingly strong when he spoke. 'We've carried the weight of that streak for some time now. This past week has been especially demanding. Now you can be just normal high school athletes. Normal kids. We have nothing to hang our heads about, but we're at a crossroads here. You can either hang your heads, or you can commit to working even harder than before. We still have lofty goals ahead of us -- the League Title and a State Championship. The coaching staff is prepared to do everything in our power to help this team get through this. Are you with us?'

The team felt helplessly empty, yet desperately latched onto Coach Reinhart's calm words. They listened with heavy hearts. Those that could speak said 'Yes'; others simply nodded their heads, powerless to fight their knotted throats. A few hit rock bottom. It was hard to imagine anything except a fretful future. His Rams were broken. He had to find a way to fix them, and help them learn to live with what just happened. He didn't want to lose them, and quickly searched for a way to bring them back. Coach looked at his kids who appeared absolutely devastated. He genuinely said, 'If losing this game is the worst thing that ever happens to you, then all of you will have good lives.'

It was the anchor they needed. In an instant, Coach Reinhart became their Rock of Gibraltar, delivering a great statement at a critical time. The media picked up on the phrase and ran with it. For every end, there is a new beginning. A door from their past was now closed. Reinhart only hoped they could find a way to open another, and start over. They had to believe in themselves.

The team traditionally marched two-by-two, with the same unity they showed 80 times before during times of triumph. Their hands were locked tighter that night, while they leaned on each other. The Rams started what felt like a march down death row. They no longer felt invincible. Parents, fans, and friends lined up and applauded the team as they walked off the field. It felt like the beginning of the end. Their heads were hung low, the weight of the streak too heavy to lift them. It would take strong character to get through this, and their coaches wondered, *Did they have enough courage?*

Players instantly forgot the comforting words that Coach Reinhart used to ease their pain, just a few moments earlier. As they approached the group, the hard knots stuck in their throats, while the horrible, empty, feeling returned in the pits of their stomachs. Players were not ready to face anyone. Brad Casciano, from the `96 Team, patiently waited under the goal post. He stepped in line with Aaron, who found it hard to look at his good friend, causing the quarterback to choke on his own words. 'I'm sorry Brad. I'm so sorry!'

'Don't worry about it Aaron. You guys just got screwed!'

Everything seemed hazy to Aaron who threw Brad a confused look.

The team wondered why so many people wanted to hug them or touch their shoulders. They thought everyone would be angry and hate them for what they lost. The desolate looks on their faces even tore at the hearts of diehard Chesaning fans, standing near the fence. Some even touched their shoulders and spoke comforting words. The remorseful scene made everyone feel terrible, as they watched the coaching staff usher players on the bus. Time stood still, while the team waited for Reinhart to finish with the media. Players stared from bus windows, watching their parents, who felt as ominous as the kids, embrace each. It made them feel terrible.

The team couldn't escape the disturbing, thick, nauseous, atmosphere on the bus, while trying to comprehend what just happened. Flashbacks started to surface, like an accident victim regaining his memory. It seemed they dominated possession of the ball, and crossed the endzone more than the score revealed. Jorod sat next to Bo and couldn't stand the quiet tension any longer. He squirmed in his seat then finally yelled, 'CAN YOU BELIEVE THAT SHIT JUST HAPPENED TO US? CAN YOU BELIEVE WHAT JUST HAPPENED?'

The game was filled with confusion, as Bo recalled some of the plays that went sour. It never registered to him during the game until that moment. His pain held an anger as his deep voice shouted, 'WE JUST GOT TOTALLY F!#$%&!'

The noise on the bus instantly halted, as if reality slapped each one of them directly across the face.

Mike Sullivan, from the `91 Team, lingered under the bleachers. He felt sick to his stomach, until he finally hurled. Sullivan was an assistant college coach, who wasn't even supposed to be at the Chesaning game. He was expected to scout a player at another school, but when he approached the Montrose exit on I-75, he simply turned on impulse and drove west instead. He never would've believed what occurred had he not witnessed the game firsthand. Another college coach waited for him to finish puking then muttered, 'It was the worst officiating I've ever seen in all my coaching days and believe me, I've seen some bad calls.'

Sullivan had the same reaction in `94 and hurled when Bo, Aaron, Loafman, Owens, and Woody were scrawny freshmen. Sullivan was a J.V.

defensive coach at the time, filling in for the freshmen offensive coach during a game. It was the last freshman game of the season against Howell, a much larger school. The undefeated Montrose Freshmen were down 0-3 with one last possession. Sullivan did his best to call offensive plays to kids that he was unfamiliar with at the time. He felt thankful that the freshmen kept suggesting plays. Howell called a timeout near the end of the game. The Freshmen Rams waited for Sullivan to finish hurling before he came on the field. They knew their own capabilities, and relied on each other that night to score in the waning seconds, capping their first undefeated high school season with a close 6-3 win.

Sullivan recalled how happy the immature freshmen were on the bus. They unmercifully teased him by making puking sounds the entire way home. Carefree freshmen couldn't believe that a coach got so nervous that he actually hurled. Those same boys had never lost a youth football game since they were eight years old. Now he wondered if the Rams had lost that freshmen game, maybe this Varsity loss would be easier. *He doubted it.* Perhaps it could've prepared them for the world of hurt they felt. Sullivan knew the bus ride home that night was full of lost souls; he couldn't imagine what kind of torment they forced upon themselves.

By the time the Montrose bus pulled into its own parking lot, Coach Kitts was still picking up their equipment inside of Chesaning's press box. The celebration had long ended on the deserted Chesaning field when two young players appeared -- dressed in street clothes and Varsity jackets. He watched them lay on their backs in the middle of the field, gazing at the clear autumn night. Smiles were pasted on their young faces, while they soaked in the remaining excitement of the evening. The scene promoted a guarded smile out of Kitts, who assumed it was the most exciting night of their young lives. Understanding their utmost thrill of victory seemed to offset the emptiness that he felt in his own heart for the Rams.

The emptiness was abundant in their parents, who were aware of their sons' dreams. Parents usually took turns hosting hungry football players after games while waiting for the late news. *Not that night.*

Everyone just went home. Like the atmosphere on the team bus, many families drove home in complete silence while sisters, girlfriends, brothers, and parents tried to understand why they felt so awful. Families decided to give their sons some space, and waited at home. But several students and fans didn't know how else to help, and waited in the parking lot at Montrose High. Players encased in their own private misery, were unsure of how to react when the quiet bus pulled into the parking lot and faced so many cars. Fans intended to show their support, but it rebounded, leaving players with an overwhelming guilt. *The streak was broken.*

Their bodies felt exhausted from their physical game, and the emotional outbreak zapped them as they departed the bus. A worried assistant coach, Scott Taylor, tried to ease their minds, hoping they could find some sort of peace during the night. 'You guys be careful driving home. Keep your heads on straight, and don't do anything to hurt yourselves. A lot of people care about you.'

Jorod couldn't go into the locker room. 'Hey Bo, I'll wait in the truck.'

Bo jammed his pads in his locker, then left without speaking to anyone. He always showered and changed after a game, but he didn't need to worry about breaking superstitions anymore. He just wanted to go home.

Josh Haney, from the '96 Team, came home from Ferris State. He once thought his final football game against dePorres was sad, but it didn't hold a candle to the scene he just witnessed. Haney walked into the locker room and provided comfort to his cousin Aaron. Haney and Casciano served as unofficial bodyguards, protecting their former teammates. Players found some sort of clemency in their compassion, as if their former player status helped resolve them of their sin. Casciano had also played quarterback and felt Aaron's pain while he sat next to him, frozen on the bench for a long, silent time.

Players eventually pulled themselves together. Some took a long, steamy shower as they tried to escape the pain and reality of what just happened. It bought them time before they had to face anyone else. Coach Taylor sat next to Woody on the bench with an arm around his shoulders. He stayed in that position for a long time, talking to him. He made sure that Woody was in the right frame of mind before driving home. When Woody reached his black S-10, he noticed Coach Reinhart walking toward the practice field by himself and yelled, 'Hey Coach, you okay?'

Reinhart's face held a sad expression as he turned around and waved Woody on. Finally, it was his turn to deal with the loss. The Rams could've swallowed an outright ass whipping, but none of them would ever understand the reasoning behind their unscored touchdowns. No one felt that they honestly lost the game, yet they couldn't help but wonder how it happened . . . *and why.* Maybe they could've accepted a loss if they could blame it on a lack of will, or even lack of skill, but to suffer defeat under the conditions they just did, was more than the toughest of them could swallow.

Coach Annese received a call from Mike Sullivan, while he sat in the coach's room on the west side of the state at Jenison High School. Annese thought Sullivan was joking until he recapped the game. Once he recognized the serious tone in Sullivan's voice he moaned, 'NO!'

It sent shivers down Sullivan's spine; he needed to hurl again. Jenison's team experienced a hard loss that same night, so his staff also adorned a downcast mood. Annese couldn't imagine what the coach's office felt like in Montrose; his heart reached out to Denny, his staff, and the team.

Loaf sat hunched over, locked in the same position on the stiff locker room bench an hour later. Josh Schlorf, a junior third string quarterback, noticed that Loaf still had his helmet on. He watched as the senior captain sat motionless with a wild, gazed expression like a drugged, caged animal.

Schlorf respected his senior team leaders, and didn't know how to react or help. Loafman was oblivious to the activity in the locker room, and was totally unaware of the dampness of his uniform. As a third year Varsity player, he had experienced the pain of losing two playoff games, but that pain didn't compare to this. Players nudged Loaf, 'Change and go home.'

But Loaf wouldn't move -- he couldn't. He just stared at the floor unable to erase the mental picture of the final scoreboard, 'Visitors 12-Home 14.' Loafman sat on the lonely bench in disbelief, reliving the last few hours of his life. He hated to lose, especially like that. Once Loaf regained his senses, he noticed the stillness of the locker room and realized that he was alone. Everyone had left. He slowly changed out of his wet, filthy uniform and joined the coaches in the small room down the hall.

He watched them review the game film . . . stop, rewind, then critique each penalty on the film, trying to make sense of the outcome. Analyzing the stats confirmed exactly what they all thought; the Rams dominated the game with a 285-115 rushing advantage, and ran the ball 54 times compared to 27 for the Indians.

The loss became an infectious disease that quickly spread, impacting everyone connected with it. Eric Hyde joined his Flint Carman-Ainsworth coaching staff, and his parents at their favorite pizzeria. They had defeated the defending Big 9 Champions and were in a festive mood, while waiting for the evening news. The pizzeria had three large TV's to capture all local stations. The first channel to start Friday night sports showed a Chesaning player catching a pass, while the crowd went nuts. Eric thought, *Hmmm, it must've been a close game.* Like other alumni, he faithfully followed the scores of Montrose games each week, naturally expecting that the Rams would always win.

All three channels featured the highly publicized Montrose-Chesaning game as their opening story. Eric's body went numb when he heard the final score. His heart dropped to his knees, and he felt appalled for the Montrose Rams. He had a flashback of the '91 Montrose-Chesaning game, that came down to the last few seconds. Eric remembered how physically exhausted he felt after that game. It was such an emotional game, which could've gone either way. His '91 Team felt tremendous pressure back then to keep the precious streak alive when it was only at 27 consecutive games. He couldn't begin to explain how horrible he felt to his fellow coaches. Eric wondered if anyone outside the Montrose Football Family could understand the morbid feeling. You either had to play the sport or be so closely involved, to even begin to relate to the emotions attached to the streak.

Led, from the '90 Team, was also at the game. He left with a broken heart, not for selfish reasons but for the team. It was the worst case scenario one could imagine in a football game, and he felt terrible for the team. It was unfortunate that 17-year-old kids had to experience that level of pressure. Sometimes life seemed unfair; *ending the streak was one of those times.*

The streak was held together by a thin thread, at times, until it finally snapped. Admittedly, players wanted the legacy to go on forever, but knew that was impractical. It was a great ride while it lasted, but no one wanted it to end, especially in the suspenseful manner that it did.

Jorod and Bo drove home in silence. Jorod took the first shower then climbed into his bed. Bo lingered in the shower longer than usual, recapping the game, which still seemed like a giant blur. He knocked the back of his head against the shower wall as steamy water beat against his face. Bo hoped the eerie feeling would wash itself down the drain. He couldn't remember feeling so ashamed or awful, and felt relieved for the privacy of his own shower. He cried with as much grief as someone who had just lost his best friend. A while later, Jorod knocked on his bedroom door. 'Hey Bo, you sleepin' yet?'

Bo's face was blotchy, while his knotted throat forced out a trembling, 'Nope. Can't.'

The night didn't seem too hopeful, and they decided to stand in their parent's doorway, wanting to raid their bed. It seemed like the only safe haven in the world. A parents love was unconditional; they wouldn't reject them. Rin Moore sat up, 'Well don't just stand there -- come on in.'

The king-sized bed barely had room for Jorod, once Bo sprawled his 6'3" body across the end. Bo was haunted by the clipping play, which in his mind had cost them the game . . . and the streak, yet he knew he was faultless. 'Dad, I did not clip that guy! I know I didn't!'

'I know Bo. I watched you. The coaches will see in on films, but it won't change anything.'

Jorod's bleak expression said it all. 'If only my touchdown would've counted, we would be celebrating right now.' His wobbly voice finally emitted his anger. 'How many times do I have to cross the damn endzone before they call it a touchdown?'

He gave all that his 160 pounds could give, without reward, and it haunted him. The four of them openly talked about the game, while letting the boys vent their frustration. Rin and his wife felt relieved once the boys finally returned to their own rooms, wondering how much longer they could fool them. Both were thankful the boys hadn't come in earlier, when they were overwhelmed with their own tears about the events of the night. It all seemed so unjust considering the importance of what was represented.

Across town, Woodys' parents laid in bed, waiting for their son to come home. A dark, heavy feeling loomed over them, while the memory of their son lying face down on the field lingered in their minds. *What does a parent say to their son at a time like that?* He was a happy-go-luck teenager, who now faced one of the hardest things life had ever dealt him. His mom anxiously glanced at the clock every two minutes. *What was taking so long to drive three miles? What if he was too upset to drive? What if something happened?* She tried not to panic, but suddenly felt extremely guilty for not waiting at the school. Her husband finally breathed a sigh of relief when the sound of Woody's S-10 made its way up the long, gravel driveway.

Woody had lingered in the locker room with Aaron, his best friend. Now, he felt uncomfortable walking into his own house, but knew he had to. He couldn't sit in his truck all night, although he was so exhausted he easily could've. Woody slowly walked into his parents' bedroom, and sat on the edge of their bed, without speaking a word. He hadn't done that since he was eight, after a bad thunderstorm had frightened him. The moonlight provided just enough gleam through the blinds to reflect Woody's firmly set jaw, a rare indication that he was extremely tense. The larger-than-life seventeen-year-old dropped his head, silhouetting a hunched over, ninety-year old man. His parents had never seen him so exhausted, so whipped and scared that he couldn't even speak. Woody just sat there, wishing that somehow they could fix his awful feeling, like they did when he was eight.

His mom didn't even try to talk above the firm lump in her own throat, and soothingly circled his back with the palm of her hand. His dad spoke in a calm voice, managing to find just the right words to comfort him in a way that only a dad could.

Woody finally spoke, 'I don't understand why she didn't score my touchdown.'

It happened on the opposite side of the field and his dad couldn't see the line. 'Well Bud, there's nothing you can do about it. All you can do is never leave any chance of doubt in a ref's mind the next time.'

Woody only nodded, feeling totally responsible for their loss. Things started to become less foggy as the night wore on. Somehow, he drew comfort from learning that others felt several decisions were questionable; and they weren't just a bunch of screw-ups. He was dog-tired and gloomily said, 'I need to go to bed.'

Exhaustion consumed Woody when he crossed the living room to his own bedroom. He closed his eyes, restlessly reliving the play when he batted down the pass before Chesaning scored their final TD. *Why didn't he catch it instead of batting it down? Why?* That play crept into his head after he dozed off, forcing him to face the demons that frequented his dreams throughout the night.

Woody was unaware that he passed his girlfriend who patiently waited on the couch in the dark living room. She felt terrible and alone, while everyone deplorably laid in their own bed, completely forgetting about her. She didn't know what to do or how to get home, and quietly called her mom in the middle of the night to pick her up.

The Montrose Rams cherished their streak that spanned a decade, and fought to keep it alive. Owens walked into his house with a gloomy heart, expecting a long, lonely night. He sunk heavily into his bed, then felt the dam break. He was distraught, and couldn't believe what had happened. Blinded by his own tears, he opened his bedroom window and swallowed a deep breath of cold, night air, feeling deceived for believing in happy endings.

Aaron subconsciously drove home; he didn't recall leaving the school parking lot. He relived the final series when he grabbed Chesaning's pass on first down. He felt the leather in his hands and couldn't help but wonder, *Why did Fedechenko knock it down? Why did that happen?* He shut the key off, threw his head back against the headrest, and closed his eyes. He felt himself jump up and grab the ball, determined to keep their winning streak alive. He held ten years of effort in the palm of his hands, if only for a brief second. It would've ended the game, and their streak would still be intact.

Fedechenko sat in his parent's driveway across town, wondering the exact same thing. In a split second, he attentively focused on preventing the TD at all cost, but averted the interception instead. It was such a crazy moment. Fedechenko was fully determined to stop anyone from catching that ball. But, he didn't realize that he stopped Aaron. *Damn. Why did it happen? Why? The game could've been over, and none of them would be experiencing the terrible hellhole there were in.*

Aaron tried to gather enough courage to go inside and face his family and his girlfriend, and wondered -- *Why is it hardest to face the ones you love the most?* He sensed their uneasiness the moment he walked into the living room. His mom reached him first, and wrapped her arms around her youngest son, feeling his shoulders drop. 'Aaron, I am so sorry.'

She took out her frustration on the caliber of officials that refereed the game. She was so angry. 'You did not lose that game. It was taken from you!'

Being the quarterback's mom was still a new role for her; she quickly learned that she needed broad shoulders. Aaron had one win and one loss under his belt. The crowd either loved her son when the play worked, or quickly criticized him when it didn't. It was the nature of the game, but she took is personal. Now, she understood why Linda Klopf never sat in the bleachers during the years that her sons were the Montrose quarterbacks.

Aaron looked at his older brother, I'm sorry for breaking your streak Jake.'

Jake felt miserable that his younger brother would go down as the quarterback when the streak was broken, in spite of the effort he gave right down to the last second. It just didn't seem fair. He hugged Aaron, feeling his pain. 'Don't worry about me Aaron.'

Sparky hugged his son next and spoke from his heart. 'Aaron, things happen for reasons we don't understand, whether the team is winning or losing. Football is about life. We had some questionable calls tonight. It was unfair and unfortunate, but we're not done yet. Even if we end up having a losing season, but the guys become better people because of it, then you guys are still winners.'

In the back of his mind, Sparky knew that he would become an official. He vowed that he would be completely fair, and never respond like that group did. He knew how much Aaron loved the game, and how hard he worked. The Saturday papers credited Aaron for a tremendous game, after gaining 180 yards. His TD run that was called back, would've added even more yardage, signifying a dazzling game under normal circumstances. Instead, it was overshadowed by their heartbreaking loss. Fans probably wouldn't notice the effort that Aaron gave.

Aaron's parents sat in their living room with their sons and their girlfriends, unsure of what to say to lift anyone's spirits. They found a form of comfort in just being together, until the unfitting ring of the phone interrupted the silence at 1 AM. It was Hodge from Ferris State; the former Rams All-State quarterback couldn't attend the game because of his football schedule. Former players Ryan Persails and Crusher were also on his team, and lived in the same dorm. Hodge punched the dresser in this dorm room when they told him the news and he shrieked, 'NO!'

He had to call Aaron to find out if it was true. If it was, he needed to be there for Aaron. He had to. Hodge rubbed his throbbing hand, while he nervously waited for someone to answer at the Emmendorfer home. His throat immediately tightened the moment he heard the voice of Aaron's mom. Hodge could barely speak. She sensed the emotion on the other end of the phone, and waited until she heard a forced, unsteady voice say -- 'It's Hodge.'

The moment he spoke, she felt her own tears return and extended the cordless phone to Aaron. 'It's Hodge.'

A massive lump knotted in Aaron's chest, as tears swelled in his saddened eyes. He felt his body tense with fear, and he shook his head. His own frightened voice sobbed, 'I can't talk to Hodge right now.'

She tried to be strong and fought back her own tears, as she handed her son the phone. 'Aaron, Hodge needs to talk to you right now and you need to talk to him.'

Aaron felt awful for letting one of his closest friends down. He swallowed hard, then forced his name, 'Hodge!'

Hodge felt a cold chill rush through his entire body, as his heart dropped to his knees. Aaron's quivering voice confirmed what Hodge tried to avoid. 'I'm so sorry I broke your streak!'

Until that moment, Hodge hoped that someone had played a cruel joke on him. He wasn't worried about the streak; he was worried about Aaron. Hodge related to the quarterback better than anyone. He painfully sobbed from his dorm room three hours away, fighting the sick feeling that lingered in the pit of his own gut. 'I'm sorry Aaron, I'm so sorry.'

The clocked ticked on. Neither of them could speak or share the details of the game. They just listened to each other sob, which connected them quarterback-to-quarterback. Hodge understood the pressure that Aaron was under, and felt the pain of his former teammates. He wished that he could do something. They held a strong bond from sweating and bleeding together, and pushing each other like they had. It produced a brotherhood, a true comradeship, that was so different at the college level. Hodge genuinely cared for his former teammates, and felt like someone opened his chest and ripped his heart out.

Hodge was stunned by his inability to talk, which made him realize just how painful their situation was. But Aaron didn't need to hear any words; he only needed to know that Hodge was still there for him. Hodge finally forced a painful good-bye. The dial tone echoed in Aaron's ear, reminding him of the flat monotone sound of the scoreboard buzzer. He clicked the cordless off as he slowly tapped the phone against his other hand, as if coddling a football. Aaron's new tears became contagious and overwhelmed his girlfriend, Jake's girlfriend, his brother, and his parents who waited with him in the darkness of the living room. A glimmering candle reflected their tear-streamed faces, while they listened to Aaron face the one former player that he felt he had let down the most -- Hodge. *It was a moment they would never forget.*

Bo tossed and turned throughout the seemingly endless hours, while dark, vicious thoughts subconsciously lingered. In the next room, exhaustion finally devoured Jorod who dozed off, escaping the evil spirits for a few hours.

They were surprised that the sun actually came up on Saturday morning; their world really didn't end because the streak had been broken. Rin sent the boys for donuts and a Saturday morning paper, hoping that the fresh air cheered them up. Facing that particular Saturday morning alone seemed unbearable to Bo and Jorod; they were thankful they had each other to lean on. Bo hoped they didn't run into anyone they knew, and intentionally avoided the local bakery. But it appeared that luck was not on their side that weekend. They ran into a former player as they walked out of the gas station, carrying a folded newspaper. The player recognized them and jokingly asked, 'Hey, I couldn't make it to the game. Did you guys win?'

A wave of guilt jolted through both of them. 'No man, we lost.'

'C'mon, what was the score?'

They both felt so guilty and seriously repeated, 'No, we really lost!'

Bo and Jorod felt their eyes search the pavement, unable to make direct eye contact with the former player. Their eyes followed his feet, and noticed how he stopped walking after realizing their serious tone. Bo and Jorod felt the horrible, gut-wrenching feeling return.

It was usually fun to wake-up early on Saturday mornings in Montrose and read the sports section. *But not that day.* Fans wanted to protect their boys, and dreaded the walk to the paper box, wondering how cruel the media had been.

The game made front cover news, as well as the main feature of the sports section. Jorod opened the paper, then felt his heart drop as he read the thick, blocked letters. 'STOPPED!' 'Montrose Streak Snapped at 80. Chesaning Pulls Upset.' He glanced over at Bo and watched his broad shoulders hug the steering wheel. Before starting the truck, Bo dropped his head and exhaled a deep sigh.

The Rams had another Bo on the team, a junior 260 pound tackle, that outweighed Bo Moore by 50 pounds. 'Bo Paxton' felt the urge to go hunting the moment his eyes opened that Saturday morning. The woods always felt like his sanctuary. The Paxton house was extremely quiet, and he knew that his family felt terrible for him. He didn't want to face them just yet, and called teammate Cary House. 'Hey, I'm on my way over. Get ready. We're goin' hunting.'

Paxton vanished into the woods with his best friend and his rifle. The woods had always been his haven, but it felt strange that day. *Life* suddenly felt strange. He couldn't help but wonder, *What would we be doing right now if we tied the streak? Life would be so different today.*

Paxton and Cary were both edgy and nervous as they walked through the woods. Paxton looked straight ahead as he spoke. 'Man, what are we gonna do? There's never been a team that's lost before since we started playing football.'

Cary also found it hard to face his best friend. 'How are we supposed to practice knowing we lost?'

The two juniors really didn't know if the team would pack up their bags and hang up the season, or become stronger. They didn't know what would happen next, as they yielded their own thoughts to the silence. *Would things be the same, or different? How did the other guys feel? The seniors had to feel even lower than they did . . . if that was possible.*

Paxton finally broke the silence. 'Cary, think we should have a bonfire at my house tonight? It might help to get everyone together.'

'Yeah, that's a good idea. It might be easier to face each other before films on Sunday.'

When Barry Paxton heard that the streak was broken, he felt disappointed. The streak had special meaning to him, since he was a member of the '88 Team that started it all. Every year the obligation to keep the streak alive grew deeper. Like links in a chain, each year was equally important. Barry was proud of the character that the '97 Team showed. He called his younger cousin and placed blame on his '88 Team. Paxton listened while Barry sympathetically said, 'We didn't have the expectations or the pressures that you guys faced. Look at it this way, if the '88 Team had won our first two games that season, then you would've tied the state record. So it's our fault. Blame it on us.'

It drew a chuckle from the younger Paxton cousin who appreciated a totally different perspective. It was the only thing that anyone had said during the entire weekend that actually made Bo Paxton feel better.

Kevin Salter was Barry's teammate on the `88 Team. He felt just as bad for this little brother Craig, another junior on the team, who went by 'Salty Dog.' Kevin knew how much heart that his little brother had, and how important maintaining the streak meant. In a strange way, he almost felt relieved for the team and wisely guided the younger Salter. 'Now you can just go out and play football without all of that pressure being placed on you.'

Salty Dog couldn't understand what his older brother meant, but felt relieved that he didn't blame him or his teammates. He admired his older brother, and wanted to play as good as he did. It was the worst Salty Dog ever remembered feeling and he wondered, *Why did it have to happen on his first Varsity game that I started in? It was supposed to be a great day.*

The maturity of the earlier streak players came through. Vinnie, from the `89 Team, couldn't believe the news when Mr. Venturino made the disappointing call to his son from Michigan to Kentucky. Vinnie closely followed the Rams, and immediately felt sorry for the team. He had never played under that kind of pressure; he couldn't imagine how the players felt. Vinnie wondered, *How do you deal with that?*

It was a strange, bizarre game that was hard to explain to someone who hadn't physically attended it. Trying to rationalize what developed didn't do the penalty calls any justice, and sounded like whining. It was simply an uncanny game that someone actually had to experience to believe.

The young Cross brothers absorbed more than people realized. When the water boys lost a close youth football game that Saturday, they fell to the ground and cried, like their heroes did the night before. It was their first loss and they thought that reaction was expected. Their youth football coaches realized they were emulating the Varsity's outcome from the night before, and tried to explain the difference.

Saturday was a dark time in Montrose. Planning the bonfire offered players an excuse to call their closest friends throughout the day. They all felt the emotional weight of the loss squash the life right out of them. Mr. Paxton was outside when the first player arrived. He noticed how the player struggled to even say hello. Mr. Paxton sensed how difficult it was for players to face anyone, and allowed his dad status to invisibly mark him as a safety net. He knew how hard the loss was for his own son, and realized that players had serious issues to work through. The sympathetic dad automatically extended his long arms to hug a kid he barely knew. The player's head dropped when his sobs started, allowing the shaken dad to feel the young man's pain. *That's how tough it was.* It took every ounce of dad power in his tall, large body to hold back his own emotions. He managed to say in a soothing voice, 'Hey, everything will be okay.'

As more players trickled in, Mr. Paxton unofficially stood in the middle of the driveway, embracing each one. If they ever needed someone to understand and console them, that was the time. Players needed to know that the world wasn't mad at them, and they weren't bad kids. However, watching big, strapping boys with anguished faces come together for the first time, was a painful memory that Mr. Paxton wouldn't easily erase.

Players were young and didn't know the ways of the world yet, and wondered if they really wanted to. That weekend, the world seemed cruel and unfair. The teenagers tried to gain their composure before venturing out to the bonfire behind the garage. No one dared to look up from their trancelike state when new teammates joined the circle around the fire, as if participating in some sort of sacred ritual. No one wanted to make eye contact. Instead, they intently focused on the stillness of the night, while deep orange and royal blue flames shot hot little sparks that danced in the brisk, night air.

They stood together as a team yet felt so all alone, as they discovered how much they honestly needed each other. They couldn't get through it alone, and drew strength from being together. Each one took on the blame, feeling like he had let the others down. No one ever imagined that ending the streak would make him feel so low. It was all they could do to be tough, but the moment someone cracked, several followed. They felt worthless and physically drained after the emotional gamut of the past 24 hours. The reality of what happened started to sink in, leaving them unsure of how to react. Players wondered, *Will we ever be able to come to grips with this, or will it scar our souls forever?* It all crashed so quickly. Even players like center Adam Powell, who normally concealed his emotions, released them in the privacy of his squad. In a way, he felt thankful not to have to face another dark night -- *alone.*

Most couldn't remember the last time they even cried. It had to be when they were young and broke a bone, or scraped a knee. Tears of shame spilled down their cheeks. Players realized they were human beings who really cared about something important; something that seemed larger than life. The massiveness of it all made the teenagers feel so far removed from the carefree life they once knew. That all changed overnight.

The streak went down as an unexplained misfortune, but none the same it was the end of the line. Montrose Football had run its battery on high for a long stretch, until it finally drained. The team tried to be strong, but felt better after releasing vented emotions. Only then could they openly talk about the game. Confusion still surrounded how they lost a game they dominated. Their parents and coaches all said, 'It happened for a reason.' They wondered just what the hell that phrase actually meant. Players had to get mentally tough and come together, or it could destroy them. Just one night on the dark side tarnished their self-esteem and their confidence, leaving them absolutely bewildered. Former players wanted them to be strong and find a way to battle through it, not roll over and die. The loss had already taken its toll on them, marking the end of an era, and the beginning of a sad saga that played on their minds for a very, long time.

Loafman never made it to the bonfire; he never left his bedroom. He tossed and turned throughout the night, trying to sort out the tormenting feelings that loomed inside. He sat on his bed and stared at the wall the entire day, replaying the game in his head --*as if it would change the outcome.* It felt like he'd lost everything. Football was his universe and it was abruptly shaken. He lived with his mom and two sisters. They were a close family, but a bunch of girls didn't know how to help him. His mom was a teacher and coach herself and could easily make him laugh. *Not that day.* Her son had never been so despondent; his unresponsive actions were totally out of character, and it worried her. His older sister, Chrissy, felt helpless too. She was still haunted from being at Aaron's the night before when Hodge called. She wished that one of his coaches would call her brother, and snap him out of his semi-comatose state.

Parents contacted each other later in the day to check on their sons, and shared how drained they felt. They decided to get together at Woodwards, a mile down the road from the bonfire. Like the boys, it was strange when everyone first arrived. They quickly discovered how much they also needed to be together. Parents embraced each other, wondering if anyone outside of their football family could possibly comprehend their state of mind. Sad stories were exchanged about important conversations held between fathers and sons after the game. The restless night had a common effect as bodies tossed and turned throughout Montrose that night. Many woke up every few hours shaken by a terrible dream that they lost a bizarre game. The hollow feeling returned once they realized the reality of it. They reminded themselves that *it was just a game,* but they all knew better. What they couldn't understand was the peculiar feeling it left them with. It felt like the ache of death, and they wondered why. Maybe it felt like something very special was taken and they couldn't prevent it from happening. Or maybe the last time anyone had cried or felt so emotionally exhausted was after a funeral, and naturally related the two.

Nervous energy quickly pervaded the Woodward home, as parents organized a community tailgate party. They would celebrate having 'The Second Longest Winning Streak in the History of Michigan High School Football.' It wouldn't be as elaborate as the record-breaking celebration originally planned, but it was still an accomplishment worthy of honoring ten years of players. Being together formed a unique bond among them. Parents drew strength from each other, like their sons did at the bonfire. They needed that strength to help their sons heal -- *all 37 of them.*

It took courage to attend films on Sunday. The players tried to ignore the aggravating feelings that gnawed in their stomachs. No one knew what to expect, since they had never before critiqued a losing game film during the regular season. Gary approached the team entrance at the back of the school, and read a hand written sign that was stuck in the ground. Its three simple words said it all -- **'Keep the Faith.'** He paused to read a second sign that was taped to the entrance of the team door, **'We Love our Rams.'** Both were out of sight and hidden from the public, intended only for the eyes of the team. Two simple signs that gave the team hope and they thought, *Wow - people still cared.* No one knew who made the signs, but no one dared to remove them. They became weathered, yet remained in the original spot for the remainder of the season.

It was still difficult to face each other, but nothing compared to the emotion they released at the bonfire Saturday night; they felt thankful that scene was behind them. The coaches had reviewed the game film numerous times, trying to make sense of it. No one could understand the clipping call against Bo. It looked like the Chesaning player fell down in front of Bo, and appeared as clear as day on tape that Bo never clipped him. Bo must've relived that play 100 times in his head since Friday night. Now that he watched the film firsthand, it eased his guilt. In a small way it helped him regain his integrity, although it didn't make Aaron's TD count, or change the score, or mend their streak.

The team closely watched as the offensive line desperately blocked; they saw Jorod actually break the plane, crossing the few inches into the endzone. They hit the rewind button and watched it, again-and-again; regret consumed them each time that it wasn't scored. They painfully watched, trying to comprehend it all, as the dreadful feelings resurfaced. Two distinct plays that made a big difference. Now. . . *it pissed them off!*

The loss couldn't be denied regardless of the circumstances, but if they didn't put it behind them soon, it would destroy them. Reinhart remembered what it felt like to be a 17-year-old kid. He wanted them to express their frustration, so they wouldn't explode. He clicked the video off, then looked at his sedated team. 'Last week is over guys. It's in the past, so I'm giving you a homework assignment. Everyone has to write a pair of essays. The first one I want you to write down your feelings about the game. In the second, I want you to write about your plans to move forward. They're due at 7:25 AM tomorrow morning.'

Gary covered up his feelings and joked with Corky, 'Hey, we never had homework in football before.'

No one complained. It was a therapeutic assignment, although some struggled to share their innermost private feelings on paper. Others found putting pen to paper easier than talking out loud about it. It took courage to attend school on Monday; skipping would've been the easy way out. Reinhart knew that facing peers and teachers would be tough, which explained his early deadline. He wasn't a bit surprised when he found most of the team waiting outside of his room when he arrived Monday morning, essays in tow.

Several shared feelings about letting their team, previous teams, and the entire community of Montrose down. Gary wrote, 'I took things for granted. Now I know what it takes to get to this level. I never thought about losing.'

Woody wrote, 'Lying on the field after the final horn, crying, not wanting to get up made me feel like somebody just died.'

Aaron wrote, 'I couldn't believe it was happening as the time was winding down. I never thought about losing. I never thought it could happen to us.'

Bo wrote, 'I'm angry with myself, the Chesaning players and the refs. I'm going to push himself and my teammates harder, and make the team better.'

The squad didn't know what to expect from their peers and teachers on Monday. It required enormous effort to attend each class and face a new set of students, as well as another teacher, every hour. It was tough, yet they felt relieved when their peers didn't ridicule them. Instead, they empathized. They were a school that needed healing. The principal and his assistant reached out to the squad. They stood tall in the hallways between classes and repeated, 'Hold your heads high. You have nothing to be ashamed of.'

Courage was tested.

Bo carried a copy of his written goals to each class, reading them for reinforcement every hour. He folded the paper, then placed it in his shoe before practice on Monday. In spite of how he felt, he remained positive, telling his teammates, 'We have a different destiny than those in the past. Most of those teams of the last nine seasons won all year, then ended their seasons with a loss. We've had our loss for the year. Now we have a chance at redemption.'

Like most players, Jorod found it hard to pay attention during school, and in practice. They all went through the motions but felt like a dark, heavy cloud hovered over them. Bo felt that he worked hard, yet couldn't escape the gnawing feeling that fought to bring him down.

An unwritten rule existed in sports that players don't moan about the officiating. The Rams paid a high price for their loss, and found comfort in supporting calls from other coaches who had scouts at the game. Some planned to insist that same combination of referees not be allowed to officiate their upcoming game against Chesaning. They suggested their actions be reviewed, but what could be done? They couldn't replay the game. No one could put a cast on the streak now that the damage was over. The Montrose A.D. felt his own guilt. Never before had he felt the need to exercise his right to bring two officials from his own county, when non-league schools played each other. If he could go back and change it, he would request the best officials from each county for such an important game.

Players tried to disguise the burden they carried, while they struggled through practice with heavy hearts. No one had the right answers and fingers were being pointed. It was a tough week and their emotions were drained.

Their voices said, 'We're doing fine' but their eyes told a different story. The coaching staff saw right through them, and discussed their choices, reiterating how they could either 'give up' or 'go on.'

The squad definitely wanted to go on.

Coach Coon observed their broken hearts, and it killed him. He was used to seeing them so full of life. He couldn't fix this. All he could do was push them to find the courage to persevere and continue.

If that blocking dummy had a name, it would be called 'Chesaning.' It was on the receiving end of the blunt of the line's frustration. If it could talk, it would claim how bruised it felt. Coon found it rewarding to see his guys take their frustration out during their drills. They had the willingness to start over and the courage to battle back; he knew they would get back on track. Their determination endeared him, and he told his line, 'Losses don't become failures, they are setbacks. I know it hurts now, but put it in perspective. We just lost a football game. Not for lack of effort or will, you battled until the very end. There were a lot of bad calls, and a lot of things went wrong. We'll start over again. We're not done yet.'

Montrose fans printed T-shirts, 'Montrose Football, 80 Wins - Oh What a Streak.' The back side sported, '2nd Longest Winning Streak in the History of MHSAA Football.' Chesaning printed shirts that boasted, 'We Broke the Streak.' The fact that they sold like hot cakes upset the Rams to no end until Coach D commented, 'Chesaning beat you *once* in *ten* years. What shirt would you rather wear?'

It was time to put the streak behind them and focus on **Goodrich.** The Rams memorized their new motto:

**'You Can't Go Back And Make A Brand New Start, But
You Can Start Now And Make A Brand New End'**

Fans greeted former streak players from 1988-1996 at the Community Tailgate party, while the aroma of grilled hotdogs filled the air. Large banners displayed ten years worth of players' names. Stories were told and games rehashed as former teammates came together. Being able to recognize their accomplishments and not totally focusing on what was lost, held a sense of healing for the football family.

Will Smith's hit, *'Here Come the Men in Black'* blared over the loud speaker when special teams prepared to take the field. They wore the home black jerseys, and needed to walk past the tailgate party in order to reach the field. Seeing so many people under the huge tent only increased their anxiety. Each wondered, *How can I face them?* The streak had snowballed into something beyond what earlier teams ever imagined. Former players didn't blame them, but the '97 Rams didn't know that. The '97 Rams wanted to go *unnoticed* when they formed their traditional two-by-two procession, with a crack in their armor. Loaf, Aaron, Bo, Woody, Owens, Jorod, Winny,

Gary, Adam, and Cary were part of the guys who tried to maintain a tough face, but couldn't ignore the gnawing ache in the pit of their stomachs. One week wasn't enough time to heal their wounds; no one felt comfortable enough to face the public. They tried to embrace themselves and dig out of the hole they were in. The moment they were spotted, hundreds of fans stood and clapped to show their support, but the team hardly felt worthy of a standing ovation.

Whatever disgruntled fan said, 'The '97 Team didn't have any heart,' should've been standing close enough to see real tears stream down their faces as they walked to the field, clinging to the small amount of dignity they had left. *Damn*. They felt like it was *them* against the world; like they ran a marathon and got tripped five yards before the finish line. It's not supposed to end like that. They wanted more than anything to be playing to *break* the state's streak record that night, not celebrating *second* place.

But Goodrich didn't care about the circumstances surrounding Montrose's loss, or how close their last game was. The seed had been planted -- the Montrose Rams could be beat. It was all Goodrich needed. In their minds, the mystique was finally broken; the Rams were fair game. The Martians invaded the Rams' field with extra hope and determination, wanting to leave town with a victory. The entire GEC League felt the same way, anxious for their chance to beat Montrose. Little did they know how badly the Rams planned to vent their frustrations on the remaining seven league opponents.

The visiting Goodrich Martians treated the Rams like they were in enemy territory, driving 80 yards on their first possession. The Rams looked like the wind had been knocked from their sails when the Martians capped the drive with a 41 yard scoring pass. When a team has a slump, it sometimes takes awhile to snap out; but the Rams didn't have awhile. Dads were heard throughout the stands, 'C'mon boys, bounce back.'

Bo practically ripped an opponent's jersey off when they drilled into each other. He ran off the field and thought, *We are just a bunch of screw-ups!* The Montrose sideline attempted to boost the Rams up. They had already put themselves through a tough week of emotional hell. Goodrich meant business. If the Rams didn't snap out of it quickly, it would bite them.

The game was scheduled on Saturday so that Tony Annese could attend what could have been, a state record breaking victory. His presence created a sense of anticipation in Aaron when he saw the former coach on the sideline. It empowered Aaron with extra drive; he wanted to make Annese proud. Aaron was the young water boy under the former coach, and wanted to show what he could do as the quarterback for the Rams. Aaron drove 66 yards on their first possession, then handed off to Jorod who scored on a two yard run. Aaron felt better after Scott's extra point tied the game at 7-7. *They all did.* They knew the only way to be successful was to never quit.

The Rams pounced on a Goodrich fumble on the first play from scrimmage, after the kickoff at the 16. Aaron ran a 19 yard TD, but was canceled out after a penalty, so Scott booted a 28 yard field goal instead. Goodrich answered right back with a 25 yard field goal, tying the game 10-10 with 4:41 left in the half. Goodrich wanted to hit the Rams hard, while they still felt the impact from the Chesaning loss. The war was on.

Aaron's unscored TD made him fearful of a possible recurrence of what happened during the Chesaning game. He became determined to find a way into the endzone. He scored a four yard TD with just over a minute left in the half. It was a small lead, but a moral victory that uplifted the Rams for a 17-10 lead at the intermission. Former players loudly cheered and whistled in an effort to refuel the Rams -- *whether the `97 squad could believe it or not.*

Goodrich dominated the third quarter after a high snap that forced Loafman to run the ball instead of punting from the Montrose 48. The Martians took over at the Montrose 39, and scored on their seventh play after breaking a tackle from 10 yards out. After the third, the game was tied 17-17; too close for comfort.

It would take a big fourth quarter for the Rams to pull out a win, but they were determined to do so. It turned into a whale of a game as both teams took pride in their defenses and played their hearts out, unwilling to surrender. Reinhart settled them down in the huddle. He focused on being disciplined and staying within their blocks during the final quarter. Owens made an awesome block, releasing some of the demons that haunted him. Five minutes into the final quarter, Winny broke the tie when he scored on a seven yard run. Aaron was in position to catch the snap on the PAT, then used his quick reflexes to turn a high snap into a two-point conversion.

The Rams became stronger the longer they played; their extra effort became contagious. Bo manhandled every opponent that he faced, making Goodrich pay for his aggravation. Their train was temporarily derailed, but now appeared back on track, halting Goodrich near midfield. It gave the offense good field position and prevented a tie ballgame. Seeing their boys back on track, warmed the hearts of former players and pleased the Montrose coaching staff. Their confidence reappeared as they marched down the field on an eight-play drive. Aaron scored a final TD in the closing seconds, sealing a '32-17' victory. Montrose made a dramatic comeback; the *Men-in-Black* were really back. The victory made them stronger, replacing a morsel of self-doubt with hope and courage.

Annese and Reinhart addressed all ten years of Montrose football players who gathered on the field after the game. They represented a cohesive group that shared common values and goals, and held a high sense of loyalty toward each other. Each team believed in their unrelenting quest to play in the Pontiac Silverdome and win a State Championship; the streak had been an added bonus along the way.

Former players merged together like old friends, possessing a mutual affection, a shared desire, for the game of football. The `97 Team situated themselves on the opposite side of the coaches, feeling ashamed and broken.

Bo was so consumed by guilt that he could barely handle standing so close to former players. He wished they were celebrating a record that night. Bo listened to Coach Annese influence the crowd like he had for so many years. He acknowledged their accomplishments, while his soothing words tried to make them all feel better.

But it would take more than words to cheer them up. The '97 players were invited to eat food after the game, but hardly anyone showed. They didn't feel like the celebration was intended for *them* and still felt empty after the game. *Facing people was overwhelming.*

Coach Clolinger needed all of them to focus on **Hamady** and used a simple motto for week four:

'Every Player – Every Play'

Reinhart felt that practice went better after Goodrich, although his team still didn't emotionally seem quite themselves. They were physically banged up after two consecutive weeks of solid hitting. Injuries prevented three Montrose starters from playing against Hamady. Loafman's neck caused him a lot of pain, but he still planned to play against the Hawks.

Other players accepted the challenge to step up, but couldn't seem to get anything going, and played a scoreless first quarter. It got uglier after Aaron fractured two bones in his left hand, forcing back-up quarterback Kris Brown to come in. Kris was a blonde-haired, quiet, athletic kid who preferred his position at receiver, over the spotlight of being in the driver's seat. But he would play where the team needed him.

Defending pass defense against Hamady was a challenge. If the Hawks connected on a deep Hail Mary pass, the Rams feared they would be hard to catch. Kris stuck to a ground game, and activated the veer option well for his first time at the helm. Owens and Jorod each scored second quarter TD's, putting the Rams ahead 14-0 at the half.

Coach lit a fire under them during the intermission, which resulted in Kris, Jorod, and Cary scoring third quarter TD's. Schlorf came in as the third string quarterback and scored after romping 35 yards. The Rams overcame adversity. They became a better football team after other players received game experience to shutout the Hamady Hawks '48-0.' The Rams finally reached the end of the denial phase; they felt ready to move on.

Coach Clolinger wanted their drive to continue without becoming overconfident. He carefully chose the next motto, while the Rams prepared for the **Lake Fenton** Blue Devils:

'If What You Did Yesterday Still Looks Big To You, You Haven't Done Much Today!'

Homecoming week laced the school with a festive atmosphere, restoring optimism on the home front. It seemed odd that a football player wasn't elected for Homecoming King, even though six players made the court. While their votes seemed to outcast each other, players chalked it up to their school going through a lot of changes. No one actually wanted to label it as the end of yet another steak. At least their Homecoming King was a former player; the team hoped that claimed some credit toward tradition.

In the first period against Lake Fenton, Jorod and Winny each rushed for over 100 yards and scored three TD's. In spite of the hairline fracture in Aaron's hand, he opened up the passing game by connecting with Joe Bob and Woody. When Joe Bob caught his pass, a defensive back hit him in the front of his face, causing his helmet to shift over his eyes. He couldn't see, and the sideline roared when he stopped on the run to adjust his helmet. It felt good for the fans to hear the team laugh in public again; a sign that time does heal.

The Rams played up to the expectations set for them, and their potential didn't go unnoticed. All Lake Fenton could do was watch Scott Visser, the flawless place kicker, set a state record, as well as a new school record after kicking four field goals from 36, 23, 34, and 39 yards out. He narrowly missed a fifth when the pigskin hit the crossbar and bounced back. Scott's face held a rightful glow by the end of the game. His success gave him confidence; he felt there wasn't anything that the Rams couldn't do.

Coach Reinhart was pleased that the Rams didn't turn the ball over, after harping on them the entire week. Schlorf helped the Rams roll out 390 yards in total offense, and 17 first downs. Loafman lead the defense with 16 tackles, followed by Corky with 11 while Adam notched six and a fumble recovery. The '40-7' victory left Montrose tied with Bendle for first place in the GEC League, as the Rams prepared to face the **Bentley** Bulldogs. Clolinger wanted the Rams hungry as they prepared to face Bentley:

'The Determining Factor On How Good We Can Be, Lies Within Each And Every Individual Out Here'

Aaron and Woody continued their tradition of eating at Fudruckers every Thursday night for burgers. Loaf and Dauber joined them that week. Aaron announced before the Bentley game, 'We're having a Team Mother Fudrucker's Night.'

Gary, and juniors Bo Paxton and Cary House, were some of the guys that joined the original crew. They no longer worried about having to eat at the same place every Thursday night. But they had other things to worry about. They almost lost their dinner on the way home from the restaurant, when Gary rolled his Ford pickup in a ditch. The driver in front of him didn't use his blinker, forcing Gary off the road to avoid a collision. Paxton felt his heart race when the vehicle came to a complete stop. He breathlessly yelled, 'You guys okay?'

Paxton and Cary were stunned for a moment, but Gary quickly jumped out of his truck yelling, 'I'm okay! I'm okay!'

He wanted it to be so before he even checked any part of his body for injuries. It scared the shit out of the carefree trio, who saw their lives instantly flash in front of their eyes. They were banged up, but not seriously injured. For a very brief moment, they realized they were not immortal; appearing more concerned about missing the game than the state of their own health.

By the time Friday night rolled around, the post-accident victims forgot about their sore muscles. They went crazy with the line, ready to rip into Bentley. Jorod and Winny each racked up two TD's in the first half. Aaron ran seven times for 152 yards and connected with Dallas, Woody, and Joe Bob, mixing up their offensive attack. Schlorf took the quarterback reign during the third period and scored the final TD for the Rams. Loafman recorded 11 hits for the defense, while Corky added seven more to help the Rams pile up a 17-3 edge in first downs. The Rams closed the score '43-0.'

John David Ruddy hardly ever got to play. When a Ram did something great on the field, John David became pumped on the sideline. He addressed Coon, 'Put me in Coach. I'm freaking out. I'm freaking crazy. I gotta go in.'

Coon loved John David's attitude. He had the same knack for providing comedy relief that his older brother Danny did for the '94-'95 Teams.

Matt Schlicht was another offensive lineman that was smaller, like John David. He didn't get to play much like his older brother on the '92 Team did, but he practiced just as hard as anyone. Coon respected his work ethic and found him fun to coach. It took guts for both of them to endure the Rams workout, knowing they wouldn't get to play much after competing with the mammoth line. But they both wanted to be a part of the '97 Team.

The Rams had a sluggish victory the week after they lost to Chesaning, but played the following two games like Reinhart knew they were capable of. The Rams still had a league streak underway and netted 75 consecutive league victories and nine straight League Championships. It was a healthy feeling to see his squad's enthusiasm when they gathered for their post-game talk in the middle of Bentley's field. Reinhart told them, 'Now the fun begins. It's time to get down to business.'

It was officially **Bendle** week. Clolinger knew the Tigers would be a challenge, but had no idea of what lied ahead when he formed the next motto:

'To Improve, You Must Make Your Weaknesses Your Strengths'

The Chesaning game planted the seed that the Rams could be beaten, which motivated the Bendle Tigers. Newspapers and television crews focused on Bendle, creating a competitive hype in the minds of viewers. *Could Bendle break their 75 game league streak?*

The competition kept the leader position in grasp. Unbeaten Bendle could decide the GEC Conference Title, as well as a berth in the state playoffs. Both Bendle and Montrose stood 5-0 in their League, after Bendle barely survived a 7-6 battle at Byron two weeks earlier when Byron missed a two-point conversion. A Montrose victory would put Byron in contention for a shot at the GEC League Title. *Competition was energizing.*

The Tigers and the Rams spent summers together at football camps, and winters together at powerlifting competitions. They were well aware of each others' strengths and held a mutual respect. After becoming friends, Bendle didn't fear the Rams like some teams did. In their eyes, they were just guys. Both teams used similar running offenses and variations of the same split-six defense. Each had strong rushing attacks and solid defenses. Powerlifting produced a large line for both teams. Each was used to having the strength advantage, but in this contest -- it would be a draw.

The media thrived on building the hype between Bendle and Montrose. They featured how Bendle's football program had a positive effect on the Burton-Bendle community, while the Rams avoided the media after the extra pressure it caused before the Chesaning game. The Bendle community was entirely wrapped up in their winning season, and went ecstatic when the Tigers took the field in front of 2,500 spectators. The Montrose fans followed suite when their team emerged from their smoke tunnel, sensing the extra hype when they jumped higher than usual on the pre-game jampile. The Rams' kickoff team felt a mammoth adrenaline rush. They were almost too pumped when Scott booted the opening kickoff, then watched the ball sail all the way to the three yard line. The battle began.

Bendle was quick, and caught the Montrose overly hyped kickoff team off-guard. The Rams got bit when they didn't stay in their lanes; their overabundance of adrenaline actually hurt them. Bendle caught the kick, dazzling their fans with a 97 yard TD return before most Montrose fans even settled in their seats. The adrenaline contagiously flowed through Bendle's side of the stadium, completely stunning a hushed Montrose crowd. Montrose players watched in horror from the sideline; wanting to kick their own kickoff team in the ass. They couldn't believe they let Bendle score. Loafman came unglued on the sideline, yelling at the player who cut across center instead of staying in his position. 'What the hell is wrong with you guys?'

The intensity level instantly jumped a few notches. Coach Coon yelled, 'Give me Salter!'

Salty Dog jumped at a chance to go in at guard, in spite of being almost a head shorter and 40 pounds lighter than the rest of the huge Montrose line. He appeared small, but was a coachable fighter with good technique. Salty

Dog always did his assignments and his blocks; his quickness gave him the edge. Coon respected that he could play with the big guys.

The Montrose offense kicked it in gear by marching 70-plus yards halfway through the second period. Jorod punched over from five yards out, then Scott booted the extra point to tie the game 7-7. Uncontested Bendle burst through a hole and rambled 54 yards to the Montrose one, setting up a quarterback sneak for a 14-7 intermission lead. Bendle's two long runs hurt the Rams; their coaches lit into them during the intermission. It was gut check time for Montrose. They all had to reach deep, and realized how much they needed the victory; but more importantly -- *they wanted it.*

Bendle didn't pick-up a first down during the entire second half, as the defense pushed them back. During each huddle, Coach D continually told his defense what to watch for. Montrose threatened to score late in the third, after reaching Bendle's 28 yard line. The Tigers had more players going both ways. They were showing signs of wearing down from the hard-hitting game, until a Tiger picked-off Aaron's pass. The Tigers jumped in celebration after returning 72 yards for a backbreaking TD. It rejuvenated the Bendle Tigers just when they needed it.

Aaron thought, *No. This can't be happening. Not again!* But the Rams didn't fold, and put together a fourth quarter drive. Owens scored from the three with 7:37 remaining in the game, then Scott's PAT put Montrose within 14-20. The Montrose defense held Bendle on its next possession deep inside their own territory, forcing the Tigers to punt. On their next possession, Aaron carried the ball, trying to get out-of-bounds to stop the clock. The quarterback used his speed to rush for 106 yards and wanted more, but was tackled just shy of the sideline. Something was very wrong. Aaron thought he heard his own bone snap the moment he went down, his left ankle pulsated with pain. Aaron screamed when the weight from his opponent rested on his injured foot, 'Get the hell off me!'

The injury occurred on the Montrose side of the field, while the crowd stood in silence. His mom held her breath and silently pleaded, *Aaron, stand up. Please, stand up.* Sparky was on the chain gang and watched his son from the opposite side of the field, unaware of the severity of his injury. A silent crowd watched as Aaron was carried to the bench. With four minutes left to play, the injured quarterback sat in pain, watching Montrose push across midfield.

In order to beat a team like Bendle, Montrose needed a back-up quarterback that was ready to play. Teddy Klopf would've been their man, but had switched schools over the summer. The Rams needed Teddy and instantly resented that he had abandoned them. Josh Schlorf stepped in as the back-up quarterback. He found himself in the middle of a scoring drive, against an undefeated team, with the League Title on the line. Schlorf's family had moved out of state the previous year to care for his grandmother. He missed playing his entire J.V. Football Season. Schlorf wasn't prepared for what he was about to face, but was willing to play quick under fire, like his brother Shane did on the `95 Team. It almost seemed unfair to hang so much weight on the young man's shoulder. Reinhart asked Schlorf, 'Are you ready?'

Shlorf replied, 'Coach, we can do anything. Just tell me what to run.'

The rookie quarterback felt his heart race as he walked on the field. Although his heart was in the right place, his nerves couldn't settle down. The squad tried to ignore Scblorf's shaky voice in the huddle. Another loss threatened to steal whatever sanity the Rams had left; they needed Schlorf to lead them with the confidence of a seasoned quarterback. Woody patted the new quarterback on the shoulder, 'It's okay Josh, we can do this.'

Schlorf took a deep breath before he called the play, trying to relax. But it was difficult to make adjustments for experience. Aaron watched in horror as Bendle tipped the pass intended for Dallas; the Tigers intercepted it. Schlorf immediately wished he would've thrown it further, but it was too late. Bendle maintained possession until their quarterback took a knee, then ran out the clock. The Tigers won. Bendle players fell to the ground in sweet exhaustion, after posting their best season record in over 50 years. Bendle rightfully celebrated like never before. Coach Jeff Setzke taught his squad how to show class to their opponents, without boasting their '14-20' victory.

Reinhart tipped his hat to Bendle who played an exceptional football game. In a single evening they came to town, had three brilliant plays, and smashed the league streak. It didn't matter that Montrose won the statistical battle. Even though they dominated with 18 first downs and 299 yards in total offense, compared to Bendle's seven first downs and 182 yards, Bendle got on the scoreboard -- *that's what wins ball games.* The `97 Season wasn't going as the Rams planned. They painfully learned that any good team could win on any given day. Obviously, it was a very difficult loss that chipped away another chunk of their soul.

It was a humbling experience that they needed to quickly put behind them. The Rams needed to worry about their next goal . . . *making the playoffs.* The loss carried a heavy and powerful blow, yet seemed easier than the Chesaning loss that was stripped away in the closing seconds. Just when things started to feel normal again, their brittle self-esteem felt threatened. Somehow, knowing that it was a clean game made it easier to swallow. But the loss cut the stitches from their fresh wounds, making them bleed again. *Accepting defeat was tough.*

Scott felt that it was their first real loss, requiring Bendle to take out the quarterback to make it happen. It was respectful for other schools to go 8-1 or 7-2, but not in Montrose. The town had forgotten how to lose during the regular season. Losing to Bendle could actually do more damage than the Chesaning loss, putting their League Title and possible playoff contention on the line. People commented, 'If Chesaning hadn't happened, Bendle would never have happened.'

Who knows? But the Rams were not dethroned yet. They still had a good shot at the Title if they could get past Byron.

Bo slept fitfully that night, facing a true test of his character. It forced him to look deep in his soul, where he found a burning desire to succeed. He learned how to endure another unfortunate loss with grace. Bo still believed in happy endings, and made up his mind to help his team get through this.

Aaron made the painful ride home after the game, then tried to get comfortable in the recliner. The sting in his voice woke his girlfriend up. She iced his swollen ankle every two hours, while trying to ease his excruciating pain. He tossed and turned in the recliner, unable to get comfortable as daggers shot up his leg. Aaron told himself, *Just get through the night.*

Ironically, Aaron had his pre-season, 'Decade of Perfection' T-shirt on when his brother handed him the Saturday paper. The words added salt to his wounds as he read, 'Montrose Decade of Dominance in the GEC is over.'

Ouch. His parents took one look at his leg and immediately rushed Aaron to the hospital. Purple streaks had shot up his leg during the night, and the bone looked unusually protruded above his left ankle. It was obviously more than a sprain, but Aaron held out hope while he waited for the x-ray results. He prayed for good news, wanting to come back for the post-season. He already endured too many disappointments, and couldn't handle ending his senior season with an injury. *No way.*

The orthopedic surgeon appeared serious and reserved when he entered Aaron's room, carrying his x-rays. He stopped at the end of his patient's bed, then seriously peered through his glasses. 'Aaron . . . I've got bad news.'

Aaron listened in horror as his doctor sympathetically explained that his fibula was broken diagonally. It required surgery with several pins to enable it to grow back together. It was the worst case scenario of the possibilities they had previously discussed. Until then, Aaron had clung to his faith that he would play again. Now he doubted that faith after hearing his doctor's dreadful words, 'You won't be able to play football again!'

Aaron's shocked expression could've stirred the dead. It felt like his doctor just handed him a death sentence. The surge of panic he felt moments earlier was now a full forced flood, threatening to doom him with fear. His breathing became heavy, and he felt like he would collapse. All he heard were the words *surgery* and *soon.*

The doctor saw tears immediately swell in three sets of eyes that stared back, pleading him to change his mind. He left them alone, knowing they were bone tired after a restless night. His mom wished that she could somehow ease his pain. Once again, she found herself apologizing to her son through her own heartfelt tears. 'Aaron, I'm so sorry.'

The Montrose quarterback was stunned. He didn't want people feeling sorry for him. Aaron just wanted to play football, and couldn't understand why all of this shit was happening. He gave everything he had for his senior season, and had such big dreams. *Why was the bottom falling out of his world?* His breathing became rapid and shallow, while he listened to everyone plan his surgery. He was only 17-years-old and had his entire life ahead of him, yet this career ending injury felt like his days were over. He appeared to be dazed when he asked, 'Why would God do this to me?'

Once again, his mom felt terribly sad for her youngest son, his teammates, and their high expectations. The team didn't need anymore bad news, or to lose their quarterback. She knew that Aaron gave so much to do his part, which cost him dearly. In a split a second, his football career was over. *One play.* One stupid play ended his dreams, his goals, and significantly impacted the course of his team. She tried to console him, 'Aaron, you're not being punished. You can't be mad at God for this. Sometimes these things happen and we don't completely understand why.'

The coaches also found themselves jumping one hurdle after another. Coach Clolinger knew that the Rams could either learn from the loss and find a way to walk away from the losing mindset, or they could quit. Reading about it in the newspaper was tough for the team. Clolinger found the right words for the **Byron** motto, realizing that the Rams were at a crossroads . . . *again.* He didn't need the gremlins to resurface:

'If You Want More, We Must Dig Deep Down Inside And Come Up With More. How Bad Do You Want It?'

The starting Montrose quarterback and lead rusher was lost for the season. Aaron had played with torn muscles and broken fingers, but he couldn't work around a broken ankle. He was screwed. Schlorf had to step up at quarterback. Adam, the center, was determined to help him. Wrestling techniques developed Adam's quickness, qualifying him as one of the greatest centers in Montrose history. The twosome practiced the snap, again-and-again, to perfect their timing.

The Rams had a decent practice after adjusting their passing game with Schlorf at the helm. The squad worked hard to overcome yet another adversity. The '97 seniors had never lost a game since they started youth football. Now they had two losses under their belt in their most important season. It simply didn't stack up. But when Bo left pre-game practice that Thursday night, he felt the Rams were starting to peak as a team. Woody felt their defense was the strongest it had been all season. *But . . . could they do it without Aaron?*

Coach D prepared them to face the Byron Eagles. Montrose and Byron were both in the thick of the state playoff hunt. Montrose was ranked third in Class CC, Region 4, and Byron was third in Class C, Region 2. Because their losses were to successful teams, it contributed to their playoff points, but neither could afford to lose. Reinhart knew that his team was full of potential, but still dealt with the frustration of losing two tough football games. Again, they discovered that they needed to absorb their loss and get over it quickly. The head coach didn't want them thinking about playoffs. He needed the squad to settle down and play mistake free football. If they didn't win their last two league games, they wouldn't need to worry.

When each player arrived at the school before the Byron game, he received a handwritten note on a piece of yellow lined tablet paper. Gary felt his own heart pound rapidly in his chest when he stared at his handwritten name on the white, letter size envelope. It read -- Gary Strappazon #76. He didn't know what to expect as he slowly opened the sealed envelope embossed from Montrose Community Schools.

> *Gary:*
> *Being a senior and two-year starter for us . . . we need your experience and leadership tonight. Help get the team prepared for victory. Give it your all out there tonight. Remember two-a-days and all of the long practices. Don't let them go to waste. We need you. Good Luck,*
>
> > *Coach Reinhart and Staff*

Woody walked off by himself and read his personal note.

> *Woody:*
> *Go out there tonight and give it your all. Be a leader, show your confidence. Pain is temporary, but Pride is Forever. Good Luck,*
>
> > *Coach Reinhart and Staff*

Scott found a quiet place in the locker room and read his note alone.

> *Scott:*
> *All season long you have been a model of consistency. Tonight is a big game in the history of Montrose Football. This is your chance to add to the tradition that we are all so proud of. We know that you have the hunger to want the ball in the last second with the fate of the game resting upon your foot. We know you will be successful because you are a Montrose Ram. You are a winner. Show your teammates tonight because we believe in you.*
>
> > *Coach Reinhart and Staff*

Gary put his note in a plastic bag and tucked it in the pads of his pants. Woody handed his note to his assigned cheerleader, who promised to protect it during the game. Scott read his note, folded it, and placed it in his helmet.

Players respected Coach Reinhart, even though some feared him. Most of them wondered what he thought of their ability; his note helped them realize that he honestly cared about them. His words meant more than he may have imagined. The team needed the confidence after they faced even more challenges with their peers. Montrose Football not only dominated on the field, but also in the halls at Montrose High for over a decade. If you were on the football team, you were labeled as somebody special.

Not anymore. After two losses, football had lost its glamour at Montrose High. The uniqueness was gone for the Rams. Their mystique was challenged and it played havoc with players' minds. They had two losses; in the minds of their peers -- they were now average. It wasn't as cool to be on the football team anymore. Human nature kicked in, while players placed blame on each other, wondering, *What was happening to Montrose Football?*

Coach Roger Bashore prepared his Eagles to host Byron's biggest game in three years. Montrose had dropped to second place in the GEC League with one win ahead of Byron, who followed in a close third. Whoever won the contest, would end up with a share of the GEC Title, if Bendle didn't win their final two games.

The game was well attended, while the crowd anxiously waited for Montrose to kickoff to the Byron Eagles. Scott booted a nice kick, then watched Byron work its way down the field to the delight of the Byron fans. It was dejevu for Montrose fans, who held their breath in disbelief, realizing that Byron obviously studied the Bendle film.

Scott was the deep defender, the last Ram on the field. His eyes never left the Byron receiver as he tight roped the sideline. Scott quickly reran the play in his head, realizing that it was exactly like the opening kickoff against Bendle. That play had haunted him the entire week, forcing him to wonder what he could've done differently to prevent it. Now he had a chance. Scott was their last hope to catch the Byron opponent. The kicker let both the returner and his blocker get past him. Then, using his blazing speed and willpower, he chased them from behind. His strategy worked. Scott made the tackle at the Montrose 15, and prevented a scoring kick return. Scott felt great to make the tackle, but the kickoff team felt like shit. They struggled with their mental state, while preparing for a royal ass chewing as they exited the field. Players knew what they were doing wrong -- they needed to stay in their lanes. Montrose prepared for a tough game, and certainly didn't need the momentum shifting on the opening kickoff.

That error led to trouble. The aggravated Montrose defense found itself doing a gut check, after failing to stop Byron on a quick 10 yard scoring pass. The Rams became even more discouraged after their own kick return team fumbled at Byron's 15. They suddenly felt like they had to prove themselves all over again. Montrose didn't need anymore ups-and-downs. Fans wondered, *Did the Rams have the courage to overcome adversity -- again?* The Rams were so preoccupied by trying *not* to make mistakes, it seemed they forgot to play football. If Byron scored again from the 15, it could put the final nail in their coffin. Bo put his good-natured personality aside. He became so angry and pissed that he yelled like a crazy man. 'There's no way. There is no FREAKING way that Byron is gonna win this ball game!'

If even one player had the slightest doubt in his head, Bo chased any remnant of fear away. The tone in his voice made them all reach deep for that extra ounce of determination. They already had enough disappointment for one season, and didn't want to lose their playoff opportunity. *No way would they go down without a fight!*

The Montrose Rams were about to discover what they were made of. They had good players with talent; they just were not making good plays. Montrose ended Byron's short-lived drive by forcing the quarterback to fumble two plays later.

Montrose offensive coaches were not overcritical with Schlorf's case of first game jitters. He needed a chance to get focused, and find his way at quarterback. They also needed a superstar, a player so talented that he could make a dramatic difference, while taking the pressure off Schlorf. Reinhart missed Aaron, his main offensive weapon, and was forced to design a new game plan. He moved Loafman from offensive guard to running back. Loaf wasn't put out there for window stuffing, and immediately sparked the offense in his new position. Even though he hadn't carried the ball since playing halfback his freshman year, Loaf was strong and capped the drive with an 18 yard burst. Scott made sure that his extra point tied the game at the half, 7-7.

The Eagles threatened twice in the second period, but Montrose held strong. Reinhart nourished their determination, while building their confidence. He could tell by their expressions, that they grasped his message. 'We lost to two very good football teams, and we're just a few plays from being unbeaten. That's the game of football. We have a chance to go out there and win this game . . . and we know we can do it.'

Aaron couldn't have felt anymore frustrated, as he watched from the sideline -- in a wheelchair. He didn't want sympathy; he only wanted to be on the field, helping his team. People constantly told him, 'There are so many good things in store for you Aaron; feeling bitter and angry won't help.'

But he was unwilling to make peace with the fact that he would never play high school football again. It only made his situation harder. Jake faithfully pushed his brother up-and-down the sideline, following the line of scrimmage. Jake protected anyone from coming too close to the new hardware in Aaron's ankle. Losing Aaron was a big blow to the team. His teammates felt awful seeing him in a wheelchair with a blanket on his lap, like an old man watching TV in a nursing home. That wasn't their Aaron. It forced the Rams to play harder; they would win for Aaron.

Schlorf wanted the win, and found himself in a must win situation for his first start. He gained confidence as the game progressed, driving 60 yards in 14 plays, determined to score. Loaf embraced the moment. He took fate into

his own hands, determined not to stop until he plowed over the goal line.
Scott sealed the PAT, putting the Rams up 14-7. It appeared that the Rams
had finally turned the corner. They needed the win more than anyone
realized.

Jorod sealed the victory with a three yard TD. He certainly was a team
player, but his ego had a tough time surrendering his workhorse position.
Coach wanted to take some pressure off Schlorf, by putting the ball in
Loafman's hands. Loaf wasn't the showy type. He didn't care about the
glamour; he just wanted to win. Loaf played hard wherever the team needed
him. When Loaf first switched positions, Jorod thought the Rams would run
an I-formation, then Loaf would fake a TD run and block for Jorod. Instead,
Jorod took a back seat, while Loaf shone on both sides of the ball. Loaf
instantly became the cornerstone of their program after racking up 109 of
their 223 yards. The defense seemed to win the game for Montrose. Loaf led
with 14 tackles, Corky followed with ten, and Woody added six, to beat
Byron by a final score of '21-7.' It was a do-or-die game; becoming the
remarkable turnaround that the Rams needed. Reinhart gathered the team
midfield afterward, praising them for showing their true character. The
victory was the turning point the Rams needed to make some noise in the
playoffs.

Aaron sat on the edge of the post-game circle, feeling strangely
disconnected to the team. He felt left out, like the kid in grade school who
never got picked to play. His senior classmates voted Aaron as having the
'Prettiest Smile,' but he found it hard to grin about anything. He tried to be
happy for his team, while struggling to make peace with the reality of his
situation. His surgery was too fresh. *It wasn't supposed to end like that!*

The Rams ended their last league game against **Atherton.** Coach
Clolinger found an appropriate motto:

**'Some Teams Succeed Because They Are Destined To.
But Most Teams Succeed Because They Are Determined To'**

Clolinger worked closely with Schlorf, building his skills and his
confidence. He helped Schlorf believe that he could lead the Rams to victory.
Montrose scaled back on plays against Byron for Schlorf's first start, to avoid
placing him in a situation where he wasn't comfortable.

Atherton was a different story. The Rams ran some one-back plays, then
switched to working on their passing game. Once Schlorf settled into the
game, he gained confidence and hit his favorite targets of Dallas, Joe Bob,
and Woody. Everybody got in on the action against Atherton, without any
injuries. Woody had a career in one night when he caught a 17 yard TD pass,
scored two punt returns, and one kickoff return for 252 yards. It seemed that
every time that he touched the ball, he scored. Jorod added two TD's, while
Dallas and Kris each contributed one. Scott kicked seven extra points. His

29 yard field goal broke a Flint-area record of eight field goals for the season. The Rams headed into the post-season with a stellar '58-0' performance over Atherton; a long overdue confidence booster.

Bendle won their final league game and captured the GEC League Championship. The Tigers survived three close wins, but managed to pull it off. Surrendering the League Championship ended yet another streak held by Montrose since 1989, while further testing the character of the '97 Rams. The Rams held their heads up knowing they still had a shot at a State Championship, which was their ultimate goal. The Flint area was beginning to see how competitive the GEC League had become when three of its nine teams made the state playoffs. League coaches credited Montrose for raising the bar, pushing them to work harder to keep pace. Bendle posted its first 9-0 season in school history and faced Byron, again, during the first playoff round.

Even though it had not been a typical Montrose season, the Rams outscored their opponents by an average of 31–8 points per game and pitched three shutouts. Their two losses were a combined margin of just eight points against two teams that made the state playoffs. Reinhart reminded them, 'We were in a position to win both of those games and dominated the field, but allowed penalties to cost us. We can't afford that in the post-season.'

Clolinger prepared the weekly motto for **Elkton Pigeon Bay Port**, building on the words that Bo Moore stated after the Chesaning loss:

'It's Time to Start Making A Brand New End'

The Rams loved playing on Friday nights. The bright lights gleamed around their football stadium, with its newly installed pristine black track surrounding a thick, grassy field. Abundant fans poured in to watch the Rams face Elkton Pigeon Bay Port Lakers for the first round of Class CC high school playoffs.

Players received another personal note in a sealed envelope from the coaching staff before the game. Gary took a few steps away from the team before he opened his, which did wonders for his confidence.

> *Gary:*
> *Your football career could come to an end at any time. Do you want it to end tonight?? Think back about all the hard work you've put into football over the years; and it's coming to a close. Let's make great memories starting tonight. Help lead the team on to victory tonight. Remember – OFFENSE wins games – DEFENSE wins championships. Let's dominate them – seek and destroy.*
>
> *Coach Reinhart and Staff*

Scott:
You have been as consistent and reliable as anyone on this team this year. Tonight, draw on that reliability to help lead us to victory. It was no accident that you received 'First Team All League' uncontested. The other coaches in the League know, as well as we do, that you are quite possibly the best in the state. Go out there tonight and prove it to everyone. Believe in yourself and your abilities.

Coach Reinhart and Staff

Woody:
Last week you had fun returning kicks, do the same tonight. Believe in your abilities – that's half the battle. Let your body ooze with confidence – that will rub off on your teammates. Seek and destroy on defense. Stay focused and disciplined.
OFFENSE wins games – DEFENSE wins Championships!

Coach Reinhart and Staff

Like his teammates, Woody felt fortunate to make the playoffs. He wanted to be the team that went all the way; to show the town how much heart the '97 Rams really had. Woody wanted to win for Aaron.

The Montrose Rams were on a redemption mission after falling short of several regular season goals. The staff hoped the experience gained in close games, worked toward their advantage in the playoffs. Montrose looked good during the first half, making the most of the field position that the defense generated. Their first scoring drive covered 61 yards. Loaf burst through a hole, then barreled over to cap the Rams first quarter drive.

The Rams pushed for a first down on their initial possession of the second half, but fumbled near midfield. The Lakers recovered and moved deep into Montrose territory. But the Rams stopped them on fourth-and-two, when Owens came up with a hit worthy of the highlight film. With eight minutes left to play, Dallas caught a 16 yard pass from Schlorf that set up Scott's 27 yard field goal. The Rams jumped ahead 10-0. The Lakers recovered another Montrose fumble at their own 27 yard line with seven minutes left to play. They graciously accepted two pass interference penalties against the Rams, before connecting on a 17 yard pass to close the gap in the waning minutes.

Montrose recovered an expected on-side kick. The Rams held on, locking in their first round playoff victory. The Rams moved the ball well, but needed to correct the fact that their turnovers kept their opponents in the game. It was only Schlorf's third start, and his first playoff game. A couple of botched snaps and handoffs, compiled by the Lakers' hard-hitting style, contributed to six Montrose fumbles. But the Rams maintained confidence in

Schlorf; they needed the junior quarterback. Montrose couldn't rely on the defense to carry them during the intensity of the playoffs.

Loafman provided the Rams with an offensive dimension. Once the Rams went ahead 10-0, the powerful fullback continued to pound inside, making their running game more effective than their passing game. Defensive coaches had preached all week to the Rams to keep them focused by saying, 'The defense will win this ball game!'

That's exactly what happened when the Montrose defense sacked the quarterback three times. The defense dominated the line of scrimmage by stuffing the Lakers' running game, holding them to 43 rushing yards.

Bo and Woody joined in the District Championship celebration, then returned to the center of the field. Hardly anyone was around to notice the duo, except for a few maintenance staff and the Athletic Boosters cleaning up the concession stand. The bleachers were now empty. Just 30 minutes earlier, they held the energy and excitement from a few thousand fans. The two seniors looked around at the deserted stadium, soaking in one final view of the team room, press box, and their awesome smoke tunnel. Their nostrils inhaled the welcoming smell of the evening dew, sealing in the nostalgia in case it ended up being their last home football game. The Rams didn't know who they faced for round two, until the following day.

Their dads silently watched the bittersweet moment from the endzone, while closing their own chapter of a very special part of their lives. Both dads had coached their sons in the youth football program, and spent hours volunteering their labor to improve the stadium. It was worth every minute; neither would trade those hard working memories for anything.

The stadium lights were turned off and the field appeared deserted when Gary returned to leave his mark. He stuck a duck feather in the middle of the field, creating a new tradition that he planned to do after each playoff game.

Montrose fell a mere 1.4 playoff points behind Capac; enough to surrender hosting round two. Schlorf's confidence at quarterback grew during practice for Capac week. The Rams worked on correcting the things that went wrong against the Lakers. They talked about ball security, realizing they couldn't fumble and be successful in the playoffs. Clolinger built on Bo Moore's phrase for the weekly motto:

'We've Started, Now Continue Making A Brand New End'

The Scout Team practiced the Wing-T Offense that **Capac** used to prepare the defense. Capac had quick, shifty backs that applied pressure on the backfield, and didn't need their line to hold holes open for long. Capac's defense played a 5-2 and liked to stunt. The Montrose defense relied on their line to keep opponents off their linebackers so they could make key plays. Capac's bread and butter was a talented rushing tandem that accounted for 1,400 yards each. Mike Glennie was their second year coach, and led them to their first Southern Thumb Association Title since 1973, their first playoff win, and their most victories since 1985. They were a team on a roll who believed in themselves, and generated some football excitement in the small town of Capac. The Chiefs had not lost at home during their 9-1 season, but that didn't bother the Rams. They would play them anywhere.

School seemed to last forever on Capac day; players found it hard to concentrate on academics. Woody stared out of the cafeteria windows during lunch, mesmerized by the heavy falling snow. His stomach already churned as he pushed a full tray of food aside. Woody couldn't eat anything and worried that his worn out receiver gloves had lost their stick power. It would be a wet game and he became apprehensive about returning punts. He called his dad at work, something he seldom did. 'Dad, will you stop on your way home and buy me some new receiver gloves?'

His dad felt as nervous as his son that entire day, appreciating an excuse to leave work early. He stopped at the new mega sporting good store to check out their gloves. The clerk suggested water repellent diving gloves with a $38 price tag. Logic reminded him of the expense of having an older son away at college, and that Woody only had two possible outdoor games left. But it was playoffs and logic often went by the wayside. *If it helped the Rams get to the Dome, it was worth every penny.* Many families found a way to stretch their budgets during football season to support the team. Money was dished out for signs, balloons, helium, team breakfasts, and food. Cheerleaders' parents dished out as much as $20 a week for decorations for players' lockers and goody bags.

Woody nervously paced the school hall, waiting for his dad to pull up. Since he hadn't seen his dad before their first playoff game, he didn't want to jinx the post-season. He quickly found Coach Clolinger and asked him to run out and get his gloves. 'Don't let my dad come into the school. Make sure to tell him thanks for me.'

Clolinger had to laugh, but completely understood superstitions. No one messed with anyone's superstitions. They all had them and he wondered if Woody's father would understand. Clolinger relayed the message, then watched the receiver's dad shake his head and laugh. As silly as it sounded, he understood, although he wanted to give his son a pep talk before the game.

Superstitions were back in full swing. Adam wore his lucky socks, the same pair that he wore during every high school football game. Joe Bob didn't seem as nervous as the others, but made sure he took a nap before every game. Gary continued his superstitions like he had the entire season, placing his pads in his pants before he left home. He made a fashion statement sporting his long black socks, his Adidas sandals, and green Army boonie hat.

Clolinger distributed their individual letters as players arrived to dress for the game. He could tell they were anxious to read them. Players thrived on the individuality, and stood a bit taller after reading each one.

Gary:
  Regional Championship Game. What a great opportunity, only 32 teams have this opportunity. Don't let it slip away. Play focused, play with great intensity, desire, emotion. Tonight we will become Regional Champions. We believe in you. Good Luck.

Coach Reinhart and Staff

Scott:
  We have the opportunity tonight to go out and win a Regional Championship for the third time this decade. We have played in six Regional Championships this decade alone with this one being our 7th. This is Capac's first ever. Right now they are just hoping that they can win, where we know that we will be victorious. Let's go out there tonight and introduce them to how playoff football is supposed to be played. Let's continue making a brand new end. Good luck.

Coach Reinhart and Staff

Woody:
  Stay Focused – Make sure your teammates are focused. You have a great opportunity tonight. The opportunity to win a Regional Championship. What a great feeling it will be when we are Regional Kings. Good Luck.

Coach Reinhart and Staff

The Football Club came prepared for November playoffs in Michigan by hauling heaters, tanks, and generators on the two-hour trek to Capac. They shoveled snow off the track, then setup shop on the visitor's side of the field, while fans tailgated in the dark, brisk night air.

Players warmed up on the snow-covered field, dubbing the game as the 'Snow Bowl.' Woody's nerves churned heavier in his stomach until he finally puked by the sideline; former Coach Sullivan would've been proud. Woody asked every parent around if they had any Tums. Someone finally delivered, then watched him eat the entire roll before the game. *Nerves.*

The Rams prepared to take the field when two Capac players ran across to the visitor's side, then stabbed a long wooden arrow inches from Reinhart's feet. They stared directly at the opposing coach for effect, then hesitated before running back. Reinhart returned a daring look, then yanked the arrow from the ground, unable to find any humor in their ritual. His reaction counteracted their incentive to intimidate, as he gruffly pumped up his Rams to take the field.

Capac's talented receiver fielded Scott's opening kickoff, then handed the ball to his tandem partner in a fake from their Starburst play. Scott watched his opponent race to the Montrose 25, determined to break the tackle if it came down to him again. His eyes intently followed the returner as the gap closed between them; then he made the tackle. The defense held strong, determined to stop Capac's momentum, pushing the Chiefs for a negative three yards on the next three plays. Woody intercepted a pass when Capac went for a fourth-and-13, stopping Capac's initial drive.

Dallas caught a 33 yard reception from Schlorf and appeared to be headed for the first score. But Capac stripped the ball, causing a fumble as it bounced into the endzone. Woody raced behind Dallas, planning to celebrate in the endzone, then quickly pounced on the loose ball. He slid across the snow with a grin on his face, while his heart pounded in overdrive. The Rams were on the board 6-0. Early in the second half, Schlorf handed off to Loaf, who handed off to Woody on a counter trap. Woody ran 41 yards to the endzone for their second TD. Montrose attempted to make up their first missed PAT by going for the conversion, but failed.

The score was 12-0 when Capac broke loose on the ensuing kickoff. Scott found himself in another do or die situation when the receiver broke through and sprinted up the middle in the slippery snow. The special teams practiced defending Capac's Starburst return, which involved three backs cutting around a handoff man. Capac's receiver handed it off on the last return, but decided to keep it. Their dark sleeves made the Starburst challenging to discover the ball carrier. The Rams were supposed to tackle every back in Capac's game of hide-and-seek, but once again depended on Scott to break the tackle after he booted a good kick. Scott backed up 15 yards after he kicked, watching the play unfold. He chased the returner while he eyed the 25 marker, then the 20. Scott knew they were running out of real estate when he reached the 15 yard line, so he dove as far as he could. Scott's heart raced when he slapped the opponent's foot with one arm, catching his back heel. Scott sharply hit the ground, then immediately looked-up to watch his opponent trip and fall at the twelve and thought, *Whew. I stopped him.*

The Montrose stingy defense wouldn't budge, preventing Capac from moving the ball. The Chiefs attempted a 32 yard field goal, then lit up the home side of the scoreboard, Montrose 12-Capac 3. The Rams marched to Capac's 15, then had a false start penalty followed by a sack. Again, they relied on their gun as Scott attempted a fourth down field goal attempt under challenging conditions. Even with four inches of snow on the ground, he booted it so high that the hazy night, lower goal post, and poor lighting prevented a clear view of its entire path. The officials signaled no score; Scott couldn't conceal his own disappointment. After 37 successful attempts, it was the first field goal that he missed during the entire season – *another broken streak.*

Playing in the snow created a new challenge for the line. Bo Paxton glanced over at his center, *I wonder if Adam can feel his fingers.* Paxton couldn't feel his own, as he tried to overlook how cold and numb he felt.

Like the rest of the line, he held them in the snow without moving -- *every single play.* After awhile, he finally got used to the numbness until his fingers stung like needles poking his skin.

Loaf sealed the deal when he picked up back-to-back first downs. He smashed up the middle, electrifying an overflow crowd when he burst open and romped 46 yards early in the fourth. Loaf hadn't seen that much time in the backfield, but earned the title as their workhorse. He rushed for 141 yards on 20 carries, while collecting a dozen tackles on defense.

The defense held Capac to a negative six yards in the second half, shutting down their star backs. Reinhart credited his defense for the win that controlled the line of scrimmage, allowing the linebackers to get to the football quick. The Rams swarmed the ball on pass coverage and held Capac, a team that averaged 40 points per game, to only three. Owens spearheaded the stingy defense with his 13 tackles closely followed by Adam, Dauber, Gary, and the huge sophomore -- Pooh Bear.

The 'Snow Bowl' was a fun football game for the Rams. The slippery snow-covered field added a different intensity to the game. The night air was cold but calm, compared to the last time the Rams played in the snow during the '95 Frankenmuth blizzard. Schlorf gained valuable experience with his fourth start, feeling protected behind an offensive line that averaged 218 pounds.

Coach Reinhart, along with captains Bo and Loaf, happily accepted the Regional Championship trophy after losing in round two during the past two years. Maybe the two losses prepared them for the post-season, but they realized it would take everything they had to continue winning. Their quest for the Dome was getting closer, each playoff win served as medicine; a remedy that mended their hearts while restoring their pride.

The post-game huddle grew larger as fans encircled the Regional Championship Team. They patiently waited for Coach Reinhart to finish speaking before they celebrated, in spite of the cold weather. They shared a happy moment with the team, realizing the courage it took to get to that point.

Once again, Aaron felt like an outsider looking in, unable to hide his desolation. He tried to celebrate, but his heart felt too heavy to disguise his eminent feelings. It was difficult to understand why their happiness made him suffer miserably. He wanted the Rams to win, yet felt helpless that he wasn't physically a part of them. Aaron had been their quarterback and leading rusher. The papers once called him 'quick, fleety and elusive.' Now, he felt like a *has been* as he carefully rested his crutches in the slippery snow. It all meant too much, and he felt totally disconnected. Life just didn't seem fair, and he couldn't understand his own bad luck. Aaron was too heartbroken to realize what a big hole he'd left in the team. Yeah, they won without him, but the Rams had to change their entire offensive attack to do it.

Gary continued his quest for redemption and quietly stuck his second duck feather in the middle of Capac's field, bringing closure to the Chiefs' opening tribal ceremony. Some of his teammates joined in the quiet ritual, secretly hoping to be faced with the dilemma of puncturing a feather in the turf of the Pontiac Silverdome in just two weeks. The squad boarded the bus, extremely happy to be in the final four, yet didn't feel satisfied. The '97 Rams yearned for more.

Cold weather provided the background for a week of hard practice, while Montrose prepared to face **Vermontville-Maple Valley (VMV)**. They were a running team coming off an 11-0 season, making their sixth playoff trip, their first since 1992. Clolinger knew VMV would be a challenge and continued to draw on Bo's theory as he wrote the semifinal motto:

'Keep Our Focus On Making Our Brand New End'

The Montrose defense was playing championship football and had seen success with the split-six system. Reinhart ranked them with the great defensive teams of '89, '90, and '94. Adam and Pooh-Bear were the defensive tackles, while Bo and Gary were the ends. All four averaged 214 pounds and asserted their quickness and strength. They were not in the limelight like linebackers Loaf and Dauber, who got credit for the majority of the tackles, but Bo and Pooh-Bear got their share of sacks.

The linemen were in the position of being washed down or double-teamed, and bought into the Rams' defensive philosophy. They didn't worry about being the star, which is often tough at the high school level. They played total team defense, allowing the linebackers to make the tackles. Playing gap control defense precluded them from going into the backfield to be the hero. Instead, they stayed on the line and made opponents come to them. Bo took care of his responsibilities on the line, then enjoyed the rush of sacking the quarterback. He racked a team high of nine sacks for the season, a practice he continued at Ferris State.

The Lions relied on their quickness. Chesaning was the quickest team on defense that the Rams had faced, but the Lions appeared to be even quicker. Montrose matched up better with a running team, and prepared for a grind-out game, hoping their opponent's running game played into their strength. Montrose coaches watched hours of game film and concluded that the VMV's best defense was their offense. They liked ball control and ran a Fullhouse-T Offense, and drove on teams.

The Rams gathered in the school's wrestling room to watch the movie *'Brian's Song'* that Friday night. Nervous parents and friends gathered down the hall, excitedly making signs, blowing up helium balloons, and packing post-game lunches. Anxious fathers prepared food for a team breakfast they planned to serve the boys and coaches the following morning.

Gary's heart raced as he drove through the decorated town of Montrose on Saturday morning. A victory would take them to the Dome, something he wanted more than people could imagine. He anxiously opened his personalized letter when Coach Clolinger handed it over.

> *Gary:*
> *The end is so near – yet so far away. Make sure you focus on each and every play. Leave all you have on the field. There is no tomorrow. Make sure you have no regrets. Play the way we know you can play. We believe in you. Good Luck.*
>
> *Coach Reinhart and Staff*

Scott walked to a secluded spot on the bench where he could be alone then opened his private letter:

> *Scott:*
> *Today's success depends on whether or not we play as a team. It's going to take our team working as one efficient unit. We are one of four teams left in the state. We are only the third team in Montrose history to make it this far. Let's be the first to go on further. If we play together we will do so. Keep our focus on making our brand new end. Good Luck.*
>
> *Coach Reinhart and Staff*

Woody waited patiently for Clolinger to hand him his envelope after teasing him. He felt the anticipation and wanted to rip it open as fast as he could. Instead, he took a deep breath then cautiously opened his white envelope after he was alone:

> *Woody:*
> *All of our hard work is going to pay off today!! Today we will be able to celebrate the biggest victory in the history of Montrose Football. Lead us on to that victory. We have great confidence in you. Play with great confidence. Good Luck.*
>
> *Coach Reinhart and Staff*

Portland was the neutral field to host the semifinal game. Montrose was marked as the visiting team, and squished into the limited visitor seating. Hundreds of additional seats were needed; much more than the few bleachers they hauled in for the 4,000 people that surrounded the field. The Rams came to play football. The Lions wondered what hit them when Montrose controlled 17 of the first 24 first-half minutes of the game. Scott split the upright with a 25 yard field goal midway through the second quarter. But when the Rams drove to the VMV's eight, their scoring drive was stalled. Bo soon recovered a Lions' fumble at their 46, determined to get the Rams going again.

Schlorf led the Rams on a 10-play, 46 yard drive using Loaf as his workhorse. Loaf was rock steady, and carried the ball 29 times for 149 yards during the first half-alone. He became their consistent guy, running over and through the VMV defense. Montrose drove to the four yard line and faced a crucial fourth-and-two situation, when Loaf plowed through for the first down.

Vermontville's head coach charged the field to the line of scrimmage, protesting the ball placement. The radio announcers questioned if that was permissible. They soon got their answer. Reinhart became furious when the Lions were not penalized for storming the field. He was so angry that he threw his hands in the air displaying his own disgust.

Schlorf capped the play on a two yard plunge with 1:23 left in the half. Montrose scored 10 points in the last five minutes of the half, and wanted more. Owens recovered the on-side kick for the Rams, catching the Lions off-guard. Scott's heart raced as he attempted a 50 yard field goal. *Fifty yards. Could he do it?*

Reinhart watched Scott boot that distance in practice, but not during a game. A successful kick would break the 45 yard school record held by Mo since 1994. Scott was 39-for-40 PAT's. His record of 10 field goals in 13 attempts was the fourth most in state history, two shy of the state record.

But the Lions prevented the Rams from scoring a quick three points, by partially blocking Scott's kick with :08 seconds left on the scoreboard. Vermontville's coach stormed the field again in protest, after the first-half clock expired before his team could hike the ball. The number of VMV coaches in the official's face soon grew, yet no penalties were bestowed. Reinhart fumed that the officials were turning the game into a fiasco when they didn't take control over the Vermontville coaches. The aftertaste still lingered from being burned earlier in the season. Reinhart wanted to ensure that the officials played by the rules. The VMV coaches appeared disgusted. They didn't offer the Lions a chance to make the long hike to the locker room. Instead, he parked the Chiefs near the visitor's side of the field. The Lions sat on the cold grass near the Montrose bleachers, allowing nearby fans to overhear a royal butt chewing.

Controlling the ball game during the first half may have made the Rams slightly confident, as they walked the long distance to Portland's locker room. Naturally, they thought they had a shot at going to the Dome while warming up in Portland's training room. Several football players were on the Montrose Wrestling Team that won states just eight months earlier. Those that didn't wrestle were at the Kellogg Center to support them. They all remembered the awesome thrill of becoming State Champions. It was the opportunity the '97 Rams needed, a perfect chance for redemption.

No other Montrose team had ever won a semifinal contest; for once they didn't face the Detroit area private Catholic schools. They had a chance. A nervous energy consumed the Montrose side of the field. They were just 24

minutes from a trip to the Silverdome, from accomplishing something that
none of the past teams had. They were only ahead 10-0; oddly the same half-
time score as the Chesaning game that ended disastrously. The thought on
everyone's mind was, *Could we pull if of? Is it really meant to be this time?*
If a team ever needed a chance to go to the Dome, *this* was the one. The
Rams believed all along that they were a decent team. The playoffs were all
the Rams had left after losing their winning streak, the League Title, and their
quarterback. Those losses hurt early on, but success eased their pain. A
victory would release the invisible dark cloud that encircled them since the
Chesaning game. A semifinal victory would serve as a peace offering to
previous Montrose players. The Rams needed to rescue themselves, but only
the `97 Team could do it.

Two intense teams faced each other for the second half. The Rams
wanted to maintain their lead; the Lions planned to catch up. The Lions
marched 65 yards on their first possession, and faced a third-and-long at the
Montrose 35. VMV's quarterback threw a long pass and Woody and Kris
double-teamed the receiver. Both of the Montrose receivers felt momentarily
relieved when they stood over their opponent and watched the ball hit the
ground. VMV's defender snatched it and rolled on his back, as if he'd caught
it. The official was slow in running down the field, and didn't arrive in time
to witness what the Montrose receivers just had. He called the pass
'complete' at the Montrose five. The Rams couldn't believe it, neither could
the newspaper photographer who captured the shot in a series. The threat of
losing again terrified the Rams, as the frustration from the Chesaning
officiating resurfaced. The Lions capped the drive and were on the board 10-
6. The Montrose defense demonstrated just how pissed off they were, and
prevented the Lions attempted conversion.

The Rams countered by coming down the field after a 15 yard late hit call
on the Lions. Loafman was the workhorse again as the Rams plowed through
the defense to Vermontville's 24, facing a second-and-six down. But a
motion penalty left the Rams facing a second-and-long situation. Instead of
coming right at the Lions, they had to do some things differently than
planned. Schlorf narrowly missed his connection with Dallas at tight end,
when the ball slipped off his fingertips at the two yard line. *Damn.*

Schlorf gained confidence at quarterback. He wanted to score so badly on
the drive, but suddenly felt the grasp of an opponent bring him down. Schlorf
hit the ground with disbelief, frustrated that the Lions halted his comeback
drive. A determined Montrose defense took the field. Loafman hit a kid with
enough force to stretch his neck. If Loafman never played another game in
his entire life, he could hang them up knowing that he got the best lick
anyone ever got. For most football players that was enough; for Loaf, he may
have smiled, but he had too much class to brag.

Woody picked-off a VMV pass at the Montrose 43, igniting the Rams as
they tried to turn the tide. The defense traded places with the offense, only to

be disappointed after Schlorf's pass was picked-off at the Montrose 43. With :48 seconds left in the third, it set up the Lions 42 yard TD drive. Montrose fans felt the surge of anticipation as the momentum shifted. From the sideline, Aaron watched the Lions run the conversion in for a 10-14 lead, their first in the game. The injured quarterback couldn't help but wonder if things would be different if *he* was in the game.

The Montrose fans skeptical celebration was short-lived after the half as their ten-point lead slipped away. They continued to cheer as hard as their team played, hoping they made a difference. The Rams dominated the first half, aided by three of the Lions' four turnovers, but suddenly found the wheels turning on them. The Rams played with emotion and intensity like they had the entire season. They were only one play away from getting back into the game. Coach D tried his best to heighten their spirits in an effort to keep their strength and concentration focused. But the ball was jarred loose, then Montrose fumbled at their own five; their fourth turnover of the game. Aaron watched helplessly as the Rams tried to regroup, but their last hope was squashed once Schlorf's pass was picked-off with 1:40 left.

The Lions parlayed four second-half Montrose turnovers into 20 points. It cost the Rams dearly and led to two Vermontville scores, changing the entire complexion of the game. Gary was frustrated. The Lions continued to run to the outside on the right side, and he couldn't stop them. The game was closer on the field than what went down in the record books as the Lions defeated the Rams '10-20.' Maple Valley would face Muskegon Oakridge at the Dome a week later, not the disheartened Rams. *Another dream shattered.*

It was the death of a hope that the Rams clung to all season. Now it felt like the fates intentionally conspired against them. Coach Reinhart talked to his team for a long time on the field, trying to ease their disappointment, while avoiding the inevitable unhappy ending. He didn't want their season to looming over them like a dark, storm cloud. Once again, he faced their disturbing gazes, while trying to hide the worn and defeated look from his own eyes.

The '97 Season would haunt the Rams for a long time, no matter what he said. That final moment was the most difficult part of coaching. He faced their sad eyes. 'You showed more heart, more class, and more guts than any other team I've been associated with over the past decade. You showed that you were a good team after we suffered two devastating losses. You could've quit, but instead you made it to the state semifinals. You are one of only three teams in Montrose history to make it to the football final four. You did everything we asked of you. It just wasn't meant to be, but you are champions no matter what the score says. You wanted to prove that you were a good football team and you did that. You were up 10-0 at half-time against a team that's going to the Dome. That shows what kind of team you are.'

The seniors tried to permit his words to ease their load, but they couldn't. It was over. They had it in their hands and tasted it, then let it slip away.

Their massive desire to be the first team to reach the Dome was immeasurable. The '97 Rams *wanted* a championship as much as the teams before them, but they *needed it more* than all other teams combined. Their quest for the Dome suddenly became another disappointing heartache; one that hurt like hell.

Their senior good-bye was tearful and difficult. The '97 Season was particularly tough for all of the coaches. They tried to find the words to explain how just a few key things affected their entire season, turning their dreams upside down. Hodge was there for them, trying to console the seniors like they had for him in '96. The former quarterback recalled the same familiar, painful feelings as he hugged Woody, trying to ease his pain. 'You were double-teamed all night long. They were all over you Wood.'

Loaf and Bo both played with everything they had, but saying good-bye to something they loved was painful. Hodge remembered that sorrowful feeling. Aaron said good-bye to football five weeks earlier, yet still found the final scene extremely difficult. He wanted to lead the Rams to the Dome, and felt guilty for not fulfilling his commitment. He would've played with his cast on, if he could. Instead, he was left hanging like a POW that never came home; he couldn't give it proper closure.

Players tried to sort out their feelings and disappointments on the long bus ride back to Montrose. Salty Dog felt that he'd played his best game ever, but it wasn't enough. When the bus arrived at the school, Woody and Gary walked out to their home field one final time. Gary pounded his third feather dead center on the 50 yard line, then said good-bye to the game. A game that provided so much enjoyment and friendship, disappointment and happiness, victory and defeat. The '97 Rams didn't quite have the season they planned. It felt like an arrow pierced through their own hearts, leaving them numb and empty.

Woody stopped by the Team Room as they walked off the field. He pounded one of his black receiver gloves on the side of the bright red building. It wasn't the mate to his pricey diving gloves, but one he'd worn all season. That glove had a history and belonged there. Woody stepped back in the snow, staring at his monument in the cold blackness of the night. Leaving a small mark of himself on the field that he loved, gave him pleasure.

By the time the banquet rolled around, players didn't feel as distraught, allowing some of the fun times to overlay the painful ones. But once the lights were cut and the highlight film rolled, the floodgates easily opened.

It wasn't by coincidence that Nirvana's *'Rape Me'* played during the recap of the Chesaning game, resurfacing painful memories. Many tears were shed in the hushed cafeteria that night. It became obvious that their heartbreaking season had touched everyone in the room. It was a season that bonded coaches and players, connecting them with their teachers, their parents, and each other. It was a difficult banquet for Coach Reinhart, probably the saddest group that he ever said good-bye to. It felt like they had been through a war.

The banquet was especially tough for Coach Coon. He knew it was his last, *but the kids didn't.* His line presented him with a Montrose Football jacket personalized with 'Coach Coon' on the front left side. He looked at Nick, Adam, Bo, and Dauber, and was suddenly caught in his own emotional rampage. He couldn't stop the tears that instantly marked his eyes. He opened up in front of the very guys that the tough Jody Coon drilled without mercy all season. They exchanged hugs, forming a huge emotional bond. Those linemen meant more to him then they realized, and would always have a special spot in his heart. It made it extremely difficult to say good-bye, far beyond the normal end-of-season parting.

Coach Coon wouldn't be back and it wasn't because he didn't want to; the incident during the Chesaning game did him in. Coon knew that he wasn't perfect, but he hoped that he made a positive impact on players' lives before they walked away from the program. Without speaking, their eyes reflected how much they meant. No one would ever forget the '97 Season, or each other.

A lot of tears were shed as hugs were exchanged in the cafeteria that night. Everyone had a hard time reflecting on their season. *Farewells are tough.*

Brian Owens wondered, *What would become of me now?* He gave up the party crowd for football, never regretting it for a moment. He proved that he belonged on the team, and played with everything that he had to give. Of all the guys that played in the League, he made Second Team All-Conference along with Aaron, Jorod, and Woody. Adam made the First Team All Conference, while Scott and Bo earned All-State kudos.

The '97 Team found the courage deep inside to face demons that no other team had to. They learned that things don't always come easy in life and that life wasn't always fair. Breaks don't always come when you need them the most. They learned how to stand by each other through the difficult times, discovering who their real friends were -- *each other.*

They leaned on each other with a steadfast courage and overcame adversity. It was a character building season, where happiness and sadness coexisted. In the deepest part of their souls, they feared people would remember them as the team that lost the streak, instead of one of three teams in Montrose Football history, at the time, to reach the state semifinals. Their final season will live with them forever, impacting decisions they make throughout their lives. Some will become better men because of it, while others may lack the confidence their missed accomplishments could've provided. *No one will ever know.*

Bo loved practical jokes, but his mood was a far cry from his typical clown-around style. His mom noticed how unusually quiet he was on the ride home from the banquet. Bo immediately took shelter in the soothing comfort

of his own room. He sat on the edge of his bed, closed his eyes, and buried
his face in his own huge hands. Finally, a chance to release the painful
emotions that he tried so hard to conceal during the banquet. He knew
college football was in his future, but that didn't ease the hole that burned
through the core of his soul. His head throbbed from all of the emotions as he
bent over to pick-up his All-Conference plaque. He looked at his Captain's
Award, and his Regional Champion medal, and thought about everything that
happened.

Things didn't quite go as planned. The Rams exposed their souls, pushed
through their pain, and became stronger. He realized they were all survivors,
no matter what life threw at them. Bo stared at their team photo on the
special plaque from the Montrose Football Club. He could still hear Sparky's
voice crack when he shook his hand, then presented his plaque. Bo knew
right then that Aaron's dad felt their pain; *they were not alone.*

The '97 Rams endured a level of stress, while experiencing a desolation
uncommon to high school athletes. Their breaking point was tested and they
underwent a tough character building lesson. Bo focused on the etched words
in the cherry wood plaque through his own tear-filled eyes. He desperately
wanted to believe they held the truth:

NO QUITTERS HERE . . . ADVERSITY MAKES MEN

'If the Size of Your Heart and Your Level of Determination
Is What Makes a Team Successful,
Then This Team's Legacy Will be What All Others Strive For'

#66 Greg 'Pooh Bear' Yeaster, #52 Adam Powell, #40 Brian Owens and
Bo Moore (squatting) after State Semifinal loss

#16 Aaron Emmendorfer, #52 Adam Powell

1997 REGIONAL CHAMPIONS
(from left): Coach Reinhart, Captains Bo Moore and Nick Loafman

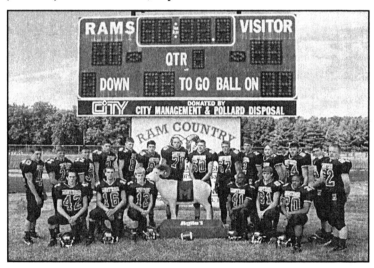

1997 SENIORS (back left): Brian Owens, Jason Hanel, Vincente Vigil, Joe Fedechenko, Ryan Caves, Dallas Parks, Bo Moore, Darren Corcoran, Trent Perior, Joe Persails, Gary Strappazon, Nick Loafman, Adam Powell and Matt Schlicht. (front left): Jacob Clark, Aaron Emmendorfer, John Ruddy, Jorod Bush, Justin Woodward and Winston Ruffin.

11. DESTINY - 1998

**Destiny is not a matter of chance; it is a matter of choice.
It is not a thing to be waited for; it is a thing to be achieved.**

-William Jennings Bryan

Coach Reinhart walked into the pre-game locker room with a serious look on his face. A respectful hush blanketed the room, while players watched his short, choppy steps approach the grease board. Coach picked up a red highlighter, then wrote one word on the board in thick letters -- 'FAMILY.'

He talked about having brothers and sisters, moms and dads. Coach confessed how much that he loved his own three sons. He paused for good measure then turned around, intently looking at the squad. 'If anyone ever took one of my kids away or tried to hurt one of them, I would search the end of the earth to get revenge because I love my kids that much.'

The emotion in his voice was powerful. Bruno felt his heart race; so did Pooh Bear. They all did. Coach gave a long, quiet stare at his team before he pointed to the board, effectively tapping the marker on the lone word -- 'FAMILY'. 'WE are a family. Last year our prized possession was taken away. This is our chance to get revenge. To get even. Tonight, we have an opportunity to get it back. We are playing the game for this team, but also for the football program and our proud tradition.'

A cold shiver passed through Bruno's thick body as the sensation of goosebumps slid up his huge arms. Even the big boys felt the bang from that speech. The entire team sensed the intense emotion in the room after Coach delivered his most emotional talk. Reinhart had their full attention, while striking a cord in each of them. The Rams felt ready to battle. Their pride was on the line; they were determined to get back on top.

Reinhart looked at his quarterback and mightily stated, 'Teddy, this is what you came back for.'

Bo Paxton felt the blow from Cary's hand whack him hard across his right cheek, then his left, then another right, and another left. Cary's nose wrinkled after each forceful blow when he forcefully screamed -- 'CHESANING!' 'CHESANING!'

Paxton grunted, then briskly paced the floor before approaching the platform, like a boxer circling the ring after throwing a knockout punch. Only his opponent was a phantom demon that reigned inside of his spirit, trying to bring him down. He was the only one who could fight the demon, and used the ritual to fine-tune his mental psyche. With his eyes firmly focused on his goal, he walked the short distance to the bar. His squat suit packed 260 pounds, and felt skin tight against the lineman's body. Its tautness prevented him from walking too fast, but the last thing on Paxton's mind at Nationals was another public blow out. Paxton grabbed the bar, benched 396.7 pounds, then glanced at the light board to confirm a clean lift. The strong lineman dropped the bar, unable to disguise the huge smile that lit up his chubby face. He jumped up and grunted, 'Yeah!'

Under his breath he muttered, 'Eat that Chesaning!'

Paxton set another national powerlifting record for a total weight of 1,461 pounds for his combined squat, bench, and dead lift. He felt on top of the world and shouted a few victory whoops as his teammates high-fived him. He finally beat his cousin Vaughn's record from the '92 Team. The new record would still show 'Paxton,' but would have a different first name. *His.*

Two others teammates set national records: Andy 'Bruno' Bernard at the 319 pound class, and Tommy Leonard at 148 pounds. Montrose left Chicago with the USA Powerlifting Teenage National Championship trophy in hand. Twelve lifters placed; seven firsts and two second places helped Montrose finish a comfortable 32 points ahead of their closest competitor. The Rams reclaimed the National Title they previously held in 1994 and 1992. Clinching the Championship provided some fame and more importantly, some desperately needed confidence.

The closing words that J.V. Coach Monty Stiles confidently spoke at the '97 football banquet seven months earlier, played heavily on Paxton's mind. 'I know a State Championship is coming to Montrose. I don't know when, but it's coming. Montrose will win a State Championship.'

Coach Stiles wasn't trying to be prophetic; he simply stated his honest feelings. The Rams worked way too hard, did all of the right things, and had more then their share of bad karma. Stiles knew that the Rams would work their way to the Dome one year, and he wanted the '98 boys to do it. They were *his boys,* the end result of his first crop as a Montrose Coach. Even when Stiles tried to be tough, the boys saw right through him and realized how much he honestly cared.

Stiles reminded Paxton about a few stories from his freshman season. Coach Stiles made him twirl his game jerseys while he ran a lap, because he left them outside overnight. He also forgot about the time when Stiles begged, 'Why don't you quit football Paxton? It's too hard and you're such a good golfer. Perhaps golf would be less hazardous to your health.'

The coaches were building character and ripped on Paxton because he had asthma and hated to run. But he loved to hit. Paxton wanted to believe the words Coach Stiles said about a 'State Championship.' He knew how close the Rams came to achieving that goal in '97; he didn't want *his* senior year to end so sad. Nothing could be shoddier then what the Rams endured in '97. *Nothing.* He had one more year to leave his mark. He was in the weight room the day after the '97 banquet, with a renewed plan to continue the Montrose Football legacy. He got as many guys to buy into that dream, spending the entire off-season getting stronger. In March of '98, Montrose won its seventh State Powerlifting Title of the 1990's at Lowell, Michigan. It felt sweet for Montrose to beat second place Bendle.

It was part of their mission after a heartbreaking season that included a string of painful memories. They hit rock bottom when they lost the streak and wondered, *How much disappointment could we be expected to handle?* They couldn't go back and change what happened; they had to learn to live with it. For the first time in ten years they were free from the pressure of maintaining that damn streak. The '98 Team had a clean slate with no place to go but up.

Powerlifting became the scapegoat that channeled their frustration, yet players felt it didn't matter to their peers. Weaker players had weaned themselves from the regimented football program, leaving the truly diehards. That was okay. *Persistence was admired.*

Those that remained didn't want any brittle links in their chain; however, the seniors felt there was one link missing. His name was Teddy Klopf. Teddy had been their quarterback since they were nine years old, until he moved away their junior year. Teddy wished that his family hadn't move to Lapeer West, then people wouldn't have called him a quitter or a traitor. He wanted to be back with his buddies, wearing the red and black for Montrose Football. Ted only played one football season at Lapeer West, after playing nine at Montrose. When the '97 Season ended at Lapeer, Ted spent more time at Montrose relinquishing his friendships. He often told his parents that he was going to the school, then drove the 45 minutes to Montrose High instead of Lapeer West.

The entire Montrose Football Team took it personal when Teddy moved away; even his closest friends resented him. They felt he could've made the difference in their '97 quest for the Dome. At the time, it seemed like it was the most important thing in their lives. Teddy was hurt, especially after his best friend, Paxton, lost touch. But Teddy never gave up on Paxton. Instead, he taught him the importance of keeping some things -- *like a best friend who moved away.* Many summer nights, the twosome ended up on the field throwing a football around. Teddy felt right at home, but always waited until dark so that people wouldn't see him. He was only a seventeen year-old kid, who worried too much about what other people thought. Teddy needed to be with his friends during his senior year, graduate with them, and play football with them. If he couldn't follow in his brothers' footsteps and be a part of the Klopf quarterback heritage at Montrose, he knew he would regret it for the rest of his life.

The Paxton family understood Teddy's distress and welcomed him back. They always treated Teddy like a second son, realizing that he was a teenager torn between family and friends. Mrs. Paxton researched Teddy's limited options with the school system. She discovered that school laws made him ineligible to play a fall sport, if he simply moved in with them.

Teddy's only option was to have his parents move back to Montrose. She told him, 'Whatever reasons your parents had for moving away is their business, and should remain that way. But Teddy, you need to talk to them. You need to tell them how much this means to you. At least give it a shot. You also need to talk to Reinhart and work it out with him. You should really do that first. I don't want to sound mean, but he might not take you back.'

Teddy shrugged, 'I can't do that yet. I'm not ready to talk to him. I just can't do it yet.'

The fear of rejection haunted him like a bad dream. Teddy's stomach felt queasy whenever he thought about talking to his old coach. He honestly didn't know how Reinhart felt about him. Whenever Cary or Paxton suggested stopping over Coach's house, Teddy felt his stomach churn and he chickened out. But Teddy knew that he would go nuts if he didn't move back to Montrose for his senior year. Crazy thoughts flooded his mind, *Would the team accept him back? Would the coaches? Would the fans?*

The coaches at Lapeer West had been good to him, but it wasn't the same. They didn't have a history. That stayed in Montrose where Teddy felt he belonged. All of his hopes and dreams surrounded Montrose Football, but he feared the snubbing rebuff. Coming back to Montrose was his goal; the pipe dream that kept him going. If Coach denied his request to return, he didn't know what he would do. He simply wasn't ready to face that ghost yet. *Not yet. Rejection was unbearable.*

One summer afternoon, Teddy cruised town in Cary's white, '92 S-10 pickup. They *happened* to drive by Reinhart's log cabin home. Cary saw Coach working in his yard, and whipped his truck into the driveway at the last second. Cary completely caught Teddy off-guard and totally unprepared when he announced, 'I already talked to Coach and he said to stop by.'

Teddy felt butterflies dance in his stomach, while his palms starting sweating. He slowly got out of the car, afraid to make eye contact with Reinhart, and stared at the gravel driveway instead. He knew it was time to face his destiny or as they say, his moment of truth. Moving away for a year played havoc with Teddy's confidence, but he wanted back on the team more than anything. Teddy finally found the guts to state his request. His worst nightmare was that Reinhart would say, *I don't want you back on the team.* Ted threw caution to the wind, as the shaky words escaped his dry, cotton mouth. 'Coach, I'm moving back to Montrose. I really want to play for the Rams again.'

There. He said it. After months of self-torture, it was finally out in the open. That heavy burden had draped itself over Teddy's shoulders for quite some time. He actually felt relieved, if even for a brief moment. He couldn't control how Coach Reinhart would react, but it felt good to face the powerful demon that commanded him. His future now rested on fate, as well as any history that Reinhart felt the Klopf quarterbacks were worthy of. Teddy didn't look Coach Reinhart directly in the eyes, but nervously focused on the ground.

Confrontation was grueling.

Reinhart sensed how difficult the scene was for Teddy, and gave him an honest answer. 'If you're coming back just to play football, then you're coming back for all the wrong reasons. If you're coming back because you really want to be with your friends and graduate from Montrose, then you're coming back for the right reasons. But you have to be willing to work hard and earn a position like everyone else. I can't promise you anything, but if you're willing to do that, then I'm willing to give you a chance.'

Whew. Teddy didn't immediately look up. He tried to ignore the prickly hairs that pecked at the base of his neck, before injecting a chill through his entire body. He bit his lip to conceal the smile that instantly shaped his face. Teddy's first impulse was to jump up and scream, then run around the car like a drunken sailor. Instead, he composed himself like a controlled quarterback should, then found the courage to face his coach. Reinhart noticed the sparks that danced in Teddy's eyes, and felt good about the encounter when they shook hands. And just like that, Cary and Teddy returned to the truck and left. The entire ordeal lasted a brief five minutes; 300 seconds that changed the course of Teddy's life. *Second chances are rewarding.*

Teddy loved his parents, but he also loved Montrose. *Was it too much to ask for both?* He didn't want to upset his family, but he needed to approach them and had to do it soon; his future relied on it. Moving away wasn't easy; moving back was even harder. He talked to his mom first, convincing her to support his dream. She also missed the people of Montrose, and decided to follow her intuition; supporting her youngest son. At the time, Jeff and Bobby both played football at Division II colleges; it was Teddy's time to be a Montrose Ram. Together, they approached Teddy's dad. He must've missed Montrose too and gave in. The Klopfs were back.

Teddy was impressed with the brand new $2,000 football passing machine that the Football Club donated. The Club purchased it with funds from their annual golf outing, then enjoyed the excitement that the new toy generated. Each receiver caught 50 balls a day during two-a-days. Coach Clolinger raised the intensity when he announced, 'For everyone you miss, you owe me a gasser.'

The linemen had fun breaking in the new toy when they were alone. The big guys adjusted the distance, then aimed and fired footballs at receivers like shells exploding from a machine gun. The machine saved the arms of the coaches and quarterbacks. Josh Shlorf would've gladly thrown passes, except his hamstring was torn during two-a-days. It gave him a taste of what Aaron felt like after breaking his ankle, forcing Schlorf to step up at quarterback. After leading the '97 Rams to the semifinals, Schlorf was anxious to use his quarterback experience during his senior year. But when it arrived, he felt shafted because the shoe was on the other foot when Teddy stepped up to replace *him.*

The Climb to the Top became the Rams annual motto. Reinhart addressed the team during their very first practice. 'Dedication, trust, be honest with yourself, and your teammates. It's harder to *stay* on top then it is to *get* to the top. Maybe we took things for granted, which caused last year to turn out the way it did. We don't know. But we can strive to get back on top.'

Players dedicated themselves during the off-season, setting a goal to reclaim the GEC League Title. A lot of football players grew up during that year, after learning a great deal from the painful '97 Season. Everyone did. The entire community had reached a point where winning was taken for granted.

But the '98 Rams lacked confidence in themselves; a result of a terrible scrimmage the week before their season opener. Offensively, the Rams scored at will and didn't look too bad, but defensively they looked horrible. Their opponents scored on the first play from scrimmage then ran it back, scoring against the Rams, again and again. The scrimmage turned into a chaotic mess. Reinhart went ballistic and told the starting defense, 'Get your worthless butts off the field. You don't deserve to be on the field. You're playing like a bunch of losers.'

The Rams got yelled at a lot, but felt they deserved every callous word. They practiced hard before their first game, working on their weak areas. By the time Friday night rolled around, they still didn't feel prepared to face the **New Lothrop Hornets.** Their annual motto held so much importance that it became their motto for their first game. The Montrose Rams felt they had no place to go but up:

'The Climb Back To TheTop'

The long time rivals hauled in a good crowd for the season opener. The visiting Hornets cheered wildly when they intercepted Teddy's pass, halting the Rams opening drive. Teddy felt terrible, especially after New Lothrop drove 61 yards and scored.

He had worked so hard to get back to Montrose, but his confidence was already at a low point. The last thing the quarterback needed was an early interception. Ted felt that his teammates accepted him back, but worried too much about the fans. He honestly believed that people wanted him to screw up. It was hard for Teddy to just be himself; knowing that he was constantly being compared to his older brothers.

Paxton saw his teammates hang their heads on the sideline. He wasn't about to let anyone screw up *his* senior year, and took on the responsibility to pump the squad up. He approached any player that appeared routed, smacked his shoulder pads, and scolded. 'Look up. What are you doing? Get into it!'

With six minutes left in the opening quarter, Teddy broke free on the option, then romped 44 yards to score. He listened to the roar of the crowd, and couldn't help but smile. It felt great to be a Ram again. Scott Visser split the uprights, giving Montrose a 7-6 lead.

Eddie Magrys pulled in an interception deep in New Lothrop territory and returned the ball to the three yard line. The Montrose offense took the field, geeking each other up in the huddle. When they took their places on the line, Paxton yelled, 'We're gonna score this. C'mon Teddy, let's go.'

Teddy tacked on his second TD with a keeper from three yards out and thought, *Maybe the people in the stands will like me now.* He let a few opinionated, boisterous men play with his head instead of appreciating the 99% of the fans who were glad that he was back.

The second TD seemed to calm the Rams down, while upsetting the Hornets. It caused back-to-back turnovers and changed the complexion of the game. But the ball slipped through Ted's hands on the PAT when the Rams yelled, 'FIRE!' The plan was for Teddy to run out and pass, but the kicker ended up with the ball. Scott looked up, saw several opponents approaching from all sides, then rolled out and threw a pass; a rare treat for a kicker. It gave him a rush, just before he got attacked from all sides by Hornets. From the ground, everything looked fuzzy seconds before Scott lifted his head in time to see his pass get intercepted in the endzone, stopping the conversion.

Mike Gibson intercepted a middle screen that was tipped at the line of scrimmage. 'Gibby' set up a one yard Cary House TD. Cary came alive by scoring two additional second quarter TD's on runs of one and 70, blowing the game wide open. Cary was a bruising 5'8"-185 pound running back, with great speed and strength. He was unstoppable when he got outside, and exploded for 172 of the Rams 325 total rushing yards. Scott booted a 38 yard field goal and kicked five PAT's, closing the game '44-6.'

Reinhart praised the team after the game. The Rams accomplished their main objective, to hang on to the ball and start their climb up the mountain. He was pleased with their performance but warned them. 'We've got a tough week ahead to prepare for Chesaning. The Indians are flat-out loaded and will be the toughest team we expect to face all season. Their quick offense will be a threat to score every single play. Facing them during week two will be a challenge.' Their motto for Chesaning became:

'Every Player – Every Play'

Chesaning. The name alone motivated the Rams during the entire off-season. When players lifted weights and appeared to give up, a teammate yelled, 'Think of Chesaning.' The weights then slammed a bit harder and the grunts became nosier, like a pissed off chain reaction that forced extra effort. 'Chesaning' became synonymous with 'swearing.'

The Rams waited an entire year for revenge after Chesaning snapped their ten-year winning streak. Reinhart packed his pre-game speech with passion, launching an emotional cord in every senior. Cary felt his entire body shake, his fingers even twitched. He sat next to Paxton on the bench in the team room, unaware that they both rocked back and forth making strange humming sounds, as if in a trance.

Paxton loved to dance; it was something that came easy for him. The big guy was fairly coordinated for a national record-setting powerlifter. But he wasn't dancing that day, the lineman only swayed in an effort to calm his own nerves. Dauber turned around after hearing a screechy noise that sounded like a dog whining. A droning 'Hmmm' came from Paxton, then Cary joined him in the crazy, psyche up ritual. Their intensity provided a contagious reaction that immediately spread through the team room.

Paxton went ballistic once the squad ran out of the team room. The Rams faced a huge crowd that packed every available bleacher seat, as well as any space along the fence. Paxton was so pumped that he started swearing, and felt the need to hit something to release his vented energy. The first thing he encountered was the fence. He rammed it as hard as he could, injuring his shoulder. The lineman immediately wondered why he did something so stupid before such a big game. By the time the game actually started, he already felt tired and emotionally drained from the extra pre-game hype.

Thick white fog oozed from the smoke tunnel, creating an eerie atmosphere against the dark, evening sky. The band played the school song the moment the Rams appeared through the smoldering haze. The effect made an awesome entrance for the opening of a high school football game.

Cary was exceptionally hyped on the opening kickoff. He ran down the field with a kill mentality, drilling his opponent as hard as he could. An intense pain jolted up his back, injuring a pinched nerve. Cary continued to play against a hard-hitting team, but it wore him down. When the pain became so intense that he couldn't concentrate, he felt that he was playing against the Indians as well as his own body.

Chesaning headed down the field on their first drive of the game. The Indians drove the ball well with a 15 yard gain, and several third-and-shorts. Cary and Dauber went in on a tackle when the Chesaning quarterback cut around a corner. Cary dove after him, then Dauber hit him high, but his knee hit Cary's helmet on the tandem tackle. Dauber went down then forced himself to stand and limp off the field on his own power; too proud to accept help. His concerned parents stood in the bleachers, unsure of the seriousness of the injury. They watched him treat a swollen knee most of the '97 Season, and became worried. Dauber planned to play college football, and had the size and G.P.A. to back him. The linebacker didn't need another knee injury

The Indians scored just five minutes into the game, but missed the PAT. The Rams countered with Anthony Vigil's one yard touchdown minutes into the second quarter, then Scott put the Rams up 7-6. Montrose grabbed an interception late in the first half, then drove within field goal range. Scott faithfully split the uprights with a 27 yard field goal, giving the Rams a slight 10-6 lead at the half.

Coach Stiles stood on the sideline, and flashed back to '95 when the seniors were *his* Freshman Team. He remembered the Labor Day weekend before their Chesaning game. Montrose beat Hemlock the prior week 21-14, but they played like absolute crap with too many turnovers. They faced Chesaning the following Wednesday, so Stiles scheduled a practice on Labor

Day. He told them, 'If your family is going out of town, you need to call me so I can set up a practice for those that can attend. For everyone that doesn't call, you get to run four gassers per man.'

Stiles thought that would add credibility. It didn't. Monday night rolled around and only six kids showed up. No one else called. Being a man of his word, that amounted to 60 gassers, which took the entire Tuesday practice to run. Consequently, with no practice on Monday, track practice on Tuesday, and a game against Chesaning on Wednesday, they were not ready. Those freshmen took a 0-36 beating by the Indians.

People that followed the upcoming freshman commented that the Rams were going down hill. Not in the eyes of Coach Stiles. He knew that they had potential; he just had to drill it into them. Stiles never gave up on those kids and felt they had the capability to become a State Championship Team. They learned their lesson, and never lost another game the rest of that freshmen year, or the following year when Stiles moved with them to J.V.

That night, Stiles joined them as seniors in the team room. A hush fell over the squad when Reinhart spoke. 'A year ago, this team took something away from us that was ours. Dearly ours. This is what you work for all year long. It's what you dedicate yourself for. It's for all of those long hours in the weight room during the off-season. It's why you go to powerlifting meets. We're in a war here. This is a battle. We can't give up and we can't give in. Chesaning is a very good team and things can change real fast.'

It agitated them when they remembered how devastated they felt exactly one year ago. Reinhart's speech caused their stomachs to churn. Horrible memories forced tears down more than a few seniors' cheeks. Coach got through to every one of them; they felt ready to kick some ass.

Coach Szappan stood 20 feet away in the opposite team room, telling his Indians that they were up against a wall. The second half determined their season, since they lost their opener to Millington by 29-26. Chesaning knew they had great potential with their lightning strike offense and dominating defense, but another loss could end their playoff hopes. Coach Szappan motivated Chesaning for an intense second half against Montrose. It worked. The Indians exploded for a 64 yard TD run, and jumped ahead 10-12 just four minutes into the third.

The Rams were not as successful during the second half, going four-and-out. Dauber went back in the game with his knee brace on, but he couldn't move 100% and came out. Matt Leitelt, their center and linebacker, also hurt his knee and was taken out of the game. Two inexperienced sophomores replaced them and gave their best, but they were young and hastily received their first real exposure to Varsity level ball. Some Rams hung their heads on the sideline, while the game was still very much in reach. The seniors become intense, as they tried to lift the others up. They had difficulty getting a response, as if the squad had shell shock. The Montrose line kept driving but couldn't get on the board, but the Indians did. Chesaning's experienced quarterback kept Montrose off balance the entire night, running the option offense with expertise. Chesaning scored late in the third for a 10-19 lead. The Indians picked-off Ted's pass on the first play of the fourth quarter, then set up two final scores to beat the Rams '10-34.' It was the most lopsided, regular-season loss that Montrose experienced in 11 years.

Reinhart addressed the team post-game. 'We've played teams that have won State Championships before, and I truly believe this Chesaning team has what it takes to win a State Title. We're a better team than what the final score indicates. One game isn't going to make our season. We still have our goals ahead of us. We'll regroup and come back. I think the way we played in the first half is the type of team we can be. We just have to put four quarters together.'

Montrose took their loss and planned to learn from it. They were still champions at heart and carried themselves off the field as winners. The Chesaning game was behind them. They told each other, 'This wasn't a severe loss. Let's just put it behind us and go on. We still have the League Championship to focus on.'

But the loss caused the bandwagon fans to surface. Players and parents overheard cruel comments that: 'The Rams lost their drive.' 'Losing will become acceptable.' 'This is the worst football team Montrose ever had,' and 'These kids don't have any heart.'

Some fans seemed to turn on a dime without any mercy; they only wanted retribution. When that didn't happen, they wanted to blame someone. Their brusque words were offensive enough, but two Varsity players felt an even stronger blow the following day at the youth football game. It shocked them when an adult youth football coach taunted, 'I'm embarrassed to see you wear that Montrose jersey.'

Every sport had its crail. For Montrose, it was their ten year football streak, which was now gone. After practice on Monday, players and coaches openly talked about the degrading comments. Reinhart told them, 'We cannot control those factors. We can only control the dynamics within this football team. We're going to keep working our tails off and bust our butts. We'll let those bandwagon fans jump off, they can jump back on when we're successful.'

The team wanted to focus on the positive; they still had their strong Montrose Football tradition. Dauber spoke up. 'Every team is going to lose sometime. This town just has to understand that and come to grips with it. Even the best teams in the NFL don't have undefeated seasons.'

On the other hand, the Rams realized they couldn't afford to lose any more games, or their playoff shot was slim. They still had tough teams to face, but were already worried about Bendle. Unfortunately, another Chesaning loss compelled football to lose most of its luster at Montrose High. It appeared that a group of students were tired of football being the sport that ruled, and intentionally caused animosity by outwardly supporting the new soccer team. They protested that Friday pep assemblies only focused on football, while neglecting other fall sports. It led to Administration changing the format to stop the bellyaching, which made the football team feel average and unimportant. Pep assemblies seemed strange after that. Players wondered why the school even bothered. Being on the football team no longer held the prestigious status that it once did.

Senior linemen compared practices to '97, when some felt a constant sick feeling in the pit of their stomachs. It came from being yelled at constantly. Their bizarre streak-breaking loss created immense pressure, causing havoc for everyone. Paxton and Bruno felt so low at times that they totally lost their self-confidence. They knew that coaches needed to bring them down, but it seemed like days before they brought them back up. Players felt their self-esteem drop to an all time low during those dark days, feeling unimportant and worthless. Some actually started to hate football. Paxton confided that he wanted to quit the sport he used to love, but knew he wouldn't. He wasn't a quitter and sucked up his pride. He endured.

The coaches critiqued each play and discovered the Rams were not prepared for Chesaning's exceptional speed and talented quarterback. The game film pointed out their weaknesses, allowing coaches to use it as a wake-up call. Their big line had exceptional strength; they just needed to work on their speed. The coaches knew the Rams had talent and potential, but hadn't clicked as a team yet. They shifted players around. The team welcomed the constructive criticism from their coaches, then went to work on a new game plan.

Two new coaches brought the linemen exactly what they felt they needed. Coach Joe Gilbert, the new teacher for the Montrose Alternative Education Program, was thrilled to join the great tradition that Montrose Football held. Gilbert had been an offensive lineman at SVSU for five years, and coached for two. He played with several former Rams and even roomed with Led, from the '90 Team, so he understood Montrose tradition. Gilbert coached the offensive and defensive lines, bringing his valuable lineman experience to the Rams. Gilbert was a big, burly, guy who was like a teddy bear on the inside, and he was funny. Paxton and Bruno appreciated that Gilbert didn't constantly yell at them, but actually showed them the proper way to do what he wanted. Gilbert treated players like his college coaches treated him. He knew how linemen reacted, and helped tap their potential. He was frank with them. 'If you work hard I won't have a problem with you.'

Gilbert couldn't have asked for a better group of kids to work with. He had the powerful likes of Bo Paxton and Bruno working on one side, while Salty Dog and Gibby worked on the other side of center, Matt Leitelt. They were the toughest group of kids Gilbert ever had the pleasure of coaching. He planned to make them champions.

Coach Cory Gildersleeve was a first year coach doing his student teaching under Reinhart. He was a football standout at inside linebacker for the

Central Michigan University Chips. Ironically, 'Sleeve' played for Monroe St. Mary, who eliminated Montrose during the '90 Regional Playoffs. Sleeve pulled in two interceptions that game; a memory that still haunted the '90 Football Team eight years later.

Sleeve helped Gilbert shore up the offensive line, but his main focus was to help Coach D's defense, concentrating on the linebackers. He also served as the J.V. defensive coordinator for Coach Stiles. Sleeve appreciated to be let in, and that Reinhart was open to his coaching ideas. The linebackers didn't complain about the new defensive pursuit drills he made them do at the end of practice. Sleeve coached the same way that he played, firey but disciplined. He believed that discipline wins. His guys were hard working, determined football players. Sleeve told them, 'We ran out of gas at the end of that Chesaning game, but we'll work on that.'

Sleeve was a tremendous influence to both the team and to Gilbert. He worked with Gilbert during offensive line individual time, playing a vital role as the motivator. Together, Sleeve and Gilbert made those kids work to their fullest potential. Gilbert and Sleeve thought they were pushing the line hard enough, until they faced Chesaning. Their line actually played tough during the first half, then struck the brick wall. Gilbert looked at Sleeve during the final quarter and vowed, 'That will never happen to the Rams again.'

Sleeve agreed. Sleeve and Gilbert became quite close and worked well together. Sleeve felt Gilbert was a great teacher of the game. He did very well with his duties and was fun to be around. The kids really liked him. Gilbert and Sleeve set new rules for the linemen to complete certain drills. If the offense fumbled or the line jumped, the linemen completed a 50 yard bear crawl followed by a run. It was killing the linemen, but the coaches made them realize how it could make them better. The offense soon wised up, trying harder to reduce their fumbles. They didn't want to cause the line extra practice because of their errors. Their line made big holes for them, and made great things happen; they didn't want to piss them off. The agonizing drill encouraged the team to help each other play error free football. *Collaboration was constructive.*

Clolinger wanted a motto for the **Goodrich** game that made players think:

'Contender Or Pretender'

The Rams wanted to show their toughness against Goodrich, proving they could snap back after a hard loss. They tried to pump each other up, but it took the entire first half for the offense to bounce out of the mental slouch they were in. The defense played rugged and prevented Goodrich from a first down the entire first half. Cary finally broke a scoreless tie when he raced 73 yards for a first quarter TD, then added the conversion. Teddy scored on a 13 yard TD early in the second quarter, while Scott's extra point gave the Rams a 15-0 lead.

Montrose tried an on-side kick, but received a penalty. A Ram pounced on the ball after it advanced only five yards. The Montrose defense controlled Goodrich upfront, but their offense seemed to be off. It wasn't just one person; it seemed everyone took a turn at making a mistake. The linemen drove down the field then the offense made big, glaring errors. They wondered, *Man, what is going wrong tonight? Did Chesaning have that much impact on our confidence?* Emotions seemed to compete with their logic, making the game in their head much tougher than the one on the field.

Goodrich recruited a cute, female soccer player for their kicker, who nipped an interview on Good Morning America. Her teammates treated her like their kid sister, grateful that she helped the team. Her dad was an assistant football coach, and protected his daughter from any other action on the field. She strictly kicked PAT's.

Scott openly resented the hype that the female kicker received from the media, especially since she didn't see any field time. After all, he was a Division I recruit who was featured in Prep-Star Magazine. His name was listed as one of the top five kickers for the Midwest, and was ranked fourth on the Michigan recruiting list. He even made the 'Fab 55' recruiting list. The attention she received turned Scott into a green-eyed, covetous kicker. He was jealous. When Goodrich had several fourth down situations inside the 20, Scott couldn't resist by yelling from the sideline, 'Where is she?'

When the Rams came within field goal range they didn't hesitate to send their All-State kicker in. Scott booted the ball so hard that it drifted high above Goodrich's shorter goal post. The officials standing directly underneath the goal post had difficulty making the call. It looked good from Scott's angle, and he felt qualified to judge an accurate kick. After all, he received All-State Honors in '97 for setting records for kicking 39 out of 40 PAT's, and was 10 for on 13 field goals. He watched his share of accurate kicks, and felt worthy of his two cents. Scott was shocked that the officials didn't respond right away after he kicked the 35 yard field goal. There wasn't a doubt in his mind that it was an honest kick. He continued to watch them turn their heads as they looked at each other, then finally waved. 'No good.'

Scott immediately jumped up-and-down like a kid throwing a tantrum and mouthed, 'What?'

He was obviously upset and applied enormous pressure to keep his stats up. Division I recruits had their eyes on him; his college career depended on every stat. Although Scott never swore at the officials he didn't contain his emotions, which was uncharacteristic of him. His little fit haunted him later in the game, after he kicked another field goal with seven minutes left. When he bent down to pick-up his block, he mumbled under his breath, 'Are you sure that one's good?'

The kicker simply spoke out loud, thinking that he was far enough away from the officials under the goal post, but he forgot about the official standing directly behind him. When Scott started to run off of the field, Kris Brown yelled at him. Scott knew something was wrong because Kris seldom got mad, but looked unreservedly pissed. Scott asked, 'What did you say?'

Kris replied, 'I said, You just got us a penalty.'

Scott turned around and saw the yellow penalty flag resting on the ground. *Shit.* About that time a livid head coach stomped on the field, sharing a few coarse words with his kicker. It was a bad reflection on the coaching staff, as well as the team, when a player received an intentional personal foul. It had never happened before, and Scott felt embarrassed that he hadn't controlled his emotions as a respectful athlete. Scott thought about what it meant to receive an unsportsmanlike penalty. He compared his to what other players physically did to receive the same penalty. It didn't make any sense and it bothered him. He never swore, never taunted, never even touched another player, yet received the same penalty. It didn't seem quite fair, yet he still felt terrible. Scott feared it could mean the difference in the game, but the field goal still scored. It didn't matter that the penalty required the Rams to kick from 10 yards deeper. Scott's frustration converted into extra adrenaline. He booted the ball deep inside the five, a distance comparable to a NFL kickoff.

The Rams were up by 18-0, but the offense played lousy after losing two fumbles. Cary's back was still in a lot of pain; he couldn't give 100%. Teddy scrambled on fourth-and-26 in the final quarter, hoping the defense could get the ball back.

But Goodrich's quarterback scored on a 10 yard run to avoid the shutout. An opponent cut Dauber's knee, causing him to go down -- hard. Dauber made a promise to himself when he was in youth football, that he would never be helped off the field. He tried to get up on his own, then fell again. Dauber's pride forced him to rise above the pain and stand. Once he steadied himself, he limped off the field for the second week in a row.

Reinhart was pissed after the game, and dramatically vented his frustration in the post-game huddle. 'We're not playing football with our heads. We've got to be a much smarter team if we're going to be successful. It's the third week. The mistakes we made are week one mistakes. We're just mixed up and have got to get it straightened out.'

The Rams had breakdowns in coverage with seven penalties for 75 yards. Goodrich had penalty trouble of its own with 10 flags for 90 yards. It was an ugly win for the Rams, but they wouldn't give it back. They didn't want people feeling disgraced when they lost, and relived when they won. The '18-6' victory was enough to keep the Rams in the driver's seat for the league race. The Rams wanted to improve when they faced **Hamady**, their next opponent.

'Unless You Try Something Beyond What You Have Already Mastered, You Will Never Grow'

Scott booted the opening kickoff, then jogged along while the play unfolded. He noticed a Hamady opponent getting closer and thought, *No one comes after the kicker; the play is way down field.* The opponent closed in on him at the last second so Scott decided, *Why not?* The kicker sprinted the last five yards, then hit his opponent hard, taking out his feet. As Scott ran to the sideline he thought, *He's not going to let me do that again.*

The following kickoff, the same opponent came after Scott again. Scott acted like he was going after him, then juked at the last second, causing his opponent to slide foolishly on the ground. On the next kickoff, the Hamady opponent came after Scott for the third time. By then, Scott had enough of his cheap shots and decided to play hard ball. Scott grabbed his facemask and pulled his opponent down. The officials never watched the kicker since the play focused down the field, but the Montrose sideline had more fun watching Scott than the actual play.

Scott wanted to break the school record by kicking eight PAT's in one game. He kicked seven during the first half, and tacked on a 37 yard field goal, before Reinhart decided to give Andy Barrett some experience. Scott needed to keep his stats high for college recruiters, and felt disappointed that Reinhart pulled him. When Barrett missed one, Scott selfishly thought to himself, *Well, there you go.*

Paxton faced a 315 pound Hamady opponent, unsure of what to expect from him. He was so big that he couldn't reach down far enough to place his fingers on the line. On the very first play, Paxton drove his opponent back ten steps and thought, *He's just a big, overstuffed pillow.* On the very next play the defender looked at Paxton and breathlessly suggested, 'I won't go hard if you won't.'

Paxton looked at his opponent and laughed. He thought, *No way. This is gonna be a fun game.* Paxton's opponent got up a bit slower after each blow. After he made him pack dirt for the third time, Paxton decided to be a sport and helped him up.

Hamady came out in a spread offense formation, throwing the ball. Dauber covered his opponent from the middle, breaking perfectly on the ball. He was only 20 yards from the endzone and thought, *I'm going to get an interception and score a touchdown. Never in my life have I scored a touchdown.* Dauber pictured himself catching the ball and crossing the goal line. But his dream was suddenly interrupted when the ball hit the linebacker's hands and bounced off his facemask, before hitting the ground. It left an embarrassed lineman eating his rare scoring opportunity. Dauber hated to face the guys in the huddle, but sheepishly soaked in their laughter. They intentionally mocked Dauber the rest of the night by saying, 'What the heck was that?'

Hamady realized that the Rams lightened up their intensity. When Montrose tried to run down the clock, Hamady showed class. 'Man, why don't you run some more plays? Can't you see we need the work? Go break some records or something.'

The Rams laughed, appreciating Hamady's sportsmanship considering the situation they were in. The Hawks got excited after a good play regardless of a lopsided '65-0' score. The Rams finally executed well and stayed focused, while rolling out 433 total offense yards. They played solid and didn't get sloppy. The coaches saw improvement.

Clolinger needed a deeper inspiration for the **Lake Fenton** motto:

**'Some People Dream Of Worthy Accomplishments
While Others Stay Awake And Do Them'**

Word quickly spread throughout the bleachers at the J.V. game that Eddie Magrys was in a car accident. Magrys was on his way to the game to hook-up with the rest of the Varsity. But he traveled too fast and lost control at the spot where the pavement turned to gravel. The next thing he knew, Magrys was on a stretcher in an ambulance headed to a Flint hospital. The entire Varsity couldn't believe that something happened to a squadmate. They felt an urgent need to be with him, and quickly piled into vehicles. Fear consumed them on the half-hour drive to the hospital, with Coach Reinhart at their side.

They arrived at the emergency room in a panic, and constantly pestered the nurses about Magry's condition. The noisy team had too many guys in the E.R., so the head nurse made a deal with them. 'You can all go in his room at once for five minutes, then you all have to leave.'

It was a deal. They just needed confirmation that Magrys was okay. The entire scene upset the carefree teenagers. Accidents happened to other teams. The team received a rude awakening of how quickly their lives could change; something they didn't care to think about at age 17.

Coach could tell they were still upset directly before the game Friday night, as thoughts of the accident bopped in their heads. He needed to calm them down and encouraged them. 'You need to play every play like it was your last. Live every day like it could be your last.'

This crazy game constantly taught them about life. Clint Galvas, a smaller kid they called Cleatus, spoke up. 'Let's dedicate the game to Magrys.'

They did, and quickly scored 21 first period points followed by four second quarter TD's. Everyone had an opportunity for some live action. Their victory made them feel that they were all a part of the team by setting a '69-0' record for the most points scored in a game. Reinhart saw great improvement in his Rams and was pleased with their performance. The offensive line seemed closer after earning each other's confidence; they called themselves 'The Boys.' If the right side was on pass protection and Paxton had a guy lined up above him, he knew that Bruno would be all over his opponent. Bruno was huge for a high school tackle at 5'11"-265 pounds. The line believed in each other, and contributed their added confidence to Coach Gilbert who brought them together. *Unity was treasured.*

Bentley was next and faced Montrose with a record of three wins, one loss. The Bulldogs hoped to beat the Rams, then have Montrose beat Bendle to force a three-way tie for the GEC Conference Title. But the Rams didn't seem too threatened by the Bentley Bulldogs. Instead, the squad mentally focused on Bendle who they faced the following week. It triggered Clolinger to pick a motto with a deep objective:

'If You Look Too Far Into the Future And Lose Focus Of The Task At Hand . . . You Can Become Bitten. Don't Be A Victim!'

The team listened intently during Reinhart's pre-game talk. 'Don't discount this team. They've got some good athletes. One broken play or one mess up can haunt us.'

The Rams felt the extra excitement surrounding the field due to Homecoming hoopla. Scott kicked off to the Bentley Bulldogs then stopped their first series. Montrose ran a 42 trap when they took over possession. Paxton created a huge hole for Cary, who busted loose, then bolted 39 yards to score less then four minutes into the game. Scott tacked on the PAT; the scoreboard blinked 7-0. One could almost see their intensity level drop and read their subconscious thoughts. *This is gonna be easy.* But then, the Bulldogs and the Rams stopped each other. Before the Rams realized it, the half was almost over and Bentley scored. The game was tied.

Shit. The Bentley Bulldogs gained confidence and had every right to think they could hang with the Rams. The Bulldogs had possession of the ball at the end of the second half when their quarterback turned to pitch the ball to their running back. Dauber was the closet Ram to take him down. He chased after him when a smaller opponent got under his shoulder pads and hit him. Dauber managed to get away and ran after the back, but his knee wouldn't cooperate. Dauber was the last hope for the Rams to catch the opponent, but his brace was so bulky that he couldn't extend his leg in a normal stride . . . and he stumbled. The running back ran over the top of Dauber's hands as he raced down the field, while Dauber lay vulnerably on the ground. From a distance, Dauber looked up to watch his opponent cross the goal line. The Rams thought, *What the hell is going wrong? Our offensive line is stacked with strength and our backs have the speed, why aren't we dominating?*

Trailing 7-14 at the half was an uncomfortable position for the Rams. A loss meant a long season; a win saved face. Reinhart didn't waste any time getting in Dauber's face the moment he reached the sideline, humiliating his captain in front of the entire team. Players remembered what people said after the Chesaning loss. 'The Rams weren't any good,' and 'Once you think you can be beat, it's easy to lose more.' It almost became a self-fulfilling prophecy. *Losing stinks.*

Bo Paxton had to make a choice, leave with the team or hang back and fulfill his role as Homecoming King. Reinhart left the decision totally up to him. Paxton was so upset with the game, that he never considered hanging back as an option. The King forfeited his opportunity to be on the field when the Queen was announced. He didn't join in any of the festivities, or strut his stuff in front of the fans, or have his picture made with the Queen. Instead, he stomped his sweaty body into the team room, yanked off his helmet, and threw it against the bench. He was so pissed that he couldn't hold back his feelings. Just three months earlier, he set two national powerlifting records and was categorized as one of the strongest seniors in the state of Michigan. He dedicated himself during the entire off-season, preparing for his senior year.

It was only week six of the season and the Rams were losing. He thought, *I don't want my senior year to end this way, not to Bentley. We've been through way too much to give it all up now.* Paxton looked at his fellow seniors and questioned, 'What the hell are we doing?'

He was so worked up that his flushed cheeks turned crimson red. Paxton's voice was packed with heartfelt emotion. 'Do you guys want to throw our season down the drain? Do you want everything we've worked for to be over now? Do you guys want to lose? DO YOU? It's too early. It's just too early! If we lose tonight, our playoff dream is over. It's all over. Our dream of winning a State Championship is over. Shit, we won't even be able to win the League, and I AM NOT READY TO BE DONE PLAYING FOOTBALL!'

Paxton was so worked up that he didn't know if he wanted to cry or punch someone. But he had the squad's complete attention as he looked at each one of them with such intensity that his voice cracked. 'WE ARE NOT LOSING TO THIS TEAM!'

The musty room immediately fell silent, as the stench grew noticeably heavier. Each player nodded his head in agreement. Bo Paxton was the guy that made them laugh, but when he laid his heart and guts on the line, they felt hollow for not trying harder. The tears that slid down the huge lineman's burning cheeks were real. Even though he wasn't an official captain, in that crucial moment he became their emotional leader. Although unrehearsed, Paxton handled the delicate moment perfectly. He challenged each one of them to a gut check. Everyone silently committed to giving everything he had in order to win. The Rams found themselves pushed to the brink. But they had been in that hole before and realized they could come back for the fight. They wouldn't quit.

The coaches couldn't have said it any better; they didn't need to rant and rave. Instead, they calmly made adjustments, then watched as Reinhart walked up to the board. He wrote down the score -- 'Montrose 7 - Bentley 14.' He didn't yell at them. He didn't swear at them. He didn't throw any water bottles. He just paced back and forth in front of the grease board, stopped, then slowly looked at his team before pointing to the board. 'This is your season fellas. This is it. We can go out the second half, dominate, and win this ball game. Or everything you've worked for the past year, everything we've talked about in the past year, will be thrown away.' He tapped the board with the marker. 'This is it fellas. This is it.'

Paxton slowly turned his head and paused to look at his teammates. He already saw a difference in them. Their expressions now reflected raw determination. He realized they were just messin' around with Bentley during the first half. He knew they were ready to go back on the field and get the job done. Dauber took off his knee brace and left it on the bench. He thought, *If we can't win here tonight then our season will be over in three weeks; I won't have a reason to save myself for anything.*

The Rams walked out of their team room with one thought on their minds. *It was now or never.* They pulled together and found a way to make it happen. Montrose outscored Bentley 21-0 during the second half, playing like they knew they were capable of. The scoreboard lit up the north end of the stadium, '28-14.' The Rams executed without penalties, demonstrating they were ready to play good football.

Beating Bentley helped the Rams turn the corner and endure an exceptionally tough practice for **Bendle** week. Players gathered after pre-game practice and listened to Reinhart. 'We were on top for nine years, always being the hunted. This year the shoe's on the other foot. That's a new experience for us. Tomorrow night we'll find out how we handle it. We want to come back and beat them. We want the GEC Title back. Maybe we won't have as much pressure on us because we're the underdogs; we're not expected to win.'

'It's Not The Game, The Half, Or The Quarter. It's The Play!'

The Bendle Tigers were ranked No.7 in Class C, and hosted the Montrose Rams who were unranked in the state. Once the Rams lost to Chesaning, they also lost their ranking -- and it bothered them.

Reinhart walked into the pre-game locker room with a serious look on his face. A respectful hush blanketed the room, while players watched his short, choppy steps approach the grease board. Coach picked up a red highlighter, then wrote one word on the board in thick letters -- **'FAMILY.'**

He talked about having brothers and sisters and moms and dads. Coach confessed how much that he loved his own three sons. He paused for good measure then turned around, intently looking at the squad. 'If anyone ever took one of my kids away or tried to hurt one of them, I would search the end of the earth to get revenge because I love my kids that much.'

The emotion in his voice was powerful. Bruno felt his heart race; so did Pooh Bear. They all did. Coach gave a long, quiet stare at his team before he pointed to the board, effectively tapping the marker on the lone word -- 'FAMILY.' 'WE are a family. Last year our prized possession was taken away. This is our chance to get revenge. To get even. Tonight, we have an opportunity to get it back. We are playing the game for this team, but also for the football program and our proud tradition.'

A cold shiver passed through Bruno's thick body as the sensation of goosebumps slid up his huge arms. Even the big boys felt the bang from that speech. The entire team sensed the intense emotion in the room after Coach delivered his most emotional talk. Reinhart had their full attention, while striking a cord in each of them. The Rams felt ready to battle. Their pride was on the line; they were determined to get back on top. Reinhart looked at his quarterback and mightily stated, 'Teddy, this is what you came back for.'

Teddy nodded in his quiet manner. He didn't outright show his emotions as he tried to keep his poker face on. But if anyone looked inside of his heart, they would see a concealed whirlwind of emotions that churned like a funnel cloud ready to attack. Over 2,000 fans were on hand to watch the rematch, wondering, *Who would break the tie for the League's first place?* Dauber stared at Paxton as they lined up on the field. He heard the lineman mumble, and noticed Paxton's clenched fists as he bounced up-and-down. Just looking at Paxton in his psyched-up state pumped Dauber up. He knew right then that the Rams would play to win. Paxton would make them.

Teddy connected with Craig Parks on a 40 yard scoring strike six minutes into the game. The Rams wanted to score again, but both teams fought hard and held each other. Bendle and Montrose knew how to run the veer, but they also knew how to stop it. Bendle tied the game early in the third when a back burst off left tackle, found his way through traffic, then blazed untouched down the left sideline. A good PAT tied the game. The Rams threatened to score again when a Tiger defender forced Anthony to fumble at goal line. It was the Rams only turnover, but a critical one that ended their drive at goal line. Bendle moved the ball, but couldn't get it in the endzone. Listening to the trash-talk forced Bruno to crack a smile as the tackle took his position. Pooh Bear played tight end. He pointed to a spot while he announced to his opponents. 'We're running right here. The ball is coming right here. Are you coming at me? C'mon, let's rock.'

The linemen loved Pooh Bear. They called him a gentle giant off the field, but on the field he turned into an animal. After the Rams made their first down, Pooh Bear took his position and once again started messing with their minds. 'You can't stop us. You can't do it.'

Cary capped a 72 yard drive after scoring a nine yard TD with less then ten minutes in the game. The Rams went ahead 14-7. Bendle had a different plan and returned the kickoff 47 yards to the Montrose 33. On second-and-third from the 14, the Tigers were called for offensive pass interference in the endzone, stalling the drive at the 25. It was a questionable call, but the official stood in the endzone. He felt the Bendle receiver made aggressive contact. From the visitors side, it looked like a defensive pass interference call against the Rams, but they weren't about to give it back.

The pressure was on. If the Rams didn't win, the doubters would return. The battle became a game of smash mouth football. It was a player's game, not necessarily a great game to watch unless you enjoyed a hard-hitting, exhausting football game. Both teams ran at each other, forcing their opponents to stop them. Bendle's defense struggled to block Pooh Bear on the strong side. He was only a junior and stood 6'1"-245 pounds, but was quick for his size. Pooh Bear already had the eye of Division I recruits. He wasn't intimidated in the least when he looked at his opponents. 'You can't block me. Do you know who I am?'

The trash-talk spread to Parks who stood 6'3", next to Dauber on the other side of the line. Parks was a quiet-natured guy off the field, but came alive on the line. 'I'm coming to get you again. What are you gonna do?'

The trash-talk distracted the intensity of the game and made it fun, in spite of a close score and the GEC Title on the line. Salty Dog played guard and ran his mouth constantly. Salty's neck was about half the size of the rest of the line; Bruno and Paxton both outweighed him by a hundred pounds. Salty looked minuscule next to the rest of the line, but he had a special way of making them laugh. The Rams communicated through their trash-talk. Parks yelled to Dauber, 'You got the Marsha on that one?'

Marsha was the line call to double-team and meant, 'I'm gonna help you.' If the offensive line said, 'Are you Boomer-Boomer?' It meant, 'You've got him on your own.'

Dauber flat-out told his opponents exactly what he planned to do. 'All right Parks, you're gonna take out #67. I'm gonna help you out, then I'm goin' after the linebacker, and you just gotta come down.'

Most of the time Bendle didn't pay attention to their trash-talk, in case they intentionally tried to throw them off. The Rams drove the ball the entire length of the field, earning five chunks of real estate at a time, until they exhaustedly reached the one yard line. The call was supposed to be a '13.' Bendle knew that Cary was the go-to-guy and loaded up on his side.

Instead, Teddy ran the option and handed off to Anthony who crossed the goal line, but was nailed by a Bendle Tiger and fumbled. The Rams broke the plane before the fumble, and felt it should count. Instead, Bendle received a big break when they got the ball at the 20. It was a critical call and the intensity level caused high blood pressure in the mildest person. Teddy felt awful, but the line remained confident that the Rams would come back.

With three minutes left in the game, the Tigers had one final chance to score on their own 29. They made it to the 16, when Tommy Leonard applied pressure on the quarterback as he threw a deep pass. Tim Hemker made an interception in the endzone, stopping any hope for a Bendle retort. The Rams ran out the clock, squashing Bendle's final hope to maintain their League Title that they took from the Rams a year ago. The war was over.

Players and coaches felt emotionally drained after the thrilling '14-7' hard-hitting and well-played victory. It was a shame that someone had to lose after that level of effort. But players didn't feel any animosity toward each other, and respectfully shook hands after a championship battle. They were competitors who played to win, yet respected each other enough to leave it on the field. The backs played hard, the line played hard and everyone felt physically exhausted. The Rams protected their family, and it felt great. Reinhart felt drained when he gathered his team post-game. 'This was a classic football game. We saw full class from both sides. You came over here tonight to take something back that Bendle took from us a year ago.'

'Family' became their motto that carried them through the remainder of the season. That victory restored their confidence; they felt reborn in the system like they just started a new season. Paxton and Teddy knew what they wanted to do. They had to. Teddy knew the Rams wouldn't settle for anything less than a State Title. Paxton yelled out to the squad, 'We're here to do it. We're gonna do it.'

Paxton reread the newspaper article that was taped on the back of his bedroom door before he went to bed. The caption read, 'Bendle Ends Rams GEC Run' and was written by Keith Morris of the Flint Journal. That very article held a worn look from hanging on the back of his bedroom door for an entire year. For 365 days he read that headline every single night when he shut his bedroom door, then fell asleep pissed off at Bendle Football. It was finally time to put the demon to rest. He ripped the article off the wall, crumbled it, and threw it on his dresser. The following morning he joined his mom, while she worked in her flowerbeds. 'Hey Mom, watch this.'

He held a lighter to the crumbled article until it was completely engulfed in flames. In a matter of seconds, the article became a small pile of ashes in his mom's flowerbed. He scooped a handful of freshly worked dirt, buried the ashes, then looked up at his mom. 'There, that's the end of that.'

From her knees, she watched the back of her 6 foot, 260 pound son. His thighs were so large that they rubbed together as he walked away. She noticed his relaxed cadence; as if he had a skip in his walk. It made her aware of the burdens that her son carried for an entire year. She stood by his side during his most painful moments, and couldn't help but smile when he doused in the pleasure of sweet revenge.

But Clolinger didn't want anyone to have a big head after their close victory, and chose an appropriate motto for **Byron**:

**'If What You Did Friday Still Looks Big To You,
You Have Not Done Much Today!'**

The Rams jumped out to a quick 17-0, first period lead against Byron. But Byron came back halfway through the second quarter and scored, followed by Teddy's 35 yard run to the goal line. Scott kicked a 36 yard field goal, giving the Rams a 23-7 edge at the intermission. Byron came ready to play. The Eagles put together a pair of impressive drives in the third period, and scored the only TD of the quarter. The Rams showed their character on their next possession. They marched the entire length of the field, scored early in the fourth, and again near the end of the period. Scott's PAT closed the score at '37-13.' The Rams played well and didn't appear too bruised. They didn't make many mistakes, clinching at least a share of the GEC Championship with one more week of league play.

Montrose didn't celebrate the GEC Title share though; they had higher goals in mind. The Rams proved they could get back on top by moving into second place in the Region 4 playoff standings. They dedicated themselves to go farther than they did a year ago when they lost in the state semifinals; their quest in '98 was a trip to the Silverdome.

Clolinger continued driving them with an inspiring weekly motto, as the Rams headed into their final league game against **Atherton**:

> **'If You Want To Accomplish More,**
> **You Must Be Willing to Give More.**
> **How Much More Do You Want?'**

The Rams prepared for Atherton but focused on the following week, which opened playoffs. They knew they didn't need to be at their best to beat Atherton and worked longer and harder hours. Even the linemen didn't complain after running farther to get in better shape for the post-season.

The coaches turned the lights on during practice for their last home game, adding an uncommon dimension to their workout. The Rams locked in their League Championship by beating Atherton '67-0' for the regular season finale. Cary opened the score with an 85 yard kick return, followed by a 30 yard scoring run later in the quarter. Anthony rushed for four consecutive TD's on runs of 8, 20, 24, and one yard. Parks, and sophomores Jeremy Cochrane and Wesley Fisk, each got a shot to score, while Scott's extra point record was 8-for-10.

The team gave Atherton credit when they made the effort to block two missed kicks. Scott constantly worried about his stats for college, by constantly applying his own pressure. He became upset after each blocked kick, which statistically counted against him as missed punts.

Their climb to the top was far from over; reclaiming the GEC League Title was the first step. They were ready to scale another peak, just in time for the first playoff round. Clolinger saw the intensity in their eyes, and knew they were already motivated to face **Almont**:

'We Have Completed One Journey, It's Now Time To
Start Climbing The Biggest Mountain Of All!
Do We Have What It Takes?'

The Almont Raiders had impressive depth with a lot of weapons; who used their speed to score quick and often. Almont had faced bigger teams, and planned to mix up their offense for diversification.

The Internet provided the Montrose coaching staff with an article from a local Almont paper that focused on the strength of each team. The Montrose offensive line was referred to as *big and slow*. Gilbert and Sleeve never showed the article to their guys, but translated the phrase to *fat and slow* in an effort to motivate the line. They opened practice with, 'Okay you fat and slow linemen, let's get to work today.'

The linemen heard the coaches taunt them during the iron sled drill, and again when they moved to the chutes. 'What's the matter, are you too fat and slow?'

It pissed Paxton off and he asked Bruno, 'How can they call us fat and slow? They don't even know us and they called us fat and slow.'

The thought alone provoked every lineman to drive the sled as hard as he could. The line worked so hard during practice that they sheered off the bolts that held the bags on the seven-man sled. Gilbert didn't think that was even possible and glanced at Sleeve with a grin on his face. 'Can you believe that?'

They both just shook their heads and grinned. *Willpower was warranted.*

The '98 Team had another chance to redeem themselves -- if they could exorcise their post-season demons. They vowed not to let another game slip away. The seniors grew up a lot over the past year and wanted to make up for '97. They planned to use their superior size and strength for the same edge that helped them during the season.

'Bond Fridays' became a new '98 tradition. Cleatus hooked-up his Nintendo 64 in the coach's office, like he had every Friday morning throughout the season. But the pressure was higher during playoffs and everyone needed a means to escape. They welcomed the distraction that took their competition to a different stage. Whenever the players or coaches had a free period, they packed into that minuscule office and played James Bond. The game never stopped, Sleeve made sure of that. He did his student teaching under Reinhart. His assignment that day was to help them unwind. At times, as many as 20 players packed into that tiny coach's office. It was a fun time to relax and battle each others' brains out. Rank and size were cast away. Even Cleatus could wrangle the huge lineman and whip them; he was the master. It was a time to forget about the demands of playoff football. The coaches didn't have to coach, and players didn't need to be coached. They were all on the same level on Bond Fridays. Sleeve and Reinhart had improved each week throughout the season, but Sleeve secretly thought that he passed Reinhart, and could take him.

Salty's recently retired dad, Dick, volunteered to cook a playoff breakfast for all of the coaches and players before school on Almont day. The Salters lived near the school, and greeted sleepy kids as they entered their home. Players either hid their emotions well or were too sleepy to show any. Dick felt confident they would come alive by game time. Nora and Dick Salter planned to enjoy their twin's senior year. Salty Dog played at guard, while his twin sister and her friends contributed to the school's spirit by decorating the hall near the football locker room every Thursday night. They squeezed so many balloons into Reinhart's office that the door hardly closed. Nora wrote a special balloon message and placed it in the coach's bathroom toilet that read, 'Kick their Butts.'

Gilbert and Sleeve appreciated one of the perks of coaching Montrose Football -- *the food*. The 24 year-old bachelors enjoyed the home-cooked team dinners before Sunday film sessions, as well as the awesome breakfasts before playoff games.

At the opening of the game, they noticed that the bandwagon fans jumped back on the playoff wagon, as if they'd never left. Montrose fans held their breath when Scott kicked off to the Almont Raiders, then watched their speedy punt returner dodge in and out. The Raiders drove down the field, progressively moving the ball. Almont ran a flair pass three times, which caused problems for the defensive backs that hadn't practiced defending it. Almont Coach Gary Carson felt their first drive set the tone for the night when the Raiders marched the length of the field to the Montrose two yard line. Dauber told Leitelt, 'Man this isn't working. We have to change something real quick or they're gonna score.'

They both looked to the sideline and saw Coach D give the double fire signal to stunt. But they didn't read their keys and darted straight ahead when the ball was snapped. Dauber realized they were close to the endzone when he stunted and dove for his opponents' legs. Dauber ended up on the bottom of a huge pile, with his face buried in the ground. He heard cheering but couldn't see anything through the pile and thought, *Shit. They scored.* He peered through a slight opening in the pile and thought that he saw his teammates bouncing up-and-down. It was easy for the immobile guy on the bottom of the pile to get disoriented, while waiting for players to peel off. Dauber wondered, *Did we stop them? Why are we acting so happy? We still have one down left.* Then he recognized Park's voice, 'We got the ball, we got the ball.'

Almont fumbled in the endzone after a hard-hit from a defender, while Pooh Bear smothered the loose ball. His huge body stood up, grinning from ear to ear while he did his famous Pooh Bear Dance.

It hurt the Raiders to lose the ball on the Montrose one yard line after their long drive. The Rams took possession, which allowed Scott to boot a field goal that landed just outside of the crossbar. The Raiders fumbled again on their next possession at their own 20 yard line. The Rams took advantage of the momentum shift by scoring five plays later. Scott's good PAT put the Rams on the scoreboard 7-0.

The Raiders drove to the Montrose 39 when a third fumble occurred and the Rams recovered. The Rams needed their opponents to make turnovers. They needed some opportunities, and they got them. The defense and offense switched places and wasted no time. Cary took a handoff from Teddy and broke clear down the left sideline, racing 63 yards to score halfway through the second. Scott's PAT lit up the scoreboard 14-0. The Raiders threatened to score when sophomore Jeremy Cochrane picked-off an Almont pass in the endzone. But the Rams were far from pompous with a 14 point first half lead. Both coaches were in their locker rooms stating that the score could very well have been 7-7, instead of 14-0. Montrose learned the hard way that anything could happen in a ball game. The Rams knew that Almont wasn't playing with its most potent weapons due to injuries; their turnovers led to Montrose scoring. Reinhart was disappointed with his defense and stressed, 'It's so important for us to set the tone during the opening play of the second half.'

The Raiders kicked off to the Rams to start the third. Cary positioned himself deep, grabbed the ball then bobbled it, while the crowd held its breath. His quick reflexes maintained control while he worked his magic, determined to reach the goal line. Nothing would stop him that night. *Nothing.*

The Rams blocked as Cary juked then raced 80 yards, untouched, for a TD. Cary was on fire after scoring his third TD in the playoff game. Scott's kick went wide, but the Rams were up 20-0.

The Raiders felt the hard blow across the field when Cary returned the kickoff, but they came back and intercepted Teddy's pass. Reinhart came unglued when his defense received a pass interference penalty on fourth-and-long. That blunder came back and bit the Rams when Almont spurted 12 yards, then broke two tackles to get on the board 20-6.

Fans wondered, *How would their Rams react?* They appeared shaken after dropping the ensuing kickoff, which backed them up at the 12. Then they fumbled on the first down, backing them up to the five. Sudden flashbacks from the '97 semifinal game surfaced and fans wondered, *Would their Rams fold under second half pressure?* Reinhart was furious on the sideline, which caused a contagious effect on Cary. He shouted in the huddle, 'We are not giving this up. No way are we letting Almont come within a TD. No way! Let's get it back. Now!'

The emotion in Cary's voice saturated the line. They wanted it too. On third-and-17, the determined line blasted a hole, allowing Cary to break loose off tackle into the secondary. His determination moved his strong legs for 95 yards, determined not to stop until he crossed. Paxton was gassed but used his adrenaline rush to pick himself off of the ground. He jogged as fast as he could toward the endzone to celebrate. Scott had his game head back, calmed himself down, then kicked a perfect PAT to make the score 27-8.

Coach Stiles joined the Varsity staff after his J.V. Season ended. He worked with the backs and quarterbacks to organize the scout team look. Stiles stood nearby Reinhart on the sideline and suggested plays, while serving as a buffer to bounce ideas off. He was prepared whenever Reinhart said, 'Gimmie a play.' Stiles knew their skills well from coaching them at the freshmen and J.V. level. He still considered the '98 seniors to be *his boys*. They were his first batch of Rams and held a special connection in his heart.

The Rams rocked their fans who now stood and cheered. Players turned around and rhythmically moved their palms upward, encouraging the fans to yell even louder. The cushion squashed away their fears, while adding confidence, making the game fun. Reinhart sent the punt team in and called for a squib. Cary found his position on the line, while his heart pounded in his chest. He totally focused his eyes on Scott's perfect kick then used his speed to pounce on it. It worked like a charm, just like in practice. The Rams marched down to the nine yard line when Teddy darted in for a TD. Scott kicked the PAT, then celebrated the '34-6' score. Hemker took the helm at quarterback and guided the Rams down the field, until Anthony made a final score. Naturally, Scott ran on the field with the special teams to kick the PAT. He didn't hear Reinhart call for Scott's little brother. An excited Tommy Visser ran up, 'What do they need coach? Water? Do you want me to take the water out?'

The little freshman was thrilled to have the honor just to dress for the game and couldn't hide his enthusiasm. He never expected to play; those dreams just don't happen in the playoffs, especially for freshman. Reinhart chuckled at his reaction, 'No Tommy, how would you like to kick the extra point?'

Little Visser's mouth dropped open, 'For real Coach?'

'Yes -- for real Tommy.'

Like the three Unangst brothers that kicked for the Rams, Tommy was the third and youngest Visser to hold the kicker position. And like the Unangst brothers, the Visser brothers were each other's biggest fan. Scott stopped running and turned around when he heard his name called. He grinned the moment he saw Tommy approach him. 'Hey Scott, care if I kick this one?'

Scott forgot about his college stats when he tapped his little brother on top of his helmet. His facemask couldn't conceal his genuine smile. 'It's your big chance Tommy. You can do it.'

That was all Tommy needed to hear before pacing off his steps. He tried to ignore his rapid, pounding heartbeat, while tuning out all of the people watching him. Tommy intently focused while he waited for the whistle. The ball was hiked. Tommy confidently stepped up and kicked it perfectly, like he had his entire freshmen season. Scott charged the field to embrace his little brother, enjoying a moment the Visser brothers would never forget.

Almont scored a TD in the waning seconds to close the game '41-14.' Reinhart talked to them after the game. 'It was a nice victory, but we need to play better defensively if we expect to make a long run in the playoffs. Defense is the key to winning championships and tonight we bent, but we didn't break. We came up with some big defensive stops when we had to, but we also gave up a lot of yards.'

Injuries and turnovers were critical and uncharacteristic for Almont. The Raiders fumbled the ball six times, while the Rams committed just one turnover. Four Almont turnovers led to Montrose TD's. Possibly, the game would have a different score if Almont's star player had been in uniform instead of crutches, or another key back had not chipped a bone in his foot. The back that scored Almont's first TD, injured himself while diving for the ball on a missed extra-point attempt. He didn't play much after that.

Playoff injuries are always unfortunate, leaving a team wondering, *What if?* The Rams experienced more than their share of post-season wounds and playoff fumbles through the years and could empathize with Almont. For once, Montrose appreciated being on the other end.

Clolinger wanted the Rams hungry for more when he wrote the motto for Round two against **Capac:**

'As We Scale The Biggest Mountain, We Must Remember
What Got Us To This Point.
Do We Want To Continue Our Journey Or Are We Satisfied?'

The cold air from the Michigan November evening filled players lungs with a numbing sensation. Coach D saw his breath turn white when he called out defensive plays on the practice field. Practice didn't involve a lot of hitting due to the cold temperature, and the fact that players were banged up after ten weeks of football.

Montrose felt that they didn't receive much respect from the Southern Thumb Association, even though they beat Capac in '97 during the second-round playoff game and stopped Almont the previous week. Coaches accessed sports articles from the Capac area on the Internet. They were left with the impression that Almont was the best team Capac had ever played -- both years. Gilbert and Sleeve decided to stretch what they read and told the line, 'Capac also mentioned they you are big and slow and that you couldn't do a whole lot.'

It only pissed them off, giving the line coaches the exact result they were after. Reinhart preached to his team all week during Capac practice, 'You can't go by comparative scores. Turnovers can really change the outcome of the game.'

He didn't want his Rams to think that Montrose had the edge, since they beat Almont 41-14 the previous week, while Capac beat Almont 21-17 during the final minute of their regular season. Capac had turned the ball over five times against Almont. But they didn't have one turnover in their opening playoff round against Livonia Clarenceville, outscoring them 48-28. Capac returned seven starters who were all eager to even the score from '97; similar to the revenge the Rams held against Chesaning. Reinhart reminded them that their last match was played on a cold night in five inches of snow, which limited both teams. 'We'll probably face a better team than the one we beat a year ago. Capac passes more and seems more diversified.'

A win would provide Capac with their first-ever Regional Championship or provide Montrose with an opportunity to claim back-to-back Regional Titles. Most of the Montrose students chose to support their Rams again and chanted from the bleachers, 'REPEAT! REPEAT!' The super fans sang the school song while the cheerleaders danced the routine, disallowing the absence of a school band to dampen their spirit. Players from Almont, Goodrich, and Lapeer West attended the game sporting varsity jackets, yet rooted for the Rams. Excitement filled the Capac stadium as fans rose to their feet for the opening kickoff. The Chiefs booted it to the Rams, then Teddy fumbled on the second play at the Montrose 29. Capac recovered, then moved the ball down the field running a back side tight-end drag. Dauber covered the end until Leitelt took over. The Rams couldn't cover it right, which made it easy for the Chiefs to pass and score in just three minutes.

The Rams demonstrated tenacity when Teddy pitched out to Cary on their first play from scrimmage, then watched him run 69 yards to score just :19 seconds later. Cary bailed the Rams out of a few games, while his excellent timing ignited the spark. Scott's extra point gave the Rams a 7-6 lead as both teams settled into hard-hitting football. The Rams started a drive at their 26, then were forced to punt from their own nine later in the first quarter. The Chiefs couldn't take it in. Instead, they kicked a 22 yard field goal to claim a 7-9 lead with over 11 minutes to play in the first half.

The Rams drove down the field, playing Montrose Football -- running first, passing when needed. Ten plays and 46 yards later, Cary plowed up the middle from the one with :30 seconds left in the half. The conversion failed, but the Rams as well as their fans were thrilled for the 12-9 lead.

Teddy took a tough hit from a Capac opponent that forcefully crammed his head into the hard ground. The quarterback was out of it. Teddy heard his coaches and trainers talk, but couldn't respond. Paxton grew concerned. He went beyond extremes to protect Teddy, not just because he was their quarterback but they were close friends. He realized what it took for Teddy to become a Ram again. Paxton stood over his quarterback, 'C'mon Teddy, you've got to pull through this. We've come too far and we're not done yet.'

Ted regrouped during the intermission and opened with a screen pass to Cary. Early in the third, he broke loose, then spurted 70 yards down the field to the one yard line. It was a huge play for the Rams that claimed the opening momentum. Paxton thought Cary was in and planned to give his little buddy a fat bear hug after hauling all of his 260 pounds to the endzone as fast as he could, screaming, 'Whoo-hoo!' He realized the jaunt exerted his last bit of energy, but planned to run over to the sideline and rest while special teams took the field. He was pissed after realizing that Cary was stopped at the one. Instead of celebrating, the exhausted lineman ran up to his friend, slamming both fists into his shoulder pads. 'So what's your problem Cary? Why didn't you score? Why didn't you take it in?'

Cary wasn't surprised by his friend's reaction, even though the fans were ecstatic that his long run provided a huge momentum swing. He laughed at Paxton, realizing that his friend expended more energy than he could spare. And now he had to run another play. On the very next play, Teddy plunged over on a keeper, then Scott made the PAT, changing the score 19-9. Cary ran up to Paxton afterward and wanted to call him a fat and slow lineman, but held back. Instead he asked, 'Do you feel better now that you got a drink?'

The Rams were an awesome team that worked great together on the field, but didn't exactly dish out compliments to each other. Paxton glared at his friend, 'Oh shut up Cary.'

Salty Dog played left guard on Dauber's side. Dauber noticed that he didn't get up after the play and walked over to Salty. 'Hey, what's the matter?'

'I don't know, my leg won't move. I threw a block then it just wouldn't move.'

The game was delayed while his leg was examined. It didn't look good when they carried him off the field. Freshman Coach Dave Beazley went to work on Salty's leg. Beazley was known for coaching the Montrose State Champion Wrestling Teams and for being a former Olympic-wrestling contender himself. Beazley could relate to being injured. He knew firsthand how tough it was for a dedicated athlete to work toward a goal, then fall short because of an injury.

Gibby willingly stepped in for Salty Dog. Gibby played right guard in '97 as a sophomore when he was positioned next to Dauber at right tackle. They played eight games together, and felt confident they could work together on the left side. Montrose earned possession after stopping Capac, then took it to the one before the determined Chiefs stopped the Rams.

Reinhart called a timeout then approached the huddle with his trademark short choppy steps. Adrenaline flashed through his body with each impending pace. By the time that he reached the huddle, his emotions were peaked. He was on fire when he pointed his index finger directly in the chest of his key back, enunciated each forceful word, 'Cary, you freaking squat 500 freaking pounds. YOU - CAN - GET - ONE – FREAKING YARD!'

Goosebumps jolted up 22 arms in the huddle, 26 if you counted the two water boys. Coach was so worked up that he probably didn't even realize the harsh choice of words he used. Adrenaline juices thrust into overdrive; not just for Cary, but for the entire team. Reinhart had the line ready to explode. Cary felt such a charge that he started hyperventilating. He took a pull of deep air to control his heavy breathing and calm down before the important play. The unwavering line used the same massive force that jarred the bolts off the sled. Their strength, combined with Cary's determination, undeniably pushed him over. It was only a one yard run, but became Cary's most exciting score. Exhilaration consumed him; he actually clapped in the endzone the moment the scoreboard changed 26-9.

Paxton was instructed to run time off the clock since the Rams were ahead. Coach Gilbert yelled to his animated lineman, mouthing the words, 'Hey #72, you slow kid. You big, fat, slow kid. Now is the time to be fat and slow. When you knock someone on the ground, get up real slow.'

Paxton looked back at his line coach, savoring the moment. He stood up, grabbed his fat, then shook it up-and-down so it jiggled like a bowl full of jello. He glanced at the sideline and yelled, 'Oh yeah, I love my fat.'

His jersey was untucked when he pointed to a Capac player on the ground, grabbed his belly and yelled, 'Look at what my fat does!'

The other linemen joined in by grabbing their stomachs when they walked up to the line. 'Oh, we're all so fat. I don't know how we're doin' this. We're sooo tired and sooo fat.'

Reinhart laughed, along with his line coaches, shaking his head as he walked away. *Linemen.*

Dauber and Kris stepped forward to accept the regional trophy from Capac's Athletic Director. The team huddled in the center of the field, an area usually privileged for the ears of players, coaches, and a few reporters. That night, parents, girlfriends, and fans invaded the sacred ground. Salty Dog stood behind his team, resting his weight on a pair of crutches. Like Aaron, he was thrilled for the victory, but felt cheated that his injury prevented him from playing in the post-season.

The team intently listened when Reinhart spoke. 'I had a vision that we were playing in the Silverdome and were in a position to put Salty Dog in for one last play at the end of the game.'

Salty looked at his Coach with moist eyes, appreciating that he was included in the post-game celebration. The injured guard only hoped that his dream became a reality. Reinhart continued, 'Tomorrow at films, we'll enjoy this game film before we watch the Hopkins game. Then, we'll go in the gym and work on some plays.'

The team captain told them to raise their helmets as the Rams sang the school song in unison. Fellow students joined in, forming a special memory. The team bus made its exit through the small town of Capac, headed toward the expressway. The bus made a routine stop at the railroad crossing, and noticed a man standing in the middle of the highway, flagging them down. It looked like Coach Reinhart. The team watched with wide eyes, trying to figure out why their coach was hitchhiking. Reinhart planned to ride back to Montrose with some of his scouts, like he did in '97 when the Rams beat Capac on the same field. But his superstitions got the best of him as they drove out of town. The head coach didn't want to jinx his Rams since they lost in the next playoff round. He didn't care how crazy it sounded, he needed to change what he did a year later and told the driver, 'Stop at the railroad tracks and let me out.'

His scouts realized how superstitions easily clouded normal judgment; that was a part of football, especially during playoffs. They laughed, 'Just do whatever it takes to get us to the Dome.'

Montrose Football was the only local team still in the semifinals, relinquishing great sports coverage from the media. For the past three weeks, sports writers constantly reiterated the heartbreaking losses of the '97 Season. Seniors from that team were college freshmen and went on with their lives. But the words of the media jabbed like a sharp knife, reopening barely healed wounds a year later. Woody threw the newspaper down after he read the sports section. 'Why do they keep beating us up?'

The article stated, 'Rams were stunned by Chesaning 12-14 on a touchdown in the final seconds that ended the Montrose nine-year, 80-game regular-season winning streak, one shy of the state record.'

A few miles down the road Bo Moore had the same reaction, 'Why can't they just leave us alone?'

Aaron had a similar reaction as he read, 'Then Bendle snapped the 75-game GEC winning streak that helped the Rams to nine straight League Titles.' How could he ever forget? He still had eight pins in his left ankle and required another surgery as a result from that game. That injury prevented him from playing college football. Hell, it practically prevented him from playing backyard football.

Three heartbreaking semifinal losses prevented the Rams from completing their quest to the Dome -- 1992. . .1994. . .1997. The thought on everyone's mind was, *Could they squeak by in '98?* It was the first time they had consecutive years in the semifinals. *Could that make a difference?* The seniors tasted success during the first half of the '97 semifinal game when they were up 10-0 at the half, then felt a deep-rooted ache that lingered for an entire year. Reinhart hoped that executing under pressure wouldn't be as difficult, since the fresh memory still haunted them. The Rams worked hard to get back to this point; they were hungry for more. It was an incentive for the '98 seniors who wanted a different ending; a happier one. They wanted their season to last two hours longer than '97.

Gilbert and Sleeve had the line practice longer than the rest, since the Chesaning game. The '98 line appeared to be in the best physical condition ever. Gilbert watched Paxton hit the chute with accurate precision. Paxton repeated more reps than anybody and told Sleeve, 'He looks like a crafty veteran. Remember how much trouble Paxton had early in the season?'

Sleeve snickered, 'Yeah. He screwed up and made the line pay.'

When a player hit the chute on the line drill, the entire group had to repeat it. Linemen had to be conditioned to stay low. Paxton never thought he would make it some days, after hitting the chute with his helmet or shoulder pads five times in a row. The entire line became frustrated, but Paxton was determined to get it down. He finally mastered it.

Gilbert and Sleeve appreciated that Reinhart did what a lot of head coaches have a hard time doing; *he let them coach*. Reinhart wanted to know what they were doing, but gave them the reigns and cut them loose. Reinhart inspired Gilbert after seeing how important the game of football was to the head coach. He saw how hard Reinhart worked to keep Montrose going in the direction that it traveled for the past decade.

Practice for the third round went flawless; the Rams started to peak at the perfect time. Previous teams peaked early in the season and never improved, but the '98 Rams seemed to continually improve each week. Everything clicked, leaving them with a strong belief in themselves. They felt they would win their semifinal game. It wasn't arrogance. It wasn't overconfidence. It was outward conviction!

Cary's crazed passion told him to order his turf shoes two weeks early, even before the semifinal game. That's how confident he was about Montrose going to the Dome. He couldn't imagine the Rams losing in the semis to **Hopkins**. It was time to erase past disappointments. Montrose had paid its dues. *Losing was not an option.*

Clolinger challenged the squad with the motto for the semifinal game:

'We Have Reached The Biggest Mountain's Summit.
Do We Have The Intestinal Fortitude To Continue On Our Journey?'

Cary and Paxton ate their pre-game dinner at their usual restaurant -- Don Pablos. Both were lost in their own thoughts about the Hopkin's game, and drove home in Paxton's black S10 pickup in complete silence. Paxton kept his eyes on the road as he made a quick grunt. Cary doubled it. Paxton grunted rowdier, then Cary rumbled louder yet. Paxton threw Cary a glance while adamantly stating, 'After tomorrow, we're goin' to the Dome.'

They both screamed at the top of their lungs, enjoying the awesome natural high. The moment Paxton pulled into his driveway, it dawned on him that he didn't remember driving home. He hadn't concentrated on the road at all; he only thought about going to the Dome. They found a note on the kitchen table from his parents, 'Let us know where you're going.'

Without hesitation, Cary grabbed a pen and hastily scribbled at the bottom of the paper, 'We're going to the Dome! Love ya Paxtons!'

Cary slept like a baby that night, while Paxton tossed and turned, wondering if morning would ever come. Dauber's dad was up early Saturday morning. He was a culinary chef and teamed up with several dads to cook the players and coaches a tasty, hearty breakfast. Later that day, Reinhart sat at his kitchen table reviewing plays, unaware that his young sons emulated him. After he reviewed everything one final time he stood up. 'Come tell Daddy good-bye. It's time to leave for the game.'

They jumped up hugged him then handed him a picture of stick figures. 'Here's your plays for the game dad.'

Reinhart tucked it in his back pocket, hoping it brought him luck.

The decorated town sent the Rams off in typical Montrose tradition, with a caravan that followed the team buses to Dewitt High School. The tailgate fans socialized with the flavor of a college game in the parking lot. Every team from the ten-year streak was well represented. Several players from the '92 Team hugged the fence near the goal line, reliving good memories of when they faced Dewitt during their first playoff round. Even though that was six years ago, they remembered specific details like it happened yesterday. The '92 Rams left DeWitt's field with a 25-14 victory; wanting the '98 Rams to do the same thing. Everyone in town wanted to advance. *It was time.*

The day was cold, but perfect. Billowy white clouds slowly danced across a brilliant blue sky. It was perfect jacket weather, especially for the third week in November. In Michigan, it could've easily been snowing. It was also prime deer hunting season, but men changed their plans to watch the semifinal game. After all, the odds were 50-50 for a ticket to the Dome; no one wanted to miss it. It would be a fairy tail ending for one team. The squad didn't have the same nervous, hyped-up feeling that they felt before the Chesaning and Bendle games. When the '98 Rams took the field to face Hopkins, they felt confident and ready to play football. They didn't have anything to lose.

Thousands watched the Hopkins Vikings boot the opening kickoff to the Montrose Rams, who marched 65 yards on their first possession. Teddy finally burst through on a four yard run on their 13th play. Scott's kick was wide because of a bad hold; he hoped it didn't come back to haunt them. The Rams controlled the ball for the first six minutes of the game, scoring first. Some Montrose players thought, *They can't stop our offense.*

Following the kickoff, Hopkins thought their offense couldn't be stopped either, after answering with a 15-play TD drive. A PAT gave Hopkins a slight 6-7 lead. The Rams had to punt on the fourth down, but when Hopkins caught the ball, they dropped it. Paxton whooped his large body down the field as fast as he could, jumping on the ball at the Hopkins 34. He was in the best shape of his life, and wanted the fumble recovery. Paxton wrestled with the ball, giving a good fight to keep possession. The hefty lineman was unaware that he was scrambling against the strong will of his own teammate until he heard, 'Paxton -- let go! It's Clint.'

Scott kicked a 32 yard field goal with 6:19 left in the half, giving the Rams a 9-7 lead. Montrose held the Vikings until they got the ball back. The

Rams kept Hopkins off balance with a short passing game mixed in with their running game. Teddy connected with Kris on a 17 yard pass on fourth-and-12 from Hopkin's 36. Teddy ran six yards then dove over Paxton, his faithful friend and lineman, capping a 64 yard, 12-play drive. The Rams were pumped as they celebrated their 16-7 lead in the endzone at the half.

Unbelievable teamwork. Unbelievable friendship.

Montrose fans were filled with protected anticipation, afraid to get overly excited. They had learned the hard way that anything can happen in a playoff game but still thought, *Maybe things would be different today.* Hopkins and Montrose were both involved in playoff semifinal games, but neither had advanced. That would change for one of them. The Vikings entered the semifinals unbeaten in 1995 and 1996, but were eliminated by Detroit St. Martin dePorres both times. The Rams would've faced Hopkins in 1996, if dePorres had not eliminated them the previous week.

The second half opened with as much excitement as the first. Fans held their breath when the Hopkin's kick returner brought the pigskin to the Montrose 32. When the Hopkin's quarterback scored four plays later, Montrose fans regretfully sighed as they tried blocking out unpleasant memories from a year ago. The Vikings seemed to click on all cylinders, as if intentionally nourishing the post-season demons for the Rams. Montrose returned the kickoff, but got stopped on four-and-out. The Rams returned the punt to Hopkins, then watched their All-State running back free himself from a host of Montrose tacklers before darting 53 yards to score. Hopkin's two-point conversion attempt failed, but the Vikings held a 16-19 lead, erasing their nine point deficit.

Incredible.

Hopkins came out and scored two back-to-back TD's in a three minute span to open the third quarter. It was dejavu for the Rams. Reinhart had flashbacks of the '97 Maple Valley semifinal game. Everyone did. Montrose faced the possibility of having a team end their season one step short. The players, the fans and the coaching staff silently prayed, *Please don't let the playoff demons strike again!*

It was eerie that Hopkins wore the same blue and white school colors, and played with the same style that Maple Valley did in the '97 semis. But when Hopkins came out and scored early in the third period after being down at the half, it was just plain weird. The seniors remembered how it felt to lose in the semis. The Rams were not ready to have the coffin nailed shut. *Not yet.* They buckled down, encouraging each other in the huddle. 'We're only down by three points. If we score a TD -- it's our game. We can do this.'

Reinhart joined his team during a timeout, and compared the battle they were in against Chesaning. 'We prepared for this moment. Hey, we've been here before. Last year we folded up our tents and went home after we got our butts kicked the second half. We are still in this ballgame. Let's show them what we're made of. We can do this.'

The cheerleaders yelled, 'We Say Hopkins – You Say Never. Hopkins.'
'Never!'
'Hopkins.'
'Never! Let's Go Rams!'
The huge group of Montrose fans screamed, hoping their voices made it so. Montrose drove the ball, but found themselves in a dilemma on fourth-and-two. The offense felt they could get the down and stay alive. Playing conservative was the last thing on their mind. They wanted to take a risk and believed in what they were supposed to do. The Rams wouldn't quit; they wanted it too much. But the offense couldn't believe that Reinhart sent the punt team in. Cary was appalled when he looked at Paxton, 'We only need two freaking yards! Why the hell are we kicking?'

The hopes and dreams of all past teams rested on their shoulders. They had one of the strongest lines in Montrose history . . . and felt insulted. Bruno thought, *You don't get that many opportunities in the playoffs. If you get a shot, you gotta go for it.* He looked at Dauber, 'We can do this. Why won't Coach let us go for it?'

The intensity on the field was strong. The guys in the huddle took control. Cary wanted the down so badly that he worked himself into a craze. His face turned beat red. Spit flew from his mouth when he yelled, 'We are NOT giving up this down.'

Paxton piped in, 'We're goin' for it. No matter what play is called, we're goin' for the fake punt.'

Everyone in the huddle nodded in agreement. Cleatus ran on the field with the punt team. He provided a lot of energy for being the smallest guy on the team at 5'5"-120 pounds. The skinny, quiet kid had several nicknames, including 'The Beav' because of his buckteeth and big smile that proudly showed them off. Cleatus was a likable kid who sported a great attitude, making the most of any field time that he saw. He appreciated that Coach D gave him a chance to play, not overlooking him because of his size.

Pressure caused athletes to react with intensity. Cary threatened Cleatus, 'You gotta call Eight-Six. I mean it! Call it or I'm gonna beat your ass.'

Cleatus wasn't smiling now. He had never heard their key back so upset. Fear consumed him. He looked at Cary, then at the huge line glaring back at him, as if their future rested in the palm of his hand. Cleatus could hardly speak. The desperation that his friends displayed frightened him to the core. His heart raced as he ran toward the sideline to get the play. *Oh my God. What if Coach doesn't call a fake punt? What am I supposed to do? I can't override Coach.*

It was the scariest moment of his young life. He was only 16-years-old, the smallest guy on the team, yet carried the weight of the world on his scrawny shoulders. He knew that his teammates had their minds made up. By the look in their eyes, nothing he said would change it. Cleatus had never challenged a coach before, and found himself in an awkward position. His heart pounded so heavily in his chest that he almost hyperventilated.

Reinhart signaled 'Eight-Six.'

Thank God! Cleatus breathed a huge sigh of relief as he returned to the team. Cary crossly waited for Cleatus to give the call then piped in an unbending response, 'Good thing, cause we're running it anyway.'

Cary had never showed such adamant determination before, which completely threw Cleatus off-guard. He pulled a deep breath, feeling grateful that he wasn't in the midst of a war zone, then exhaled.

Reinhart pulled the stick figure drawing from his back packet and rubbed it; a ritual he performed throughout the game whenever trouble brewed.

The line rushed to get in their two-point stance. Some were still unsure of what the play actually was, but would block with determined strength. Dauber looked down the line to his left, then to his right, feeling confident after realizing they all wanted the down as much as he did. They put the time in, and proved their dedication by lifting during the entire off-season. It was their moment. Their hearts raced in the seconds that followed, while they listened for the call, 'Eight'... 'Six'... 'Set Hut.'

Paxton and Dauber muttered, 'Yeah' when the ball was fired. Helmets crashed as the line went head-to-head. Fans held their breath while all eyes focused on Scott, who was easy to spot as he stood solo in the kicker position. It seemed everything moved in slow motion. Scott reached, then jumped, then turned around. Oh no! A hush fell over the crowd, as if they all tried to catch their breath at once. No one could believe what they just witnessed. Their two-time, All-State kicker shrugged his shoulders with outstretched arms, motioning like he couldn't locate the ball. It was such a critical moment for a turnover. Fans thought, *Why now? Why are the Rams consistently jinxed during second half semifinal games? Unbelievable. Of all times, Scott never fumbled the ball.*

Suddenly, their attention diverted to the commotion on the line. Pooh Bear blocked down, the backs took off, and all 120 pounds of Cleatus set his best block ever. The junior was quick, as adrenaline flowed through his body like lava erupting from an active volcano. Cleatus knocked his opponent directly on his tail.

So much about life is about second chances; that moment was a second chance for the Rams. Cary was not about to surrender his opportunity to be the first Montrose team to advance to the Dome. He took the short snap in the halfback slot from punt formation, realizing that this very play could make or break the game. He showed a true test of his will by making the two yards, then rambled another 26.

Paxton looked down the line to the right, realizing that Cary made the first down at Hopkin's 30. Cary usually juked then broke for a TD, but he was so relieved after making the down that he ran directly into an opponent. Paxton shook his head, feeling that Cary was sending a message. *We want this and we mean business!*

It seemed the Rams made their own luck that entire season. The Montrose crowd went absolutely crazy after realizing the Rams got the down. Scott's theatrical performance delightfully fooled them. Scott felt silly whenever they practiced the fake because they never used it. It felt great to finally execute the play in a game. And this wasn't just *any* game.

Players strongly grasped hands in the huddle, listening to Reinhart. 'All right boys, we're running a 38 veer. If we don't score, then go right into a 39 Veer. No offensive huddle. Got it?'

The Rams nodded, feeling extremely confident by sensing their coach's conviction in them. He believed that they could do it. Paxton grinned when he looked at his teammates. 'C'mon guys. We're gonna do this. We're gonna do it! We're just one big unit clicking on all cylinders.'

The Rams moved the ball close to the endzone then called one of their favorite plays --'BS' (short for bullshit). The line positioned itself on the goal, then Paxton blew a huge hole for Cary as the whistle blew. They were doing this together. Paxton had great strength, but had an even bigger heart, and soon found himself on the bottom of the pile. Linemen loved to be buried at the bottom of the heap on all fours, unable to see anything but 22 guys in a pile overhead. *That was football.*

The juices charged through the linemen and they wondered, *did Cary get in?* As they tried to find their bearings, players listened to which side of the field cheered. The red and black fans answered their prayers with the craziest of excitement, as Cary capped the drive with a five yard run. Scott's extra point gave Montrose a 23-19 lead, with two minutes left in the third quarter.

Hopkins threatened on its next possession when the Rams were flagged for unsportsmanlike conduct. Pooh Bear sacked the Hopkin's quarterback, then did his famous 'Pooh Bear Dance.' His dance came from Winnie the Pooh, the Disney character he enjoyed as a child. His mother dubbed the nickname on him and it stuck. His helmet hid his baby face, but when he did the Pooh Bear Dance, his 245 pound frame was easy to spot. The dance was a simple shuffle; his long arms dangled from his sides while he rocked his weight back-and-forth on stiff legs. It wasn't anything obscene, just an emotional release after making a big play. Pooh Bear did his dance whenever he got a sack. He never received a penalty or even a warning; an unsportsmanlike penalty seemed severe under the circumstances.

The official explained that a player cannot show excessive celebration, they can only face their team to celebrate, not the fans. Playoff officials were extra cautious to control the players and the fans. It was a direct result of a first round playoff game between Chesaning and Millington, that received state-wide attention after an upset fan entered the field arguing with an official. With so much at stake, playoff emotions often kicked into overdrive, putting fans on edge.

The coaching staff hoped that the penalty wouldn't break the Rams momentum. They soon discovered that it did just the opposite, relentlessly pissing off both defensive ends. Pooh Bear and Parks rushed the quarterback, then forced Hopkins to punt after making back-to-back sacks on the next two plays. The Rams were only up by four; they needed a score. Eleven plays later, Montrose made a dramatic comeback after Teddy scored from the five. The conversion failed but the Rams breathed a little easier after the scoreboard read 29-19.

Parks wasn't making any sense in the huddle. The end got rocked on a play, and didn't know exactly what was going on. His teammates asked him silly questions, then laughed at his response. Because he wasn't knocked out cold, they didn't realize the severity of his concussion. It wasn't uncommon for the brain to float in the skull after hard contact, affecting the sense of direction. But the coaches realized that Parks was out of it, and pulled him out of the game. Attitudes were changing about concussions. What once was considered a badge of courage, was taken more seriously after a few pros had memory problems after severe concussions.

The Vikings came back hard, but didn't plan on an interception with four minutes left. Hopkins Coach Rex Weaver knew that teams had to be ready for a fake in the playoffs, and admitted that the Rams caught him asleep. He wanted to keep the ball, and the lead, since Hopkins was moving the football until that point. The fake hurt Hopkins, changing the complexion of the game. Once the Rams got their momentum started, they were hard to stop. Montrose marched down the field on a 65 yard drive. Anthony ran it in from the nine to score with less than two minutes left in the game, making the score '36-19.'

Some of the Rams realized they had the game locked in, while others were too afraid to think about winning. Paxton could hardly walk back to the huddle on this last drive. He couldn't control his emotions. 'Oh my God. We're goin' to the Dome. Oh my God. We are really going.'

The Beast told Paxton, 'Shut up. The game's not over.'

Many gun-shy fans stood with their own guards up, unable to think clearly. They couldn't comprehend that the game couldn't be taken from them. Once they realized that they were safe, Montrose fans couldn't hide their excitement. Their hearts raced. Eyes swelled with tears as their bodies tingled with excitement when they hugged. 'Oh my God. The boys did it. We are finally going to the Dome!'

Every fan felt the emotional, wonderful, natural high. The coaches felt it. The players on the sideline felt it, and those on the field were beginning to realize the same awesome sensation. Paxton looked across at his opponent and grinned, 'We're downing the ball.'

The Hopkins defender could've smacked Paxton at that very moment, and he wouldn't care. Paxton went back to the huddle on the next down and repeated, 'Oh my God. We're goin' to the Dome.'

Bruno was so focused on the game that he didn't comprehend that Montrose had the win locked in. He glared back, 'Shut up Paxton. The game's not over.'

Radio channel 92.5 broadcasted the game while it blared over the loud speaker at Montrose Riverside Market. Riverside was the only grocery store in Montrose and was unusually quiet that day, since most of the town attended the game. The few shoppers enjoyed the excitement, while the cashiers and carry out workers cheered every time the Rams got possession or scored.

Montrose fans stood with frozen smiles and wide eyes, happily counting down the final ten seconds in unison . . . Three . . . Two . . . One! They tried to absorb the fact that they just won the semifinals. The Rams were going to the Dome -- the Pontiac Silverdome. The eager crowd couldn't rush the field fast enough. The small gate entrance was bottlenecked, so fans climbed the fence. Even parents that hadn't jumped a fence in twenty years found themselves scaling their own little mountain.

Paxton dropped to the ground when the buzzer sounded; his emotions obsessed his body. He was so overwhelmed that he couldn't move. He just stared at the scoreboard. *We won. We really won.* With squinted eyes and flushed cheeks, he looked at the commotion surrounding him. He didn't care that he couldn't conceal his tears; for once they were tears of happiness. It was the greatest experience of his young life and he felt someone pat him on the back, 'Are you all right? Are you sick? Are you hurt?'

He just shook his head and thought, *They really don't understand what this win is all about.* He tried to talk through the lump in his throat, 'I've never been better!'

He hugged his line, Bruno, Gibby, and Dauber. They were the biggest guys on the team, and he watched them rightfully bawl like babies. Their thrill tasted so real that it actually hurt. He looked at his teammates who all reacted differently. Some jumped and shouted, while others dropped to the ground like he did. They were so taken that their dream, their ten-year quest, had suddenly became a reality for the Rams. It was breathtaking and wonderfully awesome. Players and coaches searched for their families as 2,500 exhilarated fans rushed the field, hugging anyone wearing red and black. Players ravished every moment, while high-fiving and cavorting with fans. Winning a trip to the Dome was more special, and wonderful, and healing, then any of them had ever imagined.

Paxton's dad finally found his son. Neither could hide the honest tears that streamed down their faces until Paxton forced his cracked voice. 'We did it dad. We really did it!'

Coach Stiles joined Clolinger and Destrampe. Their faces beamed as coaches exchanged hugs, enjoying the uplifting feeling of winning a semifinal game. The Rams finally cleared that last hurdle. After so many attempts, they were going to the Dome. It was the greatest feeling a coach could have.

Fans lingered on the field, then surrounded the team as Coach Reinhart started his post-game talk. Salty Dog rested his weight on his crutches, feeling both happy and sad. He broke out in goosebumps when Reinhart presented him with the game ball. 'Remember my vision of the Rams being in a position to take a knee and have Salty Dog walk out on the turf for the last play? He's gonna be on that field next Saturday when we're at the Dome. Are you guys with me?'

They all raised their helmets and cheered, 'YEAH!'

'We talked about climbing the mountain. We're almost there. Okay? Next week, we're done climbing. Next week we conquer the mountain fellas! We conquer the mountain! This week is gonna be hectic for you guys and for all of us. We're gonna stick together to get through this. We're not going down there just for show. We're going down there to win this! Nobody remembers who finished second.'

Reinhart looked at his squad, their families, and all of the fans that focused on his words. 'Enjoy this fellas. Our fans are enjoying this. You've got something to be proud of. Everyone who ever wore the red and black is proud of you. Enjoy this until 3:00 tomorrow. We're gonna meet at the school, eat steaks, then we'll break down and watch films. We've got to get ready for next Saturday! This is a once-in-lifetime opportunity fellas. We've been trying to get to this point forever. First Coach Hayes, then Coach Annese, and now our coaching staff. We're playing this for everybody, for the entire town of Montrose, and we're going down there to win it!'

Each player raised his helmet when Dauber led the school song. Everyone joined in, basking in delight. It was what every kid that played football dreamed about since the ninth grade. They weren't playing just for themselves, but for the tradition of Montrose Football. The Rams were going to the Dome. *Finally.*

People donned in red and black were everywhere. Teddy found his grandpa who came to all of his games, even though he was in a wheelchair. Teddy told the press during his interview, 'This is for my brothers. They worked so hard and had such good teams.'

The press interviewed Dauber who racked up 17 tackles during the game. The excited senior proudly told them, 'This win is for everybody who ever wore the red and black. We've wanted this for so long and it feels awesome. We're not done yet.'

Dauber couldn't wait to call a favorite uncle who lived in Minnesota. His uncle told him when he made Varsity as a sophomore, 'If you make it to the Dome, I'll be there.'

The Montrose buses had unintentionally blocked the Hopkins buses, forcing them to watch the euphoria. Hopkins' seniors had just played their final high school football game; their sorrow was well written on their faces.

Montrose parents recognized the painful, haunted look in their eyes, recalling a similar expression on the faces of their own sons during tearful endings. They empathized with them, although no one would consider trading places. For once, they experienced what the flip side of the coin was like. It felt awesome; their immeasurable happiness was vastly overdue.

Headlines read, 'Final-ly Montrose Advances to 'CC' Title Game,' and 'Dome Sweet Dome.'

Montrose faced **Whittemore-Prescott** in the Silverdome. The coaches analyzed game films, realizing that they faced a tough team, but appreciated the beauty of their situation. The Rams were going to the State Finals and were still improving. The Montrose Rams had played error free football since the Bendle game.

The '98 seniors talked about the tremendous weight of carrying the streak. Some were glad that the streak was over. If that pressure had continued in '98; they may not have made it to the final four. People didn't realize the amount of pressure that winning streak created or the burden that intensified each year. The '98 Rams were the first team allowed to *just play football.*

The Rams had enough kids back from the '97 Team who remembered how close they came to being the first Montrose team to make it to the State Finals. They realized how one play could botch a game; that heartache had pushed them the entire season. A win would mend their broken hearts. It was for every Ram who passed the torch from one season to the next and never quit. Their contribution paved the long and winding road to the Pontiac Silverdome.

'Climb To The Top'

Football season stretched an entire month longer than most schools in the country, but the Rams appreciated every extra minute of sweat. Wrestling and basketball practices had to wait; a Football State Championship was on the line. The football team overcame all kinds of odds to reach the finals. More and more students caught the playoff spirit, as the Rams advanced in the playoff hunt. Even students that didn't usually follow football jumped on the bandwagon, making plans for the Dome. Football rejuvenated Montrose High, retrieving some of its popularity. *Reinforcement was effective.*

Players purchased turf shoes over the weekend, while coaches made arrangements to practice on available turf fields. After school on Monday, the team headed to Atwood Stadium in downtown Flint for their first exposure to outdoor turf. The turf at Michigan State University was next. Players watched in awe when the MSU Spartans walked past them after a practice. They all appeared bigger than Pooh Bear, who actually became a Spartan two years later. Scott absorbed every detail, while dreaming about a college scholarship to kick for the Spartans.

Dreams aside, the Rams looked terrible during practice, appearing to focus more on their new turf shoes and pads, than they did on plays. The sweltering field house seemed 30° hotter than the outside temperature they were used to. It felt muggier than any practice the entire season, including two-a-days. Receivers missed too many passes, placing blame on the bright lights against a brown ceiling in the field house. Class DD state finalist, Fulton-Middleton High School, arrived just as their reserved time finished. Fulton offered to share the turf for 30 minutes while they warmed-up. The Rams took advantage of their extra time and ended with a good practice, restoring their confidence in their quarterback . . . *and in each other.*

The University of Michigan campus in Ann Arbor was next on the list. Practice was held in the field house, not in the Wolverines 'Big House' that packed 110,000. Coach Cory Gildersleeve showed the kids a plaque that hung in Schembeckler Hall, proudly displaying the names of every State Championship Football Team in Michigan. The squad watched as he located his 1991 high school team then proudly touched the engraved name of Monroe St. Mary. The look of pride on his face etched in their memory. Players often admired Sleeve's enormous State Championship Ring that he often wore to entice them. He happened to wear it to practice that week. Sleeve planted an even deeper yearn when he pointed to the Class CC column and looked at them, 'Make the 1998 Montrose Rams appear here.'

Their hearts raced. Cary looked at Paxton with wide eyes. They wanted that honor. *Desire was inspiring.*

Several Wolverines walked past them after their practice, which made even the largest Ram feel small, yet motivated. Just to practice in the U of M field house infatuated them. State Champs get noticed and maybe some of them would play for Michigan one day. They ran their butts off, while coaches conditioned them for the environment of the Silverdome. The heat made the linemen want to puke.

Reinhart firmly told the squad, 'This is what it's all about fellas. We're goin' to the Dome to win, not just to make an appearance. We're goin' to work hard to become State Champs! We're goin' to run over teams.'

If the Rams heard it enough, they would believe it. The Rams focused on minimizing their mistakes. The Rams left Schembeckler Hall feeling like they finished their best practice of the year.

It was close to midnight when a bus full of exhausted players pulled into the parking lot at Montrose High. Paxton went home exhausted. He fell asleep the moment his head hit the pillow, ignoring the fact that he had an early morning practice. He boarded the school bus at 8 AM on Thanksgiving morning; the sleepy squad felt like they just left each other. The plan was to get home in time to eat turkey dinner with grandma. For their final turf practice, the coaches rented an indoor golf dome, 30 miles away. The temperature inside of that dome seemed more comparable to the Silverdome than the college field houses. The Rams ran through play after play, experiencing how the turf responded. They connected on their passes, feeling confident and prepared by the time they left.

The Rams came back to their roots for a final practice on their hometown field on Friday. Paxton felt nostalgia set in as he looked at Cary with a solemn face. 'We just finished our last football practice.'

Cary cocked his head and threw a puzzled look at his friend. 'Dang Paxton -- we're playing in the Dome tomorrow. You can't feel sad about that!'

The championship games started on Friday; Class A and D played early in the day, followed by Class B and C in the evening. Montrose played the same schedule on Saturday against Whittemore-Prescott in Class CC.

Reinhart surveyed his players and was surprised to discover over half of the team had never stepped foot in the Pontiac Silverdome. He decided to take them down for a preview. The school bus dropped the team and coaches off at a special access door used by the Detroit Lions. The coaches led players toward the tunnel entrance while Coach Clolinger brought up the back of the pack. His body swelled with pride when he pictured the Rams dressed in full uniform the following night. When he glanced up, he saw the backs of 50 black jackets, bobbing through the tunnel. Large white letters stared back at him, glowing in the darkness -- 'MONTROSE FOOTBALL.'

Players stopped at the tunnel's opening and gawked, soaking up every last detail. The turf looked so green under the bright lights; the stadium seemed huge. Class A finalists, Hudsonville and Farmington Hills Harrison, warmed-up under the lights for their 1 PM game. Their fans were noisy and excited, which made their hearts pound rapidly. Teddy looked at Paxton, 'Wow, that's us tomorrow night.'

Paxton thought, *Tomorrow we'll be dressed in uniform, running out of this very tunnel in front of all these people. Oh my God.*

Pooh Bear and Bruno felt the same way. So did little Cleatus. They all did. Once they absorbed the awesomeness of merely being there, they tried to relax and watch the game. They observed how loud the crowd reacted, how the commercial timeouts worked, and how the big screen focused on individuals. In just over 24 hours, they would be the players that warmed-up on the very turf in front of them. *Anticipation was overwhelming.*

It was MHSAA's 23rd straight year to showcase Michigan's top grid teams in the world's largest domed stadium, with capacity to seat 80,600. Over one million fans witnessed the MSHAA Football Finals at the Silverdome since 1976. Only sixteen teams earned the privilege to play in the Silverdome; the Rams realized how fortunate it was to be included. They felt comfortable when they left the Dome after adjusting to the size, brightness, and noise levels. The coaches hoped the visit helped them realize what to expect and reduce their anxiety levels. The Rams boarded the bus for the 90 minute drive home. Many of their parents passed the bus headed in the opposite direction. They were on their way to the Silverdome to cheer for Chesaning who faced Belding for the Class B Championship Game.

Chesaning. A word that was synonymous with swearing just a year ago. Many avoided shopping or eating in Chesaning for an entire year. Too many painful memories resided in that town, along with residents that were clueless about what it all meant. It simply hurt too much to hear them brag. Most towns would never experience the thrill of a ten-year football streak and couldn't be expected to understand the emotions attached to it. Having both Montrose and Chesaning make the state finals a year later confirmed the caliber of competition. The same Montrose parents that had difficulty even saying the word 'Chesaning,' headed to the Pontiac Silverdome to support the Indians, proving that time heals.

Superstitions devoured the entire team, beyond what the Rams even considered normal. In 24 hours, the Rams would either be Class CC State Champs, or second best. No one wanted second. They all wanted to win the precious championship crown jewel -- the championship ring. They bled for it, broke bones for it, and suffered for the honor to wear it.

Paxton and Teddy didn't want to jinx their championship game by skipping their usual pre-game meal, but were paranoid. It was the day after Thanksgiving, the craziest shopping day of the year, and their favorite restaurant was located near a busy intersection by the mall. They didn't want to chance having an accident with the crazy shoppers. The next day was the most important day of their life; they didn't want to botch it.

Instead, they ordered pizzas and watched Chesaning play Belding on PASS at Cary's house. Since both schools were located along M-57, the media dubbed the slogan, 'Highway of Champions.' Four of the 16 finalists, from the entire state, were located approximately 20 miles apart along M-57.

Chesaning won their championship game. While the Montrose fans were in the Dome celebrating with Chesaning, it wasn't quite as easy for the squad. Even though Chesaning was the only team that the Rams had lost to all season, the seniors felt suppressed animosity toward them, admitting they wouldn't lose sleep if the Indians won or lost.

They had their own victory to worry about, except Cary. He was the exception. Cary kicked everyone out of his house as soon as Chesaning won, and was asleep before most of players pulled into their own driveways.

Paxton felt restless on the five-mile drive home. Sleep was the farthest thing on his mind. He pulled out powerlifting videotapes the moment he walked into his house. He stared at his friends who yelled at him. He watched Cary slap him across the face to pump him up, seconds before he lifted. He remembered how excited they felt after winning the National Powerlifting Tournament, but somehow that paled in comparison for a chance to win a State Football Championship.

He thought about how close his teammates had become over the past week. They wanted to win 'States' more than anything. It only made him hungrier to play the following night. Paxton was restless when he pulled out the Maple Valley tape from the `97 semifinal game. He remembered how confident and excited the Rams felt during the intermission, but then lost their chance. He reminisced about all of the things that happened during the past year, which only stirred up crazy emotions -- *especially the Chesaning game.* The big lineman couldn't sit still, pacing the room with an abundance of energy. He grunted like a wild boar. In one year, he went from feeling the lowest point a human being could possibly feel to the opposite extreme. Making the State Finals had become the highest point of his life.

Bo Paxton's younger sister peeked through the kitchen to see what was wrong with him. Her big brother had never acted so weird before, making her leery to walk through the family room. Like her parents, she was consumed by a nervous excitement about the finals, yet was thankful that it would end the following night, one way or another. Paxton looked at his watch. He didn't care that it was after midnight, he had to talk to someone and dialed Teddy's number. 'Teddy, what are you doin' right now?'

If Teddy didn't know his friend any better, he would presume that Paxton was drunk. The quarterback sounded completely composed, 'I'm just watching old videos from our youth football games.'

Teddy's parents had dutifully taped practically every one of his games through the years. Watching Teddy relive his football childhood that night, made them appreciate the times they watched him play through the eyes of the camera, instead of watching the game. Teddy calmly replied, 'This is what we prepared all these years for Bo. Tomorrow we have the chance that my brothers never got. We could be State Champions.'

Unlike Paxton, Teddy was extremely relaxed. The Rams drew upon his calmness and confidence the next day; two traits that a good quarterback brought to the field. Teddy felt confident that the Rams would do their job, but his calmness didn't reassure the animated Paxton who seemed over the edge. Paxton yelled into the phone. 'Teddy, do you realize that we are gonna be the first Montrose team EVER to go to the Silverdome? Do you understand that?'

An easy smile formed on Teddy's face while he listened to his enthusiastic friend rant and rave until Paxton asked, 'Where's Anthony?'

He knew the running back had spent the night with the Klopfs.

Teddy replied, 'He's asleep.'

'Well, wake him up.'

Teddy walked over to the couch, shook Anthony, then handed him the phone. He sat back and watched Anthony's eyes widen, while he tried to wake-up and comprehend the yelling coming from the other end of the line. Paxton felt his insides twist and turn like a hypoglycemic victim that ate too much sugar. He wanted to motivate everyone just a bit more, except for Cary. He knew that Cary would be sound asleep. He didn't want to disturb him, and called Dauber next. Eventually, sleep kicked in and Paxton finally dozed off.

The following Saturday morning, Reinhart sat at the kitchen table, reviewing plays one final time. He pushed his chair back and called to his sons, 'Okay, it's time for Daddy to leave now.'

His oldest son handed him another drawing with stick figures. 'Okay Dad, here's your plays for the game.'

Coach folded it, stuck it in his back pocket, and thought, *It worked last week, let's hope it works today.*

Students scurried through the parking lot painting 'Domeward Bound,' and 'Rams are #1' slogans on car windows. It was the largest caravan the town had ever made. Police cars proudly led the eight-mile route to the interstate, passing good-luck signs along M-57 for both the Montrose Rams and the Chesaning Indians. Cary felt a lump in his throat when he noticed a sign nailed to a tree that read, 'Win with Honor.'

Players gasped when the Dome came into sight. For some reason, it appeared bigger than it did the day before. Goosebumps shot up Carys' arms. He felt tears mark his eyes when he stepped off the bus, looking directly at the Dome. It felt like a dream come true. He quickly glanced around to see if the guys surrounding him were really his teammates, pinching himself to validate if this was *for real.*

When the Rams walked through the tunnel for the second time, they were dressed to play. They stopped at the entrance and glanced at the empty seats surrounding them and wondered, *Where are all of our fans?* The entire Silverdome was vacated between sessions since the first session ran over. Fans were denied access to watch the pre-game warm-ups, forcing them to anxiously stand in long lines outside of the Dome. The Dome appeared extremely quiet without any fans in the building. A few lingering Detroit Catholic Central players shook their hands and wished them luck. They had just beat Rockford High School to win the Class AA State Championship Title. Their post-celebration reality started to sink in when they told the Rams, 'Enjoy every last minute.'

Another one yelled, 'Seniors, enjoy this game. It's your last one.'

The look on his face made Paxton and Dauber swallow hard. Dauber led them under the goal post in their traditional two-by-two formation, before lining up for pre-game warm-ups. Their voices clearly echoed in the empty Dome while they counted. Teddy ran on the turf and felt it slowed him down. Cary felt he moved faster on turf than on grass, and was glad they practiced on turf all week. Dauber and Paxton joined the other linemen who felt *they* even ran faster on turf, admiring the squishy sound it made when it bounced back.

Reinhart referred to the Bendle game during his pre-game talk. He reminded them how they protected their family that night. He relived everything they had overcome to advance to this point. 'You've reached the pinnacle of high school football. You're playing for everyone who ever played football for Montrose, for everyone in the Genesee County area. Most importantly, you're playing for yourselves. You have the opportunity that so many players, who ever wore the red and black, dream about. You need to play with everything you have today, and not make any mistakes. Let's go out and make them proud.'

Butterflies danced in the pit of every player, firing them up like never before. The Rams had never felt so determined about anything in their young lives; they wanted to accomplish their final goal.

Hodge came hours early and stood in line, as if he was going to a rock concert, then raced for a seat near the front. He grabbed the row directly behind the team, getting as close as he could without actually being on the turf. Hodge didn't care how silly he looked with a 12" red and black letter 'R' painted on his chest.

Damn it. They were in the Dome; in the Pontiac Silverdome. He had paid his dues for that moment. No one would take it away, nor prevent him from celebrating. Not even the attendant who insisted they put their shirts on could dampen his spirit, or that of his eleven teammates whose chests spelled out their school mascot. They tried to abide, but their shirts came off every time the cheering started. Most were now college students who didn't intend on being obnoxious; they simply couldn't disguise the excitable vigor of being in the Dome. Hodge felt a strong sense of relief knowing that it wasn't impossible for the Rams to play here. He often wondered if they had been jinxed, or barred by some unwritten statute that denied them for so long.

Bulldog, his teammate, stood nearby but didn't act crazy like the guys with the painted chests surrounding Hodge. Bulldog was voted as their 'Most Dedicated Player' his senior year, an honor well deserved after he worked so hard. Being in the Dome meant so much to Bulldog. He felt an honest happiness for the team, but couldn't deny the selfish envy lounging deep in his own heart. He wanted to be in their shoes and do this for his town, for his own dream. The team on the turf didn't have to play in a blizzard, or face a private Catholic school. Yet they overcame their own obstacles, earning integrity along the way. They were destined to play here. They made it. They actually made it. *Finally.*

It affected another former player in a different way. Bo Moore couldn't come out of the motorhome. The tailgaters shared football stories and were colorfully loud, while they partied directly outside of his door. He watched his teammates whip off their shirts and paint letters on their chests. They asked Bo what letter he wanted, but he just shook his head and walked away, unable to speak. Bo Moore couldn't join them. He just couldn't. The pain was too fresh. He stared at the outside of the building, while the ache in his chest grew deeper by the minute. Physically being at the Dome reopened his wounds, making him realize just how close he actually came to playing here. Only one word haunted him -- *Why?*

His teammates felt the same intensity, but covered it up in other ways. Bo couldn't. He stood tall, strong, and tough on the field, but once he stepped off he thought about it all too much. His mom worried that her son wouldn't compose himself in time to watch the game. His family couldn't understand his reaction. Hell, Bo didn't understand his own reaction; how did he expect anyone else to?

It hit him like a brick wall the moment they entered the parking lot. The leftover emotional baggage from his season suddenly resurfaced. Bo thought that portion of his life was buried when he went to Ferris State. He told himself, *'C'mon Bo, you play football at a successful Division II college. You've got four more years before you turn in your uniform, and you get to play on turf every week.'* For the life of him, he didn't understand why he couldn't haul his big butt out of the motorhome and join in the celebration. After all, he was Bo Moore, their class clown; the guy who made everyone laugh. Now, he took shelter in an obscured motorhome to hide his unstoppable tears.

It was finally time for the game, but Bo refused to come out. He sat frozen in the motorhome, lost in his own world. No one wanted to leave him alone in his depressed state. The principal was able to pull a few strings for an extra press pass, the final ticket that lured him.

Bo found the courage to cast his own demons aside when he entered the Dome; his high school principal, Doug Kinter, was at his side. They stood on the turf next to the team, marveling at the sensation firsthand.

He was actually here. Bo physically stood on the spongy turf of the Pontiac Silverdome, soaking in every radiant detail with a quivering mouth and wet eyes, *but he was here.*

Kinter stood tall next to Bo. His head tilted back, while his eyes looked up at the mammoth crowd. Standing on the carpet of the Pontiac Silverdome for the State Division III Football Championship was indescribable. He couldn't take his eyes away from the energized fans. Their emotion overwhelmed him, causing him to realize what a true privilege it was. Kinter came up through the ranks as a teacher, assistant principal, athletic director, then high school principal. He watched the football program grow through the years, and experienced the ups-and-downs with players through the entire streak.

It was a pleasure for him to watch the program continue to grow and prosper. The dedication that the kids displayed through the years was amazing. He thought about the endless hours that he observed, while they trained in the weight room and summer passing leagues. He watched captains work with their squads in the summer evenings, a tradition that endured time.

Kinter thought about the many dedicated people from athletes, coaches and parents that made Montrose Football the envy of their region, as well as the entire state. He realized what some principals would give to walk in his shoes. The principal felt just as guilty, as others in the community did, for overlooking the pressure they placed on 14-18 year olds boys. He had watched them enter the state playoff hunt, year-after-year, until they finally reached the Dome. It was commendable, and thrilling, and obvious that the high school principal loved every minute of it. Every person associated with the program felt the thrill of its success. The expectation that 'we are winners' was embedded in their minds. It wasn't simply their record that measured their feats, but the work ethic and dedication that the football program instilled in the Montrose Community. *They were all winners that day.*

The Montrose Rams continued their tradition, allowing Whittemore-Prescott to enter the field first. They stood back and watched the opposing fans cheer. Forceful screams echoed through the Dome, appearing loud compared to their pre-game warm-up just an hour earlier.

The hearts of the Montrose squad pounded heavily knowing that their fans would be even louder. They felt larger than life as they walked through the tunnel with locked hands; *this time it was for real.* Bruno spotted the red and black section of fans that occupied the main section seats from 10 yard line to 10 yard line and thought, *All of these people came to watch us.*

Every year of the streak was represented. Players from the GEC League, as well as from the entire state came to watch. The Bendle coaches brought their players, who sported red and black in support of the Rams. Even politicians and players from the greater Genesee County area sat on the Montrose side of the Dome. Genesee County waited 21 years to win a State Championship. They were absorbed in a region of the state much maligned to make the playoff finals. Holy Rosary defeated Class D Crystal Falls Forest Park 21-20 in 1977; that was four years before the seniors were even born. Holy Rosary High School had been closed for more than a decade. Montrose had been the county's football flag bearer since then. Genesee County was definitely ready to celebrate a State Championship. *It was time.*

Coach Bob Hayes kept his promise to be on the sideline at the Dome, and flew in from Arizona. He was afraid to make a reservation too early for fear of jinxing the Rams, then struggled to get a plane ticket at the last minute due to holiday travelers. He was a man of his word and proudly stood by the team, cane in hand, as a radiant smile outlined his face.

Hayes wasn't the only one that flew in for the game. Dauber's uncle stood true to his word and caught a flight from Minneapolis. He rose to his feet as soon as he spotted #55, feeling immensely proud of his nephew.

Coach Stiles stood behind the team, feeling strangely and wonderfully surreal. Now he understood why the Fulton-Middleton coach, who just won a State Championship in last minute dramatic fashion, acted like he did. Stiles observed his body language. That coach was so excited that he glowed, appearing to have an-out-of-body experience.

Sleeve walked through the tunnel entrance with a different perspective than the rest of the coaching staff. He was the only one that had the privilege of playing on the sacred turf. The experience held a different thrill for him; he couldn't get over the noise from the fans. Funny, he didn't remember that after playing here in '91, and he knew his town was just as excited then as Montrose was now. Sleeve was he so focused on the game that he must've completely tuned out that incredible, energizing noise. After he witnessed how overly excited the entire town of Montrose was, he felt a twinge of guilt for being a main challenger that denied the '90 Rams from playing in the Dome. That was eight years ago when he played for Monroe St. Mary. He came full circle, as if presenting an unofficial peace offering to Montrose. After all those years, Sleeve found it extremely commendable that the Montrose Rams never gave up on their quest to play in the Dome. They were here. They were actually here and he was thrilled to be a part of it -- *again*.

He stood in the dark tunnel entrance, appearing far away from the onlookers. Sleeve stared at the barrage of people that came to watch the Rams play. He felt totally accepted by the kids, the school, and the entire community during his first year as a coach, and was thankful.

A student jumped and pointed after noticing the Rams standing in the shadows of the tunnel entrance in the far endzone. Montrose fans jumped to their feet and cheered. A chain reaction inspired thousands of people to come alive, like a wild fire out of control spreading from person-to-person. Pooh Bear's heart raced when the Rams walked the short distance from the tunnel to the goal post, before facing their fans. The noise was overwhelming and he savored every wonderful moment. Montrose fans stomped their feet while they yelled, determined to have louder voices than their opponents. They shouted in unison, 'LETS GO RAMS!' LETS GO RAMS!'

Sleeve glanced at the anxious team who waited to make their entrance, allowing the clamor from the crowd to propel their adrenaline. They were a great group of kids to work with. He enjoyed watching them grow throughout the season, realizing they were eager and ready to represent and win.

Players heard the echo from their fans and enjoyed the awesome welcome. They jumped up-and-down under the goal post in the sacred Pontiac Silverdome. Their expressions revealed that it was the greatest feeling in the world. Smiles glowed through their helmets when they rushed the field, allowing their emotions to surpass their highest expectations. Cary thought he would burst as he raced across the turf toward the fans. The crowd screamed even louder as the Rams approached the sideline. The ecstatic cheers forced chills through everyone: players, coaches, fans, siblings, and neighbors. Even strangers couldn't deny the cabaret of anticipation. Nothing was sweeter for a small town. It was hard to tell who was happier to be there, the team or the town. *Happiness was awesome.*

Clolinger ran across the turf with the team, feeling just as thrilled as the players. He knew there was a reason why he couldn't stay away from Montrose Football or put an end to it. He tried. He gave it up once for the sport of baseball then blew out his shoulder, which required surgery. Now he constantly questioned himself, *Did I make the wrong decision?* Football haunted him. The sport was obviously still in his blood and he couldn't put it to rest. *Not yet.* Something felt like it was missing. His heart thumped so heavily in his chest that it echoed in his ears when he ran through the tunnel -- that awesome tunnel. They sprinted across the turf in front of thousands of people. The welcoming noise from the fans was unbelievable; and it was all for *them.* The turf was softer and newer than he expected. He bounced on the bright green carpet, feeling the spring of a tumbling mat and thought, *This could make a turtle think it was fast.* He wanted to cut loose and tear across the turf, but knew he shouldn't and held back. Only sixteen teams earned the privilege, which was unbelievable and way overdue. He never quit believing that it would happen, feeling thankful that dreams didn't come with expiration dates. Clolinger looked at the team, then at the fans, absorbing the energy of being in the Dome – a wonderful place where dreams came true and championships were won.

Montrose won the coin toss and elected to kickoff to Whittemore-Prescott. The stakes were huge and the noise astounding when both sides rocked the Dome. The great Silverdome crowd roared. The din was almost deafening. The home kicker tapped his kicking toe nervously behind him. The average built athletic senior felt unworthy to be the one to start the show. He had not made a touchdown all season – a few tackles, which he was unmercifully kidded about, some extra points, and a couple of field goals.

Still.

He shook his head to rid his mind of negative thoughts: *Be cool. Act like you've done this a hundred times. Don't miss it. Just hit it. Head down.* He raised his left arm and silently counted each of his coverage squad mates that flanked him, '… nine, ten,' he pointed to himself and mouthed, 'eleven.'

The shrill tone of the back judge's whistle cut the noise and echoed eerily about the cavernous building. The kicker gave the scene a final panoramic scan and committed it to memory, reckoning that he'd need the mental snapshot one day to explain it to his kids. He closed his eyes and breathed deep like he always did. He approached the teed-up ball gracefully in a lazy 'J' and, after what seemed like an eternity, met the ball with an outstretched foot. Barely a second later, the dull explosion of foot meeting pressurized leather rocked the Dome. Another State Championship game was on.

The Rams played tough, but struggled for yardage after racking up only 159 yards on 40 rushes. Cary took off his new turf pads during the first series. He didn't care if the turf scratched his arms, that was the last thing on his mind. He threw them on the sideline, 'I can't move fast enough with these.'

The Rams ignited their momentum by marching 92 yards in 10 plays. D'ar watched the poised quarterback gradually work his way into the pocket, while his steady eyes searched for an open receiver. Everyone was guarded so he snugly tucked the ball under his left armpit, like he'd done so many times. He quickly searched for a hole then ran, lunging forward to gain more yards than anyone expected. D'ar joined the thousands of roaring spectators who shrieked with pleasure and wondered, *Can they possibly feel as excited as I do?* He still couldn't believe they were actually in the Dome!

The instant replay lured his eyes, like a magnetic force drawing him in. He focused his gaze at the huge screen in the upper deck then watched #16 repeat the play. His face held a grin, as if he'd just watched a rerun of the best scene from his favorite movie. Strange feelings stirred inside as he watched the quarterback, #16, who seemed a little stockier, bulkier than he remembered. He even ran with a different cadence, a different confidence.

D'ar unhurriedly shook his head to get a grip, realizing #16 wasn't Jeff, *his* quarterback, but instead Jeff's little brother Teddy. A different senior in a different time who was living *his* dream.

Teddy threw two first down passes on the drive. On the next play, he faked then bolted 39 yards up the middle. He saw himself run on the Dome's big screen as the camera zoomed in. Peeking at the big screen to check if an opponent was close on his heels seemed like cheating. Hopefully, it wouldn't matter as he listened to his own body grunt from sprinting so fast. He felt on top of the world, positive that he could outrun anyone at that moment.

His eyes found the screen again as he watched himself run on the turf. The crowd's voice exploded giving him a surge of energy, while his adrenaline kicked into overdrive. His legs glided smoothly across the spongy turf as if on automatic pilot. It truly was the greatest feeling that he could ever remember; yet he still doubted the reality of it. *If this is a dream, it sure feels genuine and real and I don't ever want to wake-up.*

The camera crew strategically filmed players from several different angles. The one that patrolled the sideline made Klopf look like a pro on Monday Night Football. His parents and two brothers focused on the close up shots after Teddy scored a TD near the end of the first quarter. Their hearts overflowed with pride.

His brother Bobby thought, 'We deserve to be here. It's about time!'

Jeff, on the other hand, didn't feel the same indisputable pride. Instead, it felt more like a sense of jealously or maybe it was sheer resentment in its purest form. Whatever it was, it didn't seem fair to Jeff and he wondered, *How could it turn out this way, after I worked so hard for so long?*

Paxton ran to the endzone as fast as he could to greet Teddy. He laughed at his quarterback when he said, 'I should've done something crazy in the endzone.'

Paxton's strength easily picked him up to celebrate. 'Teddy, you're just not a go nuts kind of guy!'

Teddy had a bittersweet reaction and couldn't fully enjoy his score. Part of him felt that some fans wished another player had scored their first TD, instead of him. He continued to hammer himself for deserting the Rams a year ago. It was unfortunate that he allowed that curdled thought to pierce his mind at such a highpoint in his life.

It hit them the moment they walked into the Dome and took a seat in the Main Event Restaurant; a familiar scene to the Annese brothers. They recognized the team on the turf by their uniforms, but immediately noticed something different about them. They watched the team run through plays, but the pang of envy was a new addition. Not being on the field with them felt undeniably strange.

After watching championship game-after-game, year-after-year, the brothers could tell the teams that were absolutely thrilled to play in the Dome from the ones that were just excited. Maybe it was because some schools played in the Dome so many times that it was more of an expectation than a dream, and they lacked the wonderment. Or maybe they were a lucky team that tiptoed through their region without paying any dues, and didn't fully appreciate what an honor it was to play here. They couldn't help but notice that this game was different for the team on the field. It held a glowing ambiance that something very special was happening, not just for the team but for their entire community.

The Annese brothers watched in silence. The atmosphere seemed to cast a spell over the players donned in red and black, and their fans fully clad in corresponding colors. It felt strange, like the game was being played in a dream and they weren't part of the cast -- *or were they?* They wanted to be the coaches who stood on the sideline, not the ones who watched from the windows above the upper deck. Yeah, the restaurant had great seats and the food wasn't bad, but for once they wanted to be the team on the field below. They wanted to feel the cushion of the turf and speak into the headsets and take advantage of the TV breaks. They wanted to see the glow on players' faces when the echo from the roar of the crowd sent chills through their bodies. They wanted to win a State Championship just as much, if not more, than any coach that ever stepped foot on that magical turf.

They finished their dinner and left the restaurant, wondering, *Will we ever get here? What are we doing wrong? We have the passion, the program, the work ethic, and the talent. What else does it take? What more could we possibly do?*

Scott paced off his steps then took a deep breath, trying to slow down his heart rate before kicking his first PAT in the Dome. It was high and centered. He couldn't deny how great it felt when the camera zoomed in, capturing his huge, white smile. His little brother, Tommy, greeted him on the sideline, while his family watched the close-up replay on the large screen. It held the aura of a college game, and they felt so much pride for Scott.

The Rams were on the board 7-0, which seemed to settle them down a bit, while agitating the Cardinal's momentum. Quiet, easygoing Kris Brown transformed into the meanest player in the Dome. He was so focused on winning that he expected everyone to perform at his best, and got pissed when Montrose didn't get enough yardage. His mannerism and cutting words made the offensive line turn it up a notch. 'What's wrong with your fat ass? What's your problem? All you've got to do is block. Get your fat ass out there and block. Can't you do that?'

Kris reeked with determination. Schlorf looked at Kris when they prepared to run twins and asked him, 'Which one do you want to take?'

Kris seriously glared back at Schlorf with squinting eyes and wouldn't answer. Schlorf didn't get the response he needed, but Kris had such a determined look on his face, he knew he'd better get his guy.

Whittemore-Prescott intercepted Ted's pass at the 46 yard line just two minutes into the second quarter, then scored eleven plays later. The PAT sailed wide right, allowing the Rams to maintain a 7-6 lead.

Pooh Bear played defense end and intercepted a pass, but was caught off-guard when the quick hands of an opponent stripped the ball away. Both teams fought hard, leaving the door open for anyone's game.

Coach Gilbert watched Coach D gather his defense. Gilbert loved to watch how he connected with them, feeling lucky to work with the head defensive coach. Coach D was one of the hardest working people he had ever met, leading by a quiet example. He was always well prepared for everything; a team never caught him by surprise. Coach D was as hard-nosed as they came, showing both his mental and physical toughness to the players. On the same token, he was compassionate and cared for each and every one of the kids, and they all knew it.

Al Olah, from the '90 Team, looked over at the love of his life sitting next to him, while driving southbound on I-75. He glanced at her, then at his watch, then back at her, contemplating if he should ask. *Would she mind? Maybe they could just drop in for a quarter or two and check it out.* They were on their way to a party in Troy, Michigan; not too far from the Silverdome. He suggested the detour then carefully watched her reaction, immediately pleased with her response. After hearing so many stories about Montrose Football she welcomed the idea.

The game was underway when they entered the top level of the Dome. The bright emerald field, the professional lighting, and the crisp sound system made the scene picture perfect. They immediately felt the energy of the Montrose crowd that yelled, 'LET'S GO RAMS' like a lighthouse beckoning them over. Olah introduced her to several of his old teachers and friends. She could instantly tell which guys played football by the radiant expressions on their faces. They stood out above the rest, making it obvious there wasn't any place on earth they'd rather be.

Without exchanging any words, the guys thought about the *what ifs* that prevented *them* from playing here. A few missed blocks, and those ill-timed fumbles at critical moments, took it all away.

Still.

They were the ones who tested the waters, then stepped back and watched the seemingly rippled effect that cascaded. They sensed the uniqueness of being in the Dome together, like some kind of tribal telepathy.

Former players tasted the excitement that rocked the Dome from the moment they arrived. The couple completely lost track of time, forgetting about their party. They were glad they came. Before Olah pushed the metal bar on the exit door, he glanced over his right shoulder for a final look then shook his head in amazement. A happy calmness devoured his body, making him proud that he was a part of something so magical. He cringed as the fixed, heavy, sound of the metal door slammed shut behind him. The impact created an echo that sounded so final, as if giving closure. A slight smile shaped his face as Olah walked away. He honestly felt, in some strange way, that he left his mark.

Reinhart told the squad during the half, 'This game will remain with you for the rest of your lives. Nobody ever remembers who finished second. You've got to want this and be able to give everything you have to win. We don't want to come this far and lose. We want to go home with that trophy!'

The jubilant fans greeted both teams to open the second half. Late in the third period, the Rams covered 58 yards on seven plays, aided by a pass interference call. Cary burst up the middle from four yards out, then Scott's PAT gave the Rams a 14-6 lead.

Tim looked to his left and saw the gleam on Nate's face after the second TD was scored. He watched Nate high-five his oldest brother Cheese before they slapped hands with their dad, and Cheeses' college buddy, who appeared equally thrilled. It was hard to believe that they were actually sitting in the Pontiac Silverdome, watching their favorite team in the state finals.

The entire Leeseberg family had allowed football to be the nucleus of their lives for over a decade, becoming totally engrossed in the greatness of it all. Tim tried to ignore the selfish feeling in the pit of his stomach that gnawed at him. He questioned why *his* team wasn't the one on the field, and he wondered if his older brothers felt the same way. All three went on with their lives: Cheese was married with kids of his own, Nate was a police officer, and Tim was a senior in college.

On the drive down, they talked about the chance of Montrose winning. They openly admitted their doubts at the beginning of the season. But now as they watched them play on the turf, Tim felt that this group of players rose above their potential, proving their worthiness. It was obvious that they loved playing for their school, performing like they rightfully deserved to be there.

They made the lengthy climb to the top. He recalled the many great players that went through the program. Then, this group came along and learned to play so well together that they earned their shot at a State Championship. Watching his school lifted to this level, left him with a feeling far greater than he ever imagined.

A genuine smile formed on Tim's face as deep pride warmed every blood vessel filtering through his entire body. His hand reached out to return the high five to his dad and his brothers, while soaking in the righteousness of the memory. He savored the moment, enjoying the proud look on all of their faces. It created a lasting impression, making him feel that they all paid a small part in making that magical moment happen.

Both teams battled hard into the last period. The Cardinals didn't make their down and went back to punt from the 35 yard line. Reinhart rubbed his sons' plays in his back pocket, hoping it brought good luck on their next possession. The score was still too close. A bad snap sailed high over the Cardinal's head as he scrambled to recover it. The same Cardinal that experienced such a high when his second quarter interception set up the Cardinal's only TD, was shocked as he stumbled and fell on the ball on the three yard line.

Cary powered through two plays later, giving the Rams a 21-6 lead with seven minutes left. The score seemed to relax Reinhart who appeared to actually enjoy himself. It was his time; he blossomed as a head coach. He spoke into the headset to his assistants in the booth, like a Nascar coach talking to his driver, 'Guys, are you there?'

Clolinger responded from the booth. He was an excellent coach who had a tremendous knowledge of the offense. He was instrumental in their success; his presence alone represented a history. Clolinger wanted Reinhart to open up the playbook and showcase the offense a little more; they relied too heavily on the defense. The eyes of the entire state were upon them; they were playing too conservative for him. He worked out daily with the quarterback, running backs, and defensive backs. Clolinger was aware of their capabilities, and the willpower they possessed to accomplish their goal. But he also knew his position and respected it. Clolinger adjusted his headset, while trying to conceal his beaming smile, but the aura of being in the Pontiac Silverdome was purely overwhelming.

Harris glanced at Clolinger from the next room, where he spotted the game. Harris spent the majority of the game in the press box, with his elevated nerves that were at an all time high. The rest of the coaches were in the room next to Harris; all that separated them was a glass wall. They exchanged glances throughout the game and shrugged, as if they couldn't believe that the Rams were really in the Dome. It was such a surreal feeling that kept Harris thinking, *Okay, after all these times – we're finally here. Now we have to win this thing.*

Whitemore-Prescott came back on their second possession and scored on a 17 yard pass. A successful conversion made the score 21-14. The Cardinals were within a TD; the Rams needed to fight back.

Both teams gave everything they had, putting it all on the line. They played the most important game of their life on the biggest stage. The Cardinals kicked an on-side kick. The largest Ram on the field, Pooh Bear, jumped on the ball and held on, as if his life depended on it. He was afraid to do his famous Pooh Bear dance after receiving a personal penalty a week ago, settling for a scaled down version on the turf. Fans hoped that the officials wouldn't react negatively while he celebrated.

His eyes focused on #95, critiquing every move that Pooh Bear made. He watched the huge tackle sack the quarterback, then celebrate his huge hit like he was on top of the world. The thrill of a sack shot through his veins, carrying an honesty for a well-deserved adrenaline rush. He reminisced about his days playing tackle, figuring that he would've done the same thing, only he was a smidgen shorter and wore #79. They were seven years apart, yet he felt connected to the lineman in a mysterious way.

Would the obsession ever leave? He hoped not. He knew that he couldn't stop until he developed a program that played for a championship. He felt one step closer to his goal every day of his life. Maybe people thought he was crazy, but he loved to work with football players and watch them succeed in achieving their dreams. He never lost his love for the game. It would take a hell of a lot of desire, knowledge, and luck to win the big one. But when all three components united, the world would be a better place - at least for 48 minutes. Call it fate. Call it destiny. Whatever it was, he would be ready when his turn came. From the time he was a teenager, that all-consuming desire never left him. He hoped it never would. It was more than a strong feeling; it was a burning passion that smoldered within, like a perpetual flame.

The excited lineman on the field was totally unaware that his actions restored the invisible torch, and passed it back to a former player, now a coach. The torch was intangible to measure, but its worth was as bonafide as a family heirloom handed down from one generation to the next. The transient torch sparked a passion that the young coach still had for this crazy game. It reaffirmed that he was still on the right track, doing what he needed to do. Mike Sullivan would continue working with young people to build a passion, not just for the game of football . . . but for the game of life.

The Cardinals continued to fight hard, forcing the Rams to a fourth-and-one situation. Reinhart conservatively sent his punt team on the field. The crowd was afraid to give the Cardinals possession, fearing the Championship could be stripped from them in the final seconds. In their minds, hope far outweighed doubt. The massive crowd united in an effort of community spirit, shouting, 'GO FOR IT! GO FOR IT!'

Reinhart asked for an official measurement to buy some time. He heard Bruno's voice when he stood behind him. 'Coach, this is why we lift weights all year. We can get the down.'

Bruno was the biggest Ram on the offensive line. The tackle tipped the scales at 265 pounds and was a coach's dream. Reinhart thought about what Bruno said, while listening to the thousands of fans behind him. He consulted the press box, as he wrestled with his vision of Salty Dog taking the field on the final down. The cards were dealt. He had to make the call whether to hold or to fold. His gut reaction kicked in, as the offense traded places with special teams.

The crowd went nuts. Players on the sideline turned around, motioning for their fans to cheer even louder. Players on the field felt like their entire football life came right down to that one play, that one very important yard. Everything they worked for since they started playing football at age eight, was now on the line. It became their moment of truth. Fans instantly turned quiet so the team could hear Teddy call the play. They held their breath when Cary took the handoff. Everyone seemed to move in slow motion, while the determined line blocked. Cary ran behind his buddy, Paxton, when they needed a tough yard. That play was no exception. Paxton made a huge hole for Cary to burst through. Montrose got the down.

The Dome rocked with excitement. Fans donned in red and black jumped to their feet, screaming and high-fiving anyone within reach, even strangers. At that moment, they were all on the same team, soaking in the Rams' destiny. Tears fell down several cheeks: on the turf, in the stands, in the press box, even some watching from home -- only that time they were happy tears.

Their motto, 'One For All and All For One,' enabled Reinhart's vision to become a reality. Salty Dog dropped his crutches, while two teammates carried #50 on the field for the final play. The Rams demonstrated how a team could win with class, while proving how much they cared for one another. They were a team bonded forever -- *by that moment.*

Former Coach Coon wiped the tears that surprisingly rolled down his cheeks when he heard the radio announcer say, 'The Rams are carrying an injured player, #50 - Craig Salter, on the field.'

It reminded him of the two years that he spent in therapy for a chance to dress for his last college game. Jody Coon listened to the game while he was upnorth for Thanksgiving weekend. His heart overflowed with pride for the Montrose Rams, especially the offensive line. He pictured Salty Dog limping on the field and thought, *That kid never knew the word quit.*

It was Coon's first year away from the Rams; he yearned for Montrose Football. When August rolled around, he could barely stand not being a part of it. It was his first year away from the Rams; he craved to partake in a humid, sweaty, muscle-aching football workout. Coon missed Montrose Football more than he ever imagined. An instant smile on the former coach's proud face as the announcer said, 'Quarterback Teddy Klopf made the handoff. He quickly snapped the ball and took a knee.'

Coon ranked all three years that he coached the offensive line for Montrose, as the best of his life. He hoped that he made a difference in his players. Those three special years would keep Jody Coon entwined with the Montrose Rams forever.

Coach Gilbert felt his heart swell with pride. Salty Dog was one of his kids. Seeing the injured guard get his chance to play a down in the State

Championship Game, became the best moment of his entire season. Salty was such a hard working kid. He was undersized for a guard, but made up for it with his big heart, and had the determination to accomplish anything.

Pride oozed from Gilbert's heart. He drilled the line so hard, but they came through after being tested. It made all of the hours they put in worthwhile. The '98 Rams were the best football team he was ever associated with. He knew the game of football was important to those who played in Montrose. They demonstrated that by the amount of work they did during the off-season, as well as their continued success on Friday nights. Wherever Gilbert's career took him, the '98 Montrose Football Team would always have a special place in his heart.

As the clock ran out, the Dome became a pandemonium. Montrose had its first State Champion Football Team. The hubbub roared like being at the best New Year's Eve party ever celebrated. Players, coaches, fans, and parents felt the chill start at their upper arms, then slide down their fingers while climbing up their neck at the same time. The sensation felt both hot and cold, triggering a rush of emotions that made them want to laugh and cry. The awesome rush overwhelmed them, catching them off-guard. No one expected that high of a joy ride and honestly didn't know how to react. Some players jumped and screamed and hugged one another, while others dropped to the turf and bawled like babies. Cameras zoomed in; capturing Salty Dog as he took off his helmet, then raised it with a huge smile on his face. He warmed the hearts of everyone that watched, then panicked when Tommy ran full speed at him. His crutches were still on the sideline; he grew desperately afraid that Tommy forgot about his injured knee.

Dick Salter threw down his stat sheet and charged the field. He was a large man who excitedly ran in circles around his son, like a little kid being told he was going to Disney World for the first time. Salty was his third and youngest son to play Montrose Football. Dick kept the stats for years. He'd been through it all with the teams, but that game took the cake. Salty Dog laughed at his dad's reaction, then searched the stands for his brother, Kevin, from the '88 Team. Kevin was always there for him, through the good times and the bad, and now shared in his bliss. The injured player would remember that feeling forever. One day, he would tell his grandchildren about the time he played for the State Championship.

When the game was over, Harris ran out of the press box with the other coaches. They celebrated with as much excitement as the coaches on the field. Harris hugged Clolinger while they jumped up-and-down while yelling, 'We did it! We did it!' The press box coaches couldn't get to the turf fast enough. Harris jumped up-and-down in the elevator, trying to force it to the ground quicker. The moment it stopped, they ran through the tunnel and across the turf, grinning the entire time as the awesome feeling soaked in.

After they received the crown trophy, players couldn't contain their emotion. Some kept their helmets on to hide their tears of happiness. Others didn't care; it was the greatest moment of their young lives. Cary fell into that category. His face turned bright red from spilling his emotions, making him stand out in the crowd while they celebrated. It was the most incredible feeling, as he sobbed tears of happiness.

Genesee County waited a long time for a State Championship and enjoyed the indescribable rush. Players were so overwhelmed that tears flowed when they looked at the huge crowd cheering for *them*. It was all for them. Dauber brought the trophy over to the crowd, letting fans touch it. The crowd felt tingly, almost feverish as they shared the excitement. It was heartwarming to see athletes striving to perform their best, realizing the sacrifices they made and the effort it required to become a champion.

Teddy looked up to see thousands of fans cheering. Life never felt better. He just guided the Rams to the most important game of their lives, the State Championship. He as so overwhelmed that he dropped to his knees and cried alongside Cary. Paxton, Cary, and Dauber stood close by, their scrunched faces were blotchy red. They were so overcome with a massive high that they couldn't fight it, and bawled like babies. They didn't care; they just won a State Championship. The entire team felt a special bond, knowing they would always be connected by that game. Teddy searched the stands and spotted his brothers as they made their way through the crowd. Jeff led the '92 Team, while Bobby led the '94 Team to the state semifinals. Each brother lost by one TD to the eventual State Champion, causing Jeff and Bobby to feel both happy and envious of their little brother.

Several former players matched the bittersweet feeling. The Rams came so close to earning the honor so many times. Once players experienced how truly incredible and surreal it was, they wished *they* could've been the heroes. It was difficult to understand why undefeated teams couldn't get a spot in the playoff berth or a lucky break when they needed it. *Was it all part of a master plan? Did the '98 Team need to experience the devastation of losing their 80 game winning streak in order to appreciate this incredible high? Was it a lesson to fans that high school football players are just kids?* Once they were allowed to go out and play the game they loved and not deal with the high pressures of keeping streaks alive -- *it happened.* The effort they gave and the legacy they built provided the '98 Rams with the incentive to play their best, and bring the trophy home. They earned the crown jewel for everyone who ever wore the red and black.

The Klopf brothers reached the front row and anxiously motioned for Teddy. He started running on the turf from 30 yards away, then jumped in the stands throwing his arms around Jeff and Bobby. The three Klopf quarterbacks hugged in celebration, as tears streamed down their smiling faces. Jeff and Bobby listened as Teddy's shaky voice forced out the words, 'We did it. We did it. We did this for you guys!'

The End

#45 Wesley Fizk, #76 Mike 'Gibby' Gibson, #88 Craig Parks,
#18 Kris Brown and #95 Greg 'Pooh Bear' Yeaster

#77 Andy 'Bruno' Bernard, #72 Aaron 'Bo' Paxton, #16 Teddy Klopf,
#76 Mike 'Gibby' Gibson, #55 Jared 'Dauber' Smith in Pontiac Silverdome

TRI-COUNTY CITIZEN PHOTO

1998 STATE CHAMPIONS in Pontiac Silverdome

I would like to acknowledge the massive help given to me in creating this book. Many players and coaches sat around my dining room table and relived both wonderful and heartbreaking memories. Your patience to my endless emails and telephone conversations is appreciated. Limiting the number of characters in each chapter was difficult, but necessary in order to follow the storied history. The many 'silent characters' also provided important details.

This book could not be accurately written without stories from head coaches Tony Annese and Denny Reinhart. Thanks for your patience in answering my continuous questions. The heartwarming experiences and personal details shared by assistant coaches: Chris Clolinger, Jody Coon, Craig Destrampe, Joe Gilbert, Cory Gildersleeve, Jason Harris, Monty Stiles and Mike Sullivan are priceless. Your experiences touched the hearts of your players and your passion for coaching became blatantly obvious.

I owe a great deal to Coach Jamie Kitts who expanded my own foresight and gave me direction on the format and possibilities of the school's storied football history. A special thanks is extended to Coach Dave Beazley, to author Doug Allyn for your professional expertise and special friend Sue Paxton. A very special thanks goes to my brother Mike Pyrc for preparing the photographs. 'No Quitters Here' was edited and proofed by Ryan Gasser, Mike Pyrc and Brenda Woodward.

This book originated because of the bizarre 1997 Season and the courage that squad and coaches displayed. The '97 Season is forever etched in the memory of your football family. I appreciate your kindness while I drilled for details on a very painful chapter of your life.

A special thanks to the hundreds of players, parents, siblings, teachers, bus drivers and fans for your collective and detailed personal experiences.

I am grateful for the patience that my husband and sons displayed during the five-year research period. You served as a countless football resource and provided unconditional support.

I developed a greater appreciation and respect for sports writers that faithfully covered Montrose Football during the eleven-year chronicle. Special mention is extended to local editor Dan Lea, 'Tri-County Citizen' for his coverage and access to photo archives. Several 'Flint Journal' writers chronicled Montrose Football during the featured period. Special reference is given to: Keith Morris, Mark Csapo, Bill Kahn and Weldon Johnson for their extensive coverage and to Dave Larzelere and Brian Masck for assistance with Journal photo archives.

I have come to know so many terrific players who opened your hearts and shared your greatest and toughest football experiences. Special mention is given to the ones that openly shared personal misfortunes as well as your dreams.

Your contributions created 'NO QUITTERS HERE.'

Dialogue was relived mostly through the players' viewpoint as well as many coaches. Conversations were recreated from the emotion and recollection of multiple players since no one's memory could account for exact quotes. One player's memory often triggered the others'.

NEWSPAPER REFERENCES: Tri-County Citizen: Dan Lea. The Flint Journal: Nick Chiappetta, Mark Csapo, Bill Kahn, John Gooch, Tom Gromak, Dean Howe, Bruce Johns, Weldon Johnson, Robert King, Keith Morris, Brendan Savage, Tom Sussi, Phil Pierson, Greg Tunnicliff. Detroit Free Press: Mick McCabe, Son of Swami.

OTHERS: County Press, Detroit News, Frankenmuth News, Genesee Valley Sports Chronicle, Lansing State Journal, Saginaw News, Shiawassee Independent, Times Herald, Tri-City Times.

PLAYERS MENTIONED: Anderson, Matt (87, 88) Married, one child.   Installs telecommunications equipment. Lives in Grand Blanc, MI. **Andrews, Troy** (91,92) Attended Michigan Tech University and CMU. Played football at Tech as a walk on and played Rugby at CMU. Engineering degree, works for Rowe, Inc., Married and lives in Flushing. Asst. Coach at Bendle H.S. **Baksa, Brent** (90,91,92) Graduated from Adrian College with a teaching degree. Played defensive back at Adrian with H.S. teammates Eric Hyde and Barry Gross. Teaches and is an Assistant Football Coach at North Branch H.S. under Eric Hyde, Married. **Baksa, Tony** (89, 90) Married, three children. In charge of a Modular Home Managership. Lives in Forth Worth, TX. **Barnett, Brad** (90,91,92) Attended SVSU where he played college football with Jason Liddell, D'ar Destrampe, Rob Schlicht, Tony Bearsdley and Eddie Howell. Asst. Coach at Bendle H.S. **Barrett, Andy** (98+) Attending MSU, rooms with Pooh Bear. Majoring in Horticulture and Landscape design. Married, one daughter. **Beardsley, Jason** (92,93) Employed by Delphi in Saginaw, MI. Married, one daughter. **Beardsley, Jimmy** (94,95) Attended SVSU. Employed by General Motors in Saginaw, single. **Beardsley, Tony** (90,91,92) Attended SVSU and played college football with Jason Liddell, Brad Barnett, D'ar Destrampe, Rob Schlicht and his brother Eddie Howell. Employed by General Motors Truck and Bus Plant. **Bernard, Andy 'Bruno'** (97,98+) CMU, Education, Industrial Arts major and Geography minor. Plans to graduate in 2004. **Bowen, Scott** (90, 91) Graduated from GMI. Worked 3 years as a manufacturing engineer for Lear Corp. Currently works for Bowen's Racing Top Alcohol Dragster business, NHRA Division, as an engineer. Married and has 2 sons and 2 daughters. **Bowen, Shannon** (93,94) Single, attended SVSU two years. Works for the family business, manages the Muffler Man in Chesaning. Lives in Flushing, MI, Single. **Brown, Kris** (97,98) Attended Tri-State Univ, IN for two years and played football. Transferred to UofM, majoring in business. Employed part-time by Schwan Frozen Foods. **Buffa, Chris** (89,90) UofM Flint, 1 year, Army National Guard deployed Germany, 8 years, Trained in Home Health Care, MSU, degree is Physiology (2002), Accepted in PA program and CMU. His wife is from Germany they have two children, lives in Montrose, MI. **Bush, Jorod** (96,97) Attended FSU, currently in the U.S. Armed Forces. **Casciano, Brad** (95,96) Works for telecommunications Co. **Casteel, Cliff** (88, 89) Graduated from Augsburg College, two-time All-American wrestler, on two National Championship Wrestling Teams. Teaches elementary school in Minnesota, coaches wrestling and football. Asst. Football Coach with Tony Annese at Muskegon in 2001, married. **Caves, Ryan** (96, 97) Owns and manages a car audio shop in Montrose, MI. **Carmichael, Vince** (92) Works for Rite Aid Corporation in Waterford and lives in Holly, MI. **Clolinger, Chris 'Goose'** (87,88,89) Played baseball and graduated from University of Miami of Ohio. Asst. Offensive Coach Montrose 1995-2000. Fitness Coordinator UofM Flint Recreation Center. Working on Masters Degree in Cardiac Technology. Married in 2002. **Cochrane, Jeremy** (98+) Attending and plays football GVSU. Studying to be a teacher and plans to be a football coach and start his own dynasty. **Corcoran, Darren 'Corky'** (96,97) Apprenticeship for pipe fitter for FPS Suppression Systems and installs fire sprinklers in commercial and residential buildings. Volunteer fireman for one year in Swartz Creek and three years for the Montrose Fire Department. Single and lives in Clio, MI. **Crockett, Corey** (90,91) Attended University of Hawaii, 1990 football scholarship. Lives out of state. **Dean, B.J.** (92-94) Graduated from MSU with a bachelor's degree in Supply Chain Management. Walked-on MSU's wrestling team. Spent 3 months living in Brazil with foreign exchange student Mo Targino's family and backpacked solo through Europe for 3 months. Employed by Vector SCM. Lives in Farmington Hills, MI. Single. **Destrampe, D'ar** (90-,92) Elected to the Dream Team and played in the Michigan East-West H.S. Football All-Star game.

Currently attending SVSU, played 5 years of college football with Jason Liddell, Tony Beardsley, Brad Barnett, Ed Howell and Rob Schlicht. Coached Montrose Football (1998-2001). Substitute teaches while finishes degree, lives in Saginaw, MI, **Diem, John** (90,91) – Served in the US Air Force for 4 1/2 years. Stationed in Germany for 3 years and Montana 1 year. Married and has 2 sons and a daughter. Employed as a carpenter and lives in Montrose, MI. **Diem, Ricky** (88, 89) – Moved to Concord, TN eight years ago and loves it. Works as a foreman for a landscape company and bobcat operator. Married and has two young daughters. **Draper, Jason** (93, 94) Works for a landscaping business and is engaged. **Edenburn, Rob** (93,94) Works at a tool and die factory since 1997, divorced, one daughter. Coached Montrose Football '95 – '97 and again in 2002. **Emmendorfer, Aaron** (96,97) Graduated from MSU Electrician Program in 2000. Attended FSU one semester, long enough to make the Football Team as a walk on. Third year apprentice Genesee County Electrician's Program. Married in 2002, lives in Montrose. Coaches Montrose youth football and plays on a flag football team. **Emmendorfer, Jake** (94,95) Attending SVSU, played college baseball two years. Majoring in Special Education with a minor in Psychology. Ass't. football coach at Pinconning H.S., and Saginaw Arthur Hill, engaged. **Fedechenko, Joe** (96,97) Attended CMU for one year, and Mott CC Computer Science major. Engaged, lives in Clio, MI. **Fisher, Mike** (92,93) Produce Manager for Farmer Jack in Flint. **Fisher, Robert 'Fish'** (89,90) Married and has one child. Attended Mott CC 2 years. Works as a framing carpenter, lives in New Baltimore, MI. **Fisk, Wesley** (98+) Attending Northwood Univ. and plays linebacker. **Follett, Dave** (94,95) Graduated from MSU in 2000, major in Computer Science and a minor in Business. Works as a computer software programmer in Troy, MI. **Follett, Tim** (91, 92) Graduated from MSU with a major in Elementary Education and a minor in Biology and Earth Science. Taught elementary school in Lansing, MI, New Orleans, LA, and now teaches in Boston, MA. Single. **Galvis, Clint** (98+) Attending MSU; major in Kinesiology. Plans to become a teacher and coach. Rooms with former players Tim Hemker and Nick Persails. **Gibson, Mike 'Gibby'** (98+) Attending Kendall School of Design in Michigan. **Gross, Barry** (90,91,92) Graduated from Adrian College with a B.A. in Exercise Science in 1997. Played wide receiver for Adrian College with H.S. teammates Eric Hyde & Brent Baksa. Graduated from UofM with a Masters Degree in Physical Therapy in 2001. Married in 1998. Employed by St. Mary's Medical Center as a physical therapist. **Haney, Josh** (95,96) Graduated from FSU in 2002 and accepted to the Ferris School of Optometry. Married and has a son and a new daughter. **Harris, Jim** (88) Associates degree in Criminal Justice from Mott CC then attended Iowa University. He is a broker and owns a mortgage company. Jim is married with two children and lives in Indiana. **Harris, Jason** (95,96) Attending SVSU studying Secondary Education. Worked as an assistant coach for Montrose Football programs from '97-01. Single and coaches football at New Lothrop H.S. in '02. **Head, Scott 'Flaco'** (95,96) Attending SVSU and plans to graduate in 2002 with a double major in history. Played four years of college baseball at SVSU. **Head, Steve** (93,94) Graduated from SVSU with a double major in Sociology and History. Coached JV Football and Basketball and Freshmen Baseball at New Lothrop H.S. Currently a graduate student at Northwood University. **Hemker, Tim** (98+) Attending MSU. Rooms with Clint Galvis and Nick Persails. **Heystek, Joe** (92,93) Engineering Degree Kettering University, 1999. Currently employed by GM Powertrain as a Test Engineer. Married in 2001. **Hodges, Ryan** (94,95,96) Played in the Michigan East-West H.S. Football All-Star game. In final year at FSU, Math Education major, Physical Education minor with a concentration in Science. Played 5 years as cornerback for Ferris Football, started in 35 of the 40 games he played in. Plans to coach college football and teach. **House, Cary** (97,98) Attended SVSU for one year then enlisted in the U.S. Navy, electrician training. Shipped to Afghanistan in Sept. 2002. **Howell, Eddie** (92, 93) Attended SVSU and played two years of college football as a DB with Liddell, Barnett, D'ar, Schlicht and his brother Tony Bearsdley. Married and has one daughter. Employed as a diesel mechanic for Automotive Component Carrier, affiliated with GM parts. **Hyde, Eric** (90, 91) Graduated from Adrian College with a teaching degree in Secondary Education. Played four years of college football with Brent Baksa and Barry Gross. Taught Social Studies and was an assistant football coach at Carman-Ainsworth High School in Flint, MI. Currently head football coach and Health Education teacher at North Branch High School in MI. Married in 1999. **Katt, Jason** (88,89,90) Graduated from Hillsdale College with a teaching degree, English Major, Social Studies. Played football for Hillsdale. Taught and was an assistant coach at Powers Catholic H.S. Currently teaching and Asst. Coach at Lowell H.S., married. **Kies, Chris** (88, 89) Attended and played football for Alma College. Married, has 3 children, lives in Hart, MI and is a cement truck driver. **Klopf, Jeff** (91,92,93) Made the Michigan Dream Team. Played in the Michigan East-West H.S. Football All-Star game. Attended EMU one year. Transferred to SVSU and played football four years. Played Arena Football and tasted pro football with the Cleveland Browns for preseason games in 2000. Married, two children. Received a degree in communications from SVSU. Pursuing his teaching certificate at SVSU, works at General Motors. **Klopf, Bobby** (93,94) Working while attending Northwood University, played football until he was injured. Majoring in Business Management and plans to graduate in 2003. **Klopf, Teddy** (98) Currently attending and playing football for Olivet College, Biology major. **Kneuss, Fred** (94,95) Works for a union architectural millwork company in Oakland County, MI. Single and lives in Flint, MI. Rents an apartment with former teammate Rob Persails. **Kovl, Jerry** (89,90) Graduated from FSU with a printing degree. Started his own (small) printing business, pursuing teaching certificate in Special Ed. Works at Comstock H.S. and hopes to help coach football and baseball coaches. Married, no kids yet. Lives in Kalamazoo, MI. **Lake, Corey 'Lakester'** (89,90) Graduated from GVSU (1991-96), Sports Medicine Program and played college football two years. Certified in Athletic Training. Employed by Medhealth Wellness and Physical Therapy Clinic, Plymouth, MI. Athletic Trainer for Livonia Churchill H.S., Personal Trainer for two years. Asst.Mgr. Personal Training Dept for Lifetime Fitness of Troy. Married in 2000. Started his own lawn care, snow removal and painting business. Lives in Keego Harbor, MI. **Lange, Charlie** (87,88) Works at Haden, a company that produces paint booths for large automotive and other manufacturing facilities. Married and has a young son and daughter. Lives in Chesaning, MI. **Lange, Jeff** (93,94) Graduated from SVSU 1995-2000, Mechanical Engineering major. Married, no kids. Account Manager for a Manufacturer's Rep. in Ann Arbor, MI. Lives in Clio, MI. **Leeseberg, Matt 'Cheese'** Graduated from Northwood University and played four years college football. Married, 3 kids. Works as a Pharmaceutical Rep. and lives in Augusta, GA. **Leeseberg, Nathaniel 'Nate'** (92,93) Graduated from the Police Academy. Employed by the Alcona County Sheriff's Dept., Canine Unit. Lives in Alcona, MI. **Leeseberg, Tim** (93,94) Graduated from college and is working on his master's degree. Married in 2001 and lived in Europe for a year and Ohio. Working as a carpenter. **Leitelt, Gerrad** (93,94) Married and lives in Perry, MI. Employed by Koegel Meats in a supervisory position. Attended SVSU for three years. **Leitelt, Chris 'Bulldog'** (95,96) Attending GVSU since 1997, Communications major with emphasis on Film/Video and Broadcasting. Works as the video coordinator for the football team and is the video coordinator for Grand Rapids Rampage (Arena Football) that won the Arena Bowl in 2001. Also works for the Grand Rapids Griffins of the AHL (Detroit Red Wings new affiliate). **Leitelt, Matt** (98+) Attending FSU since 2000 and is working toward a degree in construction management. Does video cuts and taping for FSU Football. **Leonard, Tommy** (97,98) Attending the UofM in Ann Arbor, majoring in History. Delta Upsilon Fraternity, and serves as VP of Recruitment. Plans to graduate in 2003 and attend Law School to specialize in Sports and Entertainment law. **Liddell, Jason 'Led'** (89, 90) Graduated from SVSU with a Finance Degree. Played college football with Brad Barnett, Tony Beardsley, D'ar Destrampe, Robert Schlicht. Burger King Scholar-Athlete of the Week (SVSU received $25,000 scholarship in his name), MI College Football Hall of Fame Scholar – Athlete of the Year, 1995. Married, employed by an accounting firm. **Loafman, Nick** (95,96,97) Plans to graduate from Albion College with a biology degree in Dec. 2002, then attend medical school and become an orthopedic surgeon. Played four years of football for Albion College and attended and wrestled one year for Boston University. **Lyman, Dave** (95,96) Works in the computer field and is employed by the Yellow Cab Company in Chicago, IL. **MacDonald, Alan** (91,92) Attending Baker College, majoring in Aviation. Plans to graduate in 2003. Has pilot license, owns his own plane and enjoys sky diving and flying. Works at Delphi in Saginaw, MI and lives in Flushing, MI. Single. **Magrys, Eddie** (98+) Attending EMU, majoring in Psychology. Captain of the Varsity Wrestling Team at EMU. MAC place winner at 174 lbs. in 2001. **MacDougal, Micah** Married, registered nurse and also works construction. **Maviglia, Ben** (93) Attended Mott CC, Criminal Justice Major and works construction. Employed by communications company as a Supervisor and overlooks installation of equipment. Plays on a flag football team.

Mier, Brody (88,89,90) Has 3 children. Works in construction and lives in Alcona County. **Miller, Brian** (94,95) Graduated from LSSC with a Criminal Justice degree. Employed by Walmart Stores, Security and Loss Prevention. Married in June, 2002, lives in Big Rapids, MI. **Moore, Bo** (96, 97) Graduated from FSU in 2003 with a degree in Secondary Education, major in English, minor in Social Sciences. Played five years of football for Ferris State, Honorable Mention 'All American' Defensive End as a junior & potential candidate for 2002. Plans to teach high school and coach football. **Morse, Joe** (87-88) Attended SVSU and was an Assistant Coach at Montrose H.S. 91-94. Coached with Tony Annese at Ann Arbor Pioneer, Jenison High School and currently teaches and coaches at Muskegon High School. Married with two children. **Newton, Ron 'Newt'** (88,89,90) SVSU, Finance Degree. Played Football at SVSU until his car accident. Held various positions with a mortgage industry, Loan Originator, District Manager then Regional Operations Director of Indiana. Owns a successful Mortgagee Company and several other companies. Married, 2 children, lives in Linden, MI. **Noble, Matt** (87-93-Trainer) Graduated from UofM and is a sales representative for medical pacemakers. Single, lives in Clio, MI. **Olah, Al** (89,90) Married in 97, now has a son and a daughter. Driver for ACC – GM Trucking Division and lives in Grand Blanc, MI. **Owens, Brian** (97) Taking class through Mott CC. **Parks, Dallas** (96,97) Attended GVSU. Employed with commercial garage door installation. **Parks, Craig** (97,98) Attends Tri-State College in Indiana and played four years of college football. **Patterson, Chadd** (92,93) Employed by Delphi in Saginaw, MI. Married, 3 children and lives in Flushing, MI. **Paxton, Bo** (97,98) Played two years of football for SVSU before a medical discharge halted his career. Pursuing a Physical Ed. teaching degree and plans to graduate in 2004. Coaches J.V. Football at Saginaw Arthur Hill. **Paxton, Barry 'Bear'** (87-88) Graduated from MSU 1992. Worked for Duracell Consumer Marketing 1993, Ernst & Young Consultant 1994, Cleveland Clinic Foundation-Strategic Marketing Fellowship, Weatherhead School of Mgmt. MBA in 1995, Sales/Account Management/Neuroscience Relief with Eli Lilly 1995-1998. Corporate Business Analyst with Lilly and presently District Sales Manager. Married in 1995, 2 sons, lives in Canton, MI. **Paxton, Vaughn** (91,92) Attended SVSU, majored in teaching with a minor in history, math and science. Employed by Floor Serve.Incorported, a carpet manufacturing business as a Regional Manager for MI. Married and has a daughter and son. Lives in Clio, MI. **Perior, Trent** (96,97) Attended UTI. Employed by Perior Well Drilling and is a volunteer fireman for Montrose Township. Engaged to be married in 2003. **Persails, Ryan** (93,94,95) Graduated from FSU with a Public Relations degree. Student coached at Ferris Football. Works as a Sales Representative with the automotive industry. Lives in Flint and rents an apartment with former teammate Fred Kneuss. **Persails, Joe 'Joe Bob'** (96,97) Attended FSU and filmed football games. Enlisted in Army Reserves and working on Public Relations and Nursing degree. **Persails, Nick** (98+) Attending Lansing CC, plans to play college baseball. Lives with teammates Clint Galvis and Tim Hemker. **Pollard, Jason** (95,96) Completed four years in the U.S. Navy and was based in Guam; experienced Australia, Korea, Maylasia, Thailand, Japan, Singapore, Hong Kong. Works in Howell and lives in Montrose, MI. **Powell , Adam** (95,96,97) Attended MSU and Mott CC. **Powell, Nick** (95,96) Graduated from MSU with an Engineering degree. Employed by Delphi as a Mechanical Engineer. Engaged. **Powell, Scott** (90,91) Lives in Waterford, MI, completing apprenticeship in the construction field. **Richardson, Eddie** (95,96) Moved to Las Vegas after graduation and attended UNLV. **Rizk, Joey** (93,94,95) Lives in Grand Rapids, MI and is in the Management Program at Cintas. **Ross, Ryan** (94,95) Attending Mott CC, lives in Brighton, MI. **Ruddy, Dan** (94, 95) Attended CMU major in Biology (Pre-Professional Degree) accepted at the University of Detroit Mercy Dental School. Completed second year and plans to graduate in 2004 as a dentist. **Ruddy, John David** (96,97) Attending CMU pursuing a degree in Mechanical Engineering. Targeted to graduate in 2003. **Ruffin, Winston** (96,97) Attended Muskegon Community College and was on the wrestling team. Currently attending Mott CC, majoring in Criminal Justice. Ass't. Wrestling Coach at Bendle H.S. Employed by Briar Ridge Golf Course in Montrose, MI. **Rush, Corey'Crusher'** (95,96) Played five years of football for FSU, graduated with a degree in Criminal Justice. **Salter, Craig 'Salty Dog'** (97,98) Attending CMU, plans to graduate in the Spring of '04 with an Elementary Eucation degree, (Social Studies and Science). Plans to teach and become a football coach. **Salter, Kevin** (87,88) Graduated from FSU with a Criminal Justice Major. Was a police officer for one-year then joined the U.S. Army

514 SOURCES

as Military Officer and was a Captain in Bosnia. Married with two children. Police Officer in Flint, MI (volunteered to help to New York City after 9-11-01). Lives in Montrose, MI. **Schlicht, Rob 'Schlichtster'** 91,92 Attended SVSU and played college football with center with Jason Liddell, Tony Beardsley, Brad Barnett, D'ar Destrampe and Ed Howell. Employed by Wither's Steel. Lives in Montrose, MI. **Schlicht, Matt** (96,97) Attended SVSU pursing an Engineering degree. **Schlorf, Josh** (97, 98) Attended CMU one year. Currently employed by Schwann. Frozen Foods, Inc. Lives in Montrose, MI. **Schlorf, Shane** (93,94,95) Attended SVSU three years and played corner and wide receiver. Played in the Michigan East-West H.S. Football All-Star game. Married. Employed by Extreme Trailer and lives in Maple Grove, MI. **Smith, Jared 'Dauber'** (97, 98) Attending Albion College since 1999. Majoring in Economics and Management (Finance Concentration). Played defensive end on the Briton Football team with Nick Loafman (they were '99' and "01" MIAA Champs.) Plans to graduate in 2003. **Strappazon, Gary 'Strap'** (96,97) Drywall finisher for a residential company. Lives in Montrose and coaches youth football. **Stiverson, Adam** (92,93,94) Attended GVSU, Physical Therapy major. Football cheerleader before enlisting in the Army for 3 years. Competed as a powerlifter in the Army and was stationed in Fort Sill, OK. Won the USA Junior National Powerlifting Championship in 2000. Married and has a daughter. Lives in OK, works and attends Cameron Univ. Physical Therapy and Corporate Fitness major. **Sullivan, Mike 'Bulldog'** (90,91) Asst. Coach 91-94. School Board Trustee 1992, SVSU Undergrad & Masters in Teaching, Offensive Line Asst' Coach SVSU (1995-1999), Head Coach Pinconning H.S., 2000. Currently, Registrar & Academic Specialist at Northwood University Midland, MI & Director of Football Operations, Director of Champs Life Skills Program through NCAA & teaches classes in Sports Management & Entertainment Field at Northwood. Engaged to be married in 2003. **Tafoya, Jason** (88,89) Attended a Business/Automotive College in Ohio for two years. Self-employed, owns his own Drywall Company for eight years. Married and has one child. Lives in Flint, MI. **Toney, Jason** (94,95) Enlisted in Armed Forces. **Targino, Mauricinho 'Mo-the-Toe'** (94) After his year in America as a foreign exchange student Mo returned to Brazil. Attending college, B.A. degree. Worked with his father in a computer business for two years. Currently works in a family business manufacturing a popular Brazilian beverage called 'Cachaca' (similar to Tequila) that uses a sugar cane base. Single. Lives in Fortaleza-Ceara, Brazil. **Thornburg, Tony** (96) Works for a Communications Co. installing fiberoptic cable. Married in 2001 and lives in Montrose. **Brian Tripp** (96) Graduated from LSSU in 2002 with a degree in History. Worked as a disc jockey during college. Employed as a Claim Adjuster for Frankenmuth Insurance. **Unangst, Sean** (91) Attended SVSU for two years. Employed by General Motors. Married, lives in Grand Blanc, MI. **Unangst, Tim** (92,93) Graduated from SVSU Criminal Justice Major, Graduated from Northeastern Policy Academy. Currently employed by WMU Campus Police Dept. Lives in Kalamazoo, MI. Single. **Unangst, Tom 'Tommy Gun'** (95,96) Attending Mott CC, pursuing teaching degree in secondary education. Served as the head Varsity Soccer coach at Chesaning H.S. and coaches JV Soccer at Montrose since 1999. **VanGorder, Ryan** (93,94) Currently employed by U.S. Com and travels extensively laying fiberoptic cable. Lives in Grand Blanc, MI. **VanHecke, Tom** (93,94) Medical Student at MSU. Lives in Ferndale, MI. **Venturino, Matt 'Vinnie'** (88,89) Graduated from Morehead State, KY. Married, 4 kids. Works for survey company, Venturino and Associates, lives in Ortonville-Brandon, MI. **Vigil, Anthony** (97,98) Works for a mortgagee company and is in the Marine Reserves. Vigil, Vicente (96,97) Managers a Foot Action store in Waterford, MI. **Visser, Scott** (97,98) Attended Albion College and played football (kicker). Employed by Home Depot and attending Mott CC. **Visser, Steve** (95,96) Attended UofM and is a third year apprentice in the Genesee County Electrician's Program. Single and lives in Flushing, MI. Plays on a flag football team. **Visser, Tommy** (98+) kicked PAT in playoff game as freshman. Attending WMU, in ROTC Program. **Whorf, Steve** (94) Asst. football coach in Montrose and Clio for a few years. Currently in the U.S. Armed Forces. **Wingo, Chris** (92,93,94) Made Dream Team '94. Received a football Scholarship for Bowling Green but wasn't able to stay on. Currently employed by a drywall company. Single. **Wixson, Paul 'Wixy'** (88-89) Married, Works for General Motors. Plays and tours with a band 'Stoned Cold' opened for Sawyer Brown (2/98), Confederate Railroad (12/97). **Woodward, Jim** (93,94) Graduated from Olivet College in 1999 with a major in Communications and minor in

Journalism. Wrestled 2 years for Olivet then injured his shoulder. Graduated from Columbia College-Chicago in 2002 with a masters degree in Arts and Media Management. Internship at Universal Records, manages a small record label. Single. **Woodward Justin 'Woody'** (96,97). Attended SVSU for one year, member of the Cardinal Baseball Team. Third year apprentice in the Genesee County Electrician's Program. Single. Lives in Montrose and plays on a flag football team. **Wright, Chris** (88-89), BA in Economics from MSU, 1994. MBA from Harvard Business School, 2001. Financial analyst for General Electric 1994 – 1999. Lives in Los Angeles and works as an associate in private equity for TCW/Crescent Mezzanine (growth capital). Single. **Yeaster, Greg 'Pooh Bear'** (97,98+) Attending MSU on Football Scholarship. Plays defensive tackle for the Spartans. Majoring in Engineering. Received highest G.P.A. on the team in 2001 (3.48). Dean's List 2000. Plans to graduate in 2005. **Yuncker, Shawn** (93,94) Attended Olivet College, wrestled 3 years and played football 1 year. Currently employed by a communications company. Single.

MONTROSE COACHES MENTIONED:
Annese, Tony: Head Coach, Montrose ('87-94). After Montrose, coached at Pioneer in Ann Arbor, Jenison and currently at Muskegon High School. Married to Chris, 4 children.
Annese, Phil: Asst. Coach during Tony Annese years
Annese, Steve: Asst. Coach during Tony Annese years
Beazley, Dave (97-98): Athletic Director and Vice Principal Montrose High School
Clolinger , Chris (95-98+) Fitness Coordinator, U of M, former player
Coon, Jody (95-97), Genesee County Sheriff Department
Destrampe, Craig (1991 – 98+) currently Asst. Coach at Bendle H. S.
Edenburn, Rob (95-97) also former player
Gilbert, Joe (98+), Teaches and coaches in Port Huron, MI
Gildersleeve, Cory (98) Teaches and coaches in Dundee, MI
Harris, Jason (1995 – 98+), former player (95-96), Student and coaches at New Lothrop H.S.
Hayes, Bob: Head Coach at Montrose (68-86), Asst. Coach (94-98), Retired, in Arizona.
Kitts, Jamie (87-97): Teaches Sociology at Montrose H.S. Helps produce highlight videos.
Persails, Bill: (89 – 98+ Still associated with Montrose Football.
Reinhart, Denny (87-current): Teaches Physical Ed at Montrose H. S., Head Coach (since 1995), Asst. Defensive Coach 1987-1994. Has 3 young sons.
Stiles, Monty (95-98) Teaches and Coaches Varsity Football at Montrose H.S.
Sullivan, Mike (91-94): (Former player 90-01) Coaches football at Northwood University.
Taylor, Scott (97): Asst. Coach, Owner-Manager Briar Ridge Golf Course
Williams, Keith (91-94): Coach Muskegon H.S. with Annese, Taught at Holland West Ottawa

OTHERS INTERVIEWED:
Don & Shirley Andrews, Mrs. Christine Annese, Marlene Baksa, Cheryl Barrett, Karen Beardsley, Becky Bernard, April MacDonald Bowen, Stacie Brown, Bob & Debbie Brown, Judy & Les Christensen, Denny & Joanne Cochrane, Dan & Diane Corcoran, Noel Dean, Ms. Karen Dean, Denise Destrampe, Shaunae Destrampe, Bob and Bev Doyle, Chris Emmendorfer , Terry Emmendorfer, Mark Emmendorfer, Mary Jo Emmendorfer, Rich & Marilyn Fedechenko, Diane Fisher, Mary Jo Fizk, Ann Follett, Walt and Sue Head, Linda Hodges, Larry Hyde, Judy Hyde, Jan Katt, Dennis Kies, Doug Kinter, Ted Klopf, Linda Klopf, Mr & Mrs Warren Leeseberg, Betty Kay Leitelt, Sadie Leonard, Chrissy Loafman, John McAuley, Rin & Sabrina Moore, Crystal Tipton Morse, Sid & Jane Morse, Raeanne Nelson, Doug Noble, Stacy Noble, Denny & Jackie Owens, Dallas & Danielle Parks, Barry & Jules Paxton, Sr., Terry & Sue Paxton, Rob Persails, Linda Persails, Doug & Cherrie Perior, Jim Ply, Rudy Poletti, Don & Theresa Pollard, Jack Powell, Tansy Powell, Joe and Vicki Rizk, Ms. Amy Rowbotham, Dave & Karen Ruddy, Eric Rush, Dick & Nora Salter, Doug Schlorf, Pat Sidley, Mark & Cindy Smith, Tim & Mary Stiverson, Nancy Lyman, Gerry & Mary Sullivan, Mr & Mrs Doug Schlorf, Jeff Setzke, Gary Strappazon Sr., Rod Studaker, Duane & Connie Tripp, Tom & Jan Unangst, Yvonne VanGorder, Jim Venturino, Denise Visser, Les Visser, Ron Woodward, Mr. Wayne Wright, Greg & Connie Yeaster, Rick & Jean Yuncker.